ICSA GUIDE TO CRYPTOGRAPHY

ICSA Guide to Cryptography

Randall K. Nichols

McGraw-Hill

New York San Francisco Washington, D.C. Auckland Bogotá
Caracas Lisbon London Madrid Mexico City Milan
Montreal New Delhi San Juan Singapore
Sydney Tokyo Toronto

Library of Congress Cataloging-in-Publication Data

Nichols, Randall K.
    ICSA guide to cryptography / Randall K. Nichols.
        p.   cm.
    Includes index.
    ISBN 0-07-913759-8
    1. Computers—Access control.   2. Data encryption (Computer
science)   I. International Computer Security Association.
    II. Title.
    QA76.9.A25N53   1999
    005.8—dc21   98-36563
                                                              CIP

McGraw-Hill

A Division of The McGraw·Hill Companies

    2 3 4 5 6 7 8 9 0   AGM/AGM   0 3 2 1 0

P/N 0-07-047166-5
PART OF
ISBN 0-07-913759-8

The sponsoring editor for this book was Judy Brief, the editing supervisor was Curt Berkowitz, and the production supervisor was Clare Stanley. It was set in Century Schoolbook by Terry Leaden of McGraw-Hill's Desktop Composition Unit, in cooperation with Spring Point Publishing Services.

Printed and bound by Quebecor Martinsburg.

 This book is printed on recycled, acid-free paper containing a minimum of 50% recycled, de-inked fiber.

To Chuck and Mom, thanks for being there
when I needed you most.

To Montine, Kent, Phillip, Diana, and precious Michelle,
for understanding while I stole time from you all.
The Bear is back!

To Dan Ryan, for a lifetime of friendship, I thank you.

To WITZ END, for joining the party.

To my team at ICSA, thanks for the professional work.

CONTENTS

Contents

Contents

Contents

Contents

LIST OF CONTRIBUTORS

We are deeply grateful for the assistance from our colleagues on many of the practical chapters of *ICSA Guide to Cryptography*. Here is a look at the qualifications of these very special professionals.

RANDALL K. NICHOLS (Supervising Author/Editor) served as Technology Director for Cryptography and Biometrics for the International Computer Security Association (ICSA). He was the Senior Cryptology Technical Director for the ICSA Cryptography and Biometrics Products Consortia.

The *ICSA Guide to Cryptography* is his third book on cryptography. Nichols is considered an expert on cryptanalysis and classical cryptography. He has authored two textbooks on the latter subject, *Classical Cryptography Course*, Volumes I and II, published by Aegean Park Press in 1996 and 1997, respectively. Nichols has 35 years of management experience in a variety of leadership roles in cryptography and computer applications in the engineering, construction, consulting, and chemicals industries.

Nichols currently is President of COMSEC Solutions, a consulting firm specializing in cryptographic countermeasures applied to commercial computer security problems. Nichols has served as President and Vice President of the American Cryptogram Association and is presently the Aristocrats' Department Editor for the ACA's bimonthly publication *The Cryptogram*. He holds BSChE and MSChE degrees from Tulane University and Texas A & M University, respectively, and an MBA from the University of Houston.

SHAWN ABBOTT is Chief Scientist at Rainbow Technologies and an expert in intellectual property and Internet cryptographic security. Shawn has given presentations at over 50 conferences on advances made in the hardware used to support or attack cryptographic systems. Shawn's credits include not only the founding of the AND group, which pioneered CD-ROM locking, but also the responsibility for a significant portion of Rainbow Technologies Internet security group products. He is a Director of International Software, Escrow, and an advisor to Tragoes, Inc.

STEVE PETRI is Program Director of Smartcard Products at Litronic, Inc.

In this role, he directs a team of software engineers and manages the technical development of a cross-platform line of smartcard-based products. The line includes end-user products (NetSign, NetSign PRO), software developer products (CryptOS SDK, CryptOS SDK PRO, Template Toolkit), and MIS manager products (ProFile Manager). With these products, Steve has demonstrated an expertise in bringing state-of-the-art smartcard technology to real-world products, and he has become a sought-after speaker at industry events. Steve holds a BSAAE degree from Purdue University and an MSEE degree from the University of Southern California.

MARY VAN ZANDT is Director of Marketing, responsible for the strategic direction of Sterling Commerce's enterprise security products, which are key to enabling secure electronic commerce. These products address multiple security issues including authentication, access, authorization, integrity, confidentiality, and nonrepudiation of information in transit or stored. Ms. Van Zandt has more than 18 years experience in the security, database, application development, knowledge base systems, and data warehousing markets with companies such as Platinum Technology, Altai, Sybase, AICORP, Cap Gemini, and Hewlett Packard. She received her MBA from Lake Forest School of Management at Lake Forest College in 1982.

JACK OSWALD is President and CEO of RPK Security, Inc. He has more than 12 years experience in the software industry, includings 10 years in product marketing and product management. Prior to founding RPK in 1995, he led the team that developed Borland International's overall Internet strategy, its early adoption of the Java technology, and was Director of the Internet Products Division. He was Lead Product Marketing Manager for Borland's Quattro Pro spreadsheet marketing team and has worked in a variety of marketing leadership positions in high-tech startups. Early in his career, Oswald turned around a small family owned software company that specialized in database development products. He holds an MBA from Harvard Business School and an Engineering Sciences degree from Dartmouth College, specializing in Electronic Design.

COLIN SOUTAR received his B.Sc. degree in mathematics and physics and his Ph.D. degree in physics from Dundee Institute of Technology in Dundee, Scotland in 1988 and 1992, respectively. From 1992 to 1994 he worked on the use of correlation for automated vision systems as an NRC Research Associate at NASA Johnson Space Center, in Houston, Texas. In 1994, he joined Mytec Technologies Inc. in Toronto, Canada, where he is currently Director of Research and Development. He has co-authored 22 publications and holds 7 patents.

DANNY ROBERGE received his B.Ing. and M.Sc.A. degrees in physics engineering from Ecole Polytechnique de Montreal in Montreal, Canada in 1989 and 1991, respectively. He received his Ph.D. degree in optics in 1995 from the Centre d'Optique Photonique et Laser laboratory at the Université Laval, Quebec City, Canada. From 1995 to 1998, he worked as an NSERC Research Fellow at Mytec Technologies Inc. Currently, he is employed by Forensic Technology Inc., in Montreal, Canada. His research interests are image processing and pattern recognition.

ALEX STOIANOV received his M.Sc. degree in radiophysics and electronics and his Ph.D. degree in physics and mathematics from Kiev State University, Ukraine, in 1978 and 1985, respectively. Between 1978 and 1993 he served on the Faculty of Nonlinear Optics, Kiev State University, Ukraine, where he worked primarily on the theory of photorefraction and related phenomena. Since 1994 he has worked on optical processing, pattern recognition, and fingerprint verification for Mytec Technologies Inc., where he is currently a senior staff scientist. He has published over 30 journal papers and holds several patents.

RENE GILROY received her B.Sc. in mathematics from Mount Saint Vincent University in Halifax, Canada in 1995 and her M.Ma. in combinatorics and optimization from the University of Waterloo in Waterloo, Canada in 1997. Her master's thesis topic was a review of DES and differential cryptanalysis. Since 1996 she has been working as a cryptologist for Mytec Technologies Inc., where she is responsible for cryptographic analysis of the Biometric Encryption™ algorithm. She is the co-author of several publications.

B. V. K. VIJAYA KUMAR received his B. Tech. and M. Tech. degrees in electrical engineering from the Indian Institute of Technology in Kanpur, India in 1975 and 1977, respectively, and his Ph.D. in electrical engineering from Carnegie Mellon University (CMU) in Pittsburgh in 1980. Since then, he has been with the Electrical and Computer Engineering (ECE) Department at CMU where he currently serves as a professor.

Professor Kumar's current research focuses on the use of correlators for pattern recognition and on developing advanced signal processing methods for data storage systems. He has authored or co-authored five book chapters, two patent applications, and more than two hundred technical papers in various conference proceedings and journals. Professor Kumar is a Fellow of the Optical Society of America (OSA) and of SPIE, the International Society for Optical Engineering.

SHANNON BYRNE, B.Comm., B.Sc., M.C.Sc., is Chief Operating Officer, Paradata Systems Incorporated. She has an extensive background in object-oriented programming and software development of information security products. Shannon has been with Paradata Systems Inc. since 1995 and, prior to joining Paradata, worked with Geovision, Siemens, DMR Group, and Statistics Canada.

DAVID SLIK is a consultant and former Technology Architect at Paradata Systems Inc. He has performed extensive research into electronic commerce systems over the last four years. He has developed several implementations of secure soft good delivery systems for CD-ROM and Internet data delivery.

JULES PRICE (WITZ END) has been a Senior Cryptographer with the ACA since 1950 and has solved over 10,000 cryptograms. Only a few people in the world have obtained that ranking, which signals expertise in nearly 75 different classical cipher systems. In his other life, he is a Professional Engineer, and, as Vice President, Chief Engineer and Project Manager, he has been directly involved in the construction of multi-million-dollar projects ranging from highways and bridges to colleges, schools, hospitals, and Shea stadium (home of the New York Mets). His long experience working with building plans and specifications has given him a sharp eye for details. For this talent, he was chosen as a primary reviewer for this book.

HART W. DeGRAFFT has 34 years of Information Security experience serving the National Security Agency, the Defense Information Systems Agency, the U.S. Delegation to NATO, and, most recently, SPARTA, Inc. He has held a variety of technical, senior management, staff, and liaison positions while serving in both the government and private sectors. Since joining SPARTA three and a half years ago, he has served as both a program manager and chief engineer, developing security solutions in business areas such as electronic data interchange, procurement, and travel. He has also led efforts developing powerful automated information management tools, which apply expert system and Web-based technology. Mr. DeGrafft holds an MS in Electrical Engineering from the University of Maryland and a BS in Electrical Engineering from Virginia Tech.

MICHEL E. KABAY began learning Assembler at age 15 and had learned FORTRAN IV G at McGill University by 1976. In 1976, he received his Ph.D. from Dartmouth College in applied statistics and invertebrate zoology. Until 1979, he was a university professor in applied statistics. In 1979, he joined a compiler team for a new 4GL and RDBMS in the United States, responsible for developing the statistical syntax, writing the parser, error traps and code generation for statistical functions in the command language. Kabay joined Hewlett-Packard in 1980 and became a performance specialist, winning the Systems Engineer of the Year Award in 1982. He has written security columns for *Computer World, Network World, Computing Canada, Secure Computing Magazine, NCSA News*, and several other trade magazines. He attained the status of Certified Systems Security Professional (CISSP) in 1997. Dr. Kabay has published over 170 technical papers in operations management and security and has completed a college textbook, *The NCSA Guide to Enterprise Security: Protecting Information Assets*, published by McGraw-Hill. Kabay joined the National Computer Security Association as volunteer Director of Education and Chief Sysop for the CompuServe NCSA Forums in 1991 and took up these positions full-time in June 1995. He remains President of JINBU Corporation.

RICHARD E. SMITH, author of the national bestseller *Internet Cryptography* published by Addison Wesley, is a Principal Information Security Architect at Secure Computing Corporation. He provides consulting services in network security to commercial and governmental organizations, including NSA. He has managed some interesting projects, such as military network guard systems and the Sidewinder Internet Firewall. Rick is a lecturer, writer, and seminar trainer in cryptography and computer security. He holds Ph.D. and MS degrees from the University of Minnesota, and a BSEE from Boston University.

TIMOTHY L. TROWBRIDGE received his BS degree in aeronautical and astronautical engineering from Purdue University and his MS in electrical engineering–space systems from the University of Colorado. Tim has 18 years of experience in command, control, communications, and intelligence systems (C3I). He developed simulation and modeling software for two command and operations systems located within the Cheyenne Mountain Complex and performed systems engineering studies for United States Space Command intelligence support systems. He led the development of satellite telemetry processing software and is an experienced researcher, having been the principal investigator on two research and development projects involving space assets and their tactical applications. He is currently managing the development of wargame command and control simulation software at the Joint National Test Facility at Schriever Air Force Base in Colorado.

FREDERICK G. TOMPKINS is an Information Security Advisor and Deputy Program Director for the Unisys Corporation. He has over 30 years of combined experience in the fields of intelligence, information technology, industrial security, and information systems security. Mr. Tompkins is a recognized authority in the area of information security policy and risk management. He has served as consultant to a variety of federal and state governments and commercial clients. Mr. Tompkins currently is the Unisys Corporation representative to the Network Group of the President's National Security Telecommunications Advisory Committee. He recently served on the board of directors of the Information Systems Security Association as the Director of Education. Mr. Tompkins is also an advisor to the DataPro Reports in Information Security. He is a member of the Information Assurance Working Group for the Center for Strategic and International Studies Global Organized Task Force. He has served as the Chair of the Computer Security Committee of the American Society for Industrial Security. Mr. Tompkins is currently a member of the Operations Task Group of the Network Reliability and Interoperability Council. He is a member of the adjunct faculty of Eastern Michigan University, where he teaches a graduate-level course in Information Security Risk Management. Mr. Tompkins holds a BS in technology of management from The American University and a Master of Liberal Studies in interdisciplinary technology from Eastern Michigan University.

R. KEVIN HUNTER is the President of Broken Rhythm Solutions LLC. He has over 28 years experience in managing and developing commercial and military software and communication system applications. His experience includes strategic planning, project planning, resource and program management, system engineering, security engineering, software engineering, computer operations, and quality assurance. He has assisted in the development of numerous corporate policies for software development, software management, secure systems development and operations, and network management controls. He has performed security accreditation evaluations, software capability evaluations, and management audits. He has served as principal engineer for secure command and control systems, operation planning centers, information management systems, and international systems. He holds an MBA from the University of Phoenix and a BS in Management and Computer Science from Regis University.

RICHARD KOMANDO is President/CEO of Krypto-Tech, Inc. Mr. Komando and Dr. Vinh C. Nguyen are the founding partners of Krypto-Tech, Inc., a provider of data privacy hardware and software. In addition to facilitating a number of computer-related startup companies, he has been a Principal Systems Engineer for the deployment of strong authentication devices in the United States, a Division Director for a department of defense automation effort, and an Automation Analyst for a New York Fortune 500 corporation. He holds a BA from Kings College and an MBA from the University of West Florida. He has been actively involved with computer security for more than 15 years.

ROY PEREIRA is the security architect for TimeStep Corporation, a Newbridge affiliate dedicated to developing secure virtual private network (VPN) solutions that are leading the field of network security. TimeStep's PERMIT Enterprise product suite is an IPSec-compliant secure VPN solution that enables you to use the Internet as your private network.

At TimeStep, he is heavily involved with security and Internet standards, as well as product direction, new technology, product integration, and product management. Roy is well-respected in the ANX and IETF, having had been an active member and an author in IETF's IPSec and IP Compression working groups. Before becoming security architect for TimeStep Corporation, Roy owned his own software development company producing Internet server software. After having done undergraduate computer science studies at Carleton University, Roy has over 11 years experience in the software development industry, with a focus on Internet protocols, telecommunications protocols, software APIs, and email systems.

WILLIAM STALLINGS has made a unique contribution to understanding the broad sweep of technical developments in computer networking and computer architecture. He has authored 15 titles and a total of 32 books on various aspects of these subjects. In over 20 years in the field, he has been a technical contributor, technical manager, and an executive with several high-technology firms. Currently, he is an independent consultant whose clients have included computer and networking manufacturers and customers, software development firms, and leading-edge government research institutions.

He is the recipient of the 1998 Texty Award from the Textbook and Academic Authors Association for the best Computer Science and Engineering textbook of the year, awarded for his book *Operating Systems: Internals and Design Principles*, Third Edition (Prentice Hall, 1998). He received the 1997 Texty Award for his book *Data and Computer Communications*, Fifth Edition (Prentice Hall, 1997). He also received the 1996 Texty Award for his book *Computer Organization and Architecture*, Fourth Edition (Prentice Hall, 1996).

Bill has designed and implemented both TCP/IP-based and OSI-based protocol suites on a variety of computers and operating systems, ranging from microcomputers to mainframes. As a consultant, he has advised government agencies, computer and software vendors, and major users on the design, selection, and use of networking software and products. He is a frequent lecturer and the author of numerous technical papers. His books include *Data and Computer Communications*, Fifth Edition (Prentice Hall, 1997). His new book, *Cryptography and Network Security, Principles and Practice*, Second Edition, 1999, has just been released. Dr. Stallings holds a Ph.D. from MIT in Computer Science and a BS from Notre Dame in Electrical Engineering.

FOREWORD

From secret decoder rings to government policy statements, the challenges of hiding and discovering information within other information have long compelled the intellect. Cryptology is a fascinating subject with which almost every schoolchild has some hands-on familiarity. And yet, for good reasons, it is a discipline that throughout time has been shrouded in the deepest levels of secrecy and used by governments to protect their most sensitive weapons. The transformations of hieroglyphs that became cryptography may have begun as a way of adding dignity and authority to inscriptions in the tombs of the Pharaohs and evolved as a decorative calligraphy or a sort of clever game, but cryptography's role in military and diplomatic affairs has always been deadly serious. It is no exaggeration to declare that the outcome of wars and the course of history have been shaped by successes and failures of cryptography. Nor is it an exaggeration to state that our current course of history is being set by the successes and failures of cryptography.

Consider the battle of Antietam, September 16–18, 1862, in the American Civil War, when McClellan commanded the Union forces against Robert E. Lee's Confederate forces near Sharpsburg in Washington County, Maryland. A few days earlier, two Union soldiers had found a piece of paper near their camp which turned out to be a copy of an order recently issued by Lee detailing his plans for the invasion of Maryland. The order had not been encrypted. With the information it contained, McClellan knew precisely the location of the commands of Lee's scattered army and was able to push through the South Mountain passes and destroy Lee's army before they reunited.

Notwithstanding, Lee was the better general, with more imagination and drive than McClellan. In an even battle, Lee surely would have won. Had the intercepted battle order been properly encrypted, Lee might have arrived at Gettysburg in 1862 with a reunited army and plenty of time to take the best positions and set up favorable fields of fire, drawing the ever-hesitant McClellan into battle there on Lee's terms. A decisive victory for the South could have earned European diplomatic recognition and might even have convinced a majority of voters in the Northern states to repudiate the Lincoln administration in the elections of 1862, ending its policy of restoring the Union by force. The subsequent history of our nation would be very different from what we know.

Cryptographic successes and failures have shaped more recent history as well. The terrible Russian failure at Tannenberg in August 1914 was the specific and direct result of the intercept and exploitation of Russian communications by the German army. Amazingly, the Russian communications were totally in the clear—because the Russians had not equipped their field commanders with ciphers and keys. The Russians were thus unable to coordinate the activities of neighboring units within each army securely, much less coordinate a complex pincher attack by two armies in secrecy. Listening in on the Russian orders as they were relayed to commanders in the field, the German army (using secure communications itself) was able to defeat a force twice its size—an almost unheard-of military debacle. David Kahn, in his masterpiece *The Codebreakers*, says, "The case was clear-cut. Interception of unenciphered communications had awarded the Germans their triumph." The defeat was staggering on the battlefield, but, as at Antietam, the repercussions were significantly more far-reaching than the tactical loss. Back in Russia, the Bolsheviks were mounting a massive campaign against participation in the war, and the loss and capture of so many men played into their hands. Eventually, the dominos set falling by the cryptographic failure at Tannenberg led to the fall of the Tsar, and the world witnessed the emergence of what would become the "evil empire," subjugating half the peoples of the world.

The opposition to the communist "evil empire," in what was to become 50 years of Cold War, was also set up by a cryptographic failure—this time on the part of the Japanese at the battle of Midway in 1942. By winning Midway, luring out and destroying the remainder of the American fleet that had been seriously reduced at Pearl Harbor, the Japanese would have gained control of the central Pacific. Hawaii and the west coast of the United States would be vulnerable to direct attack. The United States would have been forced to concentrate on defending its homeland, leaving Japan free to advance southward, isolating Australia and securing access to the riches of Southeast Asia.

Fortunately for the United States, the Japanese were lax in communications security: their writings stressed the importance of COMSEC, but their practices and procedures were slipshod. By 1942, American cryptanalysts had broken the Japanese codes and were reading many of the messages of the Combined Fleet. Consequently, Admiral Nimitz knew the Japanese plans for the battle of Midway and was able to use the advantage of surprise upon which Yamamoto depended but lost. The Allied success at Midway stopped the Japanese eastward drive, turned the Allied strategic position in the Pacific theater from defensive to offensive, and led eventually to victory there and in the war. Cryptography thus positioned the United States to protect the freedoms of half of the world in the ensuing Cold War and ultimately to win the Cold War.

As we all heave a sigh of relief at the demise of the Cold War's geopolitical tensions, the world now turns its attention not only to the emerging promise of the information revolution, but also to the emerging threats posed by terrorism, organized crime, and drug trafficking. It is exceedingly rare today for any system to be developed that does not incorporate some aspect of information technology. Floodgates on dams are controlled remotely through the auspices of information technology. Roadways are monitored using information technology. Cars are augmented with many computer systems to enhance performance. Industrial processes are controlled and managed using highly sophisticated information technology. Every infrastructure from air traffic control to the power grid to the telephone system is based on and relies on information technology. Often these control mechanisms utilize Internet protocols over public networks. Interconnectivity between disparate elements is emphasized to increase efficiencies and reduce costs, with such interconnectivity made possible by information technology. In short, information technology is ubiquitous.

Unfortunately, increased connectivity also means increased vulnerability. The threats, in the form of hackers, computer criminals, information terrorists, and even foreign intelligence services, are becoming more sophisticated and more widespread. So, too, are the concomitant challenges of assuring information content, access, and infrastructure while maintaining confidentiality, integrity, and availability. Cryptography is a critical tool for assuring such protection. Within this emerging interconnected world lies the promise of electronic commerce, a concept poised to redefine both standards of living worldwide and relationships between geopolitical units. The enabling technology for electronic commerce is also cryptology: only when business can enforce in the courts contracts they made online, and only when citizens are assured that they will not lose their life savings through the auspices of online activities will the concept fully be embraced.

The bright promise of electronic commerce relies on the speed and connectivity of modern computer networks to facilitate commercial transactions, increase the velocity of money, and make us all richer. But the exchanges that comprise such transactions must be secure. That security, to be effective, depends upon cryptography. Fortunately, 4000 years or so of experience protecting information transactions with cryptography has ensured that today we have at hand powerful cryptography. The relatively recent advent of public-key cryptography offers a simple and effective solution to what used to be intractable and expensive key management problems. To maximize the advantages of electronic commerce we need widespread availability of high-quality codes and ciphers, and supporting key management infrastructures. Therefore, our ability to produce hardware and software products containing cryptography is very timely. And therein lies a problem.

One of the most powerful techniques for combating terrorists, drug lords, and criminals is interception of conversations and messages revealing their conspiracies and plans. Our government officials responsible for national security and law enforcement are justifiably concerned that widespread use of encryption will hamper or eliminate their ability to use interception of criminal messages in protecting public safety. Accustomed to a century of relatively easy access to communications in the ether, they argue forcefully that cryptographic products are dangerous in the wrong hands, and that such products must incorporate a way for duly authorized law enforcement and national security officers to gain access to enciphered information. Further, the complexity of digital communications and the advent of sophisticated switching techniques such as out-of-band signaling have made even the interception of clear voice transmissions increasingly difficult. The response to these advances has been to legislate continued access to information. Laws have been passed requiring the public switched networks to facilitate interception of voice or data communications, and cryptographic technologies have been developed that incorporate trapdoors, or feature key escrow or key recovery capabilities to satisfy these requirements.

To say that these actions are controversial is an understatement. Because of the complexity of the issue, it has fallen to a core band of technologists to argue against such legislation. And argue they have. Proponents of individual privacy have little sympathy for the government's position and oppose requiring the use of technologies that permit law enforcement or national security officers access, even if controlled by court orders, to encrypted information. They argue that such access is subject to abuses. Concurrently, manufacturers of computer-based systems argue that they as an industry and we as a nation cannot remain competitive in international markets if U.S. cryptographic products are known to be weaker than cryptographic products produced elsewhere. The manufacturers insist they are trying to provide U.S. officials ready access to messages and information enciphered using their products. Both argue that the government's claim that public safety will be enhanced by requirements for access is misleading. This is because drug lords, terrorists, and criminals will not use products that provide access when alternative secure products are readily available, as they indeed are throughout the world. Debate is currently raging as to what policies will best serve the nation, companies, and organizations that use computers to create, store, process, and communicate information and wish to engage in electronic commerce, and individuals who increasingly rely on online systems for their livelihoods and entertainment. How the debate concludes will set the course for the future, with the concomitant analysis by the historians of the future on how history was shaped by these decisions.

No one is more capable of enlightening an interested reader in all of the dimensions of cryptology, from its mathematical heritage to its sociological implications, than Randy Nichols. The author of two prior technical works on the subject of classical cryptography, and former President of the American Cryptogram Association, Randy has gathered together a team of extraordinary professionals to make *The ICSA Guide to Cryptography* an outstanding contribution to this important field. The book comes at a strategic point in this evolving history. It provides a timely and important contribution to the understanding of this critical technology. Whether the reader is seeking edification about cryptology itself—a fascinating body of techniques and methods that has helped shape the history of the world as we know it, and which poses an opportune issue requiring an informed citizenry to choose among competing national policies—or is a practitioner of information security as a vocation or avocation, the depth and breadth of knowledge included in these pages will be a welcome source of useful information and a valuable addition to a library.

Daniel J. RYAN
Corporate Vice President
Science Applications
International Corporation
http://members.tripod.com/~Dan_Ryan/

JULIE J. C. H. RYAN
President
Julie Ryan, Inc.
http://www.julieryan.com

PREFACE

Cryptography is a maturing science that has broad-ranging applications in business. Every commercial establishment that either markets its products internationally or uses computer networks for global communications and customer services must be concerned with protecting its assets and customers' information from a variety of attacks.. This concern increases when the Internet is the primary communications medium. The most cost-effective protection for information transmitted by or stored in computers is cryptography.

At one time the sole province of government and military organizations, cryptography has expanded into many directions and dimensions: recreational, scientific, biometric, educational, tactical, strategic, and global. The well-informed company recognizes the value that cryptography adds to the security of its computer information assets. Unfortunately, relatively few corporate managers have deployed cryptographic tools to protect their company computer communications and databases. This trend seems to be reversing dramatically as businesses expand into global markets and the cost of installing appropriate cryptosystems decreases.

Objectives

It is the purpose of this book to provide a practical survey of the principles and practice of cryptography with respect to business applications and, more specifically, commercial computer security systems. It strives to show the benefits of cryptography as a strategic and tactical tool for effective computer security in the commercial theater of operations.

This book presents an in-depth discussion of the business value gained from proper implementation of cryptography countermeasures. It covers processes, products, protocols, key management, implementation mistakes, and product certification. In addition, it provides managers with many resources (including a CD-ROM with state-of-the-art product information supplied by ICSA Cryptography Consortium Members and affiliates) for applying cryptography to commercial computer systems.

The *ICSA Guide to Cryptography* is aimed at the manager, not the specialist. It is especially aimed at the vendor community and contains much material gainfully obtained from it. This book provides a detailed look into the use of cryptography to protect commercial information resources. It describes the ICSA certification process in detail. The *ICSA Guide to Cryptography* integrates the rich history of classical cryptography and cryptanalysis into the modern realm of public-key cryptographic products and capabilities. It demonstrates the science of cryptanalysis in breaking into advanced computer security systems, and speculates on the future directions with biometric encryption. The *ICSA Guide to Cryptography* addresses the challenges associated with doing private business on a public Internet. This book stresses the proper implementation of cryptography security products on computer systems. It covers processes, products, protocols, key management, implementation mistakes, and most vitally, product certification with respect to standards. It presents ICSA's dynamic certification process, which constantly reviews industry standards and current attack methodologies and applies them in its testing of consortium crypto-products. The ultimate effect is to reduce the digital risk in the user community. Lastly, it provides resources for applying cryptography to commercial computer systems.

There is a definite momentum to this book. Part 1 establishes the rich historical basis for modern cryptographic systems. Substitution and transposition systems are introduced with attention to their historical relevance. The principle of cryptographic universality is introduced, which states that the symbols of any language (live or dead) can be quantified and used to unlock its cryptographic treasures. Part 2 presents the essential cryptographic requirements for commercial (public-key) computer security systems. Among the topics presented in Part 2 are one-way functions, cryptographic algorithms, authentication on the Internet, key management, hardware implementations, digital signatures, and certificate authorities. Part 3 should be of special interest to cryptography product vendors. It discusses common implementation mistakes and the dynamic cryptography product certification by ICSA. The role that ICSA plays in the certification of vendors and reduction of risk in the digital world is considered. Part 4 of this guide defines the role cryptography plays in protecting computer systems from attacks originating via the Internet. Part 4 is the heart of the practical side of cryptography. Seven chapters have been originated by some of best companies in the field. Each chapter is designed to be a distinct and viable unit. Protocols, smartcards, Internet cryptography, IPSec, e-business, and role-based crypto-systems are considered. Part 5 discusses the exciting art of cryptanalysis, system identification, and attacks on the security of commercial computer systems. The final chapter presents the interesting direction of combined biometrics and encryption. Appendices include short tutorials on complexity theory, number theory, and elliptic curves.

Intended Audience

Aimed at the information-technology practitioner, the *ICSA Guide to Cryptography* is valuable to CIO's, operations managers, network managers, database managers, programmers, analysts, EDI planners, and similar professionals. The *ICSA Guide to Cryptography* is suitable for a first-year graduate course in computer science, for computers in business courses, and for MBA programs. There are plenty of resources in the bibliography, URL references, and textual leads to further reading.

Plan of the Book

The *ICSA Guide to Cryptography* is written to be interesting and progressive in its presentation of the material. This book is organized to differentiate fundamental concepts of cryptographic protection for commercial computer systems. The body of cryptographic research available today did not evolve from thin air. It came from centuries of growth and learning from mistakes. In my admitted passion and zeal for unlocking the modern cryptographic treasures, I believe that we must be aware of the lessons of the past before we try to understand the growth of the present. The chapters are organized as follows:

Part 1: The Development of Cryptography

Part 1 presents the fundamentals learned from classical cryptography. The six chapters are organized as follows:

1. *Introduction:* This chapter introduces a historical slice—and a few of the people that have influenced cryptographic thought in the past.

2. *First Principles and Overview:*   Defines the various dimensions of applying cryptography to computer systems (vulnerabilities, threats, and countermeasures); defines security foundations (data integrity, confidentiality, authentication, nonrepudiation, and identification); discusses commercial goals of cost-effectiveness and "added value" rather than military goals of secrecy and disclosure; addresses the Internet as a dynamic force against privacy.

3–4. *Historical Systems I and II:*   Defines the principle of cryptographic universality based on language-based phonemes; establishes the rich history of cryptography; discusses simple substitution and transposition systems; defines W. F. Friedman's analysis of cryptosystems; expands the knowledge base to polyalphabetic and isomorphic systems; introduces Xenocrypts (cryptograms in foreign languages) and defines taxonomy of ancient and modern languages; discusses Delastelle Systems and principles of fractionation.

5. *Codes and Machines:*   Introduces the beginnings of commercial codes; discusses development of machine cryptography used in wartime and tracks how computers became a force in cryptography; covers superencryption and additives.

6. *Data Encryption Standard (DES) and Information Theory:* Covers the transition from classical to modern cryptography; covers in depth the famous Data Encryption Standard (DES), 3DES, variants to public-key (PK) cryptography, and discusses implementation.

Part 2: Commercial Cryptographic Systems

Part 2 describes the key elements of modern cryptography. The six chapters in this section are organized as follows:

7. *Public-Key (Asymmetric) Cryptography:*   Delineates symmetric and asymmetric cryptography; discusses mathematical concepts (primes, large numbers, intractable functions, trapdoor functions, one-way hash functions, and their importance in public-key systems); details the knapsack problem and the principles of a public-key cryptosystem.

8. *Algorithms:*   A core chapter that covers the RSA algorithm and defines integer factorization problems, discrete log problems, and their elliptic curve analogs.

9. *Identification, Authentication, and Authorization on the World Wide Web:* Covers Internet identification and authentication systems.

10. *Digital Signatures:* Covers the challenge of signing and authenticating documents in the digital world.

11. *Hardware Implementations:* Covers the use of application specific gateways and specialized chips to perform cryptographic functions.

12. *Certificate Authorities:* Focuses on the difficult problem of trusted third parties (TTP) and key recovery protocols; discusses public-key certificates, distribution, workstations, authority levels, and revocation.

Part 3: Implementation and Product Certification

There are significant risks in doing business in the digital world. Part 3 defines the ICSA motives for certification and explores the implementation mistakes that have been observed in the testing of vendor products.

13. *Implementation Mistakes:* An important chapter that covers the many types of implementation mistakes associated with purchase, installation, operation, and connectivity for vendor-tested cryptographic products; explores mistakes made when implementing cryptographic countermeasures; focuses on red/black separation, link encryption, point-to-point limitations, keying, and algorithm issues.

14. *ICSA Product Certification:* Discusses ICSA's Cryptography Products Consortium and approach to certification; presents the concept of raising the "bar" on security effectiveness in products.

Part 4: Practical Cryptography

Much of the material for Part 4 was prepared and submitted by senior management representatives from ICSA's Cryptography Products Consortium. The six chapters in this unit represent state-of-the-art activities. Each chapter is a self-contained unit.

15. *Internet Cryptography:* Covers the important protocols for protecting messages on the Internet.

16. *Security: Policy, Privacy, and Protocols:* Defines computer security issues specific to the Internet and discusses attack taxonomies and legal environment surrounding cryptography products.

17. *Smartcards:* Presents the technology of smartcard and its relationship to cryptography.

18. *IP Security and Secure Virtual Private Networks:* Describes virtual private networks and the developing standards on the Internet. Topics include protocol security layers, ISAKAMP, OAKLEY, key management, authentication, encryption, and router configurations.

19. *Cryptography in Electronic Commerce Systems:* Presents unique measures to meet security objectives and secure business computers.

20. *Role-Based Cryptography:* Presents the techniques of role-based cryptography—a popular alternative to standard crypto-systems.

Part 5: New Dimensions

Part 5 presents two further dimensions of the science of cryptography, cryptanalysis, and biometric encryption.

21. *Cryptanalysis and System Identification:* Discusses Shannon's information concepts, language redundancy, encryption security, work factor, and classical attacks on symmetric ciphers; presents modern attacks such as brute force key search, reflection, man-in-the-middle, and denial of service; discusses the use of feature vectors to differentiate cryptographic systems and key clustering to solve them.

22. *Biometric Encryption:* The final chapter presents the interesting direction on the technological horizon—the combination of encryption and biometric technologies.

Internet Mailing List

An Internet mailing list has been set up through COMSEC Solutions and ICSA so that interested parties can exchange information, suggestions, and questions with the author. Email requests to *RNichols@COMSEC-Solutions.com*, or browse *www.COMSEC-Solutions.com* to obtain current guide information. Current versions of the ICSA cryptography and IPSec certification criteria may be downloaded from *www.ICSA.net*.

CD-ROM

A CD-ROM is attached to the end flap which includes a variety of papers and state-of-the-art materials regarding cryptographic products, both certified and noncertified, by ICSA.

Acknowledgments

The purview of modern cryptography encompasses more than mathematics or cryptanalysis. Therefore, I solicited help and received advanced technology material from distinguished talent in the ICSA Cryptographic Products Consortium and affiliates. The team of cryptography professionals that assisted with the writing of this book represent some of the most knowledgeable and respected members of the cryptographic community. Their collective professional wisdom can be witnessed in several practical chapters. Readers are encouraged to view the biographies and qualifications of the contributors summarized at the beginning of this book.

Chapter 8 (Algorithms) includes original material submitted by Dr. William Raike, founder of RPK International: Jack Oswald, CEO of RPKUSA: and William Stallings, a talented and well-respected author of 22 books in the security field. Chapter 9 (Identification, Authentication, and Authorization on the World Wide Web) is based on original material obtained from Mich Kabay, director of education for ICSA. Chapter 10 (Digital Signatures) includes expanded materials submitted by Rich Komando, CEO of KRYPTOTECH. Chapter 11 (Hardware Implementations) was contributed by Shawn Abbott, chief scientist for

RAINBOW TECHNOLOGIES and includes new materials garnered from PKS'98. Chapter 12 (Certificate Authorities) was prepared by Hart DeGrafft, program manager and chief engineer for SPARTA. Chapter 13 (Implementation Mistakes) was prepared with the help of Fred Tompkins, previously ICSA director of policy analysis and now information security advisor and deputy program director for UNISYS Corporation. Chapter 15 (Internet Cryptography) was developed by Richard E. Smith, author of the best-selling *Internet Cryptography* and a principal information security architect for SECURE COMPUTING Corporation. Chapter 16 (Security: Policy, Privacy, and Protocols) represents a joint effort by the author, Kevin Hunter, executive vice president, Tim Trowbridge, chief engineer of BROKEN RHYTHM SOLUTIONS, formerly of DOXA ASSOCIATES, and Roy Pereira, security architect for TIMESTEP. Chapter 17 (Smartcards) became possible because of the solid efforts of Steve Petri, director of smartcard technology for LITRONICS. Chapter 18 (IPSec) was submitted by Roy Pereira of TIMESTEP, internationally renowned in the security field and a member of IETF. Chapter 19 (Cryptography in Electronic Commerce Systems) was prepared by Shannon Byrne, COO and David Slik of PARA-DATA Corporation. The fascinating Chapter 20 (Role-Based Cryptography) was developed by Mary Van Zandt, senior product line manager for STERLING COMMERCE. Chapter 22 (Biometric Encryption) was invited material on the technology of biometric encryption from MYTEC TECHNOLOGIES, prepared by Colin Soutar, chief scientist, and Rene Gilroy, senior cryptologist in conjunction with Professors Danny Roberge, Alex Stoianov, B. V. K. Vijaya Kumar, all of Carnegie Mellon University. To say the least, I am deeply grateful for all their competence, assistance, and sincere professionalism. *The ICSA Guide to Cryptography* is a professional success due to our collective efforts.

The ICSA Guide to Cryptography has benefited from review by numerous experts in the field, who gave generously of their time and expertise. The following people reviewed all or part of the manuscript: Jules M. Price, an expert on cipher technology; Alfred J. Menzes, coauthor of the *Handbook of Cryptography* and a world-class expert on elliptic curve cryptography (ECC); Dan Ryan, corporate vice president of SAIC and an expert on global computer security; Julie Ryan, internationally respected consultant to the U.S. Navy on information warfare; Leo Pluswick, ICSA cryptography products consortium manager (NSA retired); Peter Tippett, president and CEO of the International Computer Security Association (ICSA); Louis Kruh, American Cryptogram Association and coauthor of

Machine Cryptography and Modern Cryptanalysis; Frank Lewis, perhaps the greatest living cryptographer of the twentieth century and two-time U.S. Medal of Freedom winner; Jerry L. Metzger, professor of mathematics, University of North Dakota; Richard E. Smith, principal information security architech for Secure Computing Corporation and author of the best-selling book *Internet Cryptography*; Robert Moskovitz of ICSA (formerly Chrysler Corporation) and chief author of the international standards on IPSec; Hart DeGrafft and Lou Moliani of SPARTA; Kevin Hunter of Doxa Associates; Don Krysakowski; Mich Kabay; Jesse Geiman; Bobby Shipp; Steve Ratcliffe; David Kennedy; Fred Tompkins; Harry Brittain; Bob Bales; Tom Kelchner; Dave and Wendy Harper; Corinne Martin; Charles M. Thatcher, distinguished professor of chemical engineering, University of Arkansas and author of *Chemical Engineering Principles*; and, finally, those primary authors who have influenced my thoughts so deeply over the years, namely Whitfield Diffie, Alfred Menezes, Scott Vanstone, Arto Salomaa, David Kahn, Stephen Matyas, Claude Shannon, William Stallings, Dorothy Denning, I. J. Kumar, Winn Schwartau, Wayne Barker, William F. Friedman, Friedrich Bauer, Eli Biham, Bruce Schneier, Phil Zimmermann, Adi Shamir, Lambros Callimahos, Abraham Sinkov, Soloman Kullback, Frank Lewis, Stephen Kent, and many more to whom I apologize for failing to give partial or full credit. I am responsible for this material and any omissions or errors in its presentation. Please advise me by email and I will do my best to correct the errors and publish an errata list on the COMSEC Solutions listserver.

This manuscript didn't just come about without a lot of patience and effort by my two typists. I want to thank Judy Motter (ICSA) and especially Janel Linette Shipp (COMSEC Solutions) for superior work on our book. Montine Nichols deserves a commendation for her help and patience during this process. Special thanks to Alice Tung, Judy Brief, Claire Stanley, Terry Leaden, and Curt Berkowitz of the McGraw-Hill Book Company for their very professional help.

RANDY NICHOLS
President, COMSEC Solutions
Former Technology Director—Cryptography and Biometrics
International Computer Security Association (ICSA)
Email: *RNichols@COMSEC-Solutions.com*
Web://*www.COMSEC-Solutions.com*
Carlisle, Pennsylvania
September 1998

ICSA GUIDE TO CRYPTOGRAPHY

The Development of Cryptography

CHAPTER **1**

Introduction

Cryptology is the study of creating codes and ciphers (*cryptography*) and decoding or deciphering codes and ciphers (*cryptanalysis*) when the system is not known. Cryptology would not be the science it is today without the contributions of different groups of people who have become part of its rich and fascinating history over the past several thousand years. David Kahn wrote the definitive history of cryptology in his book *The Codebreakers*. Dr. Bauer at the University of Munich, in his thoroughly enjoyable book *Decrypted Secrets — Methods and Maxims of Cryptology*, extended Kahn's work to include European contributions. In his two volumes *Classical Cryptography Course*, Nichols focused on the scientists and mathematicians involved in the science of cryptanalysis of codes, ciphers, and speech.

Mathematical disciplines have played an important part in the development and especially the current state-of-the-art efforts in cryptology. A list of the disciplines would include applied and theoretical statistics, number theory, group theory, combinatory logic, complexity theory, information theory, elliptical curves study, and chaos theory. Cryptology is taught in major schools under the banner of applied mathematics and computer science. The computer scientist views cryptology as an important connection with respect to access to operating systems, databases, computer networks, and data transmission systems.

The list of contributors and their stories are exemplary — names such as Francois Viete; John Wallis of England; Rossignol of France; Auguste Kerckhoff of Holland; de Viarus, Valerio, Delastelle, Bazeries, General Givierge, all of France; Edgar Allan Poe, a rather misunderstood cryptographer and visionary; General Luigi Sacco in Italy; William Frederick Friedman, the American Master Cryptographer, who in 1920, introduced the *Index of Coincidence* and in whose brilliance the latter-day National Security Agency (NSA) placed its trust; Abraham Sinkov; Solomon Kullback; Lester S. Hill; Claude E. Shannon, who gave us modern day information theory; Alan Turing in England; Hans Rohrbach from Germany; Marian Rejewski from Poland, who originally broke Enigma; Vannevar Bush; Frank Lewis, who defeated the Japanese Army codes in 1942-1943; Maurits de Vries in the Netherlands; and Ernst S. Selmer in Norway.

Cryptography's influence on history is significant. For example, a small historical snapshot might include the following names.

Kerckhoff

Kerckhoff (aka Jean-Guillaume-Hubert-Victor-Francois-Alexandre-Auguste Kerckhoff von Nieuwenhof)—who was neither French nor Dutch, but Flemish—was the first to separate the general system from the specific key. He perfected the theory of superimposition to solve polyalphabetic systems, described the concepts of symmetry of position to glean more plain text from the cipher text, and invented the Saint-Cyr slide and named it after the French national military academy where he studied. *La Cryptographie militaire* gave the French a commanding lead in cryptography in World War I. He was the impetus for those that followed.

French Influences: Givierge, Valerio, de Viaris, Delastelle, and Bazeries

General Givierge, a military commander, wrote an early and important textbook on cryptography called *Course in Cryptography*. Givierge published letter frequencies for French, German, English, Russian, Spanish, and Italian. They differ from the Master William F. Friedman's works. Friedman's works are more authoritative and based on significantly more modern plain text. General Givierge borrowed from Paul Louis Eugene Valerio, a captain of artillery who wrote in the *Journal des Sciences militaires* in 1892. Valerio published a book called *De la cryptographie* in 1895. The General also borrowed from de Viaris (aka Marquis Gaetan Henri Leon Viarizio di Lesegno), who invented one of the first printing cipher devices in 1874. The General may have included the work of the enigmatic Felix Marie Delastelle, who wrote *Traite Elementaire de Cryptographie* in 1902. Delastelle's most famous cipher is the bifid, which is covered in a later section. Delastelle expanded Kerckhoff's symmetry of position principles published in *La Cryptographie militaire* in 1883. Lastly, the influence of Etienne Bazeries on the General was important. Bazeries invented a cylinder device for polyalphabetic encipherment, although de Viaris solved the Bazeries cylinder in 1893. (Bazeries was miffed to say the least.) In spite of this, his device was accepted for use by the U.S. Army as a field cipher device until 1922.

Rossignol

Rossignol served with a swashbuckling facility in the court of Louis XIV. His cryptographic successes gave him access to secrets of state and the court. Rossignol was the court cryptologist of France in the time when Moliere was her dramatist, Pascal her philosopher, La Fontaine her fabulist, and the supreme autocrat of the world her monarch.

Rossignol's technical improvements to the *nomenclator* (a two-part code) systems of the time were quite important. When Rossignol began his career, nomenclators were one-part, listing both the plain and the code elements in alphabetical order or numerical order if the code was numerical. Plain and code paralleled each other. This arrangement existed since the beginning of the Renaissance. Rossignol destroyed the parallel arrangements and mixed the code elements relative to the plain. Two lists were required, one in which the plain elements were in alphabetical order and the code elements were randomized. The second facilitated decoding in which the code elements were alphabetized and the plain equivalents were disarranged. The two tables were called *tables a chiffrer* and *tables a dechiffrer*. The two part codes are similar to a bilingual dictionary. The two-part construction spread rapidly to other countries and the nomenclator systems grew in number and size.

His son Bonaventure and his grandson Antoine-Bonaventure both carried on the tradition Rossignol started. Both were raised from King's counselor to president of the Chamber of Accounts. The Cabinet Noir, founded under Louvois, France's Minister of War, at the urging of Antoine Rossignol, took extraordinary precautions by switching systems, introducing 18 new nomenclator series. It was the start of France's ironclad control over the cipher business. It still has a tight access policy today. The Vienna Black Chamber—the Geheime Kabinets-Kanzlei—regularly read French ciphers up to the cabinet level.

Wallis

England had its own Black Chamber. John Wallis, Rossignol's contemporary, was first a mathematician, giving us the germ of the binomial theorem, the symbol and concept of infinity, a calculation of pi by interpolation, and the beginnings of the calculus for Newton to do his work. John Wallis's solution of Louis XIV's (France) letter of 9 June 1693 put his name in the record books.

Wallis's and Rossignol's careers paralleled each other: both n
their start on their country's civil war ciphers in their twenties, h
mathematical bent, were self-taught, lived into their eighties, c
their worldly success to cryptanalysis, and became their respective c
tries' "Father of Cryptology," in both the literal and figurative sense
they were different, too. Rossignol worked at court, whereas W
worked at Oxford. Rossignol introduced new systems for the French
supervised their use. Wallis apparently prescribed only one En
cipher and that was done informally.

It is unlikely that these cryptologic experts ever clashed cryptolo
ly despite the contentious natures of both countries.

General Luigi Sacco

One of Italy's most brilliant cryptographers, General Luigi
detailed solutions of various transposition, monoalphabetic, and p
phabetic systems. His appendix details the equations used for
interesting problems as de Viaris's polyalphabetic substitution, F
hoff's ciphers, and the Hill algebraic problem.

Changing Directions

Cryptology has flourished in secrecy itself—some might say obs
The available classic literature is hard to collect.

Professional cryptographers in the military and diplomatic se
hold their cards tight to the vest of materials cryptographic. As a
freely available literature never fully reflected the state of the
condition that is bending a little in modern-day politics. The U
States under its Freedom of Information Act (FOIA) has released
erous amount of information to satiate the public media. This is
cially true when dealing with World War II communications. U
the 1990s and only after the political disintegration of the "Old
Union" did we find that the Soviets were very adept in the cryptog
business. The French, who have not learned to cooperate with a
including the French, have the most oppressive laws regarding cr
raphy's import/export/use. The Internet is quickly dissipating thei
tion. The Germans and English have unique "Secrets Acts" b

working with the International community to improve security and maintain privacy interests for their countries.

The intelligence services do not usually reveal even the names of their leading cryptographers. Some have become too famous to hide. General Sir Stewart Graham Menzies (1890-1968), chief of M.I.6, the British Secret Intelligence Service, was known only as "C." He was in charge of nearly 8000 "Passport Control Officers" as well as the cryptanalytic unit at Bletchley Park (BP). His counterpart was Ernst C. Fetterlein (d. 1944). He was the head of the Russian cryptanalytic bureau and served the Government Code and Cipher School (GC&C) of the British Foreign Office.

The government and specifically the military consider cryptography and cryptosystems in general as weapons for defense and attack. The International Traffic in Arms Regulations (ITAR) and, most recently, the Bureau of Export (BXA) under the aegis of the Commerce Department have rules governing the release of "strong" cryptography to foreign interests without a license, which requires sub-rosa approval from the NSA or NIST. The government has approved millions of dollars of research to improve cryptosystems. Kahn and Nichols detail many stories where the battle turned because a better cryptographic system was in place. All the major powers in World War II had success in solving enemy cryptographic systems.

On the other sides are two counterforces, the commercial interests that want to bring products to market quickly and effectively to compete with foreign products that are not restricted as in the United States, and the privacy interests of civil rights groups. The politics in 1997-1998 are fierce, to say the least. The Internet is dissolving all the territorial responses to the issues. Phillip Zimmerman became a modern folk hero when he released PGP to the public over the Internet. PGP is akin to a Tinkertoy set with the right ingredients for encipherment, key exchange, trust levels, and popular appeal. Early versions of PGP found their way around the globe and became distributed well before some of the contractual arrangements could protect an author's intellectual property and to the chagrin of the U.S. government; but, the most recent PGP version includes key recovery, a definite concession to U.S. government whims.

Side by side with state cryptology in diplomatic and military services have stood the amateurs. Since 1929, the American Cryptogram Association (ACA) has been the leader in recreational cryptography. Their free courses have included students from every intelligence and military discipline, talented amateurs from educational halls, and commercial players from the computer and information industries. From the revelations

of historic events by Etienne Bazeries (1846-1931); to the amusements of Wheatstone and Lord Playfair; to the vision of Edgar Allan Poe, a talented cryptographer whose works affected literature and science; to drug-runners stopped by the U.S. Coast Guard with the help of Elizabeth F. Friedman (1892-1980); to the popular mythology around President Kennedy, who used a Playfair cipher to send a message to his base after he was shipwrecked when his PT-109 was cut in half; to President Eisenhower, who used a clever cipher system based on golf words; to Bush, who built up the HUMINT Intelligence services to a shining level only to have it gutted by President Clinton; to the love notes my ten-year-old Diana sends me by fax using the telephone code—cryptology shows a rich tapestry interwoven with history. Cryptology's many personalities make its history a particularly pleasurable field—and for me, a passion as well as a vocation.

Commercial interests take cryptography as seriously as does government. The International Computer Security Association (ICSA) pioneered the consortium model for certification of cryptography-based products. The Cryptography Products Consortium (CPC) was formed to encourage the use of cryptography as an enabling technology and to educate the user community on the benefits and proper application of cryptography. There are 40 members in the U.S. consortium and nine more in the European group. The CPC IPSEC subgroup includes the entire automotive and trucking industry and has set the cryptographic standards on VPN (virtual private networks) for the world. The Internet Service Providers Security Consortium (ISPSEC) is dedicated to implementing global measures to improve security on the Internet. The 17 "backbone" businesses use cryptography to protect $1 billion worth of business in 1997. The implementation of strong cryptography is prima facie to this effort.

The increased need for information security has given cryptology a hitherto unrecognized importance. Private commercial applications of cryptography have come to the forefront and are leading to some exciting new technologies. In particular, the asymmetric public keys first proposed by Whitfield Diffie and Martin Hellman in 1976 have revolutionized the commercial cryptography market. Computer programs that have not had adequate copyright protection now use cryptography to preclude theft or unauthorized use. Both email and e-commerce use cryptography to authenticate business relationships. The Auto Industry Group (AIG) in conjunction with ICSA set the global security standards for Virtual Private Networks (VPN) and IP security (IPSEC) for auto/truck dealerships and Tier I suppliers.

We no longer have Morse code. We have satellites and optical fiber networks. Our code books are kept in laptops, not jumpsuits. "Breaks" or "cracks" are now made using cooperative computer horsepower with thousands of stations in situ. Exploring an entire keyspace has little excitement and even less practicality. Tactically, such "hits" are high-show, low-probability, and low-functionality; considering the counterinterception capabilities, random number generation abilities, the useful key life cycles and sizes, and the array of defensive algorithms offered, modern cryptographic products are up to the challenge of practical viability.

Cryptology for the "public" raises contradictions, hysterical claims, and conflicts of interest between numerous scientists, public, privacy, legal, businesses, and government. Mutual cooperation has become the workable solution to many of the questions of the day—so that will be our tone for this book.

WRAP-UP

Cryptography's history, people, and development are intricately woven into society's fabric. We first look at the basic principles of cryptography, then show how security of the classic systems was improved through complexity and cleverness, and then move into the mechanization of cryptosystems. We end our classical look at cryptography with a study of data encryption algorithm (DEA), which evolved into the data encryption standard (DES). DES is still popular today even though official moves to replace it with an Advanced Encryption System (AES) are moving rapidly forward. DES marks the turning point from classical cryptography to modern and public key cryptosystems.

CHAPTER 2

First Principles and Overview

The explosive growth of commercial computer systems and networks over the last decade has brought with it the challenge of protecting them from unauthorized access to their contents. One of the most important tools available for computer security is cryptography. A wide variety of products using encryption technologies have become available commercially. The Cryptography Products Consortium (CPC), facilitated by the International Computer Security Association (ICSA), has been working toward joint security goals of enhanced interoperability and communications among their common products. The Open Systems Interconnect (OSI) standard is cited as a common framework for design of secure networks. Common industry practices for implementing cryptography in commercial computer systems are identified within the purview of that OSI framework.

Classical Cryptosystems

Cryptography is the science of writing messages that no one except the intended receiver can read. *Cryptanalysis* is the science of reading them anyway. "Cryptography" comes from the Greek *krypte*, meaning "hidden" or "vault" and *grafik*, meaning "writing."

Steganography also comes from Greek (meaning "covered") and is considered in the next chapter. The term *cryptographia*, meaning "secrecy in writing," was used in 1641 by John Wilkins, a founder with John Wallis of the Royal Society; the word *cryptography* was coined in 1658 by Thomas Browne, famous English physician and writer. It is the aim of cryptography to render a message incomprehensible to an unauthorized reader—*ars occulte scribendi*. One speaks of overt secret writing, *overt* in the sense of being obviously recognizable as secret writing.

The words, characters, or letters of the original intelligible message constitute the *plain text*. The words, characters, or letters of the secret form of the message are called *cipher text* or constitute a *cryptogram*.

The process of converting plain text into cipher text is *encipherment* or *encryption*. The reverse process of reducing cipher text into plain text is *decipherment* or *decryption*. A *cryptosystem* is defined as the associated items of cryptomaterial and the methods and rules by which these items are used as a unit to provide a means of encryption and decryption. A cryptosystem embraces the general enciphering-deciphering and the specific keys essential to the employment of the system.

Cipher systems are divided into two basic classes: *substitution* and *transposition*. A *substitution cipher* is a cryptogram in which the original letters of the plain text, taken either singly or in groups of constant length, have been replaced by other letters, figures, signs, or a combination of them in accordance with a definite system and key.

A *transposition cipher* is a cryptogram in which the original letters of the plain text have been rearranged according to a definite system. Modern cipher systems use extremely complex mathematical forms of both substitution and transposition to protect sensitive messages.

Purposes of Encryption

In a cryptosystem, *plain text* is acted upon by a known *algorithm* (set of mathematical rules) to determine the transformation process to cipher text and a *key* that controls the encryption/decryption algorithm to *transform* the data into cipher text. In a system using a key, the message cannot be transformed without the key. Two types of key systems exist: *symmetric* or *private key systems,* where the sender and receiver use the same key, and *asymmetric* or *public key systems,* where the sender and receiver use different keys. In an asymmetric system, the sender uses a public key, which is available to anyone, to encipher the message, but only the receiver using a unique private key can decipher the message.

The basic purpose of encryption is to protect sensitive information from unauthorized disclosure. When computer systems are involved, this information can be stored within the system or transmitted across insecure public carriers.

Modern encryption methods are used to prevent the exposure previously defined and offer desirable features for other types of exposures such as:

Data confidentiality, or secrecy, since messages must be decrypted in order for information to be understood.

Data integrity, because some algorithms additionally protect against forgery or tampering.

Authentication of message originator, because it is needed to demonstrate that the key has not been compromised and remains secret. Authentication of system occurs when the user performs a cryptographic function with a cryptographic key that is unique to the user.

Electronic certification and digital signature, using cryptographic algorithms to protect against unauthorized modification and forgery of electronic documents.

Nonrepudiation, using (a) secret key technology whereby a trusted third party (TTP) can hold a copy of the secured transaction or (b) public key technology where users impose nonrepudiation on the originator by virtue of the digital signature. Public key technology can also provide nonrepudiation of the recipient by requiring an acknowledgment signed by the recipient before a "contract" is formed. Thus, neither sender nor receiver can deny the document. The signed acknowledgment includes the signature from the original message. This is very important in the making of electronic contracts on such media as the Internet.

Cryptosystems represent a powerful *countermeasure* to computer intrusions. Cryptographic product vendors have a mission to reduce the risk in the electronic marketplace.

A Glimpse at Commercial Cryptography

The Cryptography Products Consortium (CPC) is a group of 40 talented companies specializing in the delivery of a wide variety of cryptographic products for protection of commercial computer systems and networks. In 1997, the International Computer Security Association (ICSA) initiated certification programs for many different categories of security products and services (File Encryptors; Virtual Private Networks, or VPNs; Cryptographic Toolkits; and Smartcards). ICSA's overall goal is to improve commercial security systems by improving the implementation, sales, and use of appropriate security products, services, policies, techniques, and procedures.

The CPC as a joint entity defined four values supporting their mission to produce quality *cryptographic* products for their customer facilities. These values are Quality, Service, Innovation, and Collaboration. Figure 2-1 shows the linkage between CPC performance and their corporate values.

Note that the critical success factors include both quality goals and customer satisfaction. Customer satisfaction is most important in the commercial security market because of unequal tradeoffs of risk, security, cost, and productivity. Commercial firms and government departments have different reasons and priorities to justify the purchase of security systems. Nor are the security concerns the same for commercial facilities as with government entities. The more difficult the encryption product is to understand, the less likely it will be added to customer inventory. Customers are satisfied when they are comfortable with the supporting quality controls used by the vendor. Quality is the key issue

Figure 2-1
Linking Performance
To CPC Values

What	CPC Values	How
Number of Customer Requirements Met	Quality	Standardization Documentation Audit Certification by Registrar
Improvement in Customer Satisfaction Levels	Service	Treatment of Customers
Number and Impact of Process Improvements	Innovation	Exploration of New Ideas, Publication
	Collaboration	Seeking Input, Offering Assistance, and Customer Feedback

in the commercial security market. In some firms, the technical superiority of the encryption system is of secondary importance in the decision to purchase the encryption product. Compatibility of the product line with current computer systems may have significant influence in the final decision.

How do we measure the quality of a cryptosystem? One answer is to provide products that conform to international standards of excellence.

Cryptographic Standards

To customers, quality and interoperability of encryption products are essential. Standards facilitate widespread use of cryptographically sound techniques, and interoperability of system and system components. The main standards organizations—ISO, CCITT, ANSI, IEC, and ECMA—are described by Stallings. Appendix Tables A-1 to A-7 list standards addressing particular areas. Menezes presents a detailed overview of these standards.

Table A-1 presents international (ISO and ISO/IEC) application-independent standards on cryptographic techniques. Tables A-2 and A-3 summarize banking security standards, subdivided into ANSI and ISO standards. Table A-4 considers international security architectures and frameworks (ISO and X.509). Table A-5 summarizes security-related standards for use by U.S. federal government departments. Table A-6 addresses selected Internet specifications, while Table A-7 notes selected de facto industry standards.

Importance of Standards to the Commercial Market

The telecommunications industry embraced standards to govern physical, electrical, and procedural characteristics of their communication equipment. Historically, the computer industry has not embraced this view. Computer vendors tended to bind their customers with proprietary products and protocols and have been slow to push for standardization of interfaces. The CPC realized that computers from different vendors must communicate with each other; with the ongoing evolution of protocol standards, customers would no longer accept special-purpose protocol-conversion software development. From the potential customers' standpoint, there are three key advantages of standardization:

1. Standards assure that there will be a large market for a particular piece of encryption equipment or software. Economies of scale for production are encouraged.

2. Standards allow products from multiple vendors to communicate, giving the purchaser more flexibility in equipment selection and use.

3. Standards facilitate competition, leading to better products at lower prices.

The principal disadvantage of standards is that they tend to "freeze" technology. By the time a standard is developed, subjected to review and compromise, and promulgated, more efficient technologies may have been developed. Products developed under these systems may be delayed for acceptance into the market.

It should be noted that many cryptographic standards are voluntary. Manufacturers voluntarily implement a product that conforms to a standard if they perceive a benefit to themselves; there is no legal requirement to conform. The CPC embraced standardization because: (1) standards have been developed on a basis of a broad consensus and (2) customer demand for standardized products encourages continuous improvement and implementation by consortium members.

Open Systems Interconnect (OSI) Model

How many ways can data require protection in a computer system? Conventional wisdom might say three: (1) data at rest, (2) data in motion, or

(3) data in the process of transference. Data protection is accomplished by means of hardware, software, or a combination of both.

Currently, communications usually are analyzed using the International Standards Organization's Open System Interconnect Reference Model (ISO OSI-RM). The purpose of the OSI Reference Model (OSI-RM) was to provide a framework for developing communication protocol and service standards that would allow interworking of equipment from many different vendors. The OSI model breaks down communications into seven layers. Refer to Table 2-1 for a look at the OSI model layers and their information processing/transfer functions. Table 2-2 presents ISO data processing, transfer protocols, and equivalents for each layer. Within this architecture, standards have been developed at all seven layers to support distributed computing. With the development of the OSI model, vendors were expected to quickly provide standardized communications facilities. This did not happen. The last decade has seen slow acceptance of standardized communications products.

TABLE 2-1

OSI Model Communication Layers and Their Information Processing/Transfer Functions

OSI Layer # Name	Information Processing/Transfer Functions
7 Application	Provides the interface for applications to access the OSI environment through the lower levels. Supports functions such as file transfer, virtual terminal, electronic mail, establishing the authority to communicate, systems and applications management functions,...
6 Presentation	Formats data received from Layer 7. Character code conversion, terminal standards, data compression, display rules,...
5 Session	Negotiation and establishment/termination of connections with other nodes. Manages and synchronizes the direction of data flow. Coordinates interaction among applications.
4 Transport	Provides for end-to-end data transfer between applications, data integrity, and service quality. Assembles data for routing by Layer 3.
3 Network	Routes and relays data across multiple networks.
2 Data Link	Transfers data from one network node to another over a transmission circuit. Performs data integrity functions.
1 Physical	Transmits the bit stream over a communication medium.

TABLE 2-2

ISO Data Processing, Transfer Protocols, and Equivalents

Layer # Name	ISO	ITU(T)	ANSI	ECMA
7 *Application*	8571 (FTAM) 10021 (MHS) 9041 (VT) 10026 (DTP) 9594 (DS) 8613 (ODA) 9579 (RDA) 9596 (CMIP)	— X.400 — — X.500 T.410, T.73 — —	— — — — — — — —	— — — — — ECMA-101 — —
6 *Presentation*	8823 (connection) 9596 (connectionless)	X.226 —	— —	—
5 *Session*	8327 (connection) 9548 (connectionless)	X.225 —	X3.153 —	ECMA-75 —
4 *Transport*	8073 (TP0–TP4) (connection) 8602/8072 (connectionless)	X.224 — 	X3.140 — 	ECMA-72 —
3 *Network*	8208 (layers 1–3) 8878 (use w/8208) 8348 (connection) 8473 (connectionless) 9542 (IS-IS) 8880 (LAN) 8881 (X.25 on LANs)	X.25 X.25 X.213 — — — 	— — — — — — 	— — — ECMA-92 — —
2 *Data Link*	7776 (LAPB) 3309 (HDLC) 8802.2-.7 (LAN) (IEEE 802.2-.7)	X.25 — — 	— X3.66 — 	— ECMA-40 ECMA-81, -82, -89, -90
1 *Physical*	9314 (FDDI) 2110 (EIA-232D) 4902 (EIA-449) 2593 4903	— V.24, V.28 V.24, V.28 V.35 X-series	X3.139, X3.148 X3.166 	— — — —

Truly interoperable, distributed, standardized (universal) processing requires more than the basic protocols at the seven layers. Issues concerning the choice of networks and the ability to control and manage configurations had to be addressed (e.g., ISDN protocols). Four key areas where alternative standards are developing to provide the customer with improved functionality are:

1. *Internetworking:* Both connectionless and connection-mode internetworking standards have been developed. Routing issues are being addressed.

2. *WAN* (*wide area network*): New standards for ATM (asynchronous transfer mode), SONET (synchronous optical network), and frame relay are being revised.

3. *LAN and MAN* (*local and metropolitan area networks*): FDDI (fiber distributed data interface) and 802.6 MAN standards are evolving.

4. *Network Management and Security:* The nub of complex networking is effective network management and security.

OSI-related standards have reached a level of maturity and functionality that makes standardized network management and security products practical. On the quality assurance side, in the last five years, commercial firms registering to ISO 9000 standards have quadrupled in both Europe and United States. Another useful result of international standards is international standardized profiles (ISPs). These profiles provide specifications that allow multiple vendors to build products that work together for specific application areas.

OSI Security

From a security standpoint, ISO 7498-2 may be the most important standard in the business. ISO standard No. 7498-2 (OSI Basic Reference Model—Part 2: Security Architecture) establishes an OSI security framework. It provides functional assignment of security services and mechanisms to OSI layers. The OSI security architecture addresses the issues of network security (protecting data in transmission from terminal to user or from computer to computer) rather than a single system security. Three concepts form the basis for the security architecture:

1. *Security threats:* Actions that compromise the security of information owned by an organization.

2. *Security mechanisms:* Communications mechanisms designed to detect, prevent, or recover from a security threat.

3. *Security services:* Communications services enhancing the security of an organization's data processing systems and information transfers. These services are intended to counter security threats.

ISO has been developing standards that elaborate on the concepts in

TABLE 2-3

Key ISO Security
Standards

ISO 7498-2	OSI Basic Reference Model—Part 2: Security Architecture
ISO 8649 AM 1	Service Definition for the Association Control Service Element—Amendment 1: Authentication during Association Establishment
ISO 8650 AM 1	Protocol Specification for the Association Control Service Element—Amendment 1: Authentication during Association Establishment
ISO 9160	Data Encipherment–Physical Layer Interoperability Requirements
DIS 9797	Security Techniques: Digital Signature Scheme Giving Message Recovery
ISO 9797	Data Cryptographic Techniques: Data Integrity Mechanism Using a Check Function Employing a Block Cipher Algorithm
DIS 9798-1	Security Techniques: Entity Authentication Mechanisms—Part 1: General Model
CD 9798-2	Security Techniques: Entity Authentication Mechanisms—Part 2: Entity Authentication Using Symmetric Techniques
CD 9798-3	Security Techniques: Entity Authentication Mechanisms—Part 3: Entity Authentication Using Public Key Algorithms
DIS 10116	Mode of Operation for an n-Bit Block Cipher
CD 10181-1	Security Frameworks—Part 1: Overview
CD 10181-2	Part 2: Authentication Framework
CD 10181-3	Part 3: Access Control
CD 10181-4	Part 4: Nonrepudiation
CD 10181-5	Part 5: Integrity
CD 10181-6	Part 6: Confidentiality
CD 10181-7	Part 7: Secure Audit Framework
DIS 10736	Transport Layer Security Protocol
CD 10745	OSI Upper Layers Security Model

7498-2 and specify procedures and protocols for implementation of security services. Table 2-3 lists these key ISO standards.

Security Threats

Computer and network security generally addresses secrecy, integrity, and availability requirements. Secrecy requires that information be accessible only to authorized parties. Integrity means that computer system assets be modifiable (in any form) only by authorized parties and that modifications can be detected. Availability requires that computer-system assets be available to authorized parties.

There are four categories of security threats to a network in its normal pattern: (1) Interruption (threat to availability), (2) Interception (threat to secrecy), (3) Modification (threat to integrity), and (4) Fabrication (threat to integrity). Table 2-4 (definitions from ISO 7498-2) lists the types of threats that might be faced in the context of network security.

TABLE 2-4

ISO 7498-2 Security
Threats

Threat:	A potential violation of security.
▪ Accidental	A threat with no premeditation such as software-bug malfunctions.
▪ Intentional	Premeditated threat when realized as an attack.
▪ Passive	Unauthorized disclosure of information without changing state of the system.
▪ Active	Deliberate unauthorized change to state of the system.
Release of message contents	Data transmission read by unauthorized user.
Traffic analysis	Inference of information from flow of traffic (presence, absence, amount, direction, frequency).
Masquerade	Pretense by an entity to be another entity.
Replay	Occurs when a message, or part, is repeated to produce an unauthorized effect.
Modification	Alteration of data without detection of effect.
Denial of Service (DOS)	The prevention of authorized access to resources or delaying of time-critical operations.

Refer also to Appendix A, Table A-1, which details additional ISO standards for generic cryptographic techniques, for example, digital signatures.

Security Mechanisms

ISO 7498-2 also discusses security mechanisms that are implemented in a specific layer of the OSI architecture and those that are used at any layer of the model (refer to Tables 2-5 and 2-6). The OSI security architecture distinguishes between specific security mechanisms and pervasive security mechanisms. Specific security mechanisms may be incorporated into the appropriate (N) layer in order to provide some of the OSI security services. Pervasive security mechanisms are not specific to any particular OSI layer or OSI security service.

TABLE 2-5

Specific Security
Mechanisms

Encipherment	Use of mathematical algorithms to transform data into a form that is not readily intelligible. The transformation and subsequent recovery of the data depend on the algorithm and one or more encryption keys.
Traffic padding	Insertion of bits of meaningless data in a data stream to frustrate traffic-analysis attempts.
Authentication exchange	Mechanism to ensure the identity of an entity by means of information exchange.
Digital signature	Data appended to, or a cryptographic transformation of, a data unit that allows the recipient of the data unit to prove the source and integrity of the data unit. It is a means to bond a user to data.
Access control	Mechanisms used to enforce access rights to resources.
Data integrity	Mechanisms used to ensure the integrity of a data unit or stream.
Routing control	Selection of secure routes for certain data and allows routing changes especially when security has been breached.
Notarization	Trusted third-party assurance of properties of data exchange.

TABLE 2-6

Pervasive Security
Mechanisms

Trusted functionality	That which is perceived to be correct with respect to some criteria—establishment of a security policy.
Security label	A marking bound resource that delegates the security attributes of that resource.
Event detection	Detection of security-relevant events.
Security-audit trail	Independent data for surveillance.
Security recovery	Permits recovery actions when events require or software management indicates.

Stallings presents several tables showing placement of security services and mechanisms in the various OSI layers.

Security Services

The OSI security architecture distinguishes between five classes of security services: authentication, access control, data confidentiality, data integrity, and nonrepudiation. Table 2-7 shows the relationship between ISO layers, cryptographic protocols, and security services.

TABLE 2-7

ISO Layers, Cryptographic Protocols, and Security Services

Layer # Name	Cryptographic Protocols	Security Services
7 Application	X.400, MSP, PEM, S/MIME, PGP, X.509, DNS Security, S-HTTP, Key Management, Certificate Management	Entity authentication Origin authentication Access control Message integrity Message stream integrity Selective field confidentiality Traffic flow confidentiality Connection integrity Selective field integrity Nonrepudiation
6 Presentation		Selective field confidentiality
5 Session	SSL	
4 Transport	TLSP	Entity authentication Origin authentication Access control Message integrity Message stream integrity Connection integrity
3 Network	NLSP, ESP, AH	Entity authentication Origin authentication Access control Message integrity Message stream integrity Traffic flow confidentiality Connection integrity
2 Data Link	SILS	Message integrity Message stream integrity
1 Physical	Synchronous Link	Message stream integrity Traffic flow confidentiality

Components of Authentication Systems for Secure Networks

One-Way Hash Functions

One-way functions are of central importance in cryptography. Informally speaking, a one-way function is easy to compute, but hard to invert.

Given a function $f: A \rightarrow B$ is a one way function if $f(x)$ is easy to compute for all x in A, but it is computationally infeasible when given y in $f(A) = B$ to find x in A such that $f(x) = y$.

It is not required that a one-way function be invertable, and distinct input values may be mapped to the same output values. If f is a one-way hash function, and it is also computationally infeasible to find two distinct x_1, x_2 in A such that $f(x_1) = f(x_2)$, then the function is called *collision-resistant*. Examples of collision-resistant one-way hash functions are MD4, MD5, and secure hash standard (SHS) proposed by NIST under FIPS 180.

Symmetric Key Cryptography

In *symmetric* or *secret key cryptography,* a secret key is established and shared between communicating parties, and this key is subsequently used to encrypt and decrypt messages. Nichols and Bauer are two excellent references on the algorithms supporting secret key cryptography.

Examples of secret key cryptosystems that are in widespread use today are the data encryption system, DES; triple DES; the international data encryption algorithm (IDEA); as well as RC2, RC4, and RC5. Other well-known algorithms, like FEAL, are out of use because of the invention of differential cryptanalysis.

Public-Key Cryptography

The idea of having one-way functions with trapdoors led to the invention of public-key cryptography. Public-key cryptosystems employ pairs of mathematically related keys. The pair consists of a public key and a private key. For both keys, it is computationally infeasible to derive one from the other. The most widely deployed public-key cryptosystem is RSA, invented by Rivest, Shamir, and Adleman at the Massachusetts Institute of Technology (MIT) in 1978. Other public-key systems in use and referred to in the standards include Elliptic Curve Cryptosystems (ECC), Diffie-Hellman, and discrete log systems.

Public-key cryptography is more convenient than secret key cryptography because it is not necessary for two parties to authenticate each other by sharing a secret key. Hence, the key-distribution problem is not as complex. Also, public-key cryptography makes it possible to place authentication information under the direct control of the system user. This is especially helpful for access control, since secret information need not be distributed throughout the system. The application of public-key cryptography requires an authentication framework that binds users' public keys and users' identities. A public-key certificate is a certified proof of such binding vouched for by a trusted third party, called a *certification authority* (CA). The CA removes the need for individual users to verify directly the correctness of other users' public keys.

One of the more important aspects of public-key cryptography is that it enables digital signatures, which are discussed later in this chapter. The historical drawback of slow performance on microprocessors has improved in the last five years. An additional compensating factor is the extent to which operations between the authentication system and host computer system have been reengineered. Algorithms such as the ECC provide improved performance as well. Hybrid approaches are widely used where public-key cryptography is used to distribute keys for use by secret-key cryptosystems. Pretty Good Privacy (PGP) uses RSA and MD5 for digital signature, IDEA and RSA for message encryption, ZIP for compression, RADIX 64 conversion for email compatibility, and segmentation for large messages. Messages are encrypted using IDEA with a one-time session key generated by the sender. The session key is encrypted using RSA with the recipient's public key and is included with the message. A hash code of a message is created using MD5. This message digest is encrypted using RSA with the sender's secret key and is included with the message. Menezes and Schneier are two excellent references on the algorithms comprising public-key cryptography.

Authentication Systems

Authentication refers to the process of verifying someone's claimed identity. Techniques are divided into three categories, depending on whether a technique is based on:

1. Something the claimer knows (proof of knowledge)

2. Something the claimer possesses (proof of possession)

3. Some biometric characteristic of the claimer (proof of property)

Examples of the first category are personal identification numbers (PINs), passwords, and transaction authentication numbers (TAN), whereas examples of the second category are keys, identification cards, and personal tokens. Fingerprints, retinal images, voice patterns, and DNA are biometric devices that may be used in the third category.

The three categories of authentication are:

1. *Password-based:* User chosen at login. Drawbacks include non-randomness, multiple-host issues, and eavesdropping and replay.

2. *Address-based:* Each host stores account information regarding resources. Subject to attacks, but convenient.

3. *Cryptographic:* Claimant must perform cryptographic operations based on keys. Best approach because it can be made more secure with zero-knowledge proof techniques. Drawback is the difficulty of designing realistic protocols.

There are several well-known authentication and key-distribution systems:

- *Kerberos:* Developed at MIT and is the best-known system.

- *NetSP:* Developed by IBM and features the use of one-way hash functions rather than a full-fledged cryptosystem.

- *SPX:* Prototyped by DEC. It followed a hybrid approach with both secret- and public-key cryptography.

- *TESS:* The Exponential Security System, developed at the University of Karlsruhe in Germany, is a toolbox security system of cooperative cryptographic mechanisms and functions based on the mathematical primitive of discrete exponentiation.

- *SESAME:* European research and development project that extended Kerberos by adding authorization and access services.

- *OSF DCE:* Open Software Foundation's distributed computing environment is similar to SESAME.

The preceding authentication and key-distribution systems differ in various respects. Table 2-8 shows a comparison of security services provided by the systems, Table 2-9 shows the cryptographic techniques used by the systems, and Table 2-10 shows the standards to which these systems conform.

Key Management and Distribution

Key management involves the secure generation, distribution, storage, journaling, and eventual disposal of encryption keys. Keys can be dis-

TABLE 2-8

Security Services
Provided by the
Systems

System	Authentication Services	Data Confidentiality	Data Integrity	Access Control	Nonrepudiation
Kerberos	X	X	X		
NetSP	X	X	X		
SPX	X	X	X		
TESS	X	X	X		X
SESAME	X	X	X	X	
OSF DCE	X	X	X	X	

TABLE 2-9

Cryptographic
Techniques Used
by the Systems

System	One-Way Hash Function	Secret-Key Cryptosystems	Public-Key Cryptosystems
Kerberos	X	X	
NetSP	X	X	
SPX	X	X	X
TESS	X	X	X
SESAME	X	X	X
OSF DCE	X	X	X

TABLE 2-10

Standards to Which
the Systems Con-
form

System	
Kerberos	RFC 1510, GSS-API
NetSP	GSS-API
SPX	RFC 1507, ITU-T, X.509, GSS-API
TESS	RFC 1824
SESAME	ITU-T X.509, GSS-API, ECMA
OSF DCE	GSS-API

tributed either via escorted courier; magnetic media; or master keys, that are then used to generate additional keys.

Cryptographically protected data are dependent on the protection of the encryption keys. The theft, loss, or compromise of a key can compromise the entire system. ISO, ANSI, the federal government, and the

American Banking Association have developed standards for key management. Key management is crucial to maintaining good, cost-effective, and secure communications among a large number of users.

Most of the security services associated with the OSI security architecture are based on cryptographic mechanisms. The use of these mechanisms requires key management, which is carried out by protocols. Many of these protocols, unfortunately, do not depend on the underlying cryptographic algorithms, but rather on the structure of the messages themselves. The IEEE 802.10 standard supports three classes of key-distribution systems, namely manual key distribution, center-based key distribution, and certificate-based key distribution. Opplinger details these classes.

Key Recovery

Key management techniques exist to manage the life cycle of cryptographic keys, including the creation, distribution, validation, update, storage, usage, and expiration of keys. Should keys become forgotten, damaged or rendered unavailable to authorized parties, then information recovery techniques are necessary to allow recovery of plain text, typically by first recovering the key through reconstruction or retrieval. Such techniques are an integral part of commercial key management. An independent, motivating factor for key recovery technologies is that some countries regulate the use, export, or import of strong encryption based on governments' citing law enforcement needs to access encrypted data. The use of particular key recovery technologies favored by government authorities may thus be necessary to sell or use products in such countries. Several techniques have been proposed to provide for key recovery. Related terms include key escrow, commercial key recovery, cryptographic backup and recovery, and trusted third-party techniques (TTP). These terms are defined differently by various communities of interest, and the associated schemes have overlapping and sometimes poorly delineated differences.

All techniques for key recovery may be viewed as having a position on a wide continuum. Because of this broad spectrum, the only way to clearly identify each key recovery technique is by listing its specific characteristics, rather than using terms with many definitions. Different characteristics have advantages in different environments, so there is no "best" key recovery technique.

Key recovery enables authorized persons to access the plain text of encrypted data when the decryption key is not available. Key recovery is a broad term that applies to many different techniques. The following are selected techniques identified by their characteristics.

Key Escrow

Key escrow involves storing keys or key parts directly with one or more escrow agents. Information recovery requires that the escrow agent(s) facilitate plain text recovery by providing the necessary key or key parts or by actually decrypting the information using the escrowed key. Advantages of this technique include: user selection of the escrow agent(s) and dispersion of key parts avoids a single point of attack. The disadvantages include dialog overheard with a third party during cryptographic key initiation, and storage requirements for escrow agent(s).

TTP: Key Distribution Center

One type of TTP scheme involves creation and distribution of encryption session keys by a trusted third party other than the principals involved in the secured communications. Such a scheme was defined in the banking standard ANSI X9.17, where the TTP is called a Key Distribution Center (KDC). If a KDC is adapted to store a copy of the session key for later key retrieval, then it may serve as an escrow agent. One disadvantage of such a scheme is the requirement for user interaction with the online KDC for each session key (e.g., additional, supporting infrastructure is required). A second disadvantage is that escrow-agent storage of each session key may result in a large storage requirement and cost. Both these issues impact scalability. A third concern, particularly if the TTP is an external party, is the potential for key compromise at the TTP.

Commercial Key Backup (Long-term Keys)

Another type of TTP scheme involves an "internal" third party run by the organization with which the end user is affiliated. This party stores (and/or creates) a backup copy of each user's private asymmetric decryption key. Session keys are generated by end users and are made available to another user by encrypting such keys under that user's public key. The commercial key backup scheme is configured to return a copy of private keys to the end users, if necessary, but does not have interfaces available to allow itself access to these keys. Advantages of this scheme include:

1. Interaction with the third party is not required on a per-session basis.

2. If an end user loses a private key, a single interaction allows the user to recover data from a large number of files, rather than a key recovery transaction for each stored enciphered message (e.g., mail message).

3. Concerns about trusting an external party do not arise (an entity in a corporate environment is assumed to trust its affiliated organization).

4. The same infrastructure used for ongoing key life-cycle management (e.g., key update) may be used for key recovery.

External-Party Session Key Access

The commercial key backup scheme may be altered to enable an authorized external party to have access to (but not actually possess) all user session keys. In this case, the encryption system of each user would additionally encrypt the session key under the public key of the external party. The intended recipient can still gain access to the session key (should it lose its own private key), by providing cipher text containing the extra encrypted key (but not necessarily the encrypted user data itself) to the external party, together with proper authentication. The external party can gain access to the session key to allow decryption of any available cipher text.

Key Encapsulation

In this type of scheme, neither a session key nor long-term key is stored or escrowed with an outside party. Instead, recovery information is associated with each encrypted message (or file to be archived) to support key recovery at a later time. Here, the TTP or "key recovery agent" is required to process or unpack the recovery information and to provide it to the person authorized to recover the key/plain text. However, the key recovery agent does not need to derive the decryption key directly. In this case, the agent does not have sufficient information to derive the key. Instead, the authorized requester possesses additional, essential information for key recovery, thus limiting the liability of the key recovery agent. An advantage here, as with commercial key backup and external-party session key access, is minimal overhead during normal operations. Another advantage is the avoidance of any outside party as a single point of attack, provided there are two or more key recovery agents used in each jurisdiction.

Key Recovery Stages

Several distinct stages may be identified for a generic key recovery scheme, beyond the usual cryptographic preparations. These include:

1. *Selection stage:*   Selecting an entity or entities (if any), as a trusted third party, to be involved in the key recovery process.

2. *Parameter setup stage:*   Each principal or end user obtains any necessary cryptographic parameters and/or keying material to allow preparation of recovery parameters for later use (e.g., per message or session) in key recovery. Some administrative and/or address information may also be required to allow subsequent communication with entities in the recovery process.

3. *Preparation stage:*   Preparation of parameters allowing subsequent recovery of the key, on a per-message or per-session basis. It is desirable that this stage not involve communication with the parties selected in the first stage or any party other than the principals in the communication (i.e., be self-contained).

4. *Recovery stage:*   Recovery of the key from available parameters, at some indefinite future time. This stage typically involves communication with the parties selected in the selection stage.

Since the communicating principals originally know the key, one option is to preauthorize these parties to invoke key recovery, in order to allow their recovery of destroyed or mismanaged keys. Such preauthorization parameters could be embedded in the preparation and recovery processes. To scale to the dimensions of the envisioned global information infrastructure, key recovery techniques should be analyzed with respect to potential scalability. For example, since the preparation stage will be invoked far more frequently than the recovery stage, the computational burden/overhead should be minimized in the preparation stage.

Advanced Features

Features emphasizing invincibility and immunity to cryptanalytic attack may enhance key recovery schemes. Concepts related to this include dispersion, collusion-resistance, residual work factor, and integrity checks.

DISPERSION.   Dispersion refers to the property that joint (but not necessarily unanimous) participation by multiple, designated entities be an essential step in key recovery. Here the key recovery preparation stage may involve multiple pieces of information, each associated with an independent key recovery agent (a TTP). Ideally, this information is associated with but not physically passed to the agent; this allows *modularity* (the preparation stage may be added to existing cryptographic applications with minimal effort) and *self-containment* (infrastructure overhead required to support key recovery is reduced).

COLLUSION-RESISTANCE. Whereas dispersion thwarts collusion among the (supposedly) trusted key recovery agents, an additional goal in some environments might be collusion-resistance of key recovery; even collusion among the key recovery agents is not sufficient to allow their own recovery of the original key. With collusion-resistance, no keys are exposed outside the end user's system, except to the authorized requester.

RESIDUAL WORK FACTOR. A residual work factor allows the communicating parties to retain a variable amount of information needed for key recovery, which must then be recovered through cooperation or trial-and-error techniques. A residual work factor option can be used to increase the overall work effort involved in recovery, to discourage "casual" recovery requests and to keep part of the overall security of key recovery in the hands of the user. Use of the residual work factor is optional, depending on user or regulatory requirements. For example, a residual work factor may be implemented by escrowing the 16-bit difference between 56-bit DES and the 40-bit exportable version.

INTEGRITY CHECKS. Inherent process integrity checks may be built into the key recovery technology to allow users, observers, and involved third parties to ascertain that the technology is being correctly invoked and to guarantee that key recovery preparation has not been circumvented. The moment of key recovery is too late to learn that the recovery technology has been improperly applied or bypassed.

Even though integrity checks may be needed for the 'confidence' of the commercial user, such checks are primarily required by law enforcement or national security interests to guarantee that the key recovery technology is not being circumvented.

Digital Signatures and Notations

RSA and Digital Signature Algorithm (DSA) are the best-known digital signature algorithms. The latter was invented by the NSA and approved for government use. The NIST has supported the DSA algorithm because the digital signature operation is separated from encryption. Both are tools for authenticating the user and origin of the message and the identity of the sender.

A *digital signature* (a mathematical algorithm) verifies the signer, is not reusable, cannot be forged or repudiated, and proves that the sender did sign an unaltered document. DSA is based on the SHA (Secure Hashing Algorithm) and is described in FIPS PUB 180 "Secure Hash Standard." The DSA is based upon the T. El Gamal signature system and newer work by C. Schnorr. All these systems rely for their security on a problem known as the *discrete log*. This means that given a message m and a value a, it is easy to compute $M^a \bmod p$, where p is a prime number. If you are given another value n, it is difficult and certainly infeasible to discover a value such that $M^a \bmod p = n$. That is, it is hard to take the discrete log of n. ECDSA is the elliptic curve analog of the DSA. It offers performance, bandwidth, and space advantages over the DSA and comprises the ANSI X9.62 standard.

In general, a digital signature scheme consists of a key generation algorithm that randomly selects a public key pair, a signature algorithm that takes as input a message and a private key, and that generates as output a digital signature for the message.

A signature verification algorithm that takes as input a digital signature and a public key, generates as output an information bit signifying that the signature is consistent with some valid message for the private key corresponding to the given public key.

In general, the bandwidth limitation of public key cryptography is unimportant, due to the use of one-way hash functions as auxiliaries. However, in environments where long key lengths are used, bandwidth may be a limiting factor.

Discrete Log Signature Schemes

One of the more significant signature schemes uses the strength of the discrete log problem. Many of the digital cash systems on the Internet use this algorithm. No one knows an efficient way to reverse the computation $g^a \bmod p$ if p is a large prime, g is a generator, and a is an integer. Reversing the computation means computing $g^a \bmod p$ and determining a, which provides a concise description of this system.

The classic failure in many security systems comes when the attacker learns the password. The discrete log problem can also be used to provide "zero knowledge" to the attacker, even if he or she knows the password for a system. The system is also known as a *challenge-and-*

response protocol. It is described in nonconfusing terms in the next segment.

Simple Cryptographic Networks

To form a *cryptographic network,* each network user should be provided with the same algorithm but with different keys so that messages sent by one node in the network can be deciphered only by the intended recipient node. Figures 2-2 to 2-4 show three different cryptographic networks. Each Kn represents a different key.

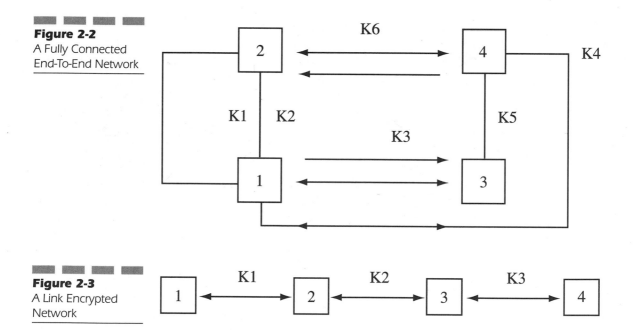

Figure 2-2
A Fully Connected
End-To-End Network

Figure 2-3
A Link Encrypted
Network

When *end-to-end encryption* is used, both the sender and receiver must be equipped with compatible hardware. After validating each other, the two units exchange encrypted data. Messages are encrypted by the sender and decrypted only at the final destination.

Link encryption involves a series of nodes, each of which decrypts, reads, and then reencrypts the message as it is transmitted through the network. With link encryption, both source and the destination remain

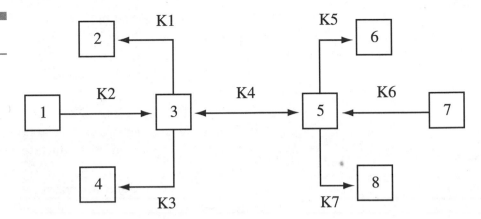

Figure 2-4
A Hybrid Network

private, and no synchronization of special equipment is required. However, more nodes means more possibilities of the message being intercepted and/or modified.

In a *hybrid network,* there is communication between a large number of secondary stations and a single main station all using separate master keys. A few stations intercommunicate with each other.

It would seem that it is preferable to use a public-key system for cryptography because of its versatility. It is slower than the equivalent private-key cryptosystems by a significant margin. The hybrid system uses the best of both kinds of systems. The speed advantage of the private-key cryptography is used for encrypting and transmitting. Public-key transactions are for the smaller transmissions. A typical combination (for a hybrid) is to employ a public dual key for encryption and for the distribution of the private keys and the private-key system for bulk data.

Implementation Considerations

Media

Cryptography can take place in software, hardware, or firmware. The least efficient, least secure, and cheapest media is software.

Configurations

Four different configurations—each with its own requirements and which need to be considered when implementing cryptosystems—are as follows:

1. *In-line:* The communications equipment is external to the cryptosystem. The handoff to the communications device occurs after encryption.

2. *Off-line:* The source controls all encryption, storage, and communications facilities.

3. *Embedded:* Configurations may be off- or online. The main requirement is that the cryptographic module be embedded or contained within the computer and the interface with that computer.

4. *Stand-alone:* These require that the cryptographic module is separately enclosed outside of the host and physically secured.

NIST FIP's 140-1 entitled "Security Requirements in Cryptographic Modules" describes four levels of security ranging from commercial-grade security to penetration/tamper resistant.

Cryptographic Algorithms

Chapter 8 introduces some key algorithms to the study of modern cryptography—of special interest is the RSA algorithm. The "Annotated Bib-

TABLE 2-11

Cryptographic
Algorithms and
Implementations

Algorithms	Implementations
DES	IBM Secret-Key Management Protocol
3DES	ISDN
IDEA	STU-III
RSA	Kerberos
DSA	KryptoKnight
Skipjack	Sesame
REDOC	Common Cryptographic Architecture
RCn	X.509
SEAL	Privacy-Enhanced Mail (PEM)
Elliptic Curve—ECC, ECAES, ECDSA	TIS/PEM
A5	MSP
PKZIP	PGP
N-HASH	PKCS
SHA-1	Clipper
MDn	Capstone

liography and Resources" presents many excellent references, which describe in detail all the cryptographic algorithms examined in this book.

Table 2-11 shows a sampling of cryptographic algorithms and implementations.

Protocols

Table 2-12 shows that the interface protocols and implementations of cryptographic algorithms are quite varied.

ISO Conformance Testing

A key element in the practical implementation of ISO is *conformance testing,* which is intended to ensure that a given implementation con-

TABLE 2-12

OSI Layers, Algorithms, LAN/WAN Interface Protocols, and Implementations

OSI Layer # Name	Algorithms	LAN/WAN Interface Protocols	Implementations
7 *Application*		File systems, mail, remote login, FTP, directory systems, print services, gateways, network management, network applications	
6 *Presentation*		Network applications, network management, gateways	
5 *Session*		Session control, gateways, sockets	
4 *Transport*	Kerberos	TCP, Novell, SNA, NT, Decnet transport, sequenced packet exchange, gateways, terminal programs	
3 *Network*	Kerberos	Decnet routing, IP, SNA, internet packet exchange, X.25, routers, gateways, terminal programs	
2 *Data Link*		Gateways, frame relay, SMDS, ATM, modems, bridges, switches, token-rings, Ethernet, ARCnet, FDDI, ISDN, PPP, SLIP	
1 *Physical*		FDDI, Ethernet, ARCnet, token-rings, ATM, ISDN, repeaters, PPP, SLIP	

TABLE 2-13

ISO Conformance
Testing Standards

Title	ISO	CCITT
General Concepts	9646-1	X.290
Abstract Test Suite		
Specification	9646-2	X.291
Tree and Tabular		
Combined Notation	9646-3	X.292
Test Realization	9646-4	X.293
Conformance Assessment	9646-5	X.294
Protocol Profile		
Test Specification	9646-6	

forms to an OSI specification. ISO standards for conformance testing are shown in Table 2-13.

International Standardized Profiles

The practical use of the ISO protocols and services has two requirements. First, implementation of ISO protocols and services must conform to relevant standards. Verifying this is the task of conformance testing. Second, any two separate implementations, if they are to participate in a cooperative application, must interwork and interoperate correctly. The two implementations must support compatible options and parameters associated with the protocols at each layer of the OSI model. ISO addresses this latter problem with the concept of International Standardized Profiles (ISPs). This is an ongoing process. The CPC is participating in this process.

Special Topics: Web Security Countermeasures

The Web represents a chaotic and exciting technology. It has become the security-balancing act of the 90s. McCarthy published a tiered approach to commercial security in 1997. He suggests the following procedure for commercial Web users: (1) identify what applications the Web will be

TABLE 2-14

Nine Basic Threats to Web Sites

1. *Data destruction:* Loss of data on Web site through accident or malice and interception of traffic (encrypted and unencrypted) both going to/from the Web site.

2. *Interference:* The intentional rerouting of traffic or the flooding of a local Web server with inappropriate traffic in an attempt to cripple or crash the server.

3. *Modification/replacement:* Altering of data on either the send or receive side of a Web transmission. The changes, whether they are accidental or not, can be difficult to detect in large transmissions.

4. *Misrepresentation/false use of data:* Offering false credentials, passwords, or other data. Also included is posting of a bogus or counterfeit home page to intercept or attract traffic away from its intended destination.

5. *Repudiation:* An after-the-fact denial that an online order or transaction took place (especially for 1-800 or 1-900 services).

6. *Inadvertent misuse:* Accidental and inappropriate actions by approved users.

7. *Unauthorized altering/downloading:* Any writing, updating, copying, and so on, performed by a person who has not been granted permission to conduct such activity.

8. *Unauthorized transactions:* Any use by a nonapproved party.

9. *Unauthorized disclosure:* Viewing of Web information by an individual not given explicit permission to have access to this information.

used for; (2) based on this stated use for a company Web site, identify the crucial threats; and then (3) map these threats to the appropriate protection technologies. He divided commerce on the Web into three basic application types: advertising, secure Internet/intranet (further subdivided into informational and transactional categories), and electronic commerce. There are nine basic threats to Web security (Table 2-14) and six safeguards (Table 2-15) that could counter these threats.

Security decisions will only become tougher as companies continue to exploit the power of the Web. Electronic commerce will especially aggravate the difficulties of setting just the right security policy. Two possible challenges include the use of select electronic transactions and high-level digital certification.

A Peek at the Future—Integrated Network Security

The convergence of technologies used in corporate computer systems such as intranets and extranets along with the Internet means that cor-

TABLE 2-15

Six Best Weapons Against Security Threats

1. *User ID / Authentication:* Range from simple passwords and callback systems to secure one-time passwords and challenge response tokens (either hardware cards or software resident).

    Usage: All Web users.

2. *Authorization:* Network confirms identity, grants access. Typical approaches include access control lists, authorization certificates, and directory services.

    Usage: Secondary-level protection to prevent data modification.

3. *Integrity control:* Aimed at the data not the user, the two key methods are encryption and message authentication, which can ensure that the message has not been altered on the way to receiver and not read by someone else.

    Usage: Excellent for validating secure Internet electronic commerce transactions.

4. *Accountability:* Web managers use various tools to monitor responsibility and ownership. Methods include audit trails, Web server logs, and receipts.

    Usage: Accountability is the backbone of enforceable and traceable security policies and practices.

5. *Confidentiality:* The keystone of most Web security policies. The technology is aimed at preventing unauthorized disclosure, or interception, or both. Encryption is the central safeguard. This can mean end-to-end encryption on the network as well as layered encryption of files, protocols, and secured links.

    Usage: These techniques are geared toward data content that must be held strictly off-limits to certain users.

6. *Available controls:* Protects the integrity of the Web site itself. Technology includes virus protection software and backup/redundancy features.

    Usage: Protection of Web and its associated data.

porations will have a greater number of options for providing connectivity to different classes of network sites or users. The ISO standards provide new alternatives for increased use of the public Internet transport as well as extranet services for tying remote users or business partners back into the corporate headquarters. The technology will be based on the same frameworks. This means that hybrid Internet/intranet/extranet solutions will be feasible.

The key to this hybrid approach is an integrated network security solution. Figure 2-5 shows what an integrated security model might include. The process of supporting trusted users across the hybrid corporate network by establishing secure encryption tunnels through untrusted networks is called *membership*. The CPC is working toward provid-

Figure 2-5
Integrated Security
Model

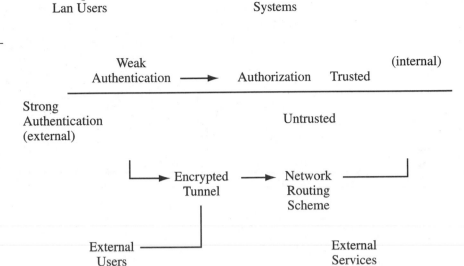

ing customers with the hardware and software to accomplish membership options for customers.

Membership is really nothing new to the CPC. It consists of three stages. First, the target network must establish the identity of users through strong authentication. Then, each party must obtain secret encryption keys so that any data sent over the network can be kept private. And finally, to avoid unnecessarily complex routing gateways, the remote workstation or branch router must join the corporate routing scheme so that the secure tunnel appears to the rest of the network and to the remote devices as a simple direct network connection.

WRAP-UP

The need for computer security and encryption products is increasing in the commercial theater. This need is especially great for firms doing business on the Internet or maintaining Web access. The most effective safeguard is cryptography. The most common practice for implementation of cryptographic solutions is in layered formats using the OSI model. In practice, the theoretical layers are combined to three or four layers. The CPC stresses that no safeguard will work unless a recognized system of international standards and procedures such as those of the ISO is in place and enforced. We have introduced many interrelated concepts in this chapter. These are some of the various concerns which must be addressed when implementing cryptographic countermeasures in a commercial theater of operations.

CHAPTER **3**

Historical
Systems I

Cryptograms are roughly divided into *ciphers* and *codes*. William F. Friedman (1891–1969), the dean of American cryptography, defined a *cipher* message as one produced by applying a method of cryptography to the individual letters of the plain text, taken either singly or in groups of constant length. Practically every cipher message is the result of the joint application of a *general system* (or *algorithm*) a method of treatment, which is invariable and a *specific key,* which is variable, at the will of the correspondents. The algorithm controls the exact steps followed under the general system. It is assumed that the general system is known by the correspondents and by the cryptanalyst. What is not generally known is the key structure.

A *code* message is a cryptogram that has been produced by using a code book consisting of arbitrary combinations of letters, entire words, figures substituted for words, partial words, phrases, or plain text. Whereas a cipher system acts upon individual letters or definite groups taken as units, a code deals with entire words or phrases or even sentences taken as units. The process of converting plain text into cipher text is *encipherment*. The reverse process of reducing cipher text into plain text is known as *decipherment*.

Substitution and Transposition Ciphers Compared

Cipher systems are divided into two classes: *substitution* and *transposition*. Modern cipher systems use both substitution and transposition to create secret messages. The fundamental difference between substitution and transposition methods is that in the former, the normal or conventional values of the letters of the plain text are changed, without any change in the relative positions of the letters in their original sequences; whereas in the latter only the relative positions of the letters of the plain text in the original sequences are changed, without any changes to the conventional values for the letters. Since the methods of encipherment are radically different in the two cases, the principles involved in the cryptanalysis of both types of ciphers are fundamentally different. It is instructive to be able to differentiate whether a cipher has been enciphered by substitution or transposition.

Simple Substitution

Probably the most popular amateur cipher is the simple *substitution cipher* (aka Aristocrat). We see them in newspapers; kids use them to fool teachers; lovers send them to each other for special meetings; and they have been used by the Masons, secret Greek societies, and by fraternal organizations. Current gangs in the Southwest use them to do drug deals. They are found in literature like the "Gold Bug" by Edgar Allan Poe and "The Dancing Men" by Arthur Conan Doyle. The death threats by the infamous Zodiac killer in San Francisco in the late 1960s were also simple substitutions.

A recurring theme of this book is that all ciphers have a common basis in mathematics and probability theory. The basis language of the cipher doesn't matter as long as it can be characterized mathematically. Mathematics is the common link for deciphering any language cipher. This is also known as the principle of *cryptographic universality*. Based on mathematical and statistical principles, we can identify the language of the cryptogram and then break open its contents.

Four Basic Operations of Cryptanalysis

William F. Friedman presented the fundamental operations for the solution of practically every cryptogram:

1. The determination of the language employed in the plain text version.

2. The determination of the general system of cryptography employed.

3. The reconstruction of the specific key in the case of a cipher system; or the reconstruction, partial or complete, of the code book, in the case of a code system; or both the key and the codebook in the case of an enciphered code system.

4. The reconstruction or establishment of the plain text gained from steps 1–3.

In some cases, step 2 may precede step 1. This is the classical approach to cryptanalysis. It may be further reduced to:

1. Arrangement and rearrangement of data to disclose nonrandom characteristics or manifestations (frequency counts, repetitions, patterns, symmetrical phenomena).

2. Recognition of the nonrandom characteristics or manifestations when disclosed (via statistics or other techniques).

3. Explanation of nonrandom characteristics when recognized (by luck, intelligence, or perseverance).

Much of the work is in determining the general system. In the final analysis, the solution of every cryptogram involving a form of substitution depends upon its reduction to monoalphabetic terms (one alphabet or one set of language symbols), if it is not originally in those terms.

A demonstration of the solution of a simple "Aristocrat" substitution may start the process of understanding the science of cryptography.

General Nature of English Language

A working knowledge of the letters, characteristics, relations with each other, and their favorite positions in words is very valuable in solving substitution ciphers. W. F. Friedman was the first to employ the principle that English language letters are mathematically distributed in a *uniliteral* frequency distribution:

```
13 9 8  8 7 7 7  6 6 4 4  3 3 3 3 2  2 2 1 1 1 - - - - -
E  T A  O N I R  S H L D  C U P F M  W Y B G V K Q X J Z
```

That is, in each 100 letters of text, E has a frequency (or number of appearances) of about 13; T a frequency of about 9; K, Q, X, J, and Z appear so seldom, that their frequency is a low decimal. Tables 3-1 and 3-2 present a historical view of English data based on military text.

Letter Characteristics and Interactions

Appendix B presents a variety of language data. Several references give letter characteristics. Gaines presents letter contact data for English, German, French, Italian, Spanish, and Portuguese. Nichols published

TABLE 3-1

Hitt's Military Text—
English Data

Basis 20,000 letters of military text:

6	Vowels: A E I O U Y	= 40%
20	Consonants:	
	5 High Frequency (D N R S T)	= 35%
	10 Medium Frequency (B C F G H L M P V W)	= 24%
	5 Low Frequency (J K Q X Z)	= <u>1%</u>
		100%

The four vowels A, E, I, and O and the four consonants N, R, S, and T constitute about two-thirds of the normal English plain text.

The most frequent English digraphs are:

TH — 50	AT — 25	ST — 20
ER — 40	EN — 25	IO — 18
ON— 39	ES — 25	LE — 18
AN— 38	OF — 25	IS — 17
RE — 36	OR— 25	OU— 17
HE— 33	NT — 24	AR — 16
IN — 31	EA — 22	AS — 16
ED— 30	TI — 22	DE — 16
ND— 30	TO— 22	RT — 16
HA— 26	IT — 20	VE — 16

The most frequent English trigraphs (three-letter combinations):

THE—89	TIO — 33	EDT — 27
AND—54	FOR — 33	TIS — 25
THA—47	NDE —31·	OFT — 23
ENT—39	HAS —28	STH — 21
ION —36	NCE — 27	MEN— 20

Frequency of initial and final letters:

Letters:	A	B	C	D	E	F	G	H	I	J	K	L	M	N	O	P	Q	R	S	T	U	V	W	X	Y	Z
Initial:	9	6	6	5	2	4	2	3	3	1	1	2	4	2	10	2	-	4	5	17	2	-	7	-	3	-
Final:	1	-	-	10	17	6	4	2	-	-	1	6	1	9	4	1	-	8	9	11	1	-	1	-	8	-

Relative frequencies of vowels:

A　19.5%　　　E　32.0%　　　I　16.7%　　　O　20.2%　　　U　8.0%　　　Y　3.6%

Average number of vowels per 20 letters, 8.

data on English and 10 different languages. It is available online at the ACA Crypto Drop Box *ACA-L@sage.und.nodak.edu.* Friedman in his *Military Cryptanalytics,* Part I, Volume 1 gives charts showing the lower and upper limits of deviation from theoretical (random) for the number of vowels; high-, low-, and medium-frequency consonants; and blanks in distributions for plain text and random text for messages of various lengths.

TABLE 3-2

Probability of Occurrence of English Letters (Friedman Data)

Letter	Probability	Letter	Probability
A	.082	N	.067
B	.015	O	.075
C	.028	P	.019
D	.043	Q	.001
E	.127	R	.060
F	.022	S	.063
G	.020	T	.091
H	.061	U	.028
I	.070	V	.010
J	.002	W	.023
K	.008	X	.001
L	.040	Y	.020
M	.024	Z	.001

Letter groups:

1. E, having a probability of about 0.127
2. T, A, O, I, N, S, H, and R, each having probabilities between 0.06–0.09.
3. D and L, having probabilities around 0.04
4. C, U, M, W, F, G, Y, P, and B, each having probabilities between 0.015–0.023
5. V, K, J, X, Q, and Z, each having probabilities less than 0.01

Letter groups:

A E I O U	38.58%
L N R S T	33.43%
J K Q X Z	1.11%
E T A O N	45.08%
E T A O N I S R H	70.02%

In *Military Cryptanalytics,* Part I, Volume 2, Friedman gives a veritable potpourri of statistical data on letter frequencies and word characteristics such as digraphs, trigraphs, tetragraphs, grouped letters, relative log data, pattern words, idiomorphic (structural) data, standard endings, initials, foreign language data (German, French, Italian, Spanish, Portuguese, and Russian), classification of systems used in concealment, nulls, and literals. Sinkov assigns log frequencies to digraphs to aid in identification. Friedman explains this procedure. Depending on the basis text we choose, we find variations in the frequency of letters. For example, literary English gives slightly different results than frequencies based on military or ordinary English text.

The important concept is that languages may be characterized by their letter behavior. It turns out that similar groups of information, such as vowel relationships with specific consonants, carry through in the cipher text and are potentially identifiable in the cipher text.

Eyeballing and Aristocrat

While reading the newspaper, you see the following cryptogram. Train your eye to look for wedges or "INs" into the cryptogram. Assume that we're dealing with English and that we have simple substitution. What do we know? Although short, there are several entries for solution. Number the words.

A-1. Elevated thinker. K2 (71)   by: LANAKI

1	2	3	4	5
F Y V	Y Z X Y V E F	I T A M G V U X V	Z E	F A

6	7	8	9	10
I T A M	F Y Q F	M V	Q D V	E J D D A J T U V U

11	12	13	14
R O	H O E F V D O.	*Q G R V D F	*E S Y M V Z F P V D

Analysis of A-1

We note that words numbered 2, 3, 7, 10, and 12 have patterns of repeated letters. We could use published lists of pattern words, which are words listed alphabetically, grouped by number of letters in the word and by the pattern of the repeated letters in the group. The solver, not having access to these pattern words lists, can easily make his or her own, but with experience, the common pattern words in newspaper cryptograms will easily be remembered. We examine words 1 and 7 and see that the first and fourth letters of word 7 are the same as the first two letters of word 1. This suggests word 7 is a very common pattern word "that" and that word 1 is most likely "the." A quick count shows that "V" occurs 11 times, approximately 15 percent of the 71 letters of the cryptogram, making it a very likely candidate for "e." Words 3 and 6 use the same four letters, I T A M. Note that there is a flow to this cryptogram: The _ _ is? _ _ and? _ _. Titles either help or should be ignored as red herrings. Elevated might mean "high" and the thinker could be the proper person. Filling in the cryptogram using [the...that] assumption we have:

```
     1           2                  3              4        5
   the       h   h e t                  e      e          t
   F Y V     Y Z X Y V E F        I T A M G V U X V    Z E    F A

     6         7        8     9               10
             t h a t       e     a   e                    e
   I T A M   F Y Q F     M V   Q D V       E J D D A J T U V U

     11           12              13                14
               t   e         a     e t         h   e   t   e
   R O       H O E F V D O   * Q G R V D F   * E S Y M V Z F P V D
```

Not bad for a start. Word 5, a two-letter word starting with "t," can only be "to." We fill in the substitution of "o" for "A." When we look at the group of words 7, 8, and 9 we see that word 9, a three-letter word starting with "a" and ending with "e" could be "ace," "ade," "age," "ale," "ape," "ate," "axe," or "awe," and word 8, a two-letter word ending in "e" can only represent "be," "he," "me," or "we." We add this information to the recovered portion of the cryptogram. No matter how hard we make the process, no matter how hard we scramble the plain text, it is only a puzzle, albeit a difficult one. Note how each wedge leads to the next wedge. Always look for confirmation that your assumptions are correct. Have an eraser ready to step back a step if necessary. Keep a tally on which letters have been placed correctly. Those that are unconfirmed guesses signify with "?". Piece by piece, we build on the opening wedge.

```
     1           2                  3              4        5
   the       h   h e s t                o   e      s      t o
   F Y V     Y Z X Y V E F        I T A M G V U X V    Z E    F A

     6         7        8     9           10
     o       t h a t       e     a r e    s   r r o       e
   I T A M   F Y Q F     M V   Q D V   E J D D A J T U V U

     11           12              13                14
               s t e r         a     e r t     s   h   e   t   e r
   R O       H O E F V D O   * Q G R V D F   * E S Y M V Z F P V D
```

Now we have some bigger wedges. The s_h is a possible "sch" from German. Word 10 could be "surrounded." Z = i. The name could be Albert Schweitzer. Let's try these guesses. Word 2 might be "highest" which goes with the title.

```
     1           2                  3              4        5
   the       h i g h e s t        n o w l e d g e   i s    t o
   F Y V     Y Z X Y V E F        I T A M G V U X V    Z E    F A
```

6	7	8	9	10
n o w	t h a t	w e	a r e	s u r r o u n d e d
I T A M	F Y Q F	M V	Q D V	E J D D A J T U V U
11	12		13	14
	s t e r		a l b e r t	s c h w e i t z e r
R O	H O E F V D O		*Q G R V D F	*E S Y M V Z F P V D

The final message is: The highest knowledge is to know that we are surrounded by mystery. Albert Schweitzer.

We have solved ("cracked") the message, but what do we know about the keying method? In problem A-1, we set up the plain text alphabet as a normal sequence [A, B,..., Z] and fill in the cipher text letters below it. Note the keyword LIGHT.

```
Plain:   a b c d e f g h i j k l m n o p q r s t u v w x y z
Cipher:  Q R S U V W X Y Z L I G H T A B C D E F J K M N O P
Keyword = LIGHT
```

Cipher text alphabets are generally mixed for more security and an easy mnemonic to remember is chosen as a translation key.

In tougher ciphers, we use the preceding key recovery procedure to go back and forth between the cryptogram and keying alphabet to yield additional information.

To summarize the "eyeball" method (more sophisticated souls call this method "by inspection"):

1. Look for common letters that appear frequently throughout the message, but don't expect an exact correspondence in popularity.

2. Look for short, common words (the, and, are, that, is, to) and common endings (tion, ing, ers, ded, ted, ess).

3. Make a guess, try out the substitutions, and keep track of your progress. Look for readability.

There is a popular game show on TV known as "Wheel of Fortune." Recognize the similarities?

Multiliteral Substitution with Single-Equivalent Cipher Alphabets

Monoalphabetic substitution methods are classified as *uniliteral* and *multiliteral* systems. Uniliteral systems maintain a strict one-to-one correspondence between the length of the units of the plain and those of the cipher text. Each letter of plain text is replaced by a single character in the cipher text. In multiliteral monoalphabetic substitution systems, this correspondence is no longer one plain to one cipher but may be one plain to two cipher, where each letter of the plain text is replaced by two characters in the cipher text; or one plain to three cipher, where a three-character combination in the cipher text represents a single letter of the plain text. We refer to these systems as *uniliteral, biliteral,* and *triliteral,* respectively. Ciphers in which one plain text letter is represented by cipher characters of two or more elements are classed as multiliteral.

Biliteral Ciphers

Friedman gives some interesting examples of biliteral monoalphabetic substitution. Many cipher systems start with a geometric shape (see Figure 3-1).

Figure 3-1

	W	H	I	T	E
W	A	B	C	D	E
H	F	G	H	IJ	K
I	L	M	N	O	P
T	Q	R	S	T	U
E	V	W	X	Y	Z

Using the square in Figure 3-1, we derive the following cipher alphabet:

```
Plain:    a   b   c   d   e   f   g   h   i   j   k   l   m
Cipher:  WW  WH  WI  WT  WE  HW  HH  HI  HT  HT  HE  IW  IH

Plain:    n   o   p   q   r   s   t   u   v   w   x   y   z
Cipher:  II  IT  IE  TW  TH  TI  TT  TE  EW  EH  EI  ET  EE
```

The alphabet derived from the cipher square or matrix is referenced by row and column coordinates, respectively. The key to this system is that when a message is enciphered by this biliteral alphabet, the cryptogram is still monoalphabetic in character. A frequency distribution based upon pairs of letters will have all the characteristics of a simple uniliteral distribution for a monoalphabetic substitution cipher.

Numbers can be used as effectively as letters in the biliteral cipher.

The simplest form is A = 01, B = 02, C = 03,..., Z = 26. So, the plain text letters have as their equivalents two-digit numbers, which indicate their position in the normal alphabet. A dinome (two-digit) cipher matrix is shown in Figure 3-2. (Note that frequently used punctuation marks can be enciphered in this matrix.) Another four are shown in Figures 3-3 through 3-6.

Figure 3-2

	1	2	3	4	5	6	7	8	9	0
1	A	B	C	D	E	F	G	H	I	J
2	K	L	M	N	O	P	Q	R	S	T
3	U	V	W	X	Y	Z	.	,	:	;

Figure 3-3

	5	6	7	8	9	0
1	A	B	C	D	E	F
2	G	H	IJ	K	L	M
3	N	O	P	Q	R	S
4	T	UV	W	X	Y	Z

Figure 3-4

	1	2	3	4	5	6	7	8	9
1	A	B	C	D	E	F	G	H	I
2	J	K	L	M	N	O	P	Q	R
3	S	T	U	V	W	X	Y	Z	*

Figure 3-5

	M	U	N	I	C	H
B	A	7	E	5	R	M
E	G	1	N	Y	B	2
R	C	3	D	4	F	6
L	H	8	I	9	J	0
I	K	L	O	P	Q	S
N	T	U	V	W	X	Z

Figure 3-6

	A	B	C	D	E	F	G	H	I
A	A	D	G	J	M	P	S	V	Y
B	B	E	H	K	N	Q	T	W	Z
C	C	F	I	L	O	R	U	X	1
D	2	3	4	5	6	7	8	9	0

Figure 3-7

	B	C	D	F	G
A	A	B	C	D	E
E	F	G	H	IJ	K
I	L	M	N	O	P
O	Q	R	S	T	U
U	V	W	X	Y	Z

It is possible to generate false or pseudo-code or artificial code language by using an enciphering matrix that uses vowels as row indicators and consonants as column indicators (Figure 3-7). Enciphering the word RAIDS would be OCABE FAFOD.

Another subterfuge used to camouflage the biliteral cipher matrix is to append a third character to the row or column indicator. This third character may be produced through the use of the cipher matrix shown in Figure 3-8 (wherein A = 611, B = 612, etc.) or the third character can be the "sum checking" digit, which is the noncarrying sum (modulo 10) of the preceding two digits such as trinomes 257, 831, and 662.

All the preceding matrices are *bipartite,* which means they can be

Figure 3-8

	1	2	3	4	5
61	A	B	C	D	E
72	F	G	H	IJ	K
83	L	M	N	O	P
94	Q	R	S	T	U
05	V	W	X	Y	Z

A = 611 B = 612 X = 053

divided into two separate parts that can be clearly defined by row and column indicators. This is the primary weakness of this type of cipher. Sinkov presents a good description of the modulo arithmetic required to solve biliteral cipher challenges.

Biliteral but Not Bipartite

Consider the cipher matrix shown in Figure 3-9.

Figure 3-9

	1	2	3	4	5
09	H	Y	D	R	A
15	U	L	IJ	C	B
21	E	F	G	K	M
27	N	O	P	Q	S
33	T	V	W	X	Z

We can produce a biliteral cipher alphabet in which the equivalent for any letter in the matrix is the sum of the two coordinates that indicate its cell in the matrix:

```
Plain:   A  B  C  D  E  F  G  H  I  J  K  L  M
Cipher: 14 20 19 12 22 23 24 10 18 18 25 17 26
Plain:   N  O  P  Q  R  S  T  U  V  W  X  Y  Z
Cipher: 28 29 30 31 13 32 34 16 35 36 37 11 38
```

$$A = 9 + 5 = 14, E = 21 + 1 = 22$$

The cipher units are biliteral but they are not bipartite—an equivalent is 14 and digits 1 and 4 have no meaning per se. Plain text letters whose cipher equivalents begin with 1 may be found in two different rows of the matrix and those of whose equivalents end in 4 appear in three different columns.

Another possibility lends itself to certain multiliteral ciphers in the use of a word spacer or word separator. The word space might be represented by a value in the matrix; that is, the separator is enciphered as a value (*dinome* 39 in Figure 3-4). The word space might be an uncimphered element. Let's break from the theory and look at four interesting multiliteral historical ciphers before discussing the general cryptanalytic attack on the multiliteral cipher.

Trithemian

The abbot Trithemius, born Johann von Heydenberg (1462–1516), invented one of the first multiliteral ciphers. It was fashioned similar to the Baconian Cipher and was a means for disguising secret text. His work *Steganographia,* published in 1499, describes several systems of "covered writing."

His alphabet, modified to include 26 letters of present-day English, is shown in Figure 3-10, and consists of all the permutations of three things taken three at a time, or $3^3 = 27$ in all. The cipher text does not have to be restricted to digits; any groupings of three things taken three at a time will do.

Figure 3-10

A—111	G—131	M—221	S—311	Y—331
B—112	H—132	N—222	T—312	Z—332
C—113	I—133	O—223	U—313	*—333
D—121	J—211	P—231	V—321	
E—122	K—212	Q—232	W—322	
F—123	L—213	R—233	X—323	

Bacon

Sir Francis Bacon (1561–1626) invented a cipher in which the cipher equivalents are five-letter groups and the resulting cipher is monoalphabetic in character. Bacon uses a 24-letter cipher with I and J, U and V used interchangeably (Table 3-3).

TABLE 3-3

Bacon's Biliteral Alphabet

A = aaaaa	I/J = abaaa	R = baaaa
B = aaaab	K = abaab	S = baaab
C = aaaba	L = ababa	T = baaba
D = aaabb	M = ababb	U/V = baabb
E = aabaa	N = abbaa	W = babaa
F = aabab	O = abbab	X = babab
G = aabba	P = abbba	Y = babba
H = aabbb	Q = abbbb	Z = babbb

Bacon described the steganographic effect of message enfolding in an innocent external message. Suppose we let capitals be the "a" element and lowercase letters represent the "b" element. The message "All is well with me today" can be made to convey the message "Help."

A	L	l	i	s	WElL	W	ItH	mE	TodaY
a	a	b	b	b	aaba	a	aba	ba	abbba
		H				E		L	P

Thus, Bacon describes several variations on the theme. Note the regularity of construction of Bacon's biliteral alphabet, a feature that permits its reconstruction from memory.

Hayes Ciphers

Probably the most corrupt political election occurred on November 7, 1876, with the election of President Rutherford B. Hayes (Republican), who defeated Samuel Jones Tilden (Democrat). Tilden had won the popular vote by 700,000 votes, but because of frauds surrounding the Electoral College, he was deprived of the high office of president. Actually, both candidates were involved with bribery, election tampering, voter fraud, conspiracy, and a host of other shady goings-on. Tilden ran on a law-and-order ticket that credited him with convicting Boss Tweed and the Tweed Ring in New York City, which controlled the city through Tammany Hall. For two years into Hayes's presidency, the scandals persisted.

With the help of the *New York Tribune,* Republicans finished the Tilden "honesty" horse. They published the Tilden Ciphers and keys. There were about 400 of them representing substitution and transposition forms. (We revisit the transposition forms at a later juncture.) They represented secret and illegal operations by Tilden's men in Florida, Louisiana, South Carolina, and Oregon. The decipherments were done by investigators of the *Tribune.* Here are two examples and their solution:

GEO. F. RANEY, Tallahassee.

```
PPYYEMNSNYYYPIMASHNSYYSSITEPAAE
NSHNSPENNSSHNSMMPIYYSNPPYEAAPIE
ISSYESHAINSSSPEEIYYSHNYNSSSYEPI
AANYITNSSHYYSPYYPINSYYSSITEMEIP
IMMEISSEIYYEISSITEIEPYYPEEIAASS
IMAAYESPNSYYIANSSSEISSMMPPNSPIN
```

S S N P I N S I M I M Y Y I T E M Y Y S S P E Y Y M M N S Y Y
S S I T S P Y Y P E E P P P M A A A Y Y P I I T

L' Engle goes up tomorrow.   Daniel

Examination of the message discloses a bipartite alphabet cipher with only 10 different letters used. Dividing the messages by twos, assigning arbitrary letters for pairs of letters, and performing a triliteral frequency distribution will yield a solution.

PP	YY	EM	NS	NY	YY	PI	MA	SH	NS	YY	SS...
A	B	C	D	E	B	F	G	H	D	B	I...

The message reads: Have Marble and Coyle telegraph for influential men from Delaware and Virginia. Indications of weakening here. Press advantage and watch board.

Here is another cryptogram using numerical substitutes:

S. PASCO AND E. M. L'ENGLE

84	55	84	25	93	34	82	31	31	75	93	82	77	33	55	42
93	20	93	66	77	66	33	84	66	31	31	93	20	82	33	66
52	48	44	55	42	82	48	89	42	93	31	82	66	75	31	93

DANIEL

There were several messages of this type. They disclosed that only 26 different numbers were used. The message reads: Cocke will be ignored, Eagan called in. Authority reliable.

The *Tribune* experts came up with the following alphabets:

AA = O	EN = Y	IT = D	NS = E	PP = H	SS = N
AI = U	EP = C	MA = B	NY = M	SH = L	YE = F
EI = I	IA = K	MM = G	PE = T	SN = P	YI = X
EM = V	IM = S	NN = J	PI = R	SP = W	YY = A

20 = D	33 = N	44 = H	62 = X	77 = G	89 = Y
25 = K	34 = W	48 = T	66 = A	82 = I	93 = E
27 = S	39 = P	52 = U	68 = F	84 = C	96 = M
31 = L	42 = R	55 = O	75 = B	87 = V	99 = J

William F. Friedman correlated these alphabets with the following amusing results. (The blank squares may have contained proper names and money designations. Key = HISPAYMENT for bribery seems to be appropriate.)

	H	I	S	P	A	Y	M	E	N	T
	1	2	3	4	5	6	7	8	9	0
H1.										
I 2.					K		S			D
S 3.		L	N	W					P	
P 4.		R		H				T		
A 5.		U			O					
Y 6.		X				A		F		
M 7.						B	G			
E 8.		I		C			V		Y	
N 9.			E				M		J	
T 0.										

Blue and Gray

One of the most fascinating stories of the American Civil War
(1861–1865) is about communications using *flag telegraphy,* also known
as the *wigwag signal system.* Wigwag is a system of positioning a flag
(or flags) at various angles to indicate the corresponding 26 letters of the
alphabet. It was created in the mid-1800s by three men working at separate locations: Navy Captain Phillip Colomb and Army Captain Francis
Bolton, in England; and surgeon-inventor Albert J. Myer in America.
Myer observed the railroad electromagnetic telegraph, developed by
Alexander Bain, and invented a touch method of communication for the
deaf and later the wigwag system. He developed companion methods
with torches and disks. The name "wigwag" derived from the flag movements.

Three main color combinations were used in flags measuring two,
four, and six feet square. The white banners had red, square centers,
while the black or red flags had white centers. Myer's method required
three motions (elements) to be used for each letter. The first position
always initiated a message sequence. Motion 1 went from head to toe
and back on the right side; motion 2 went from head to toe and back on
the left side; motion 3 went from head to toe and back in front of the
man. Each motion was made quickly. Figure 3-11 indicates the multiliteral alphabet and directional orders to convey a message.

As the Civil War wore on, Myer increased the wigwag motions to four.
This enabled more specialized words and abbreviations to be used. In
1864, Myer invented a similar daytime system with disks. For night sig-

Figure 3-11

A— 112	H— 312	O —223	V— 222
B— 121	I —213	P— 313	W—311
C— 211	J — 232	Q—131	X —321
D— 212	K— 323	R—331	Y —111
E— 221	L —231	S— 332	Z— 113
F— 122	M—132	T—133	
G— 123	N— 322	U—233	

Myer's Signal Directions
3—End of a word
33—End of a sentence
333—End of message
22.22.22.3—Signal of assent. Message understood
22.22.22.333—Cease signaling
121.121.121.3—Repeat
212121.3—Error
211.211.211.3—Move a little to the right
221.221.221.3—Move a little to the left

nals, Myer applied his system with torches on the signal poles and lanterns. A foot torch was used as a reference point. Thus, the direction of the flying wave could better be seen. Compare this to the semaphore system used by ships at sea when radio silence is necessary.

Myer continuously improved his invention through 1859 and presented his findings gratis to the Union Army (which gave him a lukewarm yawn for his trouble). Alexander Porter, his chief assistant, joined the Confederate Army and used the wigwag system in actual combat. Porter was able to warn Colonel Nathan Evans at Manassas Junction–Stone Bridge that the Union Army had reached Sudley Ford and was about to surprise General Beauregard's best division. From his observation tower, Porter sent the following message to Colonel Evans at the Stone Bridge defenses: "Look out for your left, you are turned."

Colonel Evans turned his cannons and musket fire toward the Federal troops before they could initiate their attack. Porter was later credited (and decorated) for his vigilance led to changes in the tactics of the entire struggle around Manassas Junction. The application of the new signal system had directly influenced the shocking Union defeat that eventful July day.

Myer's signaling system was catapulted into use at the Battle of Gettysburg. General Lee had invaded Northern soil in June 1863; his Potomac crossing was relayed by flag system to the War Department. General Joseph Hooker resigned under fire on June 28. General George

Meade took over command of the Army of the Potomac, headquartered at Taneytown, Maryland. Startling news came via signalmen on July 1. A skirmish on the Maryland border indicated that General Buford was facing a major force not in Maryland but in Pennsylvania. Lee himself was in command at Gettysburg. Signalmen of each army unit sent out calls for help. Reinforcements from dozens of units several miles away were committed to the fray. By July 1, 73,000 gray and 88,000 blue met in one of history's most decisive battles.

Rarely, if at all, do textbooks even hint that the secret message system of flags affected these history-changing events. Yet, the crucial sightings by Union observers directly tipped the scales against Lee's best tactics. The most famous incident was on Cemetery Ridge, when Captain Castle refused to submit to the Confederate artillery barrage as General George Pickett charged the "thin blue line," and used a wooden pole and a bedsheet to create a makeshift flag to alert Union forces under General Meade, who ordered countermeasures. Pickett's charge was stopped short of breaching the Union lines, thus dooming General Lee's gamble. Flagmen—previously disregarded—enabled George Meade to enter the shrine of heroes.

Numerical Ciphers

Cipher alphabets whose cipher components consist of numbers are practicable for telegraph or radio transmission. They may take forms corresponding to those employing letters. Standard numerical cipher alphabets are those in which the cipher component is a normal sequence of numbers.

Plain: A B C D E F G H I J K L M
Cipher: 11 12 13 14 15 16 17 18 19 20 21 22 23

Plain: N O P Q R S T U V W X Y Z
Cipher: 24 25 26 27 28 29 30 31 32 33 34 35 36

We could easily have started the cipher alphabet with A = 01, B = 02,..., Z = 26 with the same results.

Mixed numerical cipher alphabets are those that have been keyed by a keyword turned into numerical cipher equivalents or have a random combination of two or more digits for each letter of plain text.

Plain: A B C D E F G H I J K L M
Cipher: 76 88 01 67 04 80 66 99 96 96 02 69 90

Plain: N O P Q R S T U V W X Y Z
Cipher: 77 05 87 60 39 79 03 78 68 98 86 70 97

Rather than apply a brute force attack on all combinations of two-letter equivalents of the preceding cipher text, we would try a frequency count, then check for repeated digrams and trigrams, and then solve as one-for-one substitution without complicating modifications. Figures 3-3 and 3-4 could be arranged for simple numerical equivalents like this:

	1	2	3	4	5
1	A	B	C	D	E
2	F	G	H	IJ	K
3	L	M	N	O	P
4	Q	R	S	T	U
5	V	W	X	Y	Z

where: A = 11, R = 42, Z = 55

	1	2	3	4	5	6	7	8	9
1	A	B	C	D	E	F	G	H	I
2	J	K	L	M	N	O	P	Q	R
3	S	T	U	V	W	X	Y	Z	*

Numerical cipher values lend themselves to treatment by various mathematical processes to further complicate the cipher system in which they are used. These processes, mainly addition or subtraction, may be applied to each cipher equivalent individually, or to the complete numerical cipher message by considering it as one number. The Hill cipher is another good example of the use of mathematical transformation processes on ciphers. (See Bauer or Kahn for details.) In modern cryptographic systems, the DES family of ciphers use simple S-Boxes (substitution boxes) that are reorganized by ordered nonlinear mathematical rules applied several times over (known as *rounds*).

One-Time Pad

The question of "unbreakable" mathematical ciphers might be posed at this juncture. Let's look at the famous one-time pad and see what it offers. The *one-time pad* is truly an unbreakable cipher system, consisting of a nonrepetitive truly random key of letters or characters used just once. The key is written on special sheets of paper and glued together in a pad. The sender uses each key letter on the pad to encrypt exactly one plain text letter or character. The receiver has an identical pad and uses the key on the pad, in turn, to decrypt each letter of the cipher text. Each key is used exactly once and for only one message. The sender encrypts the message and destroys the pad's page. The receiver does the same thing after decrypting the message. We use a new message—new page and new key letters/numbers—each time.

The one-time pad is unbreakable both in theory and in practice. Interception of cipher text does not help the cryptographer break this cipher. No matter how much cipher text the analyst has available, or how much time he has to work on it, it can never be solved.

The reason is that no pattern can be constructed for the key. The perfect randomness of the one-time system nullifies any efforts to reconstruct the key or plain text via any of the following cryptanalytic methods described by Friedman: horizontal or lengthwise analysis, cohesion, reassembly via Kasiski or Kerckhoff's columns, repeats, or internal framework erection.

Brute force (trial and error) might bring out the true plain text but it would also yield every other text of the same length, and there is no way to tell which is the right one. It should be noted that the possible solutions increase as the message lengthens and rapidly reaches the point where all the computer power in the world, working together, would require decades and centuries to come up with all possible solutions. Only the hindsight of history would enable us to pick the right solution.

Supposing the key were stolen, would this help to predict future keys? No, because a random key has no underlying system to exploit. If it did, it would not be random. A *truly* random key sequence XORed with a nonrandom plain text message produces a completely random cipher text message, and no amount of computing will change that. The one-time pad can be extended to encryption of binary data by computer. Instead of letters, we use bits.

Fresh Key Drawback

The one-time pad has a drawback—the quantities of fresh keys required. For military messages in the field (a fluid situation) a practical limit is reached. It is impossible to produce and distribute sufficient fresh keys to the units. During World War II, the U.S. Army's European theater HQs transmitted, even before the Normandy invasion, 2 million five-letter code groups a day! It would have, therefore, consumed 10 million letters of key every 24 hours—the equivalent of a shelf of 20 average books.

Randomness

The real issue for the one-time pad is that the keys must be truly random. Attacks against the one-time pad must be against the method used to generate the key itself. Pseudorandom number generators don't count; often they have nonrandom properties. Tests at the ICSA Cryptography Laboratory have confirmed that random number generation based on deterministic machine states needs to be based on at least 20 different state functions to prevent attack on the random number generator(s). More on this issue in a later chapter.

The Structure of Language

Linguistic anthropologists have used cryptography to reconstruct ancient languages by comparing contemporary descendants and in so doing make discoveries about history. Others make inferences about universal features of language, linking them to uniformities in the brain. Still others study linguistic differences to discover varied worldviews and patterns of thought in a multitude of cultures.

The Rosetta Stone found by the Egyptian Dhautpol and the French officer Pierre-Francois Bouchard near the town of Rosetta in the Nile Delta, gave us a look at Syriac, Greek, and Egyptian hieroglyphs all of the same text. The fascinating story of its decipherment is covered in Kahn. Of special interest was the final decipherment of the Egyptian writing containing *homophones*, different signs standing for the same sound.

Until the late 1950s, linguists thought that the study of language should proceed through a sequence of stages of analysis. The first stage was *phonology*, the study of sounds used in speech. *Phones* are speech sounds present and significant in each language. They were recorded using the International Phonetic Alphabet, a series of symbols devised to describe dozens of sounds that occur in different languages.

The next stage was *morphology*, the study of forms in which sounds combine to form *morphemes*—words and their meaningful constituents. The word *cats* has two morphemes, /cat/ and /s/, indicating the animal and plurality. A *lexicon* is a dictionary of all morphemes. A morpheme is the smallest meaningful unit of speech. *Isolating* or *analytic* languages are those in which words are morphologically benign, like Chinese or Vietnamese. *Agglutinative* languages string together successive morphemes; Turkish is a good example of this. *Inflection* languages change the form of a word to mark all kinds of grammar distinctions, such as tense or gender. Indo-European languages tend to be highly inflectional. The next step was to study *syntax,* the arrangement and order of words in phrases and sentences.

Phonemes and Phones

No language contains all the sounds in the International Phonetic Alphabet. A *phoneme* is the smallest unit of distinctive sound. Although phonemes lack meaning in themselves, they distinguish meaning through sound contrasts. We find them in *minimal pairs,* words that resemble each other in all but one sound. An example is the minimal pair, *pit*/*bit.* The /p/ and /b/ are phonemes in English. Another example is *bit* and *beat,* which separates the phonemes /I/ and /i/ in English. Friedman describes similar phenomena called *homologs* and uses them to solve a variety of cryptograms.

Standard (American) English (SE), the region-free dialect of TV network newscasters, has about 35 phonemes of at least 11 vowels and 24 consonants. The number of phonemes varies from language to language—from 15 to 60, averaging between 30 and 40. The number of phonemes varies between dialects. In American English, vowel phonemes vary noticeably from dialect to dialect. Readers should pro-

Figure 3-12
Vowel Phonemes (According to Height and Position of Tongue)

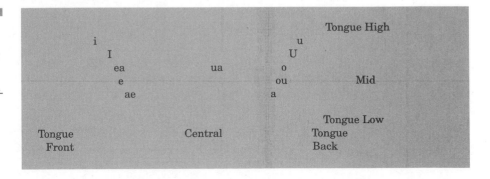

nounce the words in Figure 3-12, paying attention to whether they distinguish each of the vowel sounds. Americans do not generally pronounce them at all.

Phonetic symbols are identified by English words that include them; note that most are minimal pairs.

high front (spread)	[i] as in beat
lower high front (spread)	[I] as in bit
mid front (spread)	[ea] as in bait
lower mid front (spread)	[e] as in bet
low front	[ae] as in bat
central	[ua] as in butt
low back	[a] as in pot
lower mid back (rounded)	[ou] as in bought
mid back (rounded)	[o] as in boat
lower high back (rounded)	[U] as in put
high back (rounded)	[u] as in boot

Phonetics studies sounds in general—what people actually say in various languages. *Phonemics* is concerned with sound contrasts of a particular language. In English, /b/ and /v/ are phonemes, occurring in minimal pairs such as *bat* and *vat*. In Spanish, the contrast between [b] and [v] doesn't distinguish meaning, and they are not phonemes. The [b] sound is used in Spanish to pronounce words spelled with either b or v. (Nonphonemic phones are enclosed in brackets.)

In any language, a given phoneme extends over a phonetic range. In English, the phoneme /p/ ignores the phonetic contrast between the [pH] in *pin* and the [p] in *spin*. How many of you noticed the difference? [pH] is aspirated, so that a puff of air follows the [p]; that is not true with [p] in *spin*. To see the difference, light a match and watch the flame as you say the two words. In Chinese, the contrast between [p] and [pH] is distinguished only by the contrast between an aspirated and unaspirated [p].

Historical Linguistics

Knowledge of linguistic relationships is often valuable to determine the events of the past 5000 years. By studying contemporary *daughter languages,* past language features can be reconstructed. Daughter languages descend from the same parent language that has been changing for thousands of years. The original language from which they diverge is called a *protolanguage*. French and Spanish are daughter languages of Latin. Language evolves over time into subgroups (closely related taxonomy) but with distinct cultural differences. Figure 3-13 shows the main languages and subgroups of the Indo-European language stock.

All these daughter languages have developed out of the protolanguage (Proto-Indo-European) spoken in Northern Europe about 5000 years ago. English, a member of the Germanic branch, is more closely related to German and Dutch than it is to Italic or Romance languages such as French and Spanish. However, English shares many linguistic features with French through borrowing and diffusion.

The doctrine of *linguistic relativity* is central to cryptographic treatment of language ciphers. It states that all known languages and dialects are effective means of communication. *Nichols' Theorem* states that if they are linguistically related, they can be codified, enciphered, deciphered, and treated as cryptographic units for analysis and statistical treatment.

Dead Languages

Professor Cyrus H. Gordon, in his fascinating book *Forgotten Scripts*, shows how cryptography is used to recover ancient writings. He tells the story of the unraveling of each of these ancient languages: Egyptian, Old Persian, Sumer-Akkadian, Hittite, Ugaritic, Eteocretan, Minoan, and Eblaite. He specializes in cuneiform and hieroglyphic inscriptions and gives us a glimpse into the ancient societies that gave birth to the Western world.

Cryptographic Threads

There is a common cryptographic thread for most languages. *All known writing systems are partly or wholly phonetic, and express the sounds of a particular language.* Writing is speech put in visible form, in such a way that any reader instructed in its conventions can reconstruct the vocal message. Writing as "visible speech" was invented about 5000 years ago by Sumerians and almost simultaneously by ancient Egyptians.

The ancient Mayan knew that it was 12 cycles, 18 katuns, 16 tuns, 0 uinals, and 16 kins since the beginning of the Great Cycle. The day was

Figure 3-13
Main Languages of
Indo-European Stock

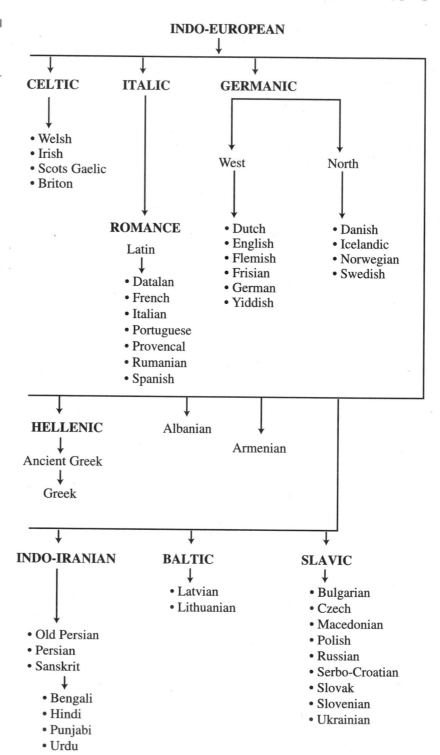

12 Cib 14 Uo and was ruled by the seventh Lord of the Night. The moon was nine days old. Precisely 5101 of our years and 235 days had passed. So said the ancient Mayan scribes. We remember the day as 14 May 1989.

Writing Systems

Three kinds of writing systems have been identified: *Rebus,* which is a combination of logograms and phonetic signs; *Syllabic,* such as CV— consonant vowel, such as Cherokee or Inuit; and *Alphabetic,* which is phonemic (the individual consonants and vowels make up the sounds of the language). Writing systems can also be classified by their signs. Table 3-4 differentiates writing systems by the number of signs used.

TABLE 3-4

Writing Systems

Writing System	No. of Signs
Logographic	
Sumerian	600+
Egyptian	2500
Hittite Hieroglyphic	497
Chinese	5000+
"Pure" Syllabic	
Persian	40
Linear B	87
Cypriote	56
Cherokee	85
Alphabetic or Consonantal	
English	26
Anglo-Saxon	31
Sanskrit	35
Etruscan	20
Russian	36
Hebrew	22
Arabic	28

Linguist Michael D. Coe classifies the entire group of Proto-Mayan languages into 14 daughter divisions of Proto-Mayan, and 31 sublanguages from Huastec to Tzuthil. He presents an extraordinary story of applied cryptanalysis and applied linguistics.

Xenocrypts—Language Ciphers

Xenocrypts are foreign language substitutions. Xenocrypts represent a cultural universal expressed at its common denominator—mathematics. It is the author's contention that any language can be learned from its cryptographic building blocks. To understand the building blocks we can look at underlying structure of language. Furthermore, most languages share the common framework of mathematics and statistics. To be able to solve xenocrypts, it is only necessary to learn the basic (group) mathematical structure of the language, to use a bidirectional translation dictionary, and to recognize the underlying cipher construct.

Ciphers start with the problem of recognizing the language and then the distribution of characters within the particular language. The legendary William F. Friedman once remarked: "Treating the frequency distribution as a statistical curve, when such treatment is possible, is one of the most useful and trustworthy methods in cryptography."

Table 3-5 gives the frequency distributions of 10 languages developed

TABLE 3-5

Xenocryptic Frequency Data, %

	16	8	7	6	5	4	2	<1	
NORWEGIAN:	E	RNS	T	AI	LDO	GKM	UVFHPA	JBO	YAECWXZQ

	10	9	7	6	4	3	<2	
LATIN:	I	E	UTA	SRN	OM	CPL	(balance)	

	18	8	7	6	5	4	3	2	<1
FRENCH:	E	AN	RSIT	UO	L	D	CMP	VB	F-Y

	14	13	12	8	6	5	4	3	2	<1
PORTUGUESE:	A	E	O	RS	IN	DMT	UCL	P	QV	(balance)

	18	11	8	7	5	4	3	2	<1
GERMAN:	E	N	I	RS	ADTU	GHO	LBM	CW	(balance)

	15	12	8	7	5	4	3	1	<1
CATALAN:	E	A	S	ILRNT	OC	DU	MP	BVQGF	(balance)

	16	13	8	6	5	4	3	<2
HUNGARIAN:	E	A	T	OS	LNZ	KIM	RGU	(balance)

	13	12	11	9	7	6	5	3	2	<1
ITALIAN:	E	A	I	O	L	NRT	SC	DMOU	VG	balance)

	20	10	7	6	5	4	3	2	<1
DUTCH:	E	N	IAT	O	DL	S	GKH	UVWBJMPZ	(balance)

	13	9	8	7	5	4	3	1	<1
SPANISH:	EA	O	S	RNI	DL	CTU	MP	GYB	(balance)

[Special characters are generally not available in classical or BC (before computer) cryptograms. They are reduced to other constructions such as an umlaut = ae.]

from various sources. Frequencies of letters and their order are not fixed quantities in any language. *Group frequencies, however, are fairly constant in every language. This is the common thread—the linguistic relativity of all languages.*

Kullback gives the following tables for Monoalphabetic and Digraphic texts for eight languages correlated with the number of letters N in a cryptogram. The constants may be derived from probability data for a given language (Table 3-6).

TABLE 3-6

Monoalphabetic and Digraphic Texts

Monoalphabetic Text	Digraphic Text	Trigraphic Text
English	$0.0661N(N-1)$	$0.0069N(N-1)$
French	$0.0778N(N-1)$	$0.0093N(N-1)$
German	$0.0762N(N-1)$	$0.0112N(N-1)$
Italian	$0.0738N(N-1)$	$0.0081N(N-1)$
Japanese	$0.0819N(N-1)$	$0.0116N(N-1)$
Portuguese	$0.0791N(N-1)$	
Russian	$0.0529N(N-1)$	$0.0058N(N-1)$
Spanish	$0.0775N(N-1)$	$0.0093N(N-1)$
Random Text		
$.038N(N-1)$	$.0015N(N-1)$	$.000057N(N-1)$

German Reduction Ciphers— Traffic Analysis

A small sister to cryptanalysis is the science of traffic analysis. *Traffic analysis* is the branch of signal intelligence analysis that deals with the study of external characteristics of signal communications.

The information was used: (1) to effect interception, (2) to aid cryptanalysis, (3) to rate the level and value of intelligence in the absence of the specific message contents, and (4) to improve the security in the communication nets. Traffic analysis was a primary reason for the cracking of the German codes in World War II. (Unfortunately, the same principles worked on the British and American codes as well.) The German Army was dedicated to unquestioned organization. Paperwork and radio messages must flow to the various military units in a prescribed manner.

Components

Allowing for historical differences in language, procedure signs, and signals, there were six standard elements for military radio communications systems. These were: (1) call-up, (2) order of traffic, (3) transmission of traffic, (4) receipting for traffic, (5) corrections and services, and (6) signing off.

In order to insure proper handling of messages in the field and message center, some information was sent in the clear or by using simple coding. This information about routing and accounting was usually in the beginning or ending of a message. This included: (1) Serial numbers, message center number; (2) Group Count; (3) File Date and Time (like a PGP signature); (4) Routing System—origin, destination, and relay (distinction is made as to action or FYI locations); (5) Priority (important information was originally signal flashed—hence the term FLASH message for urgent message); (6) transmission and delivery procedure; (7) addresses and signatures; and (8) special instructions. As a rule, German high-echelon traffic contained most of these items and German low-echelon traffic cut them to a minimum.

The German penchant for organization could be seen in the way they handled serial numbers. Any radio message flowing from division level to soldier in the field would have a reference serial number attached in clear or matrix cipher, by the writer, the HQ message center, the signal center or code room, the "in desk," the transmitter, linkage, and/or operator. The routing system usually consisted of a code and syllabary that represented the location or unit.

You can see where modern email and word processing systems have made some of this information easier to handle by the portable desk idea, but traffic analysis would still apply. Compare the preceding six traffic elements to the modern network computer packet. Look at the information flow in terms of the OSI model and notice that all six elements have their corresponding "sisters" in the headers and protocols used to route information.

American cryptographers were adept in determining the German order of battle from their cryptonets (e.g., from intercepts from corps to theater). Traffic analysis not only gave the locations but the communication relationships between units or groups of units in the field. Some German commands were allowed latitude in their compositions of codes and ciphers. This proved to be an exploitable fault in the German security.

Applications to Cryptanalysis

Traffic analysis yields information via Crib messages, Isologs, and Chatter. *Crib messages* assume a partial knowledge of the underlying plain text through recognition of the external characteristics. Command "sitreps" (situation reports) up and down German channels were especially easy for American "crypees." The origin, serial number range, the cryptonet id, report type, the file date and time, message length, and error messages in the clear gave an explicit picture of the German command process. German order of battle, troop dispositions, and movements were deduced by traffic analysis.

An *Isolog* exists when the underlying plain text is encrypted in two different systems. They exist because of relay repetition requirements, book messages to multiple receivers (spamming would have been a definite no-no), or error by the code clerk. American cryptographers were particularly effective in obtaining intelligence by this method.

Traffic analysis boils down to finding the contact relationships among units, tracking their movements, building up the cryptonet authorities, capitalizing on lack of randomness in their structures, and exploiting book and relay cribs. American intelligence was quite successful in this endeavor against the Germans as well as the Japanese in World War II.

ADFGVX

"Weh dem der leugt und Klartext funkt"—Lieutenant Jaeger German 5th Army ("Woe to him who lies and radios in the clear"). Jaeger was a German code expert sent to stiffen the German code discipline in France in 1918. Ironically, the double "e" in Jaeger's name gave U.S. Army traffic analysis experts a fix on code changes in 1918.

ADFGVX is one of the best known field ciphers in the history of cryptology. Originally a 5×5 matrix of just five letters, ADFGX, the system was expanded on June 1, 1918, to a sixth letter V. The letters were chosen for their clarity in Morse code: **A** .-, **D** -.., **F** ..-., **G** --., **V** ...-, and **X** -..-. Friedman describes one of the first traffic analysis charts regarding battle activity from May to August 1918 at Marne and Rheims, France. It was based solely on the ebb and flow of traffic in the ADFGVX cipher. This cipher was restricted to German high command communications between and among the headquarters of divisions and army corps.

The ADFGVX cipher was considered secure because it combined both a good substitution (bipartite fractionation or two-part fractionation enciphering system) and an excellent transposition in one system. During the eight-month history of this cipher, only 10 keys were recovered by the Allies (in 10 days of heavy traffic) and 50 percent of the messages on these days were read. These intercepts effected the reverse of the German advances (15 divisions) under Ludendorff at Montdidier and Compiegne, about 50 miles north of Paris. Solution by the famed French Captain Georges Painvin was based on just two specialized cases. No general solution for the cipher was found by the Allies, but in 1933, William Friedman and the SIS found a general solution. French General Givierge of the Deuxieme Bureau also published a solution to the general case.

The June 3 message that Painvin cracked changed the course of World War I: From German High Command in Remaugies: Munitionierung beschleunigen Punkt Soweit nicht eingesehen auch bei Tag or "Rush Munitions Stop Even by day if not seen."

Cipher text starts: CHI-126: FGAXA XAXFF FAFFA AVDFA GAXFX FAAAG

This told the Allies where and when the bombardment preceding the next major German push was planned.

ADFGVX Cryptanalysis

According to William F. Friedman, there were only three viable ways to attack this cipher (at the time). The first method required two or more messages with identical plain text beginnings to uncover the transposition. Under the second method, two or more messages with plain text endings were required to break the flat distribution shield (the flatter the distribution the more random the cipher text and hence, the more difficult the cracking of the cipher) of the substitution part of the cipher. The German addiction to stereotyped phraseology was so prevalent in all German military communications that in each day's traffic, messages with similar endings and beginnings were found (sometimes both). The third method required messages with the exact same number of letters. Painvin used the first two methods when he cracked the five-letter ADFGX version in April 1918.

Lest we underestimate the difficulty of this cipher, we might step behind Painvin's shoulders as he worked. At 4:30 AM on March 21, 6000 guns opened fire on the Allied line at Somme. Five hours later, 62 German divisions pushed forward on a 40-mile front. Radio traffic increased dramatically; Painvin had just a few intercepts in the ADFGX cipher and the longer ones had been split in three parts to prevent anagramming. Five letters—a checkerboard perhaps? Maybe. Simple monoalphabetic cipher? No, too flat of a distribution.

The German oddity of first parts of messages with identical bits and pieces of text in the same order in the cryptograms begin to show. Painvin feels the oddity could most likely have resulted from transposed beginnings according to the same key; the identical tops of the columns of the transposition table. Painvin sections the cryptograms by timeframe:

chi-110:	(1) ADXDA	(2) XGFXG	(3) DAXXGX	(4) GDADFF
chi-114:	(1) ADXDD	(2) XGFFD	(3) DAXAGD	(4) GDGXD

He does this with 20 blocks to reconstruct the transposition key. Using the principle of long columns to the left, he finds segments 3, 6, 14, and 18 to the left, the balance clustered to the right. Using other messages with common endings (repeated), he segments the columns to the left. Correctly? No. He uses 18 additional intercepts to juxtaposition 60 letters, AAs, ADs, and so forth. Using frequency count, he finds a monoalphabetic substitution. He finds column 5-8 and 8-5 are inverted.

Painvin sets up a skeleton checkerboard—he assumes correctly the order to be side-top:

```
  A  D  F  G  X
A
D           e
F
G
X
```

Since the message was 20 letters, the order might be side-top, repeated—meaning side coordinates would fall on the first, third, and fifth positions during encipherment—so he separates them by frequency characteristics. In 48 hours of incredible labor, Painvin pairs the correct letters and builds the checkerboard, solving the toughest field cipher the world had yet seen: a cipher that defends itself by *fractionation,* the breaking up of plain text letter equivalents into pieces, with the consequent dissipation of its ordinary characteristics. The transposition further scatters these characteristics in a particularly effective fashion, while dulling the clues that normally help to reconstruct a transposition.

Arabian Contributors to Cryptology

Dr. Ibrahim A. Al-Kadi gave an outstanding 1990 paper to the Swedish Royal Institute of Technology in Stockholm regarding the Arabic contributions to cryptology.

Dr. Al-Kadi reported on the Arabic scientist by the name of Abu Yusuf Yaqub ibn Is-haq ibn as Sabbah ibn 'omran ibn Ismail Al-Kindi, who authored a book on cryptology, the *Risalah fi Istikhraj al-Mu'amma* (*Manuscript for the Deciphering of Cryptographic Messages*) circa 750 AD. Al-Kindi introduced cryptanalysis techniques; classification of ciphers; Arabic Phonetics and Syntax; and, most important, described the use of several statistical techniques for cryptanalysis. (This book apparently antedates other cryptology references by 300 years. It also predates writings on probability and statistics by Pascal and Fermat by nearly 800 years.)

Dr. Al-Kadi also reported on the mathematical writings of Al-Khwarizmi (780–847) who introduced common technical terms such as *zero, cipher, algorithm, algebra*, and *Arabic numerals*. The decimal number system and the concept of zero were originally developed in India.

In the early ninth century the Arabs translated Brahmagupta's *Siddharta* from Sanskrit into Arabic. The new numerals were quickly adopted throughout the Islamic Empire from China to Spain. Translations of Al-Khwarizmi's book on arithmetic by Robert of Chester, John of Halifax, and the Italian Leonardo of Pisa (aka Fibonacci) strongly advocated the use of Arabic numerals over the previous Roman standard numerals (I, V, X, C, D, M).

The Roman system was very cumbersome because there was no concept of zero (or empty space). The concept of zero, which we all think of as natural, was just the opposite in medieval Europe. In Sanskrit, the zero was called *sunya* or "empty." The Arabs translated the Indian into the Arabic equivalent *sifr*. Europeans adopted the concept and symbol but not the name, but transformed it into Latin equivalent *cifra* and *cephirium* (Fibonacci did this), the Italian equivalent of which was *zefiro, zefro,* and *zevero*. The latter was shortened to *zero*.

The French formed the word *chiffre* and conceded the Italian word *zero*. The English used *zero* and *cipher* from the word ciphering as a means of computing. The Germans used the words *ziffer* and *chiffer*.

The concept of zero or sifr or cipher was so confusing and ambiguous to common Europeans that in arguments people would say "talk clearly and not so far fetched as a cipher." *Cipher* came to mean concealment of clear messages or simply, encryption. Dr. Al-Kadi concluded that the Arabic word *sifr,* for the digit zero, developed into the European technical term for encryption.

Nihilist Substitution

For some reason, Russian prisoners were not allowed computers in their cells. This might have been because at the time computers were too big to be hidden under their shirts. Russian prisoners were forbidden to communicate with each other. To outwit their jailers, they invented a "knock" system to indicate the rows and columns of a simple checkerboard (Polybius square at 5 × 5 for English or 6 × 6 for 35 Russian letters). For example:

```
    1  2  3  4  5
1   U  N  Ij T  E
2   D  S  A  O  F
3   M  R  C  B  G
4   H  K  L  P  Q
5   V  W  X  Y  Z
```

Keyword = United States of America

Repeated letters in the keyword were used only once in the square the first time encountered.

Plain text:	g	o	t		a	c	i	g	a	r	e		t	t	e
Cipher text:	35	24	14		23	33	13	35	23	32	15		14	14	15

Prisoners memorized the proper numbers and "talked" at about 10 to 15 words per minute. One of the advantages was that it afforded communication by a great variety of media—anything that could be dotted, knotted, pierced, flashed, or indicate numerals in any way could be used. The innocuous letter was always suspicious.

Cipher text letters were indicated by the number of letters written together; breaks in count by spaces in handwriting; or upstrokes, downstrokes, thumbnail prints, all subtly used to bootleg secrets in and out of prisons. The system was universal in penal institutions. American POWs used it in Vietnam. Transposition of the keyword provided a further mixed alphabet:

```
B L  A C K S M I T H
D E  F G N O P Q R U
V W  X Y Z
```

Taken off by columns:

```
B D V L E W A F X C G Y K N Z S O M P I Q T R H U
```

the Polybius square would be:

```
   1  2  3  4  5
1  B  D  V  L  E
2  W  A  F  X  C
3  G  Y  K  N  Z
4  S  O  M  P  I
5  Q  T  R  H  U
```

The Nihilists, so named for their opposition to the czarist regime, added a repeating numerical keyword (KW), which made the cipher a periodic similar to the Vigenere (discussed later) but with additional weaknesses.

```
Let the KW = ARISE = 22 53 45 41 15
Plain:       b   o   m   b   w    i   n   t   e   r   p   a   l   a   c   e
Numerical: 11 42 43 11 21  45 34 52 15 53 44 22 14 22 25 15
Key:       22 53 45 41 15  22 53 45 41 15 22 53 45 41 15 22
Cipher:    33 97 88 52 36  67 87 97 56 68 66 75 59 63 40 37
```

or with bifurcation into five number groups:

```
33978 85236 67879 75668 66755 96340 37774
    nulls = 774
```

Nihilist Transposition

A simpler form of the Nihilist is a double transposition. The plain text was written in by rows (or diagonals); a keyword switched the rows; a same or different keyword switched the columns; and the resulting cipher text was removed by columns or by one of forty (40) or more routes out of the square.

Example: KW = SCOTIA or 524631

Plain: let us hear from you at once concerning jewels xxxx

Transpose by Columns **Transpose by Rows**

```
    S  C  O  T  I  A
    5  2  4  6  3  1                  1  2  3  4  5  6
 1  S  E  U  H  T  L (let us h)   S  5  E  U  J  W  T  O
 2  R  A  F  O  R  E              C  2  R  A  F  O  R  E
 3  A  Y  U  T  O  M              O  4  A  N  E  B  C  O
 4  A  N  E  B  C  O              T  6  X  L  X  X  S  E
 5  E  U  J  W  T  O              I  3  A  Y  U  T  O  M
 6  X  L  X  X  S  E              A  1  S  E  U  H  T  L
```

X is a bad choice for nulls because it is obviously a low-frequency letter and therefore gives positional information about the keyword length.

The resulting cryptogram:

EUJWT   ORAFO   REANE   BCOXL   XXSEA

YUTOM   SEUHT   L.

(message length and fifth group are entries to solution)

Clues to cryptanalysis of the Nihilist systems were reconstructing the routes, evenness of distribution of vowels, period determination, and digram/trigram frequency in cipher text.

Chinese Cryptography

Dr. Dan August found that the Four-Corner System and the Chinese Phonetic Alphabet System lent themselves to manual cryptographic treatment. His treatment of these two systems is easier to understand than some military texts on the subject. Let a message in Chinese be X_1, X_2, and X_3; X_n, where X_i represents a character. The code for X_i is a vector union of three sets, v_1, v_2, and v_3—v_1 is a single-digit code for tone; v_2 is a four- or five-digit Four-Corner representation code; and v_3 is a six-digit phonetic code representing three phonetic symbols each by two digits.

$$X_j = \cup \sum_{1-3}^{3} v_1 \qquad \text{[Eq. 3-1]}$$

This union is called an *asymmetric code*. The Four-Corner System encodes characters into several generic shapes. Each character is broken into four quadrants, and assigned a digit to the generic shape that best corresponds to the actual shape.

The Chinese Phonetic Alphabet is Pinyin, with symbols instead of English letters. Each symbol corresponds to one of 37 ordered phonetic sounds. The 21 initial, 3 medial, and 13 finals are a unique ordered set— a true alphabet. The strength of encryption of Chinese is dependent on the specific Chinese encoding character schemes. Three cases are:

1. *Phonetic Alphabet Only:*   The cipher must include both a transposition (to hide cohesion and positional limitations) and a substitution (to hide the frequency patterns).

2. *Four-Corner System:*   The cipher can be based on ring operations (performed on codewords rather than characters, either on an individual basis or over the whole message; the name comes from the algebraic operations involving integers mod 10 or mod 37) which superencipher the encoded text.

3. *Combination of Methods 1 and 2:*   A text encoded by a combination of both methods will need a cipher employing both transposition and substitution. The transposition needs to mix up the symbols within codewords and the message itself. This prevents a bifurcated analysis.

In Chinese there is more dependence between encoding and enciphering operations than in English. The choice of the encoding system influences the type of enciphering operations.

Historical Perspectives—China

China appears to have had a much-delayed entry into the cipher business; partially because so many Chinese did not read or write, and partially because the language was so complex, Chinese cryptography was limited until the nineteenth century. But there were seeds.

The Chinese strategist Sun Tzu (500 BC) recommended a true but small code, which limited the plain text to 40 elements and assigned them to the first 40 characters of a poem, forming a substitution table. Richard Deacon describes a method of code encryption, which the secret society Triads used in the early 1800s. The Tongs in San Francisco used the same system. This method limited the plain text space and based codewords on multiples of three.

The "Inner Ring" techniques taught to "Sa Bu Nims" (teachers) by the masters of Korean Tae Kwon Do (which came from the Ancient Tae Kwan and before that Kung Fu) were passed on by means of codeword transposition ciphers. In 1885, Sun Yat-Sen used codes to transmit information by telegraph. During World War II, Herbert Yardley taught Kuomintang (Chinese Nationalist) soldiers to cryptanalyze Japanese ciphers. However, the Japanese had already outpaced the Chinese in cryptanalytical abilities.

Japan's Chuo tokujobu (Central Bureau of Signal Intelligence) was responsible for crypto-communication and signal intelligence, including cryptanalysis, translation, interception, and direction finding against the Soviet Union, China, and Britain. It began operations in 1921.

In May 1928, the Angohan (Codes and Ciphers Office) obtained excellent results in intercepting and decoding Chinese codes during the Sino-Japanese clash at Tsinan between Chiang Kai-shek's Northern Expeditionary Army and the IJA (Imperial Japanese Army).

The warlord Chang Tso-lin was murdered in June 1928. Angohan succeeded in decoding "Young Marshal" Chang Hsueh-liang's secret communications and made a substantial contribution to the understanding of the warlord politics of Manchuria. The Angohan not only mastered the basics of Chinese codes and ciphers but also broke the Nanking Government and the Chinese Legation codes in Tokyo.

The Chinese codes in 1935 were called *Mingma*. They were basically made up of four-digit numbers. The Chinese did not encode the name of either the sender or receiver, nor the date or the time of the message. The China Garrison Army's Tokujohan office was able to disclose the composition, strength, and activities of Chiang Kai-shek's branch armies, such as those led by Sung Che-yuan and Chang Hseuh-liang. It was not able to decode the Chinese Communist or Air Force messages.

By the time of the 1937 Sino-Japanese War, Japanese cryptanalytical experts had been able to greatly expand their knowledge of the Chinese system of codes and ciphers, as well as improve their decoding skills. About 80 percent of what was intercepted was then decoded. This included military and diplomatic codes but not the Communist code messages.

The Kuomintang upgraded their Mingma codes in 1938. They adopted a different system, called *tokushu daihon* (special codebook) in Japanese, which complicated by mixing compound words. By October 1940, Chiang Kai-shek's main forces were using a repeating key system. This stumped the Japanese cryptanalysts for a short time, then they returned to a 75 percent decoding level during the war. They continued to make great contributions to major military operations in China.

The Japanese broke the Kuomintang codes during the Chungyuang Operation in the Southern Shansi or Chungt'iao Mountain Campaign. In February 1941, significant penetration of Communist signal traffic was obtained.

The tokujo operations against the North China Area Army and the Chinese Communist codes were a tragic failure. The IJA's China experts held a highly negative image toward the Chinese. This may have prejudiced their attitude toward intelligence estimates of China and the Chinese, which in turn adversely affected their operational (crypto-intelligence) thinking on China in general.

When the Sian mutiny broke out and Chiang Kai-shek was kidnapped in December 1936, Major General Isogai (IJA's leading expert in COMINT for China) toasted (more like roasted) the demise of Chiang. Colonel Kanji Ishiwara (Japan's chief military strategist) deplored the incident because he felt China was on the brink of unity because of Chiang Kai-shek's efforts. He considered the ability to read Chiang's codes just a matter of doing the business of war.

WRAP-UP

The history of cryptography holds many surprises and innovations. Of special interest is the *universality of cryptography* as applied to all languages. This important concept reports that all languages, both live and dead, may be characterized by their letter, sound, or symbolic behavior. It turns out that similar groups of information, such as vowel relationships with specific consonants, carry through in the cipher text and are potentially identifiable in the cipher text. This is true even in the most difficult of cipher text. The doctrine of linguistic relativity is central to cryptographic treatment of language ciphers. It states that all known languages and dialects are effective means of communication. Nichols' Theorem states that if *they are linguistically related, they can be codified, enciphered, deciphered, and treated as cryptographic units for analysis and statistical treatment.*

CHAPTER **4**

Historical
Systems II

Zen Crypto

For the first few chapters, we have chosen not to indulge in any of the rigorous mathematics of cryptography. Everything to be presented can be reduced to mathematical models and computerized for ease of work.

BUT those who embark on a course of 'only the computer' do this without knowing the real effort - the brain power - the shortcuts - the tradecraft - the historical implications; in our opinion, they have lost the real heart of cryptography. The "ah-ha's" of inspiration are what make the difference. The hours of writing/testing, the sleepless nights, the rush we feel when the letters fall in place, these are the delights of real cryptographers.

There are several problems with the "computer only" solution. First, there is a fundamental problem in that computer models do not apply to all variant cases. Simple changes to the system can fool even the most adept computer program. For example, placing clever *nulls* (arbitrary letters, having no meaning inserted into the plain text to complete a geometric pattern or to confuse or confound the cryptanalyst) will defeat many a statistically based model.

Second, we lose the sense of urgency that was required for wartime cryptography. If John F. Kennedy's *Playfair* message (a form of simple substitution cipher using pairs of letters; that's right, it was not English and was not plain text, as in the movie *PT-109*) on the back of a coconut had been intercepted and deciphered by the Japanese (which they were very capable of doing), we might not have had the graceful light of his presidency or, who knows, the moon landings. As another case in point, the solution of ENIGMA during the midfinal Atlantic campaigns of World War II reduced the operational effectiveness of the U-boat to one day and, hence, saved allied tonnage and warships supplying Europe. The American and British cryptographers thought like their German counterparts and so could develop clues that enabled them to gain access into the cryptosystems. Because of the types of computers available during World War II, computer solutions were bulky, machine dependent, and not reliable until 1945. People made the difference. They always will.

A very brilliant engineer, Seymour Cray, died recently. In his lifetime, he did more for the advancement of computers than many could imagine. He thought about supercooling systems, Josephson Junctions, parallel processing, distributed work loads, optical computing, laser-sound interaction, supercharged transfer devices, and computing machines capable of one quadrillion operations per second. When you brought him down from high altitude, he advocated that one must understand the problem, its growth, its effects, and its conscience before applying the computer to bring forth a "better" solution.

Simple Route Transpositions (TRAMPS)

Transposition ciphers have been defined as that type of cipher in which the elements or units of the plain text—whether one is dealing with individual letters or groups of letters—retain their original identities but undergo some change in their relative positions or sequences so that the message becomes unintelligible. The majority of transposition methods involve the use of a design or geometric figure, such as a square, rectangle, triangle, trapezoid, and the like, in which the letters of the plain text are first *inscribed* or written into the design according to a previously agreed-upon direction of writing and then *transcribed* or taken off according to another and different previously agreed-upon direction, to form the text of the cryptogram.

In their simplest form, TRAMPS may take any of the following routes when employing rectangles or squares for transposing text of a message as illustrated below. The plain-text message is assumed to be merely the normal sequence from A to X, for ease in following the route.

Any geometrical form can be used, but it must be *full* block; if the letters of a message do not complete the assigned block, nulls (arbitrary letters) must be added.

Example 1—Let the message be (military text):
At fourteen hundred sighted submarine bearing two three five degrees true.
(63 letters)

Suppose we agree to use a completely filled square of eight rows by eight columns, and then to add 1 null to give us a multiple of eight (64 letters). We agree that alternate diagonals will be used for inscription.

```
  1 2 3 4 5 6 7 8
1 A T R T R E M A
2 F U E D D B R O
3 O E N S U I W T
4 N U I S N T H E
5 H G D E G R D G
6 H E B N E E R R
7 T E I E V E T U
8 A R F I E S E N
```

Next the letters are taken off by simple vertical to form the cryptogram:

AFONH   HTATU   EUGEE   RRENI   DBIFT   DSSEN
EIRDU   NGEVE   EBITR   EESMR   WHDRT   EAOTE   GRUN

To decipher the cryptogram, the process is reversed. The total number of letters in the cipher text is used to reconstruct the rectangle. Then the cryptogram is inscribed by the agreed-upon route and the plain text is taken off by the other agreed upon route. It should be noted that legitimate correspondents know the system and the key(s). The cryptanalyst would break into this type of system by searching for common trigraphs (the, and) and common digraphs (er, th) and the columns until reasonable plain text appeared in each row.

Transposition ciphers come in several simple varieties. The oldest form may be *reversed writing*. The reversing process may be applied to regular or irregular groups of plain-text letters:

Let the plain text be: Bridge destroyed at eleven PM.

Words Reversed:

E G D I R B D E Y O R T S E D T A N E V E L E M P

Words Reversed and Regrouped into False Lengths:

E G D I R B D E Y O R T S E D T A N E V E L E M P

Text Reversed and Regrouped into Five's:

MPNEV ELETA DEYOR TSEDE GDIRB

Text Reversed and Regrouped into Five's with Nulls every Fifth Position:

TRIMM PNEVP ELETA ADEYR ORTSL EDEGU DIRBM

Rail Fence Cipher

Just as the name implies, the *Rail Fence Cipher*, with its zigzag appearance, resembles an old rail fence found in many parts of New England today.

Plain: Prepare to get underway.

P E A E O E U D R A
R P R T G T N E W Y

Cipher text is taken off horizontally:

PEAEO   EUDRA   RPRTG   TNEWY

It may be composed of any number of rails (or letters in depth), which may be written up or down, coming from a point and then reversing the direction to the end of the message, either filling the final stroke or being short a letter or more.

Any message may be written in with the normal sequence up and down, or vice versa, or it may be written into the points first, and then into successive horizontal rows. It is then taken out by the alternate process.

Example:

TAOET NMFOA TNEHM NHWKS POIDI SLFMU HSOBE ALEEW

AUFHE ASNES P. (51 letters)

Any figure can be used for cipher transposition, including stars, polygons, and irregulars. It is merely necessary to agree on the figure and the starting points for inscription and transcription processes.

Civil War Messages

David Kahn, author of *The Codebreakers,* gives us an interesting look at Civil War cryptography. One of the reasons that the North won was it practiced superior cryptography. Anson Stager, first superintendent of the Western Union Telegraph Company, was charged by Major General George B. McClellan with drawing up a military cipher along the lines that Stager had devised for Governor Dennison of Ohio.

Stager complied. Soon McClellan was relying on the cipher to protect his communications during his successful campaign in West Virginia. One of the first users was Allan Pinkerton, founder of the agency that bears his name and bodyguard to President Lincoln. The key was very short; it was dependable and was used by the Union forces throughout the Civil War. It was used extensively because the Civil War first employed the telegraph on a large scale.

Communications from Washington could take 10 days to their troops depending on the weather, health of the telegraph operators, and availability of lines (which sometimes took a circuitous route). During Sherman's march to the sea, the Union had to rely on Southern newspapers for accounts of his slash and burn campaign. So effective was the Stager cipher that those same Southern newspapers advertised for help from anyone who recognized or could break the Yankee cipher.

Stager's cipher was a word transposition. Stager's telegraphic experience evidently led him to a system in which the cipher text consisted—as in the new telegraph codes—of ordinary words, which are far less subject to dangerous garbles than groups of incoherent letters. There is a funny story how one of the Rebel commanders could not read the cipher message sent to him by one of his forward patrols—prior to Gettysburg no less—so he sent a messenger to the forward post to get a clarification of the cryptogram received. The messenger returned to find his commander under arrest. The message was a warning of a Union trap. The lines were affected by rain that particular day.

The Stager cipher was appealing because of its simplicity: the plain text was written out in lines and transcribed by columns, up some and down others in a specified order. His cipher was improved by adding nulls, mazed routes of diagonals, and interrupted columns through larger rectangles; and per Samuel H. Beckwith, Grant's cipher operator, important terms were represented by codewords, which were carefully chosen to minimize telegraph error. The cipher expanded from one listed on a single card to one that, by the end of the war, required 12 pages to list routes and 36 pages for the 1608 codewords. This was Cipher 4, the last of a series of 12 that the North employed at various times during the war.

A good example of the system is given by encipherment of the message by President Lincoln on 1 June 1863:

> For Colonel Ludlow. Richardson and Brown, correspondents of the Tribune, captured at Vicksburg, are detained in Richmond. Please ascertain why they are detained and get them off if you can. The President.

Cipher No. 9 was in use and provided for the following codeword substitutions: VENUS for colonel; WAYLAND for captured; ODOR for Vicksburg; NEPTUNE for Richmond; ADAM for President of U.S.; and NELLY for 4:30 PM time of dispatch. The keyword of GUARD set the size of the rectangle and routes. Nulls were added to the end of each column.

The encipherer chose to write out the message in seven lines of five words each with three nulls to complete the rectangle. The plain text was:

For	VENUS	Ludlow	Richardson	and
Brown	correspondents	of	the	Tribune
WAYLAND	at	ODOR	are	detained

At	NEPTUNE	please	ascertain	why
they	are	detained	and	get
them	off	if	you	can
ADAM	NELLY	THIS	FILLS	UP

Cipher text: [up the first column,(kissing = null),down second,(turning = null),up fifth,(times = null),down fourth, (belly = null), up third column]

GUARD ADAM THEM THEY AT WAYLAND BROWN FOR KISSING VENUS CORRESPONDENTS AT NEPTUNE ARE OFF NELLY TURNING UP CAN GET WHY DETAINED TRIBUNE AND TIMES RICHARDSON THE ARE ASCERTAIN AND YOU FILLS BELLY THIS IF DETAINED PLEASE ODOR OF LUDLOW COMMISSIONER.

Confederate cryptography centered on the Vigenere polyalphabetic cipher. The South employed only three keywords: MANCHESTER BLUFF, COMPLETE VICTORY, and COME RETRIBUTION. Known also as the Vicksburg cipher, the team of Tinker, Chandler, and Bates (very early yuppies) were able to read a whopping 90 percent of the Confederates' messages and report them to Lincoln. For example, Grant's troops intercepted a message on eight captured rebels at Vicksburg trying to slip into Vicksburg with 200,000 percussion caps.

The cipher text message read:

Jackson, May 25, 1863

Lieutenant General Pemberton: My XAFV. USLX WAS VVUFLSJP by the BRCYAJ. 200000 VEGT. SUAJ. NERP. ZIFM. It will be GFOECSZOD as they NTYMNX. Bragg MJTPHINZG a QRCMKBSE. When it DDZGJX. I will YOIG. AS. QHY. NITWM do you YTIAM the IIKM. VFVEY. How and where is the JSQMLGUGSFTVE. HBFY is your ROEEL.

J. E. Johnston.

Note the flow of the message and hints along the way—the word separators; the clear text leads you into the next word. The size of the words is known and might be guessed.

The plain text based on the keywords MANCHESTER BLUFF is:

Lieutenant General Pemberton: My last note was captured by the picket. 200000 caps have been sent. It will be increased as they arrive. Bragg is sending a division. When it joins I will come to you. Which do you think the best route? How and where is the enemy encamped? What is your force?

J. E. Johnston.

AMSCO Cipher

The *AMSCO Cipher* is another type of incomplete columnar transposition. Its column-letters are not limited to a column of single letters, but rather alternating single, double, single, double throughout the plain text length. A numerical key is employed. For example:

```
3    1    4    2    5          2    4    6    1    5    3
TH   E    WE   A    RI         T    HE   W    EA   R    IN
N    GO   F    DE   C          GO   F    DE   C    OR   A
OR   A    TI   V    EM         T    IV   E    ME   D    AL
E    DA   L    SW   A          SW   A    SC   O    MM   O
SC   O    MM   O    NI         N    IN   E    NG   L    AN
N    EN   G    LA   N          DD   U    RI   N    GT   H
DD   U    RI   N    GT         E    RE   I    GN   O    FH
H    ER   E    IG   N          EN   R    YT   H    EE   I
OF   H    EN   R    YT         G    HT   H
H    EE   I    GH   T
HX
          (A)                            (B)
```

In matrix A the alternating pattern of 2-1-2-1 follows from one end of one line to the next line but in matrix B it is possible to have two 1s or two 2s in the continuation from one line to the next—a peculiarity of this cipher. Use of a probable word is important for this cipher. Columns are extracted in numerical order.

Polyalphabetic Substitution

A cipher system, which employs two or more cipher alphabets and includes a method for designating which cipher alphabet is to be used for the encipherment of each plain-text letter, is called a *polyalphabetic substitution* system. What is amazing about these systems is how long they remained secure. The Vigenere system was considered unbreakable for over 200 years. Along comes Major Kasiski—and poof—we have recreational cryptography.

Cipher systems employing variant values may appear to use more than one alphabet, but they have characteristics of monoalphabetic substitution and are properly classified as such.

Polyalphabetic substitution systems consist of two general types, *periodic* and *nonperiodic*:

1. In the periodic type the text of a message is divided into definite, regular groups or cycles of letters that are enciphered with identical portions of the key. Periodic systems are further subdivided as follows:

    a. *Multiple Alphabet Ciphers,* in which any number of cipher alphabets are used in the order designated by a prearranged key.

    b. *Progressive Alphabet Ciphers,* in which a primary cipher alphabet and its 25 secondary alphabets are used either in *regular* succession, sliding the components one letter at a time, or in *irregular* order according to a prearranged shift.

2. In the nonperiodic type there are no *cyclic* repetitions of the key.

The cipher alphabets employed in multiple alphabet substitution systems may be constructed by any number of methods. For example:

```
Plain:    A B C D E F G H I J K L M N O P Q R S T U V W X Y Z
Cipher:  1 R T U V W X Y Z P E N C I L S A B D F G H J K M O Q
         2 E N C I L S A B D F G H J K M O Q R T U V W X Y Z P
         3 D F G H J K M O Q R T U V W X Y Z P E N C I L S A B
```

Here the plain component is a normal sequence and the cipher component is identical keyword sequences. The same keyword sequences may be used in both the plain cipher components, or different sequences may be used. The key, which determines the setting of the cipher alphabets against the plain component (RED), may be any prearranged word or phrase. Also, each cipher alphabet may be assigned a number and the alphabets used in accordance with a prearranged numerical key.

The process of enciphering a message with the preceding multiple alphabet system would appear as follows:

```
Cipher Alphabet No.

        1- 2- 3- 1- 2- 3- 1- 2- 3- 1- 2- 3- 1- 2-  3- 1-  2- 3- 1 -2- 3- 1- 2- 3
Plain:  M Y C O U R S E Z E R O T H  R E  E Z E R O A T T
Cipher: I Z G S V P F L B W R X G B  P  W L  B W R X R U N

        1- 2- 3- 1- 2- 3- 1- 2- 3- 1- 2- 3- 1- 2- 3- 1- 2- 3
Plain:  H I R T E E N T H I R T Y T H R E E
Cipher: Z D P G L J L U O P R N O U O D L J
```

In order to reduce the chances of encipherment by the wrong alphabet, the plain text is often written so that the letters designated by the key for encipherment by each alphabet are placed in the same vertical column and each entire column is enciphered in turn.

Solving a Periodic Polyalphabetic Cipher

There are three fundamental steps to solve a periodic cipher:

1. Determine the period. This sets up the correct geometrical positioning of cipher-text alphabets.
2. Identify the cipher system and reduce or consolidate the multiple alphabet distribution into a series of monoalphabetic frequency distributions.
3. Solve the monoalphabetic distributions by known principles.

Principles of Factoring

Major Friedrich W. Kasiski (1805-1881) was a career officer in East Prussia's 33rd Infantry Regiment. He is credited with a revolutionary insight regarding polyalphabetic repeating key systems—that the conjuction of a repeated portion of the key with the repetition in the plain text produces a repetition in the cipher text. Like causes produce like effects. The interval between plain-text or cipher-text repetitions is noted throughout the cryptogram and is factored; the commonality of the factor is a good indication of the key and number of alphabets used to encipher the original methods. The fall of the Vigenere family of ciphers is attributed to Kasiski's examination.

If there are several long repetitions in the cipher text of an unknown system, the intervals between the initial letters of this repetition have a common factor; this factor represents the number of alphabets used to encipher the message and the exact number of repetitions of the key.

A simple example: Given the cryptogram

```
IZGSV   PFLBW   RXGBP   WLBWR   XRUNZ
DPGLJ   LUOPR   NOUOD   LJ
```

Factoring:

Repetition	Interval	Factors	Common Factor(s)
LBWRX	9	3, 3	3
LJ	12	2, 2, 3	3
UO	6	2, 3	3

The "period" or common factor is 3 and this is the number of alphabets employed. Digraph and trigraph repetitions may be the result of chance instead of plain-text repetitions. When factoring results in more than one common factor we shall use the highest common factor and check with frequencies of the expected alphabets to see how close to normal they are. Only short messages fail to lead to the correct determination of the number of cipher alphabets employed in the system. When factoring fails on a longer message, an aperiodic cipher may have been employed.

The Long and Short of Kasiski

Step one is finding the period. There are at least two ways to find the period. The short approach makes use of the distances between patent cipher-text repetitions and factors the differentials. The long approach is used when there are no patent repetitions to factor. In this case, we set up a possibility matrix and factor every combination looking for the highest probable common factor. Both methods are attributed to Kasiski. As an example of the first case take:

```
        10          20        30        40
BGZEY DKFWK  BZVRM LUNYB QNUKA YCRYB GWMKC DDTSP
        50          60        70        80
OFIAK OWWHM  RFBLJ JQFRM PNIQA VQCUP  IFLAZ HKATJ
        90         100       110       120
UVVQE EKESZ  DUDWE  KKESL IZQAT SBYUZ  UUVAZ IXYEZ
       130         140
JFTAJ EMRAS  QKZSQ  FOPHM W.
```

We tabulate the repetitions and the cipher-text letter differences between repetitions.

Delta	Factors
BG 29	—
RM 45	3, 5, 9
KA 53	—
MR 77	7, 11
QA 39	3, 13
VQ 17	—
AZ 40	4, 5, 8, 10
AT 26	13
UV 31	—
EK 9	3, 9
KES 10	5, 10*
SQ 4	4

*Trigraph KES is more important than QA
or AT digraphs. This suggests that the
period is either 5 or 10. The larger number
is usually the proper guess.

But suppose there are no repeats or those that do exist do not establish a period. What then?

Given:

```
          10          20          30          40
RNQJH AUKGV WGIVO BBSEJ CRYUS FMQLP OFTLC MRHKB
          50          60          70          80
BUTNA WXZQS NFWLM OHYOF VMKTV HKVPK KSWEI  TGSRB
          90         100         110         120
LNAGJ BFLAM EAEJW WVGZG SVLBK IXHGT JKYUC HLKTU

MWWK.
```

We set up the following vertical tally. We note the actual position of every letter.

```
A   6 45 83 89 92 115
B   16 17 40 41 80 86 104
C   21 35
D   —
E   19 74 91 93
F   26 32 52 60 87
G   9 12 77 84 98 100 109
H   5 38 57 66 108 116
I   13 75 106
```

```
J   4 20 85 94 111
K   8 39 63 67 70 71 105 112 118 124
L   29 34 54 81 88 103 117
M   27 36 55 62 90 121
N   2 44 51 82
O   15 31 56 59
P   30 69
Q   3 28 49
R   1 22 37 79
S   18 25 50 72 78 101
T   33 43 64 76 110 119
U   7 24 42 114 120
V   10 14 61 65 68 97 102
W   11 46 53 73 95 96 122 123
X   107
Y   23 47 58 113
Z   48 99
```

Now we take each and every difference in each case. For example, A45-6, 83-6, 89-6, 92-6, 115-6; and 83-45, 89-45, 92-45, 115-45; and 89-83, 92-83, 115-83; and 92-89, 115-89, and 115-92. Then we factor these differences, setting up a matrix (Table 4-1) of potential periods from 3-12 inclusive and total the tabulations for each factor in each of the letters of the alphabet. The highest column total represents the period. This number is correct more than 98 percent of the time.

TABLE 4-1

	3	4	5	6	7	8	9	10	11	12
$\Sigma(A, \ldots, Z)$	87	61	47	43	57	30	35	21	25	16

Column Totals × Period

$$87 \times 3 = 261$$

$$61 \times 4 = 244$$

$$47 \times 5 = 235$$

$$43 \times 6 = 258$$

$$57 \times 7 = 399***$$

$$30 \times 8 = 240$$

$$35 \times 9 = 315$$

$$21 \times 10 = 210$$

$$25 \times 11 = 275$$

$$16 \times 12 = 192$$

The period is 7.

Viggy's Family

The *Vigenere family* is a group of ciphers related to each other by the polyalphabetic system used for encipherment. These ciphers were invented at different times by different authors, sometimes with confusion of authorship, and in different countries. They are similar in that they represent permutations of the same cryptographic concept and can be cracked with the same general methodology, albeit with slight variations in procedure. What is also interesting is that these ciphers can be viewed in table form, in slide form, or matrix form.

The theory of polyalphabetic substitution is simple. The encipherer has at his or her disposal several simple substitution alphabets, usually 26, using one such alphabet to encipher only one letter, another alphabet for the second letter, and so forth, until some established plan has been followed. The earliest known ciphers of this kind, the Porta (1563) and the Vigenere (1586) used tables for encipherment, in which all the alphabets were written out in full below each other. The Gronsfield (1655) had a mental key and the Beaufort (1857), which came 200 years later, again used tables. The process was reduced to strips or slides in 1880 at the French military academy at Saint-Cyr. The polyalphabetic deciphering slides now bear that name.

The Vigenere Cipher

The father of the Viggy family is the Vigenere Cipher. Like most of the periodic ciphers, the "Viggy" is actually a series of monoalphabetic substitutions. The plain text is divided into groups that are the same length as the keyword and each group is written below the keyword. The keyword establishes the starting letter for each column and then the Vigenere Table (Table 4-2) is used to determine the substitution for each letter of the message.

Attributed to Blaise de Vigenere, the cipher was invented by him in 1586 and published in his *Traite des Chiffres*. He also invented an autokey system, which used a priming key and which did not recommence his plain-text key with each word, but kept it running continuously. He described a second autokey system, which was more open but still secure. Both systems were forgotten and then were reinvented in the nineteenth century. Historians have credited Vigenere with the simpler polyalphabetic substitution system. Legend grew around this cipher that it was "impossible of translation" as late as 1917.

TABLE 4-2

The Modern
Vigenere Table

	a	b	c	d	e	f	g	h	I	j		k	l	m	n	o	p	q	r	s	t	u	v	w	x	y	z
A	A	B	C	D	E	F	G	H	I	J	K	L	M	N	O	P	Q	R	S	T	U	V	W	X	Y	Z
B	B	C	D	E	F	G	H	I	J	K	L	M	N	O	P	Q	R	S	T	U	V	W	X	Y	Z	A
C	C	D	E	F	G	H	I	J	K	L	M	N	O	P	Q	R	S	T	U	V	W	X	Y	Z	A	B
D	D	E	F	G	H	I	J	K	L	M	N	O	P	Q	R	S	T	U	V	W	X	Y	Z	A	B	C
E	E	F	G	H	I	J	K	L	M	N	O	P	Q	R	S	T	U	V	W	X	Y	Z	A	B	C	D
F	F	G	H	I	J	K	L	M	N	O	P	Q	R	S	T	U	V	W	X	Y	Z	A	B	C	D	E
G	G	H	I	J	K	L	M	N	O	P	Q	R	S	T	U	V	W	X	Y	Z	A	B	C	D	E	F
H	H	I	J	K	L	M	N	O	P	Q	R	S	T	U	V	W	X	Y	Z	A	B	C	D	E	F	G
I	I	J	K	L	M	N	O	P	Q	R	S	T	U	V	W	X	Y	Z	A	B	C	D	E	F	G	H
J	J	K	L	M	N	O	P	Q	R	S	T	U	V	W	X	Y	Z	A	B	C	D	E	F	G	H	I
K	K	L	M	N	O	P	Q	R	S	T	U	V	W	X	Y	Z	A	B	C	D	E	F	G	H	I	J
L	L	M	N	O	P	Q	R	S	T	U	V	W	X	Y	Z	A	B	C	D	E	F	G	H	I	J	K
M	M	N	O	P	Q	R	S	T	U	V	W	X	Y	Z	A	B	C	D	E	F	G	H	I	J	K	L
N	N	O	P	Q	R	S	T	U	V	W	X	Y	Z	A	B	C	D	E	F	G	H	I	J	K	L	M
O	O	P	Q	R	S	T	U	V	W	X	Y	Z	A	B	C	D	E	F	G	H	I	J	K	L	M	N
P	P	Q	R	S	T	U	V	W	X	Y	Z	A	B	C	D	E	F	G	H	I	J	K	L	M	N	O
Q	Q	R	S	T	U	V	W	X	Y	Z	A	B	C	D	E	F	G	H	I	J	K	L	M	N	O	P
R	R	S	T	U	V	W	X	Y	Z	A	B	C	D	E	F	G	H	I	J	K	L	M	N	O	P	Q
S	S	T	U	V	W	X	Y	Z	A	B	C	D	E	F	G	H	I	J	K	L	M	N	O	P	Q	R
T	T	U	V	W	X	Y	Z	A	B	C	D	E	F	G	H	I	J	K	L	M	N	O	P	Q	R	S
U	U	V	W	X	Y	Z	A	B	C	D	E	F	G	H	I	J	K	L	M	N	O	P	Q	R	S	T
V	V	W	X	Y	Z	A	B	C	D	E	F	G	H	I	J	K	L	M	N	O	P	Q	R	S	T	U
W	W	X	Y	Z	A	B	C	D	E	F	G	H	I	J	K	L	M	N	O	P	Q	R	S	T	U	V
X	X	Y	Z	A	B	C	D	E	F	G	H	I	J	K	L	M	N	O	P	Q	R	S	T	U	V	W
Y	Y	Z	A	B	C	D	E	F	G	H	I	J	K	L	M	N	O	P	Q	R	S	T	U	V	W	X
Z	Z	A	B	C	D	E	F	G	H	I	J	K	L	M	N	O	P	Q	R	S	T	U	V	W	X	Y

The original Viggy was composed of an enciphering and deciphering table. Letters were enciphered and deciphered one letter at a time. The modern Vigenere Table is shown in Table 4-2.

The normal alphabet at the top of Table 4-2 is for Pplain text and the keyletters are shown at the extreme left under the "A" of the top row. Where the two lines intersect in the body of Table 4-2, the cipher text is found.

For example, using the keyword TENT, we encipher "COME AT ONCE" so that we have:

```
TENT    TENT
COME    VSZX (cipher text)
ATON    TXBG
CE      VI—
```

The enciphering and deciphering problems are done as a group of letters to improve the speed and accuracy of the process.

Which Way?

Does it matter with the Viggy that we encipher S by B (B alphabet or Key B) to find cipher T or encipher B by S (S alphabet or Key S) to find T? No. This is an interesting characteristic not shared by all in the Viggy family. It also was its downfall.

For instance, the message: "Send Supplies To Morley's Station" enciphered with the repeating key BED, under the original method of encipherment as might be described by Blaise de Vigenere, would be:

```
Key:     BEDB  EDBEDBE  DB  EDBEDBE  DBEDBED
Plain:   SEND  SUPPLIES TO  MORLEYS  STATION
Cipher:  TIQE  WXQTOJIV US  PPVOFCV  TXDUMRO
```

Decipherment by Probable Word

Modern cryptographers use automated attacks that are similar to their historical antecedents.

Deciphering with the Key:

```
Key:    B E D B E D B E D B E D
Cipher: T I Q E W X Q T O J I V
Plain:  S E N D S U P P L I E S
```

Deciphering with the Message:

```
Plain:  S E N D S U P P L I E S ........... (trial key)
Cipher: T I Q E W X Q T O J I V
Key:    B E D B E D B E D B E D .......... (true key)
```

The message fragment works well as a trial key, and if applied in the same manner as the true key, the true original key will be revealed. The Vigenere Cipher works equally well in reverse. It is this peculiarity that portends the use of a probable word attack.

Suppose we have the cryptogram:

```
U S Z H L   W D B P B   G G F S...
```

in which we suspect the presence of the word SUPPLIES.

We decipher the first eight letters using this probable word as a trial key, and obtain the jumbled series: C Y K S A O Z J, which is unsatisfactory. We next drop the first U and obtain the group: A F S W L V X X. We fail again on the third and fourth trials. The fifth decipherment obtains the series TCOMETCO. We see the TCO repeats and the key word COMET. A more organized approach is shown as follows:

Cryptogram Fragment: U S Z H L W D B P B G G F S ......

Probable Word:

S		C A H P **T** E L J X J O O N A
U		Y F N R **C** J H V H M M L Y
P		S W H **O** M A M R R Q D
P		W H O **M** A M R R Q D
L		L S Q **E** Q V V U H
I		V T H **T** Y Y X K
E		X L X C C B O
S		**O**

Look down the diagonals we find the key word **COMET.** The first letter S was used to decipher every possible key letter that can produce S. The entire row of equivalents was produced at the same time. The resulting rows of decipherment indicate all the possible key letters that could produce S, then U, then P, and so on. Carter actually shortened the procedure to three full rows and then partials thereafter. He assumed that the keyword was readable and discarded nonreadable text.

Primary Components

Equivalents obtainable from use of square tables may be duplicated by slides or revolving disks or computer models. Cryptographically, the results may be quite diverse from different methods of using such paraphernalia, since the specific equivalents obtained from one method may be altogether different from those obtained from another method. But from the cryptanalytic point of view, the diversity referred to is of little significance.

There are not two, but four letters involved in every case of finding equivalents by means of sliding components; furthermore, the determination of an equivalent for a given plain-text letter is represented by two equations involving four equally important elements, usually letters. Consider this juxtaposition:

1. A B C D E F G H I J K L M N O P Q R S T U V W X Y Z
2. F B P Y R C Q Z I G S E H T D J U M K V A L W N O X

Question: What is the equivalent of plain when the key letter is K? Answer: Without further specification, the cipher equivalent cannot be stated. Which letter do we set K against and in which alphabet? We have previously assumed that the K cipher would be put against A in the plain. But this is only a convention.

```
                                        Index              Plain
                                        *                  *
1. Plain:                               ABCDEFGHIJKLMNOPQRSTUVWXYZ
2. Cipher:  FBPYRCQZIGSEHTDJUMKVALWNOXFBPYRCQZIGSEHTJUMK
                                        *                  *
                                        Key                Cipher
```

With this setting Pplain = Zcipher. The four elements are:

1. The key letter, Θk

2. The index letter, $\Theta 1$

3. The plain text letter, Θp

4. The cipher letter, Θc

The index letter is commonly the initial letter of the component, but by convention only. We will assume from now on that $\Theta 1$ is the initial letter of the component in which it is located.

The preceding enciphering equations are:

$$\text{(I) } K_k = A_1; \qquad P_p = Z_c \qquad \qquad \textbf{[Eq. 4-1]}$$

where: k = key
$\qquad p$ = plain
$\qquad c$ = cipher
$\qquad 1$ = initial

There is nothing sacred about the sliding components. Consider the following:

```
                                        Index              Cipher
                                        *                  *
1. Plain:                               ABCDEFGHIJKLMNOPQRSTUVWXYZ
2. Cipher:  FBPYRCQZIGSEHTDJUMKVALWNOXFBPYRCQZIGSHTJUMKV
                                        *                  *
                                        Key                Plain
```

Thus

$$\text{(II) } Kk = A1; \qquad Pp = Kc \qquad \text{[Eq. 4-2]}$$

Since equations (I) and (II) yield different results even with the same index, key, and plain-text letters, it is obvious that a more precise formula is required. Adding locations to these equations does the trick.

$$\text{(I) } Kk \text{ in component (2) = A1 in component (1);} \qquad \text{[Eq. 4-3]}$$

$$Pp \text{ in component (1) = Zc in component (2).} \qquad \text{[Eq. 4-4]}$$

$$\text{(II) } Kk \text{ in component (2) = A1 in component (1);} \qquad \text{[Eq. 4-5]}$$

$$Pp \text{ in component (2) = Zc in component (1).} \qquad \text{[Eq. 4-6]}$$

In shorthand notation:

$$\text{(1) } Kk/2 = A1/1; Pp/1 + Zc/2 \qquad \text{[Eq. 4-7]}$$

$$\text{(2) } Kk/2 = A1/1; Pp/2 + Zc/1 \qquad \text{[Eq. 4-8]}$$

Employing two sliding components and four letters implies twelve different resulting systems for the same set of components and twelve enciphering conditions. These constitute the Viggy family (see Table 4-3).

TABLE 4-3

The Viggy Family

1. $\Theta k/2 = \Theta 1/1; \Theta p/1 = \Theta c/2$ **[Eq. 4-9]**	7. $\Theta k/2 = \Theta p/1; \Theta 1/2 = \Theta c/1$ **[Eq. 4-15]**
2. $\Theta k/2 = \Theta 1/1; \Theta p/2 = \Theta c/1$ **[Eq. 4-10]**	8. $\Theta k/2 = \Theta c/1; \Theta 1/2 = \Theta p/1$ **[Eq. 4-16]**
3. $\Theta k/1 = \Theta 1/2; \Theta p/1 = \Theta c/2$ **[Eq. 4-11]**	9. $\Theta k/1 = \Theta p/2; \Theta 1/1 = \Theta c/2$ **[Eq. 4-17]**
4. $\Theta k/1 = \Theta 1/2; \Theta p/2 = \Theta c/1$ **[Eq. 4-12]**	10. $\Theta k/1 = \Theta c/2; \Theta 1/1 = \Theta p/2$ **[Eq. 4-18]**
5. $\Theta k/2 = \Theta p/1; \Theta 1/1 = \Theta c/2$ **[Eq. 4-13]**	11. $\Theta k/1 = \Theta p/2; \Theta 1/2 = \Theta c/1$ **[Eq. 4-19]**
6. $\Theta k/2 = \Theta c/1; \Theta p/1 = \Theta p/2$ **[Eq. 4-14]**	12. $\Theta k/1 = \Theta c/2; \Theta 1/2 = \Theta p/1$ **[Eq. 4-20]**

Equations 4-9 and 4-10 define the *Vigenere* type of encipherment and are widely used; Equations 4-13 and 4-14 define the *Beaufort* type; and Equations 4-17 and 4-18 define the *Delastelle* type of encipherment.

Beaufort Cipher

Another member of the Viggy family is the *Beaufort* Cipher. Although the same procedure is applied, the slides (or tables) are different. One is a normal alphabet, extending double length A-Z; the other is reversed, double length Z-A. So if I = T at one setting, then T = I at the same setting. It does not matter what the index for the key is; the results are the same. So:

ABCDEFGHIJKLMNOPQRSTUVWXYZABCDEFGHIJKL
TSRQPONMLKJIHGFEDCBAZYWXVUTSRQPONMLKJI

Again the simple example:

```
T E N T      T E N T
C O M E      R Q B P
.A T O N      T L Z G
C E - -      R A —
```

Some interesting relationships between the Vigenere, Variant, and Beaufort are as follows: Let A = 0, B = 1, C = 2,..., Z = 25, then:

Vigenere: Cipher letter = Plain text letter + key letter (modulo 26)

Variant: Cipher letter = Plain text letter − key letter (modulo 26)

Beaufort: Cipher letter = Key letter − Plain text letter (modulo 26)

Suppose plain text = B and key = C. Since B = 1 and C = 2, Vigenere cipher text = 1 + 2 = 3 or D; for Variant cipher text 1−2 = −1 + 26 = 25 = Z. For Vigenere and Variant if key letter = A, since A = 0,the cipher text = plain text. If we reconstruct a cipher assuming it is a Vigenere, but it is actually a Variant, we will get the true plain text but a strange keyword. By subtracting the Variant equation from the Vigenere equation and setting cipher text (Viggy) = cipher text (Variant) and similarly plain text (Viggy) = plain text (Variant), we get the key letter (Variant) = −key letter (Vigenere), the same relationship as that between cipher text and plain text when the key letter is A in the Beaufort (since A = 0). Hence, we encipher our strange key word with the A Beaufort alphabet to get the Variant key. The same holds true if we have a Variant and assume it a Viggy.

If we have a Vigenere and a fragment of the same message enciphered with the same key in Variant (or vice versa) then:

$$\text{Plain text} = [\text{Cipher text (Variant)} + \text{Cipher text (Vigenere)}]/2(\text{modulo 13}) \qquad \textbf{[Eq. 4-21]}$$

$$\text{Key} = [\text{Cipher text (Vigenere)} - \text{Cipher text (Variant)}]/2(\text{modulo 13}) \qquad \textbf{[Eq. 4-22]}$$

If we have a Vigenere and a fragment of a Beaufort for the same key and plain text or vice versa then:

Plain text = [Cipher text (Vigenere) − Cipher text (Beaufort)]/
2(modulo 13) [**Eq. 4-23**]

Key = [Cipher text (Vigenere) + Cipher text (Beaufort)]/
2(modulo 13) [**Eq. 4-24**]

In Equations 4-21 to 4-24 two answers are produced because modulo 13 will give one number from 0-12 and another from 13-25.

PORTA Cipher (aka Napoleon's Table)

Table 4-4 defines the PORTA Cipher. In this table the alphabets are all reciprocal; for example, Gplain(Wkey) = Rcipher, Rplain(Wkey) = Gcipher. They are called *complementary alphabets*. Either of two letters may serve as a key letter: Gplain(Wkey) or Gplain(Xkey) = Rcipher. The Porta Cipher permits 13 different ways to disguise a plain letter.

Nihilist Substitution

Gaines suggests that cracking this cipher parallels the Viggy to the extent of determining the period (keyword length). The period is found through repeated sequences, or in their absence, through repeated single letters, yielding individual frequency counts on the several alphabets of the period. If the arrangement of the cipher text follows the normal Polybius (aka Checkerboard) Square, the frequency counts will follow the graph of the normal alphabet less one letter. Even with the keyword mixed cipher-text alphabet, no matter how badly mixed, the frequency counts are parallel and the several alphabets combined follow one graph, and can be "lined up."

The primary alphabet contains only the digits 1-2-3-4-5. The maximum difference is 4 and addition of any number to all of them does not change this fact. The maximum difference between any two sums is still 4. Now the number added during encipherment is also a number containing no digit other than 1-2-3-4-5; thus any number found in the cryptogram can be considered as carrying two separate additions, one

TABLE 4-4

The PORTA Cipher

	A B C	D	E	F G H	I	J	K L M
AB	N O P Q		R	S T U		V	W X Y Z
CD	O P Q	R	S	T U V		W X	Y Z N
EF	P Q R	S		T U V W	X	Y	Z N O
GH	Q R S	T		U V W X	Y Z		N O P
IJ	R S	T	U	V W X Y		Z	N O P Q
KL	S T U	V		W X Y Z		N O	P Q R
MN	T U V	W	X	Y Z N		O	P Q R S
OP	U V W X	Y		Z N O		P Q	R S T
QR	V W X Y	Z		N O P		Q R	S T U
ST	W X Y Z	N		O P Q		R S	T U V
UV	X Y Z	N	O	P Q R		S T	U V W
WX	X Y Z	N	O	P Q R		S T	U V W
YZ	Z N O	P		Q R S T		U	V W X Y

for 10s and one for 1s. The two 5s added give us the revealing 0; the carried digit 1 can be mentally borrowed back, by decreasing the size of the digit preceding the zero. If we find a 40, we look at it as 3 tens with 10 units or finding 110; we may regard this as 10 tens and 10 units. If we find the numbers 29 and 87 in the cryptogram, we know they were not enciphered by the same key. This is because a difference greater than 4 in the respective 10s units exists, and no digit whatever added to any two digits of the original square can produce a difference greater than 4. Say we have 30 and 77, with no difference greater than 4, the presence of the zero needs to be accounted for. The number 30 has 2 tens and 10 units; $7 - 2 > 4$, hence, we reject the same key hypothesis.

Consider the following challenge:

24 66 35 77 37 77 55 59 55 45 55 88 28 66 46

88 37 67 33 59 58 65 45 66 67 58 44 55 34 79

44 59 55 45 42 87 28 76 43 78 46 86 26 67 24

85 26 67 28 76 26 78 46 65 65 88 36 49 54 67

28 65 42 88 36 49 44 89 57 58 54 66 47 67 26

Try period = 2. Starting at the first number 24, we scan the line looking for differences greater than 4 using a constant difference of 2. We come to 33 and 38 and stop.

Try period = 3. The first comparison fails at 24 and 77.

Try period = 4. We are able to go through the entire cryptogram, comparing numbers at an interval of 4, without finding any difference in either tens or units greater than 4. We now must look at the numbers collectively in columns to verify the period is 4. We recopy the cryptogram into a block.

Key = 4?

24 66 35 77
37 77 55 59
55 45 55 88
28 66 46 88
37 67 33 59
58 65 45 66
67 58 44 55
34 79 44 59
55 45 42 87
28 76 43 78
46 86 26 67
28 76 26 78
46 65 65 88
36 49 54 67
28 65 42 88
36 49 44 89
57 58 54 65
47 67 26 -

Alphabet 1: The tens-half of the first column contains the digit 2 and since this can only come from the addition of 1 plus 1, the only possible key digit is 1. The units-half has a range of 4-5-6-7-8, the maximum range possible. The smallest digit to result in 8 is 3, the largest digit to result in 4 is also 3; that is, the only digit that can result in all of the digits 4-5-6-7-8 is 3, so that the cipher key for this column is 13. It cannot be anything else.

Alphabet 2: The tens-half of the second column ranges over the full five digits 4-5-6-7-8 (key 3), and the units-half ranges over 5-6-7-8-9 (key 4). This suggests the key digit is 34.

Alphabet 3: The tens-half of the third column contains the "giveaway" digit of 2 and the units-half also contains the digit 2. The key digit to produce this situation is 11.

Alphabet 4: The tens-half of the fourth column ranges only over the digits 5-6-7-8, with nothing to indicate whether the missing digit is 4 or 9. The key might be either 3 or 4. The units-half has the full range of digits 5-6-7-8-9, hence key = 4. So we have either 34 or 44 for our key digit. The normal square suggests COAO or COAT as the keyword. We decipher the whole cryptogram a column at a time:

C	O	A	T
A	M	I	N
I	S	T	E
R	A	T	T
E	M	P	T
I	N	G	E
U	L	O	G
Y	I	N	A
F	U	N	E
R	A	L	S
E	R	M	O
M	W	E	H
A	V	E	H
E	R	E	O
N	L	Y	T
H	E	S	H
E	L	L	T
H	E	N	U
T	I	S	G
O	N	E	

Reads: A minister attempting eulogy in a funeral sermon: We have here only the shell, the nut has gone.

For the difficult case presenting multiple key possibilities, we line up the alphabets graphically against their frequency counts to eliminate the extra key digits.

Digraphic Ciphers: Playfair

Perhaps the most famous cipher of 1943 involved the future president of United States, John F. Kennedy. On August 2, 1943, Australian Coast-watcher Lieutenant Arthur Reginald Evans, of the Royal Australian Naval Volunteer Reserve, saw a pinpoint of flame on the dark waters of Blackett Strait from his jungle ridge on Kolombangara Island, one of the Solomons. He did not know that the Japanese destroyer *Amagiri* had rammed, and sliced in half, an American patrol boat, *PT-109,* under the command of Lieutenant John F. Kennedy, United States Naval Reserve. Evans received the following message at 0930 on the morning of August 2, 1943:

20 groups

KXJEY UREBE ZWEHE WRYTU HEYFS

KREHE GOYFI WTTTU OLKSY CAJPO

BOTEI ZONTX BYBWT GONEY CUZWR

GDSON SXBOU YWRHE BAAHY USEDQ

/0930/2

Translation:

PT BOAT ONE OWE NINE LOST IN ACTION IN BLACKETT STRAIT

TWO MILES SW MERESU COVE X CREW OF TWELVE

X REQUEST ANY INFORMATION.

The coastwatchers regularly used the Playfair system. Evans deci-phered it with the key ROYAL NEW ZEALAND NAVY and learned of Kennedy's fate. Evans reported the find to the coastwatcher near Munda, call sign PWD, that Object still floating between Merusu and Gizo. At 1:12 PM, Evans was told by Coastwatcher KEN on Guadalcanal that there was a possibility of survivors landing either on Vangavanga or nearby islands. That is what Kennedy and his crew had done. They had swum to Plum Pudding Island on the southeastern tip of Gizo Island.

Several messages passed between PWD, KEN, and GSE (Evans). The Japanese made no attempt to capture Kennedy even though they had access to the various messages. The importance to them was missed even though many P-40s were spotted in the search and rescue (SAR) attempt. Maybe the Japanese didn't want to waste the time or men because the exact location of the crew was not specified. A Japanese barge chugged past Kennedy's hideout. At 0920 AM on Saturday morning, August 7, 1943, two natives found the sailors, who had moved to Gross Island, and reported the find to Evans. He wrote a brief message: Eleven survivors PT boat on Gross Is X Have sent food and letter advising senior come here without delay X Warn aviation of canoes crossing Ferguson RE. The square Evans used was based on the key PHYSICAL EXAMINATION:

```
P H Y S I
C A L E X
M N T O B
D F G K Q
R U V W Z
```

The encipherment did not split the doubled letters as is the rule:

XELWA	OHWUW	YZMWI	HOMNE	OBTFW
MSSPI	AJLUO	EAONG	OOFCM	FEXTT
CWCFZ	YIPTF	EOBHM	WEMOC	SAWCZ
SNYNW	MGXEL	HEZCU	FNZYL	NSBTB
DANFK	OPEWM	SSHBK	GCWFV	EKMUE

There were 335 letters in five messages, in the same key beginning XYAWO GAOOA GPEMO HPQCW IPNLG RPIXL TXLOA NNYCS YXBOY MNBIN YOBTY QYNAI..., for Lieut. Kennedy considers it advisable that he pilot PT boat tonight X...These five messages detailed the rescue arrangements, which offered the Japanese a chance to get not only the crew (and change all history!) but also the force coming out to save it. The Japanese failed to solve what an experienced crypee could solve in one hour. At 1000 hours that same day Kennedy and his crew were rescued.

Digraphic substitution refers to the use of pairs of letters to substitute for other pairs of letters. The Playfair system was originated by the noted British scientist, Sir Charles Wheatstone (1802-1875) but, as far as is known, it was not employed for military or diplomatic use during his lifetime. About 1890 it was adopted for use by the British Foreign Office on the recommendation of Lord Lyon Playfair (1818-1898) and thereafter identified with its sponsor.

Encipherment

The Playfair is based on a 25-letter alphabet (omit J) set up in a 5×5 square. A keyword is written in horizontally into the top rows of the square and the remaining letters follow in regular order. So for the key = LOGARITHM, we have:

```
L O G A R
I T H M B
C D E F K
N P Q S U
V W X Y Z
```

In preparation for encipherment, the plain text is separated into pairs. Doubled letters such as SS or NN are separated by a null. For example, "COME QUICKLY WE NEED HELP" we have

CO ME QU IC KL YW EN EX ED HE LP
There are three rules governing encipherment:

1. When the two letters of a plain-text pair are in the same column of the square, each is enciphered by the letter directly below it in that column. The letter at the bottom is enciphered by the letter at the top of the same column.

Plain	Cipher
OP	TW
IC	CN
EX	QG

2. When the two letters of a plain-text pair are in the same row of the square, each is enciphered by the letter directly to its right in that row. The letter at the extreme right of the row is enciphered by the letter at the extreme left of the same row.

Plain	Cipher
YW	ZX
ED	FE
QU	SN

3. When two letters are located in different rows and columns, they are enciphered by the two letters that form a rectangle with them, beginning with the letter in the SAME ROW with the first letter of the plain-text pair. (This occurs about two-thirds of the time.)

```
Plain    Cipher
CO       DL
ME       HF
KL       CR
LP       ON
```

When the keyword is known, decipherment is accomplished by using the rules in reverse.

Identification of the Playfair

The following features apply to the Playfair:

1. It is a substitution cipher.

2. The cipher message contains an even number of letters.

3. A frequency count will show no more than 25 letters. (The letter J is not found.)

4. If long repeats occur, they will be at irregular intervals. In most cases, repeated sequences will be an even number of letters.

5. Many reversals of digraphs occur.

Peculiarities

1. No plain-text letter can be represented in the cipher by itself.

2. Any given letter can be represented by five other letters.

3. Any given letter can represent five other letters.

4. Any given letter cannot represent a letter that it combines with diagonally.

5. It is twice as probable that the two letters of any pair are at the corners of a rectangle, than as in the same row or column.

6. When a cipher letter has once been identified as a substitute for a plain-text letter, there is a 20 percent chance that it represents the same plain-text letter in each other appearance.

Delastelle Systems—Foursquare Cipher

Felix Delastelle, the enigmatic Frenchman, created several nasty but very interesting cipher systems. We discuss three of his systems. They are the Foursquare, Bifid, and Trifid. The Foursquare employs four 25-letter alphabets set up in four 5×5 squares. The alphabets in the upper-left and lower-right squares are straight alphabets sans J, and the alphabets in the upper-right and lower-left squares are mixed, usually by means of a key word.

Plain-text letters are found in the two straight-alphabet squares and the cipher equivalents are located in the two mixed-alphabet squares.

Encipherment follows only one rule: the plain-text letters are divided into pairs. The first letter is found in square 1, the second in square three. The two cells are thought of as opposite corners of diagonals of an imaginary rectangle. The first cipher letter is found in square 2 and the second is found in square 4. The operation continues until all letters are enciphered.

Encipherment, for example, given:

```
        1                    2
  A B C  D E    .    G R D L  U
  F G H  I K    .    E Y F N  V
  L M N  O P    .    O A H P  W
  Q R S  T U    .    M B I Q  X
  V W X  Y Z    .    T C K S  Z
                .
  L I  C N V    .    A B C D  E
  O T  D P W    .    F G H I  K
  G H  E Q X    .    L M N O  P
  A M  F S Y    .    Q R S T  U
  R B  K U Z    .    V W X Y  Z
                .
        4                    3
```

Plain: CO ME QU IC KL YW EN EE DH EL PX
Cipher: LE WI XA FN EX CU DX UV DP GX HZ

Decipherment, when keywords are known, is the reverse.

Using GEOM(E)TRY and LOGARITHM squares for the following cipher text:

```
Plain:   XF WX PO DY DG GN AH
Cipher:  SU PP LI ES AN DA MM
```

Identification of the Foursquare

1. It is a substitution cipher.

2. It has an even number of letters.

3. Frequency count of 25 letters without J.

4. Doubled letters may occur, eliminating a Playfair.

5. Long repeats occur at irregular intervals. Even sequences are most frequent.

6. Few reversals in comparison to Playfair.

Peculiarities of the Foursquare

1. A plain text can be represented by itself in the cipher.

2. Any cipher-text letter can be represented by five letters.

3. Any given plain-text letter can be represented by five cipher-text letters.

4. A cipher letter can represent itself or the other letter of the pair.

5. Every cell frequency is known or can be calculated because of the straight alphabets.

6. The fixed locations of the letters in squares 1 and 3 makes it possible to spot the location of probable words that form a pattern when enciphered by the Foursquare.

Cell Frequencies

Bower and Meaker have derived the probabilities of the normal cipher text based on the normal distributions for the straight alphabets in 1 and 3 based on 100 diagraphs.

1	2
A B C D E	5 5 8 8 4
F G H I K	2 1 4 5 2
L M N O P	4 4 4 8 5
Q R S T U	2 2 8 8 5
V W X Y Z	1 1 1 2 1

```
4 5 8 5 5        A B C D E
2 2 4 8 2        F G H I K
4 2 4 8 5        L M N O P
4 2 5 8 8        Q R S T U
1 1 1 1 1        V W X Y Z
    4                3
```

The Foursquare follows the normal distribution of letters:

High

Letter	E	T	A	O	N	I	R	S	H
Normal frequency	13	9	8	8	7	7	7	6	6

Normal 4-square freq.	8	8	8	8	8	5	5	5	5	5
Square 2 cell	44	14	13	34	43	12	45	24	11	35
Square 4 cell	13	44	34	24	45	14	12	15	43	35

Medium   Low

```
L D C U P F M W Y B G V K Q X Z
4 4 3 3 3 3 2 2 2 1 1 1 0 0 0 0
```

Square 2 cell = A
Square 4 cell = B

	4	4	4	4	4		2	2	2	2	2	1	1	1	1	1
A =	31	33	32	23	15		25	41	21	42	54	22	55	53	51	52
B =	31	41	23	33	11		22	32	42	21	25	54	51	55	53	52

The figures represent row × column frequencies.

Observations

1. Nulls are not required as in Playfair.

2. Probable position of letters can be spotted through cell frequency.

3. Probable words can be definitely placed if they produce a pattern.

Delastelle Systems—Bifid Cipher

Friedman, Bowers, and Lewis discuss the intricacies of the Bifid Cipher. The Bifid and Trifid ciphers represent a new and tougher breed of classical cipher—Fractionated Ciphers. The process of fractionation, whereby the substitute unit is 1/2 or 1/3 or 1/part for each letter, represents a more involved problem for analysis that some of the ciphers presented to date. What we do is combine substitution and transposition processes to produce a clever mixed cipher. Modern ciphers do the same thing many times over (called rounds or S-Boxes in DES).

Method of Encipherment of Bifid

The secretive Delastelle designed the Bifid to use a checkerboard square with 25 letters, sans J. We start with a keyworded square:

```
  1 2  3  4  5
1 M A  N  Y  O
2 T H  E  R  S
3 B C  D  F  G
4 I K  L  P  Q
5 U V  W  X  Z
```

Key = MANY OTHERS

The encipherment process is periodic and the number of letters in each group is usually an odd number. Even Bifids are actually easier to solve than odd. We will focus on the odd Bifid to illustrate the process. Period lengths of 7, 9, 11, or 13 are those most frequently employed.

Encipherment is a combination of substitution and transposition, which is best shown by example. We will encipher the message COME QUICKLY WE NEED HELP in period 7.

Step 1: Period Length.   First divide the plain-text message into groups of seven letters. Write the numerical equivalents for row and column vertically under the plain-text letters.

	C O M E Q U I	C K L Y W E N	E E D H E L P
Row	3 1 1 2 4 5 2	3 4 4 1 5 2 1	2 2 3 2 2 4 4
Column	2 5 1 3 5 1 1	2 2 3 4 3 3 3	3 3 3 2 3 3 4

Step 2: Horizontal Transposition and Takeoff.   The next step is a form of transposition, wherein the numerical substitutes are taken off horizontally by pairs. In each individual group this takeoff continues, without interruption, through the two rows of numbers. The last number of the top row pairs with the first number of the bottom row. The

first number of each horizontal pair indicates the row of a cipher letter and the second number of the pair indicates the column of that cipher letter.

Step 3: Recombination.   Find the cipher letters in the square using the new row × column coordinates.

```
Plain     C O M E Q U I
Row       3 1 1 2 4 5 4
Col       2 5 1 3 5 1 1
Cipher    B A Q K U G M
```

31 = B; 12 = A; 45 = Q; **42** = **K**; 51 = U; 35 = G; 11 = M

Each cipher letter results from the some combination of half values of the two plaintext letters. Due to this characteristic, the Bifid (and Trifid with thirds) is classified as *Fractional Substitution*.

Deciphering the Bifid with Known Elements

Step 1:   Fractionate the cipher letters into their row and column components.

Step 2:   Write into two rows horizontally of periodic length.

Step 3:   Write the numerical values into the two horizontal rows below the fractionated letters.

Step 4:   Recover plain-text letters vertically.

```
Cipher Fractionated    Br Bc Ar Ac Qr Qc Kr
                       Kc Ur Uc Gr Gc Mr Mc
Plain-text Row          3  1  1  2  4  5  4
Plain-text Column       2  5  1  3  5  1  1
Plain text              C  O  M  E  Q  U  I
```

Identification of the Bifid

1. It is a substitution cipher with substitution units = to ½ of the cipher letter, represented by row or column index.

2. Frequency count of 25 letters (J omitted), but not more for 5×5 Bifid.

3. Long repeats occur at irregular intervals.

4. Repeated patterns dependent upon the length of the repeated sequence and the period.

5. A frequency count will show a flat profile compared to normal plain text.

Peculiarities of the Bifid

1. When the cipher letters are set up in the correct period a few "naturals" will occur. A *natural* is the term for a vertical cipher pair, arranged in row-column order, in which both components are the same letter. When this happens the plain-text letter is revealed. This is not true when the cipher letters are column-row unless the letter happens to be one of the five on the diagonal of the square running from 1-1 to 5-5.

For:

```
      1  2  3  4  5
   1  M  A  N  Y  O
   2  T  H  E  R  S
   3  B  C  D  F  G
   4  I  K  L  P  Q
   5  U  V  W  X  Z
```

Cipher   Hr Hc Ar Ac Hr
          Hc Cr Cc Ar Ac
          ————————
Plain   H E A T H
          *

The first plain-text letter H is a natural but the T on the fourth is not. The great majority of naturals will be high-frequency plain-text letters. *If low frequency plain-text letters appear as naturals, it is almost a certainty that the cipher message is set up in an incorrect period.*

2. Half-naturals occur quite frequently, when the cipher is set up in the correct period. One of the letters of the vertical pair, in row-column order, is the same as the plain-text letter it represents.

Cipher	Tr Tc	Qr Qc	Sr
	Sc Wr	Wc Er	Ec

--- --- --- --- --- --- ---

Plain	S O	L V	E
	*	*	

The probability that one of the letters in row-column pair is a half-natural is 8 in 25, or 32 percent. The probability of a half-natural in column-row order (along the diagonal) is $\frac{1}{5}$ of 32 percent or 6.4 percent. Half-naturals are a function of the expected appearances of the plain-text letter. For instance, in a cipher of 100 letters, we find 10 Es and 10 Zs.

Cipher Letter E = $10 \times 0.32 = 3.2$ half-naturals
Cipher Letter Z = $10 \times 0.32 = 3.2$ half-naturals

but the E is 13 times more likely than the Z. So the E is expected to appear 13 times in 100 letters so the 3-4 half-naturals are possible, but the Z will occur only 1 time in 100, so we may expect no half-naturals.

3. Half-naturals are the Bifid's most vulnerable feature because they play a large part in spotting probable words.

4. The Bifid, fractionated for decipherment, engenders two separate and different alphabets. One applies to odd-numbered vertical pairs, found in the basic square and the other applies to even vertical pairs in each periodic group.

5. Repeated plain-text sequences produce patterns as long as the repeat starts in the same relative location in the group as of its first appearance.

The search for repeated patterns is the first step to finding the correct period for solution of the Bifid. Patterns are formed by plain-text components, which serve to make up complete cipher pairs. It does not make any difference what letters may be in other places of the group; the same patterns will always show for the word in question, whenever it is enciphered in the same period.

Delastelle Systems—Trifid Cipher

Both Bowers and Linz cover the Trifid Cipher in detail. Topics include keyword block recovery, periodic group structure, Trifid patterns, pattern uncertainty, tetragraphic patterns, and part naturals. In the case of the Trifid, the block takes the same form with an additional dimension. The Trifid setup will be shown as a 27 × 3 block containing all possible changes in order of the three numbers 1-2-3, taken three at a time and arranged in ascending order. The numbers within the block, when read vertically, serve as components of the letters of the alphabet that is added, externally, to the block. So:

```
Component
  T R I F D ALP H B E C G J K M N O Q S U V W X YZ#
1|1 1 1 1 1  1 1 1 1 2 2  2 2 2 2  2 2 3 3 3 3 3  3  3  3 3 3
2|1 1 1 2 2  2 2 3 3 3 1  1 1 2 2  2 3 3 3 1 1 1  2  2  2 3 3 3
3|1 2 3 1 2  3 1 2 3 1 2  3 1 2 3  1 2 3 1 2 3 1  2  3  1 2 3
```

The fact that 27 letters are required for the Trifid is a weak feature of the system. We can use a ZA and ZB to represent the 27th letter and the true Z, respectively. A scrambled alphabet is always used to prevent some letters from being represented all the time by the same combination. Based on keyword COUNTERSPY:

```
1 2 3 4 5 6 7 8 9 10
C O U N T E R S P Y
A B D F G H I J K L
M Q V W X Z #
```

The letters are taken off vertically in order of columns. We set up two tables:

Deciphering Table

```
C A M O B Q U D V N F W T G X E H Z R I # S J P K Y L
1 1 1 1 1 1 1 1 1 2 2 2 2 2 2 2 2 2 3 3 3 3 3 3 3 3 3
1 1 1 2 2 2 3 3 3 1 1 1 2 2 2 3 3 3 1 1 1 2 2 2 3 3 3
1 2 3 1 2 3 1 2 3 1 2 3 1 2 3 1 2 3 1 2 3 1 2 3 1 2 3
```

Enciphering Table

```
A B C D E F G H I J K L M N O P Q R S T U V W X Y Z #
1 1 1 1 2 2 2 2 3 3 3 3 1 2 1 3 1 3 3 2 1 1 2 2 3 2 3
1 2 1 3 3 1 2 3 1 2 3 3 1 1 2 2 2 1 2 2 3 3 1 2 3 3 1
2 2 1 2 1 2 2 2 2 2 1 3 3 1 1 3 3 1 1 1 1 3 3 3 2 3 3
```

Method of Encipherment

Encipherment follows the same general pattern as the Bifid. The plain text is divided into groups of a chosen periodic length and the numerical components are written vertically below each letter. Periods of multiples of 3 + 1 are popular, such as 7−10−13, with 10 being the most popular. For example, with period = 10:

```
Plain     C O M E Q U I C K L    |   Y I N E E D H E L P
          1 1 1 2 1 1 3 1 3 3    |   3 3 2 2 2 1 2 2 3 3
          1 2 1 3 2 3 1 1 3 3    |   3 1 1 3 3 3 3 3 3 2
          1 1 3 1 3 1 2 1 1 3    |   2 2 1 1 1 2 2 1 3 3
Cipher    C N # I D R K U I M    |   Y T X K V L J N B V
```

The first letter C is represented by vertical 111; plain O by 121; M by 113; and so forth. The first cipher letter C is derived by the horizontal take off 111. The dot represents the break between trigraphic units. Note that the C is derived from the first three components from COM. The fourth cipher letter I derives from the first component of the tenth letter L and the second 2 components of CO. We go to the end of the row and back to the first letter on the second row, to the end and drop down to the first letter on the third row.

Decipherment

The decipherment process reverses that of encipherment, in that the numerical components of the cipher letters are written horizontally in three rows of periodic length and are then read vertically to produce the plain text.

Identification of the Trifid

1. It is a substitution (fractionated) cipher with 27 letters.

2. If long repeats occur, they will be at irregular intervals.

3. Repeated patterns will occur:

Peculiarities of the Trifid

1. Naturals, similar to those of the Bifid, are extremely rare.

1. Each plain-text letter can be represented by 729 (**3) different arrangements of fractions of itself and other letters.

3. The table of numerical components is inflexible. Any given digit 1-2-3 must appear as first, second, and third component for nine letters—no more, no less.

4. Not more than three letters can have the same two identical components; and for these three letters the other component must be a different figure in each case. This is a good rule for cryptanalysis of the trifid.

5. Repeated plain-text sequences produce patterns that are recognizable. Bower devotes a substantial chapter to this rule. The surest way to determine the period is through repeat patterns.

6. Repeated cipher patterns do not always represent the same plain-text letters. The period is key.

WRAP-UP

The diversity of classical cryptosystems prepares us for their modern encryption equivalents. Many of the more elegant attacks on classical cryptosystems are not brute force searches of entire key spaces but revolve around finding the appropriate wedge(s) or weaknesses in a cryptosystem as shown using classical techniques. Cryptography has evolved from the language structures and pattern recognition techniques via known or natural relationships in the plain text-cipher text to solutions based on mathematical or structural constructs. Modern cryptography rests on the shoulders of its cryptographic predecessors.

CHAPTER **5**

Codes and Machines

This chapter discusses two fascinating cryptographic dimensions: (1) the historical use of codes before computers (BC) and (2) the development of rotor machines to automate cryptosystems. We examine several famous code systems. The underlying principles used to develop code systems are still relevant in modern system design.

Rotor machine cryptography became popular in the 1930s, 40s and 50s. It was thought that longer keys in polyalphabetic substitution systems would provide stronger cryptograms and hence strong cryptosystems. Machines were developed to extend the cryptographic key. Unfortunately, machine cryptograms were breakable (with some heavy use of logic and a little bit of early computer help).

Code Systems

A *code system* is a highly specialized form of substitution. The basic principle underlying code systems is the replacement of entire words, long phrases, or complete sentences constituting the plain text of a message by arbitrarily selected equivalents having little or no relation to the elements they replace; these equivalents may be other words, groups of letters, groups of figures, or combinations thereof.

This replacement process is rarely applied to elements smaller than whole words and when this is done the elements are single letters, groups of letters, or syllables. In a *codebook,* the words, phrases, and sentences are listed in a systematic manner and accompanied by their code equivalents; correspondents must possess identical copies of the document in order to be able to communicate with each other. An ordinary dictionary may serve the purpose of code communication, so far as single words are concerned, but as a rule a specially prepared document containing the words, phrases, and sentences suited to particular types of correspondence is used. In the United States, they are called *codebooks* or *codes.* Other names come from different locations: *repertories, wordbooks,* and *cipher dictionaries.*

Tritheim Code Book

One of the earliest codebooks was developed by the Benedictine abbot, John Tritheim. He collected many of the ciphers used in the European courts. He was familiar with the occult and proposed a code based on cabalistic words, wherein he tried to hide the real meaning under cover of a mysterious language. The courts burned his book *Polygraphia* in great pomp and ceremony—John was lucky that he didn't go with the fire. The first edition was published in Latin in 1518; a French translation was produced in 1541, followed by a German translation.

Part one of *Polygraphia* consisted of a number of code words for each letter of the alphabet, but arranged in such a manner that if each letter of the message was replaced by a code word, the result was a complete sentence having an innocent meaning. Table 5-1 shows a section of the 14 coded alphabets.

TABLE 5-1

Tritheim's Code Alphabets

	First	Second	Third	Fourth
A	Jesus	Immortal	Producing	Angels
B	God	Omnipotent	Saving	Archangels
C	Saviour	Compassionate	Illuminating	Saints
D	King	Ineffable	Conferring	Spheres
E	Pastor	Universal	Moderating	Heavens
F	Author	Almighty	Expressing	Sea
G	Redempter	Magnificent	Governing	Earth
H	Prince	Puissant	Disposing(of)	World
IJ	Maker	Just	Dominating	Men
K	Conservator	Sempiterneal	Creating	Sun
L	Governor	Celestial	Cognising	Moon
M	Emperor	Divine	Guiding	All
N	Moderator	Excellent	Blessing	Hierarchies
O	Rector	Triumphant	Constituting	Bodies
P	Judge	Clement	Confirming	Spirits
Q	Illustrator	Peaceful	Conducting	Souls
R	Illuminator	Pacific	Sanctifying	Times
S	Consolator	Invisible	Honoring	Humanity
T	Sire	Eternal	Ministrating	Ages
UVW	Dominator	Invincible	Exorcising	Eternity
X	Creator	Benign	Elevating	Firmaments
Y	Psalmist	Pitiable	Sustaining	Stars
Z	Sovereign	Incomprehensible	Vilifying	Air
&	Protector	Excellent	Ordering	Cosmos

An example Tritheim code cipher text might read:

(The) King Triumphant Blessing (the) Bodies Manifests (to the) Catholics Pure Consolation (together with) His Servants (in) Perpetuity The Majesty (of the) Rector Devotedly Treated. Amen.

Note the interesting and rich language in Tritheim's alphabets. Unfortunately, messages using Tritheim's codes required as many words as there were letters in the plain text, which made for a long cryptogram.

From Lloyd to Marconi

Edward Lloyd ran a coffeehouse in Tower Street, London, during the late seventeenth century. An enterprising man, he noted that several brokers used to discuss their business over coffee. To sell more coffee, he decided he must make things easier for them. Therefore, in 1688, he instituted a blackboard, and then a weekly bulletin of shipping information. More brokers that were independent came and consumed his coffee while doing their business. He later moved his coffeehouse to Lombard Street, in the very center of the old city of London frequented by merchants of the highest class. It was not until 1774, with the rapid increase of marine insurance business, that a committee was set up and a constitution formed, which has remained practically unaltered to the present day. There is no longer a Lloyd's coffeehouse, yet the name is preserved, and Lloyd's is known all over the world as the center of the marine insurance business.

Lloyd's devised a method of signaling between sea and shore, so that advance news of ships and cargoes might be received. A primitive projector was set up and a system of light signals based on the Polybius' system was started. This gave rise to the use of codes for commercial purposes; and apart from the Venetian merchants in the eighteenth century, Lloyd's signals were the first to come into general use.

A system of rapid communications known as *aerial telegraphy*, employing semaphores on high towers visible at considerable distances, was instituted in Europe in 1794. Whole phrases or sentences could be expressed by one group of signals.

In 1825, codes employing figure groups were in common use and the Telegraphic Vocabulary Code was used between Liverpool and Holyhead for the semaphore telegraph. Words, phrases, and long sentences appear in this code, each represented by groups of one to four digits.

The earliest practical trial of electric telegraphy was made in 1837 on the London and North Western Railway, and the first public telegraph line, under Wheatstone and Coke Patents, was laid from Paddington to Slough along the Great Western railway in 1843.

Brewell published his Mercantile Cipher for condensing telegrams in New York in 1860. It used five-letter code groups to indicate English dictionary words producing a complete vocabulary sorted by categories.

ABC Code

The *ABC code,* also based on dictionary words, first appeared in 1874. (Refer to Table 5-2.) Up to 1872, the telegraph companies, by international agreement, charged pronounceable code language words as plain text; the higher tariff applied only to cipher or numeral language. These were charged for at a rate of five characters per word; and in 1875, at St. Petersburg, the maximum length was fixed for either plain text or code words at seven syllables. This led to abuse, such as words like Chinesiskslutningsdon—21 letters, but only six syllables—that were used by coders.

Code No.	Half Code Word	Meaning
00000	ABAAA	'ABC' CODE
00001	ABADE	Please use 'ABC' Code 6th edition
00002	ABAEF	Please use 'ABC' Code 6th edition and Code — — (s)
00003	ABAFG	Please Use 'ABC' Code 6th edition and private Code
00004	ABAGH	Using 'ABC' Code 6th edition
00005	ABAHI	Using 'ABC' Code 6th edition and Code — — — — -
00006	ABAIJ	Abandon
00007	ABAJK	Abandon altogether
00008	ABAKL	Abandon for the present
00009	ABALM	Abandon or (—-)
00010	ABAMN	Abandon the action

TABLE 5-2

Example of ABC Code Page

The rule was changed to apply to European or Latin words but not artificial words. In 1903, code words of ten characters were allowed. They had to be pronounceable to be authorized for transmission at the cost of plain text words.

In 1904, Whitewall's Telegraph Ciphers appeared with 400 million pronounceable words. Not really a codebook, it was a list of "artificials" used for private codes. These code words were composed of five letters only—for example, FORAB, LUFFA, LOZOJ—as are all words used in commercial codes today. Twenty-thousand words of five letters each were given, and since each was pronounceable, and any two of these words could be joined together to form a compound word (which was chargeable according to telegraph regulations as one word), so $20,000^2$ gave the total of potential words as 400 million.

In 1906, Bentley's Code appeared, a compact phrase book based on five-letter groups, applicable to business affairs in general. It cut the cost of international transmissions by half.

Morse Code

Samuel Finley Breese Morse was born in 1791 in Charlestown, Massachusetts. An artist by profession, his invention of the electric telegraph and development of the familiar dots and dashes of the Morse Code is one of the major precursors of the modern Communication Age. He based his Morse Code on the frequencies of letters calculated on quantities of type found in the printing office. Since his frequency tables are an enormous help in deciphering every code, let's compare here the original calculation made by Morse with the normal frequency and the telegraph frequency (see Table 5-3).

For the most frequently occurring letters, he used the simplest combination of dots and dashes. An automatic contrivance was used to alternately transmit and suspend electrical current during longer or shorter intervals and reproduce the effect at the other end of the wire on strips of paper.

The Morse Code was used not only in telegraphy but also in signaling by flags, by flashes of lights, by long and short blasts from a whistle, and knocks on the wooden cages, cell walls, and pipes to fellow prisoners in Viet Nam, Korea, and World War II prisoner-of-war camps. The practice may date back to the American Civil War and probably was not used in the Spanish American War because it was too short to establish a need for prisoner communications. It is alleged that the Count of Monte Cristo used a similar code during his imprisonment.

A simple method to learn the Morse Code was invented by Morse and is shown in Table 5-4. He developed a short list of words, one for each letter of the alphabet, the long and short syllables indicating dashes and dots.

Observe that each of these words contains as many syllables as there are dots and dashes in the corresponding Morse alphabet; but owing to

TABLE 5-3

Comparative Table of Order of Morse's Count with Telegraph Frequencies

Printer Frequency	Morse's Original Order	Actual Number of Letters Found by Morse at His Printer	Order of Normal Frequency
E	1st	12,000	1st
T	2nd	9,000	2nd
A	3rd	8,000	3rd
I	3rd	8,000	6th
N	3rd	8,000	5th
O	3rd	8,000	4th
S	3rd	8,000	8th
H	4th	6,400	9th
R	5th	6,200	7th
D	6th	4,400	11th
L	7th	4,000	10th
U	8th	3,400	13th
C	9th	3,000	12th
M	9th	3,000	16th
F	10th	2,500	15th
W	11th	2,000	17th
Y	11th	2,000	18th
G	12th	1,700	20th
P	12th	1,700	14th
B	13th	1,600	19th
V	14th	1,200	21st
K	15th	800	22th
Q	16th	500	23rd
J	17th	400	25th
X	17th	400	24th
Z	18th	200	26th

Comparative Table of Order of Morse's Count with Telegraph Frequencies

Order	1	2	3	3	3	3	3	4	5	6	7	8	9
Morse:	E,	T,	A,	I,	N,	O,	S,	H,	R,	D,	L,	U,	C,M
Telegraph:	E,	O,	A,	N,	I,	R,	S,	T,	D,	H,	L,	U,	C

Order	10	11	12	13	14	15	16	17	18
Morse:	F,	W, Y,	G,P,	B,	V,	K,	Q,	J, X,	Z
Telegraph:	M,	P,	Y,F,	G,	W,	B,	V,	K, X, J,	Q,Z

the difficulty of finding suitable words, it was assumed that vowels followed by two or more consonants are long and those by single ones short. In the words *Katherine* and *offensive,* for instance, the final syllables must be considered long. Morse put together the following memorization aid:

TABLE 5-4

Learning Morse
Code

(Invented by Morse
and Symbolization by
Morse)

			Morse	Phonetic
A	Ag-ainst		. -	dit dah
B	Bar-ba-ri-an		- . . .	dah dit dit dit
C	Cont-in-ent-al		- . - .	dah dit dah dit
D	Dah-li-a		- . .	dah dit dit
E	(short)		.	dit
F	Fu-ri-ous-ly		. . - .	dit dit dah dit
G	Gal-lant-ly		- - .	dah dah dit
H	Hu-mi-li-ty		. . . .	dit dit dit dit
I	I-vy		. .	dit dit
J	Ju-ris-dic-tion		. - - -	dit dah dah dah
K	Kan-ga-roo		- . -	dah dit dah
L	Le-gis-la-tor		. - . .	dit dah dit dit
M	Moun-tain		- -	dah dah
N	Nob-le		- .	dah dit
O	Off-ens-ive		- - -	dah dah dah
P	Pho-tog-rapher-er		. - - .	dit dah dah dit
Q	Queen Kath-er-ine		- - . -	dah dah dit dah
R	Re-bec-ca		. - .	dah dit dah
S	Sev-er-al		. . .	dit dit dit
T	Tea		-	dah
U	Un-i-form		. . -	dit dit dah
V	Ve-ry Var-ied		. . . -	dit dit dit dah
W	Wa-ter-loo		. - -	dit dah dah
X	Ex-hi-bi-tion		- . . -	dah dit dit dah
Y	Youth-ful and Fair		- . - -	dah dit dah dah
Z	(two long, two short)		- - . .	dah dah dit dit

GALLANTLY and FURIOUSLY, he fought AGAINST the foe at WATERLOO.
IVY creeping along the ground suggests HUMILITY.
The JURISDICTION of the NOBLE LEGISLATOR was OFFENSIVE to the
BARBARIAN.
A PHOTOGRAPHER saw SEVERAL KANGAROOS on the MOUNTAIN.

Early Commercial Codes

Historically, commercial codes were not so much used for secrecy as for
saving money on long telegrams. Authorized, pronounceable words of
maximum length of ten letters were being used to cover several sentences. The code words used were entirely fictitious, and followed each
other in alphabetical order, being made up of five letters each, so that
two codewords could be sent by telegraph for the price of one. Modern
day email on the Net has completely made this a nonissue. In any day,
we may write to friends in England, Germany, Italy, Japan, and Spain,

in less than 30 minutes have answers, with attachments, and be charged a flat rate for the service on this end! Other codes constructed on these principles were Bentley's and Webster's. They allow two words, or even short sentences, to be formed into one telegraph word of ten letters. There are commercial codes today with equivalent translations into every European language, so that English, German, or Italian businessmen, without knowing each other's languages, can exchange telegrams (or faxes).

Marconi Code

Senator Guglielmo Marconi was devoted to an idea—the sending and receiving of wireless signals through space. His wireless inventions are legendary. Marconi also invented and perfected the Marconi codes. The complete Marconi Code consists of four volumes comprising English, Spanish, Japanese, Russian, Italian, Portuguese, German, and Dutch equivalents. The English text is alphabetical, and every other language has a complete index of all the words. The code is divided into two parts, one containing general phrases and the other a numerical system.

The chief aim of standard code was to reduce the cost of cable charges and the time required coding the messages. Upwards of 17,050 combinations could be obtained by the Marconi Code. A checking system was used to ensure accuracy.

The code words in the Marconi Code were composed of five letters each, corresponding to a word or sentence used in trade or business. The code words could be combined into a telegraph word of ten letters by the International Telegraph regulations.

There were some differences with codes such as the ABC code. Each code word has a two-letter difference from each other code word. This two-letter difference ensured that no two words would have the same four letters in the same position. A code word like BOPEZ would eliminate code words like COPEZ, DOPEZ, and also such forms as BAPEZ and BEPEZ.

The Marconi Numerical System was arranged so that a range of figures in combination with some of the most commonly used qualifying phrases, together with an accuracy check, could be transmitted in one complete pronounceable word of ten letters. The first syllable in the numerical section consisted of two consonants, thereby distinguishing it from a phrase section in which none of the code words began with two consonants. As the code words in the numerical section were only two letters long, five words or phrases could be included in one telegraph word of ten letters.

The Marconi arrangement is shown in Table 5-5:

- *1st Syllable:* Provided for a variety of phrases that were employed in combination with the figures or phrases in the following syllables, described as "qualifying phrases" (e.g., "TH" = remit by cable; "TW" = ship immediately).

- *2nd Syllable:* Provides for an extensive variety of phrases descriptive of the following weights and measures (i.e., "OM" = pounds; "WG" = tons).

- *3rd Syllable:* Provides for figures from fractions to 100.

- *4th Syllable:* Provides for more figures to be used in conjunction with the third syllable. If unnecessary, a blank must be used here, or short phrase to qualify, such as "ZA" = per month.

- *5th Syllable:* Provides for a further series of phrases to be used in conjunction with the foregoing (e.g., "AL" = for immediate shipment). It also supplies a check for the whole coded word.

The checking system is very simple. The check numbers given in brackets on each code syllable are added together for the four syllables used; tens are disregarded, and for the fifth syllable the letters are chosen from the column bearing the same number as the total arrived at from the addition of the first four syllables. Compare the ABC code in Table 5-2 with the Marconi Code in Table 5-5.

Nonsecret Codes

Various codes are suited to particular types of correspondence. Many large commercial firms have their own private codes. For example, an early commercial codebook was made by ACME Commercial Code Company in the 1930s. Most industries have highly specialized technical language (part of the mystique in every industry or profession—Latin for doctors and lawyers; mathematics for engineers; ISO 9000 terms for quality managers; snake-oil terms for computer types; plus a whole bevy of terms for cryptographers, etc.). The purposes of many of these codebooks are brevity and compression, not secrecy. The military and diplomatic applications call for security and speed of communications, especially for frontline communications.

The PKZIP program, which is used so widely on the Net, is a compression "codebook." It provides economy of transmission and minimal

TABLE 5-5

The First Part of the
Marconi Code

(General Phrases
Code Words, Five Let-
ters Phrase System.
Code Word of Two
Letters)

No.	Code Word	English	French	Spanish
00000	ABABA	A or an	un, une	un, uno, una
00001	ABAHB	A1 at Lloyds	A1 chez Lloyds	A1 en el registro de Lloyd
00002	ABALC	Abandon(s)	Abandonn(r)(z)	Abandona(r)(u)
00003	ABAND	Abandon all claims	Abandonne toutes reclamations	Abandona todas las reclamaciones
00004	ABAPE	Abandon negotiations	Abandonne les negociations	Abandona las negociaciones
00003	ABARF	Abandon proceedings	Abandonne les demarches	Abandona los procedimientes

1st Syllable

Check No. in Red	Code Syllable	English	French	Spanish
(0)	BL	Blank or At	Blanc ou A	Blanco o A
(5)	BR	Bid (they)	Ils offrent	ofrecen
(8)	CH	Bid (we)	Nous offrons	ofrencemos
(1)	CL	Bought (we have)	Nous avons achete	Hemos comprado
(6)	CR	Breadth (or thickness)	Largeur (ou epaisseur)	Anchura (o espesura)

2nd Syllable

(5)	AB	Blank	Blanc	Blanco
(6)	AC	Acre(s)	Acre(s)	Acre(s)
(7)	AD	Ampere(s)	Ampere(s)	Amperio(s)
(8)	AF	Anna(s)	Anna(s)	Anna(s)
(9)	AG	Ante Meredian (A.M.)	Matin, avant midi	Antes de mediodia (A.M.)

3rd Syllable

(5)	AB	Blank	Blanc	Blanco
(6)	AC	0	0	0
(7)	AD	1/16	1/16	1/16
(8)	BI	1	1	1
(7)	BO	1/14	1/14	1/14

TABLE 5-5

The First Part of the Marconi Code

(General Phrases Code Words, Five Letters Phrase System. Code Word of Two Letters) (*Continued*)

Check No. in Red	Code Syllable	English	French	Spanish
			4th Syllable	
(9)	YA	000	000	000
(0)	YB	100	100	100
(1)	YC	200	200	200
(1)	YM	per annum	par an	por ano
(2)	YN	per centimeter	par centmetre	por centmetro

5th Syllable: Control of Check

	0	1	2	3	4	5	6	7	8	9
Blanc	AR	EN	BU	HI	JA	NA	OY	TO	VA	YG
Anout	AC	EP	BY	HO	JE	NE	OZ	TU	YE	YH
Average	AD	ER	CA	HU	JI	NI	PA	TY	VI	YI
C.I.F. (Cost Insurance Freight)	AF	ES	CE	HY	JO	NO	PE	WB	VO	YJ
Each	AG	ET	CI	IB	JU	NU	PI	UC	VU	YK

cryptosecurity. The power of the program lies in the ability to delineate and hold entire directories and then to create an indexed tree of the coagulated sum of files with indexed repetitions. PKZIP is an example of a *nonsecret code*. Compression can be as valuable as secrecy. The condensing power of a code is dependent on its vocabulary. When we add the goal of secrecy to economy, we then have a *secret code*. Actually, code transmissions save money because of the fewer number of characters to be transmitted over the channel.

Brevity Codes

In military cryptography, the greatest degree of condensation is afforded by *prearranged-message codes* (or *brevity codes*), which are tactical codes adapted to the use of units requiring special or technical vocabularies; they are comprised almost exclusively of groups representing complete or nearly complete messages and are intended for shortening messages and concealing their content. The police "10" codes fall into this category.

A *brevity code* has, as its sole purpose, the shortening of messages. A *field code* is a small tactical code that contains a large number of code groups representing words and a few common short phrases, from which sentences can be composed; a *syllabary,* which is a list of code groups representing individual letters, combinations of letters, or syllables, is used for spelling out proper names; and *numerical tables,* which are lists of code groups representing numbers, dates, and jargon. The Army Special Forces codes fall into this category. A *jargon code* is a very short code in which bona fide dictionary words, baptismal names, rivers, lakes, and the like, are used as code groups. Lincoln's wartime codes fall into this category. A *voice code* or *recognition code* is used for transmission by small radiotelephone sets used in combat. Other names are *combat code* or *operations code.* The Navy had a special brand of codes used for protection of marine traffic. An early example of this code system is the International Code of Signals.

International Code of Signals for Visual, Sound, and Radio Communications (INTERCO)

The Defense Mapping Agency, Hydrographic/Topographic Center issued in 1969 and again in 1981, their Publication No. 102, "International Code of Signals For Visual, Sound, and Radio Communications," United States Edition. This code was adopted by the Fourth Assembly of the intergovernmental Maritime Consultative Organization in 1975. The document was prepared in nine languages—English, French, Italian, German, Japanese, Spanish, Norwegian, Russian, and Greek—and is a very good example of the brevity and nonsecret codes that had wide distribution for ocean-going vessels. Modern-day vessels use uplinks to satellites in geosynchronous orbits to navigate and communicate.

The INTERCO was designed to communicate for situations relating to the safety of navigation and persons, especially when language difficulties arise. It is suitable for transmission of communication, including radiotelephony and radiotelegraphy. The INTERCO embodies the principle that each signal has a complete and distinct meaning.

The INTERCO was broken into four parts: (1) Signal Instructions; (2) General Signal Code; (3) Medical Signal Code, Distress and Lifesaving Signals; and (4) Radio Procedures. The INTERCO appendix included National Identity Signals for Ships and Aircraft, plus US/USSR Supplementary Signals for Naval Vessels.

General Signal Code includes sections on: Distress, Emergency, Casualties, Damages, Aids to Navigation, Hydrography, Maneuvers, Cargo, Ballast, Meteorology, Communications, and Sanitary Regulations. See Table 5-6 for sample entries. In Table 5-6, capitalized headings represent major topics; predominantly lowercase headings represent subtopics. You can see from the small sample in Table 5-6 that the INTERCO deals with serious situations. In a U.S. Coast Guard (USCG) radio room, specialists listen to 11 or more radios at the same time. It can be very intense. A MAYDAY may be heard only once and rarely in a calm voice. Sending the cutter is serious business. The USCG does its job exceptionally well.

Basics of Classical Code Construction

The encoding and reverse procedure of decoding is accomplished by replacing various words, phrases, sentences, and numbers by their code equivalents. The code text is built up from code units, each representing the longest possible plain-text unit the codebook affords. Encoding the phrase "enemy force estimated at one battalion" would require the lookup in the codebook. We might find phrases such as "enemy force" and "estimated at" and the individual words—we would write down the phrase equivalents.

The elements of which code groups are composed may be one or more of the following:

1. Bona fide words—real words from Dutch, English, French, German, Italian, Latin, Portuguese, and Spanish.

2. Artificial words—groups of letters without meaning with vowels and consonants arranged to appear like real words.

3. Random groups of letters.

4. Groups of Arabic figures.

5. Intermix groups, that is, call signs for stations K2KAA or W5AZZ.

6. All of the above.

Parallel Sets

A code may contain two or more *parallel sets* of code groups of different types. In many commercial codes and some military codes, there is one

TABLE 5-6

Sample Entries from INTERCO Codebook

(Distress—Emergency)

Code	Meaning
	ABANDON
AD	I am abandoning my vessel which has suffered a nuclear accident and is a possible source of radiation danger.
	Accident
SB	I am proceeding to the position of the accident.
GC 2	I have searched area of accident but have found no trace of derelict or survivors.
	Doctor
AM	Have you a doctor on board?
AP	I have...(number) casualties.
	ASSISTANCE
	Required
CB	I require immediate assistance.
CB 1	I require immediate assistance; I have a dangerous list.
CB 6	I require immediate assistance; I am on fire.
	Given-Not Given
CN 1	You should give immediate assistance to pick up survivors.
CO 1	I cannot give the assistance required (for vessel/aircraft indicated).
	DISABLED-DRIFTING-SINKING
DS	I have sighted disabled aircraft in lat... long...at time indicated.
DX	I am sinking.
	SEARCH AND RESCUE
	Proceeding To Assistance
FE	I am proceeding to the position of the accident at full speed. Expect to arrive at time indicated.

TABLE 5-6

Sample Entries
from INTERCO
Codebook

(Distress—Emer-
gency) (Continued)

Code	Meaning

Position of Distress or Accident

FF	I have intercepted SOS/MAYDAY from vessel (name or identity signal or air-craft) in pos lat... long... at time indicated.

Results of Search

GJ 1	Wreckage is reported in lat... long....No survivors appear to be in vicinity.

ICEBREAKER

WC 1	Icebreaker is being sent to your assistance.

SEA

WY	The state of the sea is...(Complements 0–9 corresponding to following table):

		Height	
		In Meters	**In Feet**
0	Calm (glassy)	0	0
1	Calm (rippled)	0–0.1	$0-\frac{1}{3}$
2	Smooth (wavelets)	0.1–0.5	$\frac{1}{3}-1\frac{2}{3}$
3	Slight	0.5–1.25	$1\frac{2}{3}-4$
4	Moderate	1.25–2.5	4–8
5	Rough	2.5–4	8–13
6	Very Rough	4–6	13–20
7	High	6–9	20–30
8	Very High	9–14	30–45
9	Phenomenal	over 14	over 45

MEDICAL

Diseases of Respiratory System

MIF	Patient is coughing up blood.
MIM	Patient has blueness of face.

Special Treatment

MRW	Give frequent gargles one teaspoon of salt in a tumblerful of water.

TABLE 5-6

Sample Entries
from INTERCO
Codebook

(Distress—Emer-
gency) (*Continued*)

RECEPTION OF SAFETY MESSAGES

MAYDAY (Distress)	Indicates that the ship, aircraft, or other vehicle is threatened by grave and imminent danger and requests immediate assistance.
PAN (Urgency)	Indicates the calling station has a very urgent message to transmit concerning the safety of a ship, aircraft or other vehicle, or the safety of a person.
SECURITE (Safety)	Indicates that the station is about to transmit a message concerning the safety of navigation or giving important meteorological warnings.

To *indicate* DISTRESS:

1. If possible transmit ALARM SIGNAL (i.e., two tone signal) for 30 seconds to one minute, but do not delay the message if there is insufficient time in which to transmit the Alarm Signal.

2. Send the following DISTRESS CALL:

MAYDAY MAYDAY MAYDAY. This is...(name or call sign of ship spoken three times).

3. Then send the DISTRESS MESSAGE composed of:

MAYDAY followed by the name or call sign of the ship;

Position of ship;

Nature of distress;

And if necessary, transmit nature of the aid required and any other information which will help the rescue.

USE PLAIN LANGUAGE WHENEVER POSSIBLE or send the word INTERCO to indicate that the message will be in the International Code of Signals.

Example:

MAYDAY MAYDAY MAYDAY...(name of ship spoken three times, or call sign of ship spelled using Phonetic Alphabet in Table 5-7); MAYDAY...(name or call sign of ship) Position 54 25 North 016 33 West **I am on Fire and require immediate assistance.**

series of code groups of the bona fide type or artificial word type and another series of the figure-group type, both applying to the same series of words, phrases, and sentences of the code. In parts of the world where English letters are used for writing, letters possess greater advantages in accuracy of reading than figures—especially for telegraph or radio transmissions. For communications to China and Russia or obscure ports, Arabic figures are well accepted and code groups composed of figures are used. The main reason for this is to ensure the correct trans-

TABLE 5-7
Phonetic Alphabet
Used with INTER-
CO

Letter/Number	Word	Pronounced
A	Alfa	**AL** FAH
B	Bravo	**BRAH** VOH
C	Charlie	**CHAR** LEE or **SHAR** LEE
D	Delta	**DELL** TAH
E	Echo	**ECK** OH
F	Foxtrot	**FOKS** TROT
G	Golf	GOLF
H	Hotel	HOH **TELL**
I	India	**IN** DEE AH
J	Juliett	**JEW** LEE ETT
K	Kilo	**KEY** LOH
L	Lima	**LEE** MAH
M	Mike	MIKE
N	November	NO **VEM** BER
O	Oscar	**OSS** CAR
P	Papa	PAH **PAH**
Q	Quebec	KEH **BECK**
R	Romeo	**ROW** ME OH
S	Sierra	SEE **AIR** RAH
T	Tango	**TANG** GO
U	Uniform	**YOU** NEE FORM or **OO** NEE FORM
V	Victor	**VIK** TAH
W	Whiskey	**WISS** KEY
X	Xray	**ECKS** RAY
Y	Yankee	**YANG** KEE
Z	Zulu	**ZOO** LOO
0	NADAZERO	NAH-DAH-ZAY-ROH
1	UNAONE	OO-NAH-WUN
2	BISSOTWO	BEES-SO-TOO
3	TERRATHREE	TAY-REE-TREE
4	KARTEFOUR	KAR-TAY-FOWER
5	PANTAFIVE	PAN-TAH-FIVE
6	SOXISIX	SOK-SEE-SIX
7	SETTESEVEN	SAY-TAH-SEVEN
8	OKTOEIGHT	OH-TAY-AIT
9	NOVENINE	NO-VAY-NINER
.	DECIMAL	DAY-SEE-MAL

mission and reception of messages in all parts of the world. Another reason is that certain methods of enciphering code messages for the sake of greater secrecy, figure groups often form the basis for encipherment more readily than do letter groups.

    The greatest advantage possessed by letter groups over figure groups lies in the availability of a far greater number of *permutations,* or interchanges, of letter groups, because there are 26 letters that may be permuted to form letter groups compared to 10 digits for figure groups (assumes base 10 historical use). If code groups of five letters are used, then there are 26^5 or 11,881,376 groups of five letters versus 10^5, or 100,000 groups of five figures. Letter code groups are usually constructed to reduce error in transmission.

The length of code groups used, whether the groups consist of two, three, four, or five elements, depends upon the size of the code. This applies almost exclusively to field military or naval codes, where transmission is through a governmental agency; in commercial messages or governmental communications transmitted over privately operated lines, five-figure or five-letter groups are the standard.

Code groups of modern codes are constructed by the use of tables, which permit more or less automatic and systematic construction in the form desired—these are called *permutation tables*. Because they may be used to correct most errors made in transmission or writing, such tables are usually included in the codebook and are called *mutilation tables, garble tables,* or *error-detector charts*.

Two-Letter Differential

The average telegraph or radio operator did not work without error. One-letter-different code groups such as ABABA and ABABE were easy to mistake and the message could be made unintelligible by only a few transmission errors. However, if every code group in the codebook was distinguished from all other code groups in the same code by a difference of at least two letters, then there would have to be two errors in a single group and these two errors would have to produce a code group actually present in the code before a wrong meaning would be conveyed. The principle of making code groups differ by a minimum of two letters was called the *two-letter differential*. The two-letter differential reduced the possibilities for constructing letter-code groups from 26^5 to 26^4 (456,976) but considering the advantages, the sacrifice was worthwhile. Permutation tables for construction of figure-code groups are similar in nature and purpose to tables for construction of letter-coded groups. Because of a more limited number of characters available for permutations, the maximum number of two-figure difference groups possible in a five-figure code is 10^4, or 10,000. This does not account for ASCII code derivations.

Types

In their construction or arrangement, codes are generally of two types:

1. *One-part, or alphabetical codes:*   The plain-text groups are arranged in alphabetical order accompanied by their code groups in alphabetical or numerical order. Such a code serves for decoding as well as encoding.

2. *Two-part, or randomized codes:*   The plain-text groups are arranged in alphabetical order accompanied by their code groups in a nonsystematic order. The code groups are assigned to the plain-text groups at random by drawing the code groups out of a box in which they have been thoroughly mixed. Such a list serves for encoding. For decoding, another list must be provided in which the code groups are arranged in alphabetical or numerical order and are accompanied by their meanings as given in the encoding section. Another name for the two-part codes is *cross-reference codes*. Here are extracts from typical one-part and two-part codes (Tables 5-8 and 5-9).

TABLE 5-8

One-Part Code

ABABD	A
ABACF	Abaft
ABAHK	Abandon
ABAJL	.....it
ABALN	Abandoned
ABAMP	.....by
ABAWZ	Abandoning
ABBAD	Abandonment
...	...
...	...
ZYZYZ	Zero

TABLE 5-9

Two-Part Code

Encoding Section		Decoding Section	
GAJVY	A	ABABD	Obstructed
TOGTY	Abaft	ABACF	Term
FEHIL	Abandon	ABAHK	Zero
BAYLT	.....it	ABAJL	If it has not
ZYZYZ	Abandoned	ABALN	To be sent by
NYSYZ	.....by	ABAMP	Acceding
IFWUZ	Abandoning	ABAWZ	Building
RUMGO	Abandonment	ABBAD	Do not attempt
...	...	...	...
...	...	...	...
ABAHK	Zero	ZYZYZ	Abandoned

Between the two extremes are codes that have features of both; that is, complete sections may be arranged in random sequence, but within each section the contents are arranged in some logical order.

When a strict alphabetic arrangement is used in the sequence of the phrases, the code is said to be a *strictly alphabetical code*. When the phrases are listed under separate headings based upon the principal word or idea in the whole expression, the code is called a *caption code* (Tables 5-10 and 5-11).

TABLE 5-10		**TABLE 5-11**	
Caption Code	Assistance	Strictly Alphabetical Code	Assistance
	Give assistance		Assistance for
	Require assistance		Assistance from
	No assistance		Assistance has been sent
	Assistance has been sent		Assistance to
	Assistance for		Assistant
	Assistance from		Assisted
	Assistance to		Give
	Assistant		Give assistance
	Assisted		No
			No assistance required
			Require
			Require assistance

More precise and economical coding was possible with a caption code than with an alphabetical code. With a caption code, it was easier to assemble an extended variety of expressions and shades of meaning under specific headings than with alphabetical code. On the other hand, the use of a caption code involved more time and labor in encoding.

Two-part codes were used by many governments for their secret diplomatic, military, and naval communications because of the advantages they offer over one-part codes. Some disadvantages: two-part codes are twice as large in context, printing, and distribution costs; compilation is four times greater because of the requirement of accurate cross-references. The advantages of two-part codes are greater security and greater accuracy.

In some commercial code messages there were sometimes encountered the practice of mixing plain text and code text. In governmental and naval communications, such intermixtures were rare because they present an abysmal ignorance of the fundamental rules of cryptographic security. Because the plain-text words give definite clues to the meaning of the adjacent code groups—even though the former convey no meaning in themselves (such words as *and, but, by, comma, for, in, period, stop, that, the,* etc.)—this constitutes a fatal danger to the message security.

Enciphered Code Systems

Sometimes the code groups of a code message underwent a further process of encipherment; the resulting cryptogram constituted an *enciphered code message*. Both transposition and substitution may be used to encipher the code. Enciphered code is used under the following circumstances:

1. When the code has a wide distribution and may fall into enemy hands
2. To improve the security of commercial codes and nonsecret codes
3. When increased security is necessary for highly classified communications

Transposition methods are generally used within code groups, such as rearranging or shifting the letters or figures composing them. A common method was keyed columnar transposition with special matrices with nulls. All the substitution methods previously reviewed may be used for "superencipherment" of the code. However, the most effective methods of enciphering code are arithmetical methods.

If the code groups are numerical, by adding (usually mod 10) an arbitrarily selected number (called the *additive*) to each code, the resulting group message constitutes a simple form of encipherment. The additive may be fixed.

Additive methods may actually be weak cryptographically if the basic codebook and code groups embody limitations in construction. Instead of adding a fixed number in encipherment, the latter is subtracted, in which case, in decipherment; the fixed number must be added to the enciphered-code groups as received. Such a group (called *subtractive* or *subtractor*) in decipherment becomes an additive. A third method used commonly is the *minuend method*, which involves the subtraction of the plain code group from the key to yield the enciphered-code group in encipherment, and the subtraction of the enciphered-code group from the key in decipherment. Addition and subtraction of a fixed-numerical group may be alternated within the same message such as +200, +100, +400 as a cycle or + 200, −100, +400, −200, and so forth. Instead of a fixed additive, it is possible to employ a repeating large key.

When special tables are employed as the source of the additives or subtractors for enciphered code, a much more secure system is provided. These tables were called a *key book,* or *additive book,* or *subtractor book.* By applying identifying symbols called *indicators* to the pages, as well as to the rows and columns on each page of the key book, it is possible to provide for secure encipherment of a large volume of traffic. All correspondents must have the same key books. In employing the key book, the indicators tell the recipient of the message which key groups were used and where to begin the decipherment of the enciphered code. In actual practice, indicators are often disguised or encrypted by a special key or set of keys; this procedure may add considerably to the security of the system.

Table 5-12 shows a page from a typical key book. It contains two sets of 100 four-digit key groups, dispersed in numbered blocks each containing 10 rows and 10 columns of groups. To designate a group as the initial one to be employed in encipherment or decipherment, we give the block number, the row, and column numbers of the group. For example, 0116 is the indicator for the group 8790. It is usual to take the successive groups in the normal order of reading. Some key books consist of 50 + pages containing 200+ groups making 10,000 in all. The digits in each block are random numbers. If the key book is used once and only once, security of the system approaches the one-time pad. The messages are one-time system secure even if the enemy has the basic codebook.

Dictionary Codes

Dictionary codes are highly specialized forms of substitution systems. Codebooks (modified dictionaries) used by the Department of State and military represent a greater condensation of words than commercial systems—a single code group may represent a long phrase. The average condensation of a diplomatic code is 1:5 while a commercial code is only 1:3. By way of comparison, modern PKZIP compression is 1:3–1:4 on normal text.

Codes used in conjunction with ciphers (*superencipherment*) can be very difficult to break; but the work and time involved in making this combination can be significant (if done by hand in the field). Computers

TABLE 5-12

Indicators and Key
Blocks

Block 00

	1	2	3	4	5	6	7	8	9	0
1	0378	9197	3260	3607	2699	9053	9733	1844	6622	4213
2	7185	0135	6091	2387	4957	3113	7284	0750	3501	1945
3	5037	3365	1294	8261	2149	0718	3678	2510	7238	5268
4	8004	5199	3859	1293	5311	3550	9915	0512	1518	3776
5	9282	6893	4229	9736	0927	1418	1930	9864	0090	8974
6	7259	9399	0769	3144	9801	1378	4732	5134	1435	5282
7	2878	9963	7943	4519	3404	9810	1090	4467	7069	5348
8	1620	5879	0218	1064	9560	5732	6661	0883	1883	2619
9	3868	1905	2500	6654	0824	3710	3875	6332	1503	7259
0	4319	3298	7819	8721	1549	6630	6301	5701	3586	1907

Block 01

	1	2	3	4	5	6	7	8	9	0
1	9328	1135	3871	1549	0839	8790	1771	8251	3274	1173
2	2297	9550	5033	0102	6817	5579	0847	4038	1200	2949
3	3640	3984	3299	1181	3811	8844	2500	4557	4133	0487
4	1256	9614	5520	8372	1941	2417	1098	4039	3943	8282
5	1751	4254	8479	8647	2684	5511	8680	4660	2315	4857
6	4587	5968	2568	1254	0258	1254	3568	2548	4521	8795
7	1258	6241	0125	2458	4587	5632	2589	1548	1235	1458
8	1254	2548	0004	4561	2565	2437	7849	1245	3265	4879
9	4582	1546	2589	2145	7854	7895	4589	6369	3698	1254
0	1255	1544	7850	2569	9989	8754	2548	1220	0387	0589

handle the repetitious analysis very efficiently. Modern devices are extremely compact and have a lot of computer horsepower.

The typical dictionary code protocol was as follows:

1. Agree with the recipient on the exact edition of the dictionary to be used, that is, *Concise Oxford English Dictionary*, and current edition, by Fowler and Le Mesurier.

2. Use the number of the page, and the number of the word down the page to encipher:

Given Plain: "Reunion Berlin Tomorrow"
Code:
1006 (page no.), 12 (word no.) = Reunion
0104 (pages with fewer than four numbers would have a 0 added in front to keep it uniform), 17 (word no.) = Berlin 1291−08 (on the same principles) = Tomorrow
Cipher text: 100612   010417   129108

These figures, if greater secrecy is required, could again be enciphered and thus converted into letters by means of an agreed-upon cipher.

3. Prepare for superencipherment by dividing the figures into pairs and then convert them into letters by means of a table such as Table 5-13.

TABLE 5-13

Digraphic Equivalents for Superencipherment

	1	3	5	2	4	9	7	8	6	0
9	AN	DA	HN	JT	MB	KC	GF	ES	BZ	ZA
2	CK	AO	DB	HO	JS	GE	ER	BY	FR	YB
7	IR	CJ	AP	DC	GD	EQ	BT	FQ	LH	VA
4	MC	IY	CI	AR	DD	BS	FP	LI	NL	VB
8	MA	KB	GC	CG	AS	DF	HP	JU	OB	VC
1	KA	GB	EP	BR	CE	AT	DG	HQ	JQ	TZ
5	GA	EO	BP	FO	IX	CC	AX	DH	HR	TY
3	EN	BO	FN	LJ	NK	IZ	CB	AY	DJ	SB
6	BN	FM	LK	NJ	OA	OC	IV	CB	AZ	QA
0	XY	YA	BY	YB	XC	XE	YD	YE	YX	QC

Nulls: WA WE W, to end message in groups of five letters.

The numbers enciphered into letters:

TZYXBR   XYXCDG   BRANYE

and the cryptogram for transmission:

TZYXB   RXYXC   DGBRA   NYEWA

The suggested cipher can easily be arranged to make pronounceable words suitable for telegraph or radiotelegraph transmission.

Certain dictionaries have been issued that give two columns on each page, with words directly opposite to each other. Then it is possible to give the word opposite the one we really mean, or a word, which is 5 or 3 or 10 places either above or below the one we want to encode. Codes of this kind can be solved readily.

Cryptanalysis of a Simple Dictionary Code

The Australian criminologist Mansfield presented some interesting principles for solving dictionary codes. He calculated dictionary progressive lists, giving numbers of words beginning with any two letters in dictionaries of 10,000 to 100,000 words.

Given:

55381	42872	35284	44381	45174	56037	55381	46882
23171	44234	55366	55381	00723	12050	61571	36173
55381	56442						

We rearrange the list from lowest numbers to highest.

00723	42872	55381	(5 times)
12050	44234	56037	
23171	45174	56442	
35284	46882	61571	
36173	55366		

Words beginning with XYZ are seldom used, so we can take it that the highest number indicates a word beginning with a W or a T. Mansfield made big assumptions about nulls and standardization of the dictionary. However, the list of bigram frequencies gives us the commonest initial group as TH or THE, and if we fix any repetition of such nature, then we may have the T in that dictionary. Naturally, we start with 55381 occurring five times and assume it is THE. The highest number after that is 61571, so that it could indicate a word beginning with a W. This gives us a clue to the probable number of words in the dictionary used for the code. It cannot be over 65,000 words as XYZ words are very few, seldom more than 3000. (This part of Manfield's analysis is an extraordinary jump of faith—what is more extraordinary is that it will work more than 60 percent of the time on simpler dictionary codes.)

According to Mansfield's Progressive Dictionary Lists, we attempt to fix the probable first two letters of each word in the code. For instance, the second group 12050 will be between 11646 (terminating words beginning with DA) and 12850 (terminating words beginning with DE), so that it is probable to be a word beginning with DE. Using Mansfield's lists we obtain:

THE RE--- OF THE RO--- TO- THE SE- -HA - RE- TH- THE
RE- DE- - WA- OV- THE TO-

We locate in the dictionary the word THE (55381) and count back 20 words for 55366 (TH). This gives us an area covering words THANE, THANK, THAT, THATCH; we try the most likely, THAT. We note the two words starting with letters TO- 56037 and 56442.

Words beginning with TO start at 56037 and stop at 56466, so that it is a reasonable guess to assume the first are TO and the second (56442), we count 20 words back to find the word TOWN. The R group is -RE- (42872) and RE- (44234) and RO- (45174). RE stands 300 words from the end of the RAs, which stop at 42573, according to Mansfield's tables. This gives us the following words to select from: RECLINE, RECOM-MEND, RECOMPOSE, RECONNAISSANCE, RECOUP, and RECOV-ER. We choose RECONNAISSANCE. The next look at our cipher is:

THE RECONNAISSANCE OF THE ROUTE TO THE SE- HAS-
REVEALED THAT THE AE- DE- WA- OV- THE TOWN.

We apply the same process to the AE- 00723 and get airplane, while the DE- 12050 occurring one-quarter of the way from the end of the DA to the end of the DE brings us to DEF, limited by DEFACE and DEFY, where only DEFEAT, DEFENSE, DEFEND, and DEFENSIVE are prob-able. We select airplane defensive use near the mark.

SE- should be sea 46882 and OVER for OV- 36173. The of- is in fact OF, and the HA- is has, and the WA- is was. The complete message reads:

THE RECONNAISSANCE OF THE ROUTE TO THE SEA HAS
REVEALED THAT THE AIRPLANE DEFENSIVE WAS OVER THE
TOWN.

tells us that the real message was off by two words. Instead of AIR-PLANE DEFENSIVE, it was AIR DEFENSES, but the meaning was essentially the same.

What Mansfield did show us in 1936 was that the laws of probability work with dictionary codes. The search in the area of possible words could give us the root of the plain text so that we may deduce the whole meaning of the code.

Diplomatic Codes

One of the best references on historical codes (1775–1938) in the United States was written by Professor Ralph Weber. He describes one interesting code used in 1867 by the State Department, known as *WE029* (refer to Table 5-14). It used a simple substitution-masking procedure, eliminated the use of the letter W because it was not used in European or Latin nations, focused on 24 letters of the alphabet and assigned them to the 24 most common parts of speech such as articles and other words (s = plural; a = THE; e = AND, etc.); other ordinary words were assigned to the approximately 600 combinations of two of the letters. Three letters were used for the remainder of the vocabulary required for common diplomatic usage; a fourth letter was added for plurals, participles, and genitives. When encoding the plural, genitive, or participle of a two-letter word, the third letter would be placed apart in order to avoid confusion.

TABLE 5-14

Segment of a Sample Page from WE029

ekf	Lamentation	fbf	Later	frf	Lay		
elf	Language	fcf	Laugh	fsf	Laziness		
emf	Languid	fdf	Launch	ftf	Lazy		
enf	Languidly	fef	Lavish	fuf	Leader		
eof	Languish	fff	Lavishly	fvf	League		
epf	Languishing	fgf	Lawyer	fxf	Leak		
eqr	Lapse	fhf	Lawful	fzf	Lean		
erf	Large	fif	Lawfully	gaf	Leap		
esf	Largely	fjf	Lawfulness	gbf	Learning		
etf	Lasting	fkf	Lawless	gcf	Leave		
euf	Lastly	flf	Lawlessly	gdf	Lecture		
evf	Late	fmf	Lawlessness	gef	Lecturer		
exf	Latent	fnf	Lax	gff	Left		
eyf	Latently	fof	Laxity	ggf	Legal		
ezf	Latin	fpf	Laxly	ghf	Legally		
faf	Latitude	fqf	Laxness	gif	Legibility		

Code symbols were prepared for principal countries and cities in the world, for states, major cities, and territories of the United States, and for proper names of men in English. A cipher table was to be used for those words not on the list. The first 74 pages of the code was the encode section, and contained the words in alphabetical order together with the code symbols; for example, the very first word was Aaron with the symbol ABA and the last word of the first page was Acknowledge with a symbol of EA. The decode section (three-letter symbols) was not published in one sequential alphabet and was time-consuming. Transmission of the code by cable was awkward because the number of characters was not standard. It was not until 1876 that the five-digit form became standard in the American ciphers. This code became the secret communication mask for American ministers in foreign legations in the years to 1876.

Another cryptographic dimension (precomputer) that yields new clues into the science concerns the use of rotor machines. The invention of the rotor was ingenious. The best reference on machine cryptography is Devours. Kahn is also a good source of material.

History of Machine Cryptography

If we examine the 1769 cryptography-related patents issued between 1861–1980, we find that the 1920s were the most productive era, during which decade six inventors, in particular, stand out: Arvid Gerhard Damm, Edward Hugh Hebern, Hugo Alexander Koch, Arthur Scherbius, Willi Korn, and Alexander von Kryha. Twenty-two U.S. patents are credited to this group during the decade. William F. Friedman's name joined the list in the 1930s. Herbern was the most prolific, being credited with nine U.S. patents.

The first cryptographs produced under Damm's patent were clumsy and unreliable. The most important of Damm's cryptographic ideas was a rotor invention under U.S. patent 1,502,376, July 22, 1924, which he was never able to exploit fully. The rotor principle was, in one form or another, the most widely used method of machine cryptography. The rotors took two forms: pinwheel rotors and wired rotors. *Pinwheel rotors* were classified as "active" and "inactive" based on their projecting positions. The *wired code-wheel* was a disk constructed of some nonconducting material having on each face, a series of equally spaced contact studs which are interconnected so that the current entering on one face will be switched to exit from a different position on the other face of the rotor. Each face may have 26 studs (26 letters). The rotor acted as an electrical commutator (i.e., switch) and essentially caused a monoalphabetic substitution. By moving the rotors or employing a cascade of rotors, repeated substitutions were obtained and varied to produce polyalphabetic ciphers of great complexity.

Boris Caesar Hagelin, an employee of Damm's, created the B-211 cryptograph, which used two electrical rotors in conjunction with four pinwheel rotors, to sell the first commercially successful cryptograph.

By the end of World War I, the wired rotor was an idea whose time had come. Without knowledge of each other, Damm and three others conceived of using the wired rotor for cryptographic machines. In 1917, Edward H. Hebern created his famous Electronic Code machine under patent 1,510,441 awarded on September 30, 1924. This machine greatly influenced American cryptosecurity systems throughout World War II. Hebern's rotors had the 26 contact A–Z sequence. To Hebern must also go credit for the idea of wiring rotors according to the "interval method." Up to Hebern, designers randomly connected the contacts to each face of their rotors. Hebern chose his wiring to produce as flat a polyalphabetic frequency distribution as possible. The interval method of wiring rotors was used in the ECM.

An example of the interval procedure of wiring a rotor is:

Given:

Input Contact:

A B C D E F G H I J K L M N O P Q R S T U V W X Y Z

Output Contact:

G A D B O C T K N U Z X I W H F Q Y J V P M E L S R

Displacement was defined for any input contact, and measured the shift taken by the current traversing the rotor, so:

AG 06	BA 25	CD 01
DB 24	EO 10	FC 23
GT 13	HK 03	IN 03
JU 11	KZ 15	LX 12
MI 22	NW 09	OH 19
PF 16	QQ 00	RY 07
SL 17	TV 02	UP 21
VM 17	WE 08	XL 14
YS 20	ZR 18	

Of the 26 possible displacements values, 0 to 25, every displacement occurs in this set except 4, while displacement 17 occurs twice. This was the construction of the Hebern rotors.

The rotor machine destined to be the most famous of all time, fathered by Koch and Scherbius, was named *Enigma*. The machine attained its real potential, however, in patents held by Korn. Korn explicitly set forth the idea of interchangeable rotors and allowed for reversibility of the rotor turning. On October 29, 1929, Korn received

U.S. patent 1,733,886, which provided for a feed check apparatus to ensure correct rotor positioning and movement. In 1933, two more patents were issued for the Enigma in final form.

During the same period, German cryptographers were altering Korn's commercial Enigma into a more secure form. In England, the British modified the Enigma for military use and called it the Typex. William F. Friedman started development on a tactical level rotor machine based on the Enigma. Friedman's machine, M-325, failed to work well under field conditions and was not accepted—this was William F. Friedman's only failure.

The Enigma was such a commercial success that many countries bought the machine for use and study. The Japanese Enigma, known as the GREEN machine, had rotors mounted on the top of the machine with characteristic Japanese design eccentricity.

Probably the most mechanically and cryptographically complex wired rotor machine was the American top-level machine, known as the ECM Mark II or SIGABA (also known as the M-134-C in the Army and CSP-888/889 in the Navy). The device was based on an idea by Frank Rowlett and was considered insolvable, and that it was back then.

In 1924, Alexander von Kryha of Germany invented a simple spring-driven arrangement of concentric disks, which became widely used for two decades thereafter. European interests used many of the Kryha machines in banking, industrial, and transportation industries.

During World War II, the Germans used the Kryha machine and the U.S. cryptographic teams successfully analyzed intercepted diplomatic traffic. When proposed to be used in the U.S. Army, Friedman, Rowlett, Kullback, and Sinkov solved an atypically long test message of 1135 letters to demonstrate the weakness of the machine's ciphers. Statistical analysis was used extensively in the solution. The Japanese actively pursued the development of machine ciphers during the 1920s and 1930s. Their RED ORANGE and PURPLE series were wired rotor machines based on the Hebern machine and German Enigma. Their RED machine had the distinction of being the first electromechanical cipher device to be broken by the American cryptanalysts.

While the German Enigma dominated the wired rotor market, Hagelin designed a series of machines first for the French and Russian Armies (the B-211). He then came up with the idea for using variable pin rotors in conjunction with a cage of horizontal bars containing lugs to develop a new series of machines known as the "C" machines. The variations and elaborations of the "C" machines are still debated today. The most famous was the C-38 (the number indicates the year of release) which became the standard low-echelon cryptograph for both the Army (M-209) and Navy (CSP 1500).

During 1941–42, the Germans penetrated the C-38 traffic successfully in North Africa. This is why the Americans failed to maintain the tactical advantage in the earlier battles. After World War II, Hagelin ran Damm's old Swedish organization and moved it to Switzerland under the name Crypto AG. Hagelin's lug-and-pin machines were very commonly used in embassies everywhere.

After 1931, the Germans developed a series of cipher teleprinters dubbed the *Geheimschreiber* (secret writer). The story of the Polish attack, then British, then American attack on the Enigma has been well documented. The English expanded Friedman's coincidence calculations published decades earlier to attack the Enigma.

In general, Axis code breakers never scored regular penetration of the C-36 or M-209 systems. The Americans and British did a better day-to-day job on the details of cryptographic security. It has been demonstrated that failure to observe routine procedures in messages, and not changing keys, pointed to disaster. The machine ciphers of the 1930s and 1940s were often more than adequate to defeat normal cryptanalysis, if used with care.

The role of computing technology in cryptanalysis has often been to aid in the rapid location of encipherment blunders in intercepted enemy traffic. The most fruitful cryptanalysis against the Russians in the 1980s and 90s has resulted from this approach rather than from any great conceptual advances caused by the development of computers.

By 1950, the increasing appropriations and diminishing success of the U.S. cryptanalytic effort in penetrating high-level Soviet and Eastern-bloc cryptosystems forced a reorganization of the communications intelligence (COMINT) activities. At that time, there were four principal U.S. cryptanalytical agencies: the Army Security Agency (ASA), the Naval Security Group, the Air Force Security Services, and the Armed Forces Security Agency (AFSA). In practice all these groups worked independently.

President Harry Truman directed the Secretary of Defense to establish a committee to survey COMINT activities in the United States and to recommend actions. Based on this committee's report, the National Security Agency (NSA) was formed via a secret executive order of October 24, 1952. The NSA was given clear responsibility over all U.S. COMINT activities. The NSA has a military director and a civil deputy director.

Today, cryptography is virtually all electronic in the United States. There is a tendency for our newer "sci.crypt" gurus to believe those faster and faster machines and larger storage devices could change the fundamental problems facing cryptanalysts after World War II. They tend to forget that the Third World's mail is the raison d'être of NSA. These systems are usually easier to crack than those of the major powers and reveal much more information of highest priority and importance. ***The fact that cryptography is microcomputer-based does not take away some of the conflicting system design aims, just as decades ago.***

Classifications of Cipher Machines

Cryptographic principles or methods, which are too complicated for hand operation, may nonetheless be readily mechanized and become highly practical. Electrical and electromechanical cipher machines have been developed, which are capable of producing cryptograms of great complexity; these cipher machines are to be differentiated from cipher devices, which are relatively simple mechanical contrivances for encipherment and decipherment, usually hand-operated or manipulated by the fingers, such as sliding strips or rotating disks.

Circa 1930, machine cipher systems could be classified into two broad categories: (1) *literal systems,* in which the plain-text and cipher-text symbols produced or accepted are alphabetical characters and digits; and (2) *nonliteral systems,* designed for the transmission of data in which the symbols or signals produced or accepted are other than the normal alphabet and the digits (e.g., teleprinter, ciphony, cifax, civision, etc.). Literal cipher machines may be divided into two general classes of key generators and alphabet generators, or a combination of the two; nonliteral machines are usually of the key generator class.

Transposition Cipher Machines

Transposition machines were rarely encountered. Rudolf Zschweigert was granted a patent on November 12, 1920, in Germany on the first transposition cipher machine. The problems of letter storage and automatic transposing of letters within lines and the irregular displacements of the key were not easily accomplished prior to 1970.

Substitution Cipher Machines

Substitution methods lend themselves much more readily to automatic encipherment than do transposition methods. The substitution principle lends itself ideally to mechanization by cipher machines; these cipher machines range from the most primitive types, which afford only monoalphabetic substitution, to very complex types, in which the number of alphabets and the length of the keying cycle run into the millions. If the encipherment is monoalphabetic for a succession of 20 or more letters before alphabet changes, the cryptosecurity is low, especially if the various alphabets are interrelated because of their derivation from a limited number of primary components. In some cipher machines the number of secondary alphabets is quite limited, or the manner in which the mechanism operates to bring cipher alphabets into play is so ingenious that the solution of cryptograms produced by means of the machine is exceedingly difficult.

Other things being equal, the manner of shifting about or varying the cipher alphabets contributes more to the cryptosecurity than does the number of alphabets involved, or their type. It is possible to employ 26 direct-standard alphabets in such an irregular sequence as to yield greater security than is afforded by use of 1000 or more different random-mixed alphabets in a regular way or an easily ascertained method—inventors sometimes forget this principle.

Three Machine Cipher Systems

Let's briefly examine three period machines: the CSP 1500, the Enigma, and the SIGABA.

Hagelin C-38 Cipher Machine Family

Historically, in the United States the Hagelin Cryptograph is probably best known as the U.S. Army's M-209 or the U.S. Navy's CSP 1500. Later versions were designated by Hagelin as C-48. This machine was one of an array of ingenious machines invented and manufactured by a Swedish engineer, Boris Caesar Wilhelm Hagelin. The C-38 (CSP 1500 or M-209A) was a small, compact, hand-operated, tape-printing, mechanical cipher machine, weighing 6 pounds, with overall dimensions of 7.25"×5.50"×3.5". The CSP 1500, the U.S. Navy version of the Hagelin C-38 cipher machine was a typical key generator; soldiers wore the CSP 1500 on their knee and typed in a crouched position. The instructions on the box told the encipherer to destroy at all costs. Since the box was solid steel, a normal way to destroy the box was to blow it up with a hand grenade.

The cryptographic principle employed was polyalphabetic substitution. The CSP 1500 employed a complex mechanical rotor arrangement to generate a long running key which is used in conjunction with reversed standard alphabets for the primary components. In encipherment, the machine in effect subtracts (mod 26) each Θp from the key to yield the Θc, and subtracts each Θc from the key to yield the Θp. Actually, the machine adds the key to the complements of the plain or of the cipher. In Chapter 3, we used the designation of "theta," i.e., Θc, Θp, Θk for the cipher, plain, and key, to represent characters or letters without indicating its identity. So rather than "any letter of the plain text," we use the symbol Θp and so forth. Because of the subtraction feature, the C-38 and machines of similar genre have been called *letter subtractor machines*. The CSP 1500 photos (Figure 5-1) are courtesy of the National Maritime Museum. The reader is invited to visit their Web site at: *www.maritime.org/pamphome.shtml* and *www.maritime.org/csp1500.htm*.

Wheels or Rotors. The CSP 1500 has six wheels or rotors of identical diameters; these wheels have individual periods of 26, 25, 23, 21, 19, and 17. Equidistant around the peripheries of the wheels are engraved the following sequences of letters:

Rotor I or "26 wheel": ABCDEFGHIJKLMNOPQRSTUVWXYZ

Rotor II or "25 wheel": ABCDEFGHIJKLMNOPQRSTUVXYZ

Rotor III or "23 wheel": ABCDEFGHIJKLMNOPQRSTUVX

Rotor IV or "21 wheel": ABCDEFGHIJKLMNOPQRSTU

Rotor V or "19 wheel": ABCDEFGHIJKLMNOPQRS

Rotor VI or "17 wheel": ABCDEFGHIJKLMNOPQ

At each lettered position there is associated a small pin near the edge of the wheel, which pin may be pushed to the left (or "inactive position") or to the right (or "active position"). The six wheels of the CSP 1500 move one step with each encipherment or decipherment. If they are initially aligned at AAAAAA, the second alignment will be BBBBBB, the 18th

Figure 5-1
(a) CSP 1500 show-
ing M-209 style carry-
ing case, cipher
machine, small tube
containing ink pads,
screwdriver, tweez-
ers, and small tube
containing oil. The
tubes and tools all fit
inside the top cover.
(b) CSP 1500 show-
ing the top cover
and inner cover
opened.

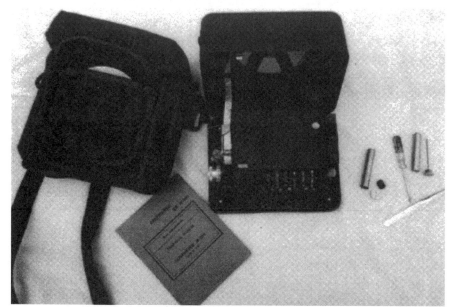

(a)

(b)

will be RRRRRA, and the 27th will be ABDFHJ. The formal name of these wheels is *variable pin rotors,* to distinguish them both from *fixed pin rotors* used in some types of cipher machines and from "wired rotors" used in electrical cipher machines.

Since the number of wheels is relatively prime to each other, the cycle of the machine will be the product $(26 \times 25 \times 23 \times 21 \times 19 \times 17)$ or 101,405,850; in other words, the wheels will not return to their initial position until after this number of letters has been enciphered.

The Squirrel Cage. Just behind the six wheels is a revolving drum something like a squirrel cage, composed of two circular retaining plates holding 27 horizontal bars, on each of which are two *lugs,* one or both of which may be set at six effective positions (corresponding to the six wheels) on the bar, or to neutral positions. The retaining plates actually had 29 slots, and in some models were equipped with 29 bars. The pins, when in the active position on a specific wheel, serve to engage those lugs which have been set opposite that wheel causing the particular bars to be displaced slightly to the left; these displaced bars act as teeth of a gear wheel, displacing the reversed standard alphabets a corresponding number of positions. In reality, an "active" pin, when it reaches the sensing or "reading" position, pushes back a key-wheel lever situated behind its wheel, and it is this lever that engages the lugs in that wheel position and causes the bars to move to the left; a lever in the forward position does not come into contact with lugs. If Rotors I–VI are aligned at the apparent or "window" setting of AAAAAA on the benchmark, the reading or effective positions of the six wheels will be at PONMLK.

The number of lugs in the path of a particular wheel is known as the *kick* of that wheel; the total kick or *key* is the sum of all the kicks contributed at a given position of the six key wheels, as governed by those key-wheel levers that are in a position to contact the lugs on the drum. When both lugs on a bar have been set to effective positions, the activity of either one or both of the wheels involved will still contribute only one kick for that bar, since the bar acts as one tooth of a gear. This situation is known as the *double lug effect,* and the amount of *overlap* (i.e., the number of displaced bars having two effective lugs) must be subtracted from the total number of lugs actuated at a given setting to ascertain the actual total key; for example, if wheels with kicks of 1, 4, and 7 are the only ones at a given position with effective kicks, and if among the bars displaced there is an overlap of 2, the total key is $(1 + 4 + 7) - 2 = 10$.

Letter Encipherment. The encipherment (or decipherment) of a letter was accomplished by obtaining the sum mod 26 of the key and the complement of the letter. For example, assuming the juxtaposition of the reversed standard alphabets to be fixed as:

Plain: Z Y X W V U T S R Q P O N M L K J I H G F E D C B A
Cipher: A B C D E F G H I J K L M N O P Q R S T U V W X Y Z

If R (plain) is enciphered at a setting of the machine where the total key is 5, the cipher equivalent is N (cipher), measured 5 intervals to the right of the complement, I: if the key were 6, E (plain) would be enciphered as B (cipher), and so forth. In the operation of the CSP 1500, the kick imparted to the type wheel is in the order of the ascending alphabet, whereas the sequence on the indicating disk moves in the reverse direction. The relative juxtaposition of the reverse standard alphabets may be varied by what is known as a *slide,* which has the effect of adding a constant to all the elements of key being generated by the machine. The slide is brought about mechanically by adjusting the relative displacement of the type wheel and the indicating disk. In the preceding example, the slide was really A = Z (= 0, mod 26). If instead of K−P = C, we express the Hagelin formula as P (bar) + (K + S) = C, where P (bar) is the complement (the complement of a number a, mod m, is $m - a$), of the plain and S is the slide, and if we use the mod 26 scale:

A B C D E F G H I J K L M N O P Q R S T U V W X Y Z
1 2 3 4 5 6 7 8 9 10 11 12 13 14 15 16 17 18 19 20 21 22 23 24 25 0

It can be seen that if R (plain) is enciphered with a kick of 7 and a slide of 22, then:

$$\text{R (bar-plain)} + (7 + 22) = (26\text{-}18) + (7 + 22) = 37 =$$
$$(11, \text{mod } 26) = \text{K (cipher)}$$

Since the CSP 1500 employed reciprocal alphabets, the operations of encipherment and decipherment were complementary; therefore, the decipherment formula was C (bar) + (K + S) = P, as shown by the example:

$$\text{K (bar-cipher)} + (7 + 22) = (26 - 11) + (7 + 22) =$$
$$44 = (18, \text{mod } 26) = \text{R (plain)}$$

Message Encipherment. The following are detailed steps performed in the encipherment of a message with the CSP 1500:

1. First, the pins and lugs are set up according to the key for the particular date. A slide is selected and is set on the machine. An initial message rotor alignment is chosen and recorded for future use. The slide and the initial alignment will be incorporated as indicator groups, which are usually included with the final cryptogram. These indicator groups are usually not sent in the clear. The letter counter is reset to a multiple of 5 and recorded; the knob is set to "C" for cipher position.

2. The first letter of the message plain text is now set on the indicating disk against a benchmark and the drive knob is given a clockwise turn. This causes the drum to make a complete revolution, imparting a kick to the print-wheel assembly equal to the number of bars which have been displaced by the action of the pins against the key-wheel levers, and the enciphered letter is printed on the tape at the end of the operating cycle. The six key wheels have moved one step each during the process, and new pins have come into contact with the key levers to set up the key for the encipherment of the next letter.

3. The succeeding plain-text letters are treated in the same fashion; at the end of every word, a fixed letter (usually Z or K) may be enciphered as a word separator. After the encipherment of every fifth letter, the machine causes the tape to advance another space so that the final cryptogram is in five-letter groups ready for transmission.

4. In decipherment, the pins and lugs of the machine are set up according to the key, and the slide and the message rotor alignment for the particular message are established from the indicators. The encipher-decipher knob is set to the "D" position, and the first letter of the cipher message is set on the indicating disk against the benchmark; when the drive knob is operated, the decipherment is printed on the tape. The "D" position also suppresses the Z plain word separator.

The Hagelin C-38 was used during World War II by the United States armed forces as a low-echelon cipher machine, under the nomenclature of M-209 in the Army and CSP 1500 in the Navy; the U.S. machines, however, were not generally equipped with a settable slide; the reversed standard alphabets were set at A = Z.

Next we examine the historical implications of the Enigma machine—perhaps the most famous rotor machine in history. It also is arguable that PURPLE was the most famous because thousands of Allied lives in the Pacific were saved; victory in the Pacific was primarily due to intercept information. The PURPLE machine is discussed in many of the references. Its lifetime was relatively short compared to Enigma, which was still in use by Third World countries into the 1950s. The Enigma solutions prevented the Nazis from getting their jets and *fliegende bombe* into mass production. It could be contended that the Nazis could have killed millions, developed the atomic bomb, and forced a negotiated peace rather than an unconditional surrender.

Enigma

Enigma was the generic term for the German machine ciphers. It was both the name of the first enciphering device and the many variations used during World War II. *ULTRA* was the British code name for intelligence derived from cracking the Enigma machine ciphers by an organization of about 10,000 staff at Bletchley Park (BP), England. The extent of the penetration of the German command structure was so profound and so pervasive that it is clear that BP's work changed not only the conduct but also the outcome of Allied European and North African Operations in World War II. Most brilliant of ULTRA successes was against the German Afrika Korps whereby the 8th Army HQ read Enigma telegrams before Rommel himself.

There exists a fair amount of material on Enigma—a few resources in the bibliography are devoted to this subject. Enigma was central to the Battle of the Atlantic in World War II. Professor Jurgen Rohwer's *Comparative Analysis of Allied and Axis Radio-Intelligence in the Battle of the Atlantic,* presents Enigma's history in eight phases.

From September 1939 to June 1940, German U-boats cruised west of the British Isles and Bay of Biscay to intercept Allied merchant ships. U-boats found enough targets. Radio signals were as indispensable to the German Commander in Chief, U-boats for directing his U-boat groups or wolf packs as they were for Allied commanders directing the convoys of merchant ships and their escorts. The aim of the Axis powers was to sever the lines of communication by surface radars, aircraft, and especially U-boats to attack ships in the convoys and thus sink more vessels and tonnage than the Allied shipbuilding yards could replace.

In the first two phases of the Battle of the Atlantic, there was a clear superiority with cryptanalytic success on the German side. Intelligence was of limited value to actual operations. The Germans introduced the short signal system, using a codebook to shorten communications to a few four-letter groups, which were superenciphered with daily settings of the *Schlussel M* (M Key) in the circuit of *Heimische Gewasser* (home waters). The Royal Navy used two cryptosystems—the first was the Naval Cipher, which used four-figure codebooks, and the second was the five-figure codebook naval code. Both used subtractor tables of 5000 groups changed monthly. B-dienst (Germany's NSA equivalent) was reading about 30 to 50 percent of the Naval Cipher, used by officers. The Merchant Navy Code was broken by the B-dienst in March 1940.

In the third phase, BP mastered the German machine known as the Schlussel M-3 and saved about 400 ships by rerouting convoys. The Schlussel M-3 used three rotors out of a stock of eight rotors. BP had no success against rotors VI–VIII and limited success against rotors I–IV.

The boarding of the German ship "Krebs" gave the British a box of five rotors. A key to Enigma is its two inner settings, the *Walzenlage,* or rotor order, and the *Ringstellung,* the setting of the alphabet rings. In addition to these were the plug board, the *Steckerverbindungen,* of ten pairs of letters and the *Grundstellung,* the starting positions of the rotors. The capture of *U-110* gave BP a consistent set of settings and grid maps to reference. The British STR (Submarine Tracking Room) became key to rerouting ships valued at 1.5 mm Gross Registered Tonnage.

Phase 4 clearly went to the Germans because of their score of ships sunk off the Americas. In Phase 5, 1942, the German BdU had many interceptions because the B-dienst decrypted the rerouting signals more effectively. The Triton was introduced and stumped BP. In March 1943, BP solved the Triton, and the British Admiralty changed the ship operation patterns.

The sixth and seventh phases: German cipher improvements were broken by use of U.S. and British high-speed computer "Bombes." The code name *bombe* was ill-chosen by the British—the Germans were listening in to their communications and the Enigma secret could have been compromised. Introduction of the German Kurier system for high-speed transmissions to new U-boat type XXI was released too late to stop operation Overlord.

Allied shipping losses were significant and import tonnage to Britain was reduced because of the U-boat success. T. J. Runyan and Jan M. Copes present details in *To Die Gallantly.*

David Kahn presents an Enigma chronology in terms of world events. A clearer picture of the effect of information derived from ULTRA cannot be found. Timelines were based on his and the honorable F. H. Hinsley's books.

Enigma was a class of machines. In *Machine Cryptography and Modern Cryptanalysis,* Cipher A. Deavours and Louis Kruh provide detailed descriptions with pictures, rotor order, settings, plug board, and their influence on frequency distribution. Numerous sources show the various Enigma variations: Dr. Klaus Brunnstein has cataloged excellent graph interface formats (GIFs) available for downloading (see Bibliography) from the online museum at University of Hamburg and at the ACA Crypto drop box site.

Electric Cipher Machine Mark II (ECM MARK II aka SIGABA)

The ECM Mark II (also known in the Navy as CSP-888/889 and SIGABA by the Army) was a cipher machine used for sensitive communications during World War II. According to the National Maritime Museum, it was used aboard the submarine, USS *Pampanito* (*SS-383*), a World War II Balao-class fleet submarine that has been preserved as a National Historical Landmark located at San Francisco's Fisherman's Wharf. *Pampanito* made six patrols in the Pacific during World War II, sank six Japanese ships, and damaged four others. It is operated by the National Maritime Museum Association. The USS *Pampanito* has its own Web site, where you can take a closer look at the many issues involved in managing a tactical submarine: *http://www.maritime.org.*

The ECM Mark II aboard *Pampanito* was provided by the Naval Security Group. After cleaning, lubrication, and minor repair it was put on display in July 1996. It is currently the only fully operable ECM Mark II in existence. This machine was built in June 1943 as a CSP-889, and sometime circa 1950, it was modified into a CSP-889-2900. The minor modifications added one switch and a knob that allow operation compatible with CSP-889 machines, or enhanced security when operated as a CSP-2900. (*CSP* stands for Code and Signal Publication; its usage started during World War I.)

In early September 1944, U.S. Fleet Radio Unit Pacific (FRUPAC) in Hawaii recorded a Japanese cipher radio message that originated from Singapore. Unknown to the Japanese, U.S. forces had analyzed many Japanese messages and as a result of much brilliant and hard work were able to cryptanalyze their enemy's inadequately designed and implemented cryptographic system. FRUPAC deciphered the message that announced the route of an important Japanese convoy from Singapore to Japan. The timing and expected path of the convoy from the message was enciphered on an ECM in Hawaii and sent to the *Pampanito* where it was deciphered on an ECM. Although *Pampanito*'s crew did not know how FRUPAC got its information, they were able to go directly to the convoy's path and attack with great efficiency. *Pampanito*'s attack was kept secret by the superior U.S. cryptographic system that revolved around the ECM Mark II.

The ECM Mark II–based cryptographic system is not known ever to have been broken by an enemy and was secure throughout World War II. The system was retired by the U.S. Navy in 1959 because it was too slow to meet the demands of modern naval communications. Axis powers (primarily Germany), however, did periodically break the lower-grade systems used by Allied forces. Early in the war (notably during the convoy battle of the Atlantic and the North Africa campaign) the breaking of Allied systems contributed to Axis success.

In contrast, the Allies were able to break Axis communications for most of the war, supplying many of the targets attacked by *Pampanito*. Intercepted messages provided not only the location of potential targets, but often insight into the thinking of enemy commanders. In the Pacific, this information was critical to success in the battles of Midway and the Coral Sea in 1942.

However, intelligence, including cryptanalysis, can be a double-edged sword. The intercepted message that directed the *Pampanito* to attack the convoy during September 1944 did not indicate that 2000 Australian and British POWs were aboard the Japanese ships.

Navy Systems. The Navy commenced World War II with three principal cryptographic systems (besides codes): (1) the ECM (for high-level communications); (2) a Hagelin cryptographic machine adapted from the C-36 (1936), the CSP 1500 (for medium-level communications); and (3) a strip cipher (for tactical-level communications and sometimes higher-level signals). The ECM was in use during Corregidor when immense quantities of enciphered poems, baseball scores, and the like, were sent to provide artificially high traffic levels to confuse the Japanese.

Army Systems. The Army used the ECM (SIGABA) and the five-rotor wired wheel M-134-A (SIGMYK), which was driven by a one-time Baudot tape to control its rotor movements. The two-tape Vernam system was also used, being later replaced by the M-228 (SIGCUM), a five-rotor teletype machine. The Hagelin C-38 (1938) (M-209) was used for tactical communications along with a variety of hand systems. The strip system was used extensively for all levels of communications.

Combined U.S.–British System—CSP 1700. During the war, communication between the United States and Britain was paramount in importance. Don Seiler of the Navy designed the adapter system for the British Typex and the U.S. ECM. It was called the CSP 1600. The hybrid machine was designated the CCM for Combined Cipher Machine, or CSP 1700. At the conclusion of World War II, the CSP 1700 was adopted by the U.S. State Department for its highest-level ciphers. It stayed in place for more than ten years.

WRAP-UP

During the period preceding World War II and up through about 1960, two interesting dimensions of cryptographic activity were witnessed. Codes for both commercial and military applications proliferated. Condensation and brevity were as important as the goal for secrecy in some of these systems. The invention of the rotor ushered in an era where machines were used to extend the security of the key(s) of established polyalphabetic cryptosystems. Three rotor machines, the CSP 1500, Enigma, and SIGABA were briefly discussed as examples of the period.

CHAPTER 6

Data Encryption Standard (DES) and Information Theory

one that has a flat distribution for all statistical properties of the cipher, implying that the redundant qualities of the natural language have been obscured.

In 1948, research performed by Shannon characterized the two main methods of uniformly distributing the redundant characteristics of a natural language. First through *diffusion,* which spreads the correlations and dependencies of the messages over substrings as long as feasible so as to maximize the *unicity* distance, which indicates the number of characters needed to determine the key. The second approach is *confusion,* where the functional dependencies of the related variables are made as complex as possible so as to increase the time needed to analyze the system. DES takes maximum advantage of both of these approaches.

The *noisy channel problem* is analogous to the problem of secure communication in cryptography—the noise corresponding to the enciphering transformation and the received message as the cipher text. The role of the sender, though, is to make the recovery of the original message as difficult as possible, if not impossible (see Figure 6-1). *Cryptographers seek to devise encryption techniques that produce cipher text that cannot be distinguished from purely random bit strings by the opponent.*

Figure 6-1
Noisy Channel

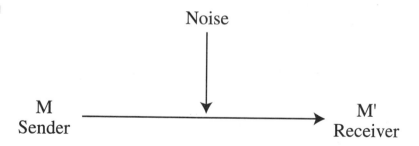

The statistical communication channel of the coding/decoding model has been replaced by a game theoretic channel; nature has been replaced by an intelligent opponent. Game theory is a mathematical theory that deals with the general features of competitive situations, placing particular emphasis on the decision-making process of adversaries.

It is not sufficient that a cryptosystem be able to thwart cryptanalysis alone. It should frustrate any aims of unauthorized parties attempting to subvert the integrity of a supposedly secure channel.

Opponent Attacks Against a Cryptosystem

The typical aims of an opponent are:

1. To determine the content of the message M

2. To alter message M to M' and have M' accepted by the receiver as a message from the transmitter of M

3. To initiate communications to a receiver and have the interloper posing as an authorized transmitter. This is also called "spoofing."

The first aim, traditionally known as the *privacy problem,* has been the focus of much research. Electronic communications has acquired a ubiquitous presence in public and private spheres. The latter two aims have become more important in systems design, and foiling these aims, known respectively as *authentication* and *repudiation,* is of equal importance.

Denning Model

A cipher is considered breakable if it is possible to determine the plain text or key from the cipher text, or to determine the key from plain text–cipher text pairs.

Dr. Dorothy Denning of Georgetown University defined four basic methods of attack to determine the adequacy of a prospective cryptosystem: (1) cipher text-only, (2) known-plain text, (3) chosen-plain text, and (4) chosen-cipher text.

Under a *cipher text-only* attack, a cryptanalyst must determine the key solely from the intercepted cipher text, through the method of encryption, the plain-text language, the subject matter of the cipher text, and certain probable words may be known.

Under a *known-plain text* attack, a cryptanalyst knows some plain text–cipher text pairs. Knowledge of probable words allows a close approximation to the known-plain text attack. Encrypted programs are particularly vulnerable because of the appearance of keywords—for example, begin, end, var, procedure, if, then. Even if the positions of these words are not known, reasonable guesses may be made.

Under a *chosen-plain text* attack, a cryptanalyst is able to acquire the cipher text corresponding to selected plain text. This is the most favorable condition for the cryptanalyst. A database system may be particularly vulnerable to this type of attack if users can insert elements into the database, and then observe the changes in the stored cipher text. This is called the *planted record problem.*

Public-key systems have introduced a fourth kind of attack: a *chosen-cipher text* attack. Although the plain text is not likely intelligible, the key may be deduced.

A cipher is *unconditionally secure* if, no matter how much cipher text is available or intercepted, there is not enough information in the cipher text to determine the plain text uniquely. With one exception, the one-time pad, all ciphers are breakable given unlimited resources, so we are more interested in ciphers that are computationally infeasible to break. A cipher is *computationally secure* or strong if it cannot be broken by systematic analysis with available computing resources or time.

Threats to Data Stored in Computer Systems

Information transmitted over electronic lines is vulnerable to passive wiretapping, which threatens secrecy, and to active wiretapping, which threatens authenticity. Passive wiretapping (eavesdropping) refers to the interception of messages, usually without detection. Active wiretapping (tampering) refers to deliberate modifications made to the message stream. Encryption protects against message modification and injection of false messages by making it infeasible for the opponent to create cipher text that deciphers into meaningful plain text. Note that, whereas it can be used to detect message modification, it cannot prevent it. Encryption does not necessarily, ipso facto, protect against replay, because an opponent could simply replay the previous cipher text. Protocols requiring acknowledgements normally prevent against intentional message deletion.

Data in computer systems are subject to similar threats. Threats to secrecy include: browsing, leakage, and inference. *Browsing* refers to searching through main memory or storage for information and confidential programs. If access controls are not employed, cipher text searching for identical information pairs may be effective. *Leakage* refers to the transmission of data to unauthorized persons by computer processes with legitimate access to the data. *Inference* refers to the deduction of confidential data about a particular subject from known or published information.

Threats to authenticity include tampering and accidental destruction. *Tampering* with data in computer systems is analogous to active wire-tapping on communication channels. *Accidental destruction* refers to the unintentional overwriting or deletion of data. Computer programs like Norton Utilities© and Nuts and Bolts© have been a great help in this area.

Computer systems are also vulnerable to another problem: *masquerading* (or spoofing), by which an intruder can gain access to a system under another user's account, thereby gaining access to all the information within that user's domain. *Digital signatures* provide a means to authenticate users and processes.

Information Theory—Shannon's Concepts

Security is directly related to the difficulty associated with the inverting encryption transformation(s) of a cryptosystem. The protection afforded by the encryption procedure can be evaluated by the uncertainty facing an opponent in determining the permissible keys used. Shannon characterized a system that has perfect security with the following property: if an opponent knows E (the encryption transformation; see Eqs. 6-1 through 6-4) and has an arbitrary amount of cipher, he/she is still left with a choice between all messages from the message space when attempting to recover the corresponding plain text for some cipher text.

Let $P_c(M)$ be the probability that a message M was sent given that C was received, with $C = E(M)$. Perfect security is defined as:

$$P_c(M) = P(M) \qquad \text{[Eq. 6-5]}$$

where $P(M)$ is the probability that message M will occur. Let $P_m(C)$ be the probability of receiving cipher text C given that M was sent. Then $P_m(C)$ is the sum of the probabilities $P(K)$ of the keys that encipher M as C:

$$P_m(C) = \sum^{K} P(K) \qquad \text{[Eq. 6-6]}$$

$$K, E_k(M) = C \qquad \text{[Eq. 6-7]}$$

where the bold $\boldsymbol{K}$ means across the space of keyspace K. Usually there will only be one key k that satisfies

$$E_k(M) = C \qquad \text{[Eq. 6-8]}$$

A necessary and sufficient condition for perfect secrecy is that for every C,

$$P_m(C) = P(C) \qquad \text{[Eq. 6-9]}$$

This means that the probability of receiving cipher text C is independent of encrypting it with plain text M. Perfect secrecy can only be assured if the length of the key is as long as the message sent, and the cardinality of the key space is the same as that of the message space. These conditions ensure that the uncertainty of the key and cipher are maintained and maximized.

Ciphers that could not be shown to have perfect secrecy but did not disclose sufficient information to allow the key to be determined, Shannon called *ideally secret*. By not revealing more information than the unicity distance, these systems were effectively unbreakable.

The opponent is faced with at least as much uncertainty with respect to the message as he/she is with the key. The only system that fits this definition is the one-time pad. The key used is a nonrepeating stream of random bits, and is discarded after each transmission. A separate key is used for each transmission as two cipher texts encrypted with the same key could be correlated. Being in possession of C adds no information to the task of recovering $M = D_k(C)$. Systems based on Shannon's equivocation are unconditionally secure, meaning the system will resist cryptanalysis even in the presence of infinite computing power. The security of the system is derived from statistical uncertainty. If $H_c(K)$, the *entropy* of the key, never approaches zero for any message length, then the cipher is considered unconditionally secure.

In devising his perfect ciphers, Shannon assumed that opponents have access to unlimited computing power. It is far from unreasonable, though, to believe that any single opponent, or cartel of opponents, except NSA, is in possession of inexhaustible computing resources. Such security measures as warranted by Shannon would appear excessive, for what they are guarding against is not a tangible threat. Modern cryptosystems look beyond uncertainty and unicity distances to establish a basis of security and, in particular, the work factor, the ratio of the complexity (Appendix C) of cryptanalyzing a system to decryption, is taken as a strong indication of a system's security. Security can be cited in terms of the number of person/computer years needed to break the system. The subtle distinction can be drawn between *perfect secrecy* and *cryptosecrecy*, the first being asymptotically defined while the latter appeals to the concept of intractability. There does not really exist a completely general method to prove a cryptosystem is cryptosecure.

Designers have come to rely upon certification by cryptanalysts, who with considerable zest attempt to compromise the system using ad hoc and heuristic measures, as an indication of a system's security. History has repeatedly shown that systems purported to be unbreakable by their inventors were demonstrated to be far less secure than thought after being scrutinized by cryptanalysts.

We have described the four basic attacks on a cryptosystem. The systems security does not depend on the concealment of its encryption transformation or algorithm. Kerckhoff's principle provides that the algorithm is available for all to examine and study. When E is revealed, a very difficult or inefficient method is also revealed to compute the inverse of E. Given the cipher text C, the cryptanalyst can examine the message space exhaustively until M is found such that $E(M) = C$. This method is also called *brute force*. Whenever a key of finite length is employed, it can always be compromised by direct search methods. The success of such an attack depends upon the work factor associated with the cipher, that is, the minimal number of computations needed to invert the system. It should be noted that the unicity distance indicates the number of characters needed to determine the key, but it makes no comment on the complexity of this task. A system can disclose more cipher text than its unicity distance considers safe but still may remain cryptosecure.

A system is considered computationally secure if the task of inverting E is computationally infeasible or intractable. You might recognize this as similar to the properties of NP (nondeterministic polynomial) problems. (Appendix C gives an additional tutorial on this subject.)

Entropy and Equivocation

Information theory measures the amount of information in a message by the average number of bits needed to encode all possible messages in an optimal encoding. For example, the sex field in a personnel database, contains only one bit of information because a 0 can represent a male and a 1 can represent a female. We could spell the words out, take up more space, but not yield more information. In computer systems, programs and text files are usually encoded in eight-bit ASCII codes, regardless of the amount of information in them. Furthermore, text files can be compressed by about 40 percent without losing any information.

The amount of information in a message is formally measured by the entropy of the message, where the *entropy* is a function of the probability distribution over the set of all possible messages.

Let $X_1,\ldots, X_n$ be n possible messages occurring with probabilities of $p(X_1),\ldots, p(X_n)$, where:

$$\sum_{i=1}^{n} p(X_i) = 1 \qquad \text{[Eq. 6-10]}$$

The entropy of a given message is defined by the weighted average:

$$H(x) = -\sum_{i=1}^{n} p(X_i) \log_2 p(X_i) \qquad \text{[Eq. 6-11]}$$

If we write this sum over all messages X:

$$H(x) = -\sum_{X} p(X) \log_2 \left[\frac{1}{Px}\right] \qquad \text{[Eq. 6-12]}$$

In the preceding example, with the $p(\text{male}) = p(\text{female}) = \frac{1}{2}$

$$H(X) = \frac{1}{2} \log_2 (2) + \frac{1}{2} \log_2 (2) = \frac{1}{2} + \frac{1}{2} = 1 \qquad \text{[Eq. 6-13]}$$

which confirms our observation that only 1 bit of information is required in the sex field of the database.

Intuitively, each term $\log_2 (1/p(X))$ represents the number of bits needed to encode message X in an optimal encoding—that is, it minimizes the expected number of bits transmitted over a channel. The weighted average $H(X)$ gives the expected number of bits in the optimally encoded message.

Because $1/p(X)$ decreases as $p(X)$ increases, an optimal encoding uses short codes for frequently occurring messages at the expense of using longer ones for infrequent messages. Morse Code applies this principle: the most frequent letters use the shortest codes.

The entropy of a message $H(M)$, also measures its uncertainty, in that it indicates the number of bits of information that must be required to recover a message distorted by a noisy channel or concealed through ciphers. The uncertainty of a message cannot exceed $\log_2 n$ bits, where n is the possible number of messages.

The rate of language r for messages of length k is defined as:

$$r = H(X)/k \qquad \text{[Eq. 6-14]}$$

which denotes the average number of bits of information in each character. For English, when k is large, r has been estimated to lie between 1.0
bits/letter and 1.5 bits/letter. The absolute rate of a language is the maximum number of bits of information that could be encoded in each character assuming all combinations of characters are equally likely. If there
are K letters in the language, then the absolute rate is given by

$$R = \log_2 K \qquad \text{[Eq. 6-15]}$$

which is the maximum entropy of the individual characters. For English, this is 4.7 bits/letter. The actual rate of English (3.2 bits/letter) is
much less as it is highly redundant, like all natural languages. Redundancy stems from the underlying structure of a language, in particular
certain letter and combinations of letters occur frequently, whereas others have a negligible likelihood of occurring (e.g., the letters E, T, A, I, N,
and O occur very frequently, as do digrams TH and EN, whereas Z and
X are infrequent). The redundancy of a language with rate r is defined
as $D = R - r$. When $r = 1$ and $R = 4.7$, the ratio D/R shows that English
is about 79 percent redundant! *We note that the more redundant a language is, the stronger the statistical relations between the letters in a
sequence.* On the other hand, if a language has no redundancy, then
occurrences of subsequent letters are statistically independent.

We can easily calculate the entropy of a single letter $H_1(M)$; also, the
entropy $H_2(M)$ of two-letter words can be found relatively easily. Unfortunately, the amount of calculation for $H_n(M)$ grows exponentially as a
function of n. The *practical redundancy* of a language is expressed as:

$$r^\infty = \text{limit } H_n(M)/n \qquad \text{[Eq. 6-16]}$$
$$n \to \infty$$
$$(\infty = \text{infinity})$$

Equivocation, defined as the conditional entropy of message M given
that cipher text C has occurred, is:

$$H_c(M) = \sum_C P(C) \sum_M P_c(M) \log_2 \left[\frac{1}{P_c(M)} \right] \qquad \text{[Eq. 6-17]}$$

where $P_c(M)$ is the conditional probability of message M given cipher
text C has occurred. Shannon measured the secrecy of a cipher with
respect to its key equivocation $H_c(K)$; for cipher text C and key K, it may
be interpreted as the degree of uncertainty in K given C, and expressed
as:

$$H_c(K) = \sum_C P(C) \sum_K P_c(K) \log_2 \left[\frac{1}{P_c(K)} \right] \qquad \textbf{[Eq. 6-18]}$$

where $P_c(K)$ is the probability of K given C. If $H_c(K)$ is zero then there is no uncertainty in the cipher, making it unbreakable.

The *unicity distance* of a cipher is defined as the minimum message length that forces $H_c(K)$ to approximate zero—so, the unicity distance of a cipher is the amount of cipher text needed to uniquely determine the key. Intuitively, as the length of the cipher text increases, the equivocation of the cipher decreases.

The equivocation of a simple cryptographic system becomes more complex as the number of messages and keys grows. The unicity distance of a cipher may be calculated or estimated, but, unfortunately, we may not be able to use this knowledge to break the cipher. Based on unicity, all ciphers can be divided into two classes:

1. The class of ciphers whose unicity distances exist and are finite.

2. The class of ciphers whose unicity distances are infinite. Ciphers of this class are unbreakable (so-called *ideal* ciphers).

Shannon defined the unicity distance of a cipher in order to be able to get some quantitative measure of:

1. The security of the cipher (if the unicity distance of a code is small then the cipher is insecure)

2. An indication of the amount of cipher text N needed to break the cipher

It is given by:

$$N \cong \frac{H(K)}{D} \qquad \textbf{[Eq. 6-19]}$$

where D is the redundancy of the language (3.2 bits per letter for English) and $H(K)$ is the information content of the key.

Symmetric Algorithms—Product Cipher

A product cipher E is the composition of t functions (ciphers) $F_1, ..., F_t$, where each F_i may be a substitution or a transposition. Rotor machines are product ciphers, where F_i is implemented by rotor R_i, $1 < i < t$. The famous Enigma machine used by Germany, Japan, and their allies were of the multiple-rotor type. A variation, the Hagelin machine, was used extensively by diplomatic posts for many years. These machines used symmetric algorithms. Both the sender and receiver knew the same secret key.

Mixing Transformations

Shannon proposed composing different kinds of functions to create *mixing transformations,* which randomly distribute the meaningful messages uniformly over the set of all possible cipher text messages.

Mixing transformations could be created, for example, by applying a transposition followed by an alternating sequence of substitutions and simple linear operations. An algorithm embodying this approach was known as LUCIFER and was designed by IBM in the early 1970s. LUCIFER used a transformation that alternately applied substitutions and transpositions. Table 6-1 shows how the principle works with some small blocks (in practice, much longer blocks are used). Table 6-1 gives a minute illustration of how substitutions and then permutations may be used to encipher using involutions only. The first three letters are substituted by removing one to the right in the alphabet and the second three letters are moved two to the right. This can be deciphered by reversing the order of the operations and applying the inverse of each substitution and permutation.

TABLE 6-1

Involution Example

	A	B	C	D	E	F
S1	B	C	D	F	G	H
P1	H	F	G	C	D	B
S2	I	G	H	E	F	D
P2	G	I	E	H	D	F

Iterated Cryptosystems

We define an *iterated cryptosystem* as part of a family of cryptographically strong functions based on iterating a weaker function n times. Each iteration is called a *round* and the cryptosystem is called an *n-round* cryptosystem. The round-function is a function of output of the previous round and a subkey, which is a key-dependent value calculated via a key-scheduling algorithm. The round-function is usually based on lookup tables (also known as S Boxes), bit permutations, arithmetic operations, and the exclusive-or operation denoted as $\oplus$.

In the late 1960s, IBM set up a research project in computer cryptography led by Horst Feistal. The project concluded in 1971 with the development of an algorithm known as LUCIFER. LUCIFER was sold to Lloyd's of London for use in cash dispensing systems, also designed by IBM. LUCIFER was a block cipher that operated on 128-bit blocks, using a key size of 128 bits. Carl Meyer and Walter Tuchman headed up an effort to make LUCIFER a commercial product that could be implemented on a single chip. They gained advice from outside consultants and NSA. The outcome of this effort was a more resistant algorithm with a shorter key size of 56 bits. It was this version that was submitted to the National Bureau of Standards (NBS) in response to an RFP (Request for Proposal) for a national cipher standard. IBM submitted the results of the Tuchman-Meyer project. It was by far the best algorithm proposed and was adopted in 1977 as the Data Encryption Standard (DES).

DES was not adopted without intense criticism. The reduced key size of 56 bits rather than the original 128 bits and the design of the S boxes (per help of NSA) were both questioned as possible political weakpoints. The debate has been healthy. DES has enjoyed many years of commercial service—especially in the financial community.

Data Encryption Standard (DES)

The *Data Encryption Standard* (DES) is an improved version of LUCIFER. DES is not, as my HAZMAT friend suggests, "a synthetic estrogen, diethylstilbestrol, used as a growth stimulant in food animals. Residues in meat are thought to be carcinogenic."

The round-function of LUCIFER had a combination of nonlinear substitution (S boxes) and a bit permutation. The input bits are divided into groups of four consecutive bits. Each group is translated by a reversible S box giving a four-bit result. The output bits of all the S boxes are permuted in order to mix them when they become input to the following round. In LUCIFER only two fixed S boxes (S_0 and S_1) were chosen. Each S box can be used at any S-box location and the choice is key dependent. For a block size of 128 bits and a 16-round cryptosystem there are 512 S-box entries for which 512 key bits are needed (for the eight-round variants, 256 key bits are needed). A key expansion algorithm that repeats each key bit four times reduces the key size to 128 bits. Decryption is accomplished by running the data backwards using the inverse of each S box.

The Data Encryption Standard is a mathematical algorithm used for the cryptographic protection of computer data. The algorithm is designed for use with binary-coded data and uses a 64-bit key to encipher 64 bits of information. The 64-bit key is of prime importance since a unique key results in the cryptographic generation of a unique set of 64 bits of cipher text from 64 bits of plain text. Since the general public knows the algorithm, the cryptographic security of the DES is dependent on the security used to protect the key. Encrypted information can be transformed into the original plain text through a reversal of the algorithm process using the same key that was employed for encryption.

The *Data Encryption Algorithm* (DEA) was designed so that 56 bits of the 64-bit key are used for the encryption process and the remaining 8 bits are used only for parity error-detecting bits. The key is divided into eight 8-bit bytes (8 bits = 1 byte). In an 8-bit byte, 7 bits are used by the algorithm and the eighth bit can be used to maintain odd parity to form a complete 64-bit block of plain text enciphered with a 56-bit key.

Overview of DEA

DEA incorporates the following steps to encipher a 64-bit message (block of data) using a 64-bit key:

1. A transposition operation, referred to as the *initial permutation* (IP). This transposition does not use the 64-bit key and operates solely on the 64 data bits.

2. A complex key-dependent product transformation that uses block ciphering to increase the number of substitution and reordering patterns.

3. A final transposition operation, referred to as the *inverse initial permutation* (IP^{-1}), which is an actual reversal of the transformation performed in the first step.

The three major steps for DEA are shown in Figure 6-2.

The IP and IP^{-1} are simple bit transpositions; the product transformation is fairly complex. Product transformations are successive applications of substitution and transposition ciphers. Large blocks of data are transformed as a unit, providing the advantage of increasing the

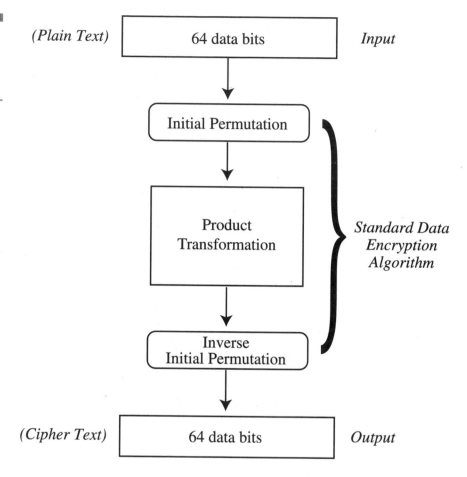

number of substitutions and reordering patterns. This is also called *block ciphering*.

In the product-ciphering step of DEA, the block-cipher substitutions are under the control of a cipher key while transpositions are performed according to a fixed sequence. Figure 6-3 depicts one iteration of the product transformation, which includes the following operations:

1. The 64-bit block of plain text is divided into two 32-bit blocks, denoted by L_i and R_i for the left and right halves, respectively.

2. The rightmost 32 bits of the input block become the leftmost 32 bits of the output block.

3. The rightmost 32 bits of the input block, R_{i-1}, goes through a selection process yielding 48-bit data block. This is a fixed selec-

Figure 6-3
Overview of One Iteration of the Computations in the Product Transformation of the Standard Data Encryption Algorithm

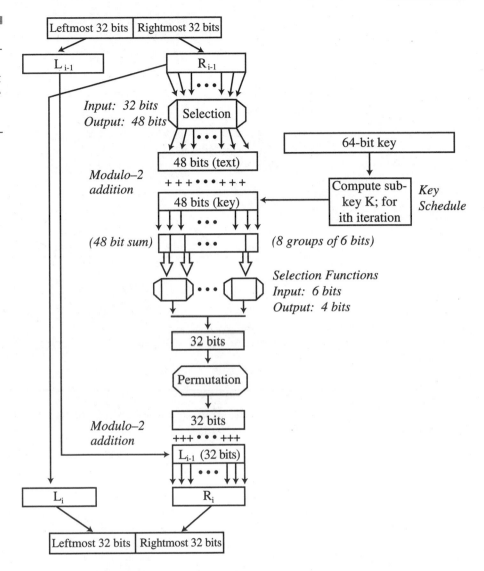

tion and it is not key dependent (called an *expansion permutation*).

4. The 64-bit key is used to generate a 48-bit subkey K_n, where $1 < n < 16$. Each K_i is unique and corresponds to the iteration of the product transformation.

5. The 48-bit subkey is added (modulo 2) to the output of step 3 yielding a 48-bit result (called XORed $\oplus$).

6. The 48-bit output of step 5 is divided into eight 6-bit groups, which are each subjected to a unique substitution cipher that yields eight 4-bit groups, which in turn are concatenated to form a 32-bit output.

7. The 32-bit output of step 6 is permuted by simple transposition to produce a 32-bit block.

8. The 32-bit output of step 7 is added modulo 2 to the leftmost 32 bits of the input block, denoted L_{i-1}, yielding R_i, which is the rightmost 32 bits of the 64-bit output block.

Steps 1–8 are repeated 16 times; this constitutes the major part of the product transformation. The last step is a block transformation (i.e., exchange) of the left and right halves of the output of the last iteration.

The deciphering process is the exact reversal of the encipherment process, in reverse order, K_{16} to K_1.

Components of the Decryption Algorithm

There are six components that make up the DEA:

1. The key schedule calculations, which generate 16 subkeys

2. The XOR or modulo-2 addition $\oplus$

3. The cipher function, which comprises the main operations in the product transformation

4. The block transposition that yields the "preoutput block," which serves as input to the inverse initial permutation

5. The initial permutation, described as a selection table

6. The inverse initial permutation, described as a selection table

Key Schedule Calculations

The key schedule calculations generate 16 subkeys, referred to as K_n, required for enciphering and deciphering processes. Each K_n is 48 bits long and is derived through the use of permutation, selection, and shifting operations. The bits are numbered 1–64, going from left to right. Parity bits are numbered 8, 16, 24, 32, 40, 48, 56, and 64, leaving the following bits for key schedule computations:

■ 1 through 7

- 9 through 15
- 17 through 23
- 25 through 31
- 33 through 39
- 49 through 55
- 57 through 63

The key schedule calculations are executed as follows:

1. The nonparity bits in the key go through a permutation operation yielding two 28-bit blocks denoted by C_0 and D_0. This is the starting point for computing the subkeys.
2. C_0 and D_0 are circularly left shifted one place, yielding C_1 and D_1.
3. Selected bits from C_1 and D_1 are tapped off, yielding subkey K_1.
4. C_1 and D_1 are circularly left shifted one place, yielding C_2 and D_2.
5. Selected bits from C_2 and D_2 are tapped off, yielding subkey K_2.
6. The process continues for subkeys K_3 through K_{16}. Each C_i and D_i is obtained from the preceding value after a prescribed number of circular left shifts.

The key schedule calculations are summarized in Figures 6-4 a, b, and c. Each subkey, denoted by K_i, is obtained through a selection operation from C_i and D_i. C_i and D_i are obtained from C_{i-1} and D_{i-1}, respectively, through prescribed shift operations.

Initially, C_0 and D_0 are obtained from the 64-bit key with permuted choice 1, which is summarized in Table 6-2 and Figure 6-5.

The cipher key active bits used to determine C_0 are 57, 49,..., 36, and so forth. Similarly, the bits of D_0 are, respectively, bits 63, 55,..., 4 of the cipher key.

Permuted choice 2 is used to select a particular key K_n from the concatenation of C_n and D_n. C_n and D_n are 28 bits long so that $C_n D_n$ combined has bits that run from 1–56 (Figure 6-6).

The number of circular left shifts for each iteration in the key schedule calculation are shown in Table 6-2.

Cipher Function

The *cipher function* (Figure 6-7) comprises the main operations in the product transformation $f(A, K_n)$ where A is a string of 32 data bits repre-

Figure 6-4(a)
Summary of the Key
Schedule Calculations

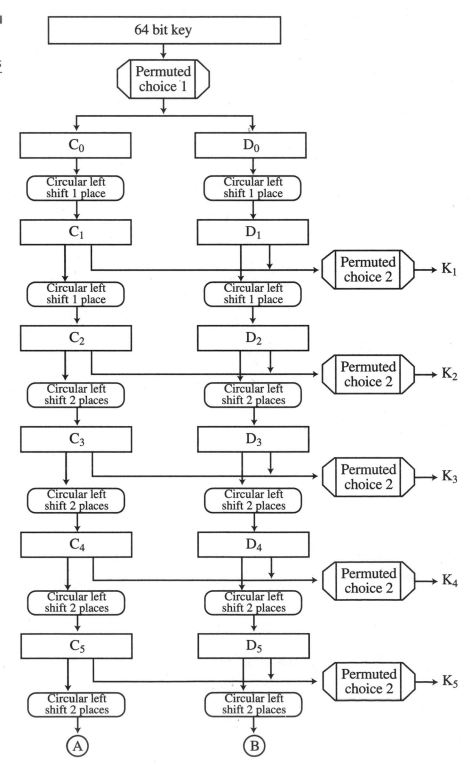

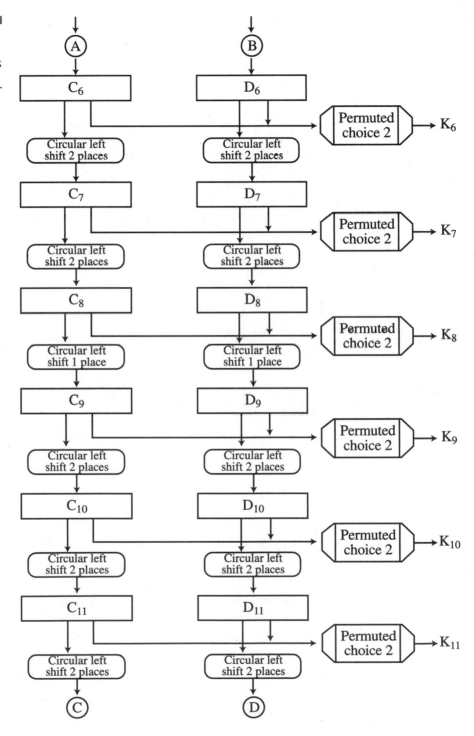

Figure 6-4(c)
Summary of the Key
Schedule Calculations
(*Continued*)

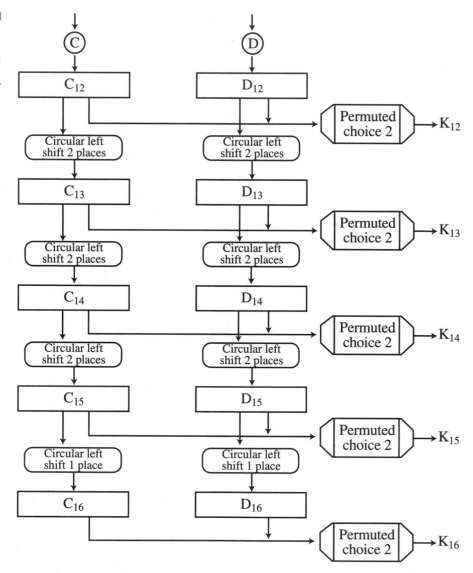

senting R_i for encryption or L_i for decryption, and K_n is a 48-bit subkey determined by the key schedule.

The cipher function combines the following operations:

1. A selection operation E that operates on the argument A of 32 bits and produces a 48-bit result.

2. An XOR addition that adds the result of the selection operation E and the 48-bit key K_n on a bit-by-bit basis, yielding a 48-bit result.

Figure 6-5
Permuted Choice 1,
Used in the Calcula-
tion of C_0 and D_0

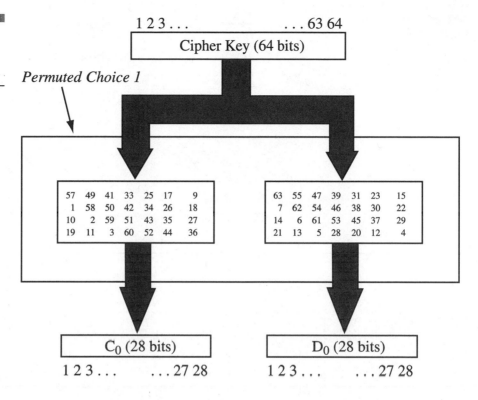

3. A unique set of selection functions S_i that converts the 48-bit result of step 2 to a set of 32 bits.

4. A permutation operation P that operates on the result of step 3 and produces a 32-bit result.

The selection operation function E shown in Figure 6-8, yields a 48-bit result wherein the bits of the result are respectively 32, 1, 2,..., 1, and so on, of the symbolic argument A, which may represent R_i or L_i depending on the function.

S Boxes

The unique set of selection functions S_i take a 6-bit block as input and yield a 4-bit result. A selection function is represented by a 4×16 matrix of numbers used in a prescribed manner (see Figure 6-9).

Input to the unique S Boxes 1–8 (selection functions S_i) is a 48-bit block, denoted symbolically as $B_1B_2B_3B_4B_5B_6B_7B_8$. Each B_i contains 8

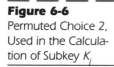

Figure 6-6
Permuted Choice 2,
Used in the Calculation of Subkey K_i

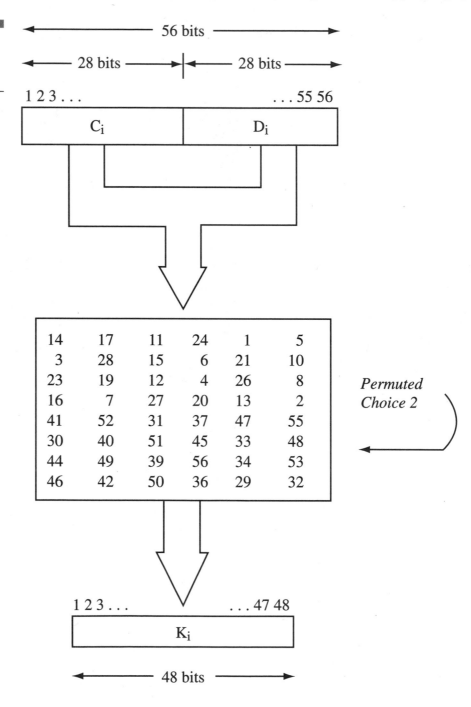

TABLE 6-2

Key Schedule
Calculation

Iteration	# of Circular Left Shifts
1	1
2	1
3	2
4	2
5	2
6	2
7	2
8	2
9	1
10	2
11	2
12	2
13	2
14	2
15	2
16	1

bits. S_1 is used for B_1, and so on. The result of the selection of S_i with B_i as an argument $S_i(B_i)$ is computed:

1. The first and last bits of B_i represent a binary number in the range of 0–3, denoted m.

2. The middle four bits of B_i represent a binary number in the range of 0–15, denoted n.

3. Using zero-origin indexing, the number located in the mth row and nth column of the S_i's matrix is selected as a 4-bit binary block.

4. The result of step 3 is the output of the selection function S_i.

The output of a complete set of selection functions is a bit string:

$$S_1(B_1)S_2(B_2)S_3(B_3)S_4(B_4)S_5(B_5)S_6(B_6)S_7(B_7)S_8(B_8)$$

Each of the S_i's is a 4-bit output.

Table 6-3 gives the matrices corresponding to the selection function S_1 through S_8.

The output of the set of eight selection functions S_1 through S_8 is a string of 32 bits. This 32-bit output goes through a permutation operation P that yields a 32-bit result and completes the cipher function. P does not complete the algorithm, but only the cipher function denoted by $f(A, K_n)$. This final permutation in the cipher function is given in Figure

Figure 6-7

Overview of Cipher
Function

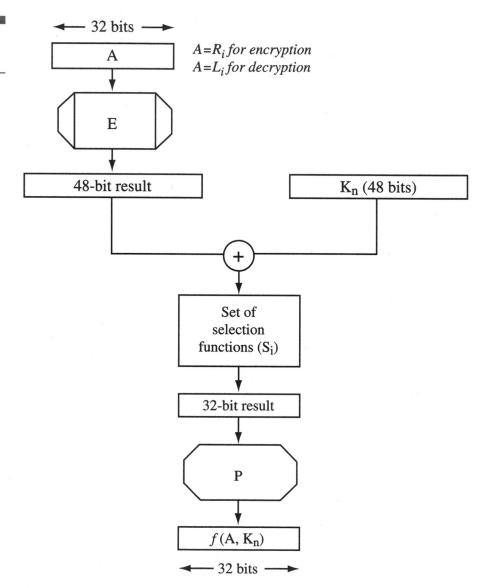

6-10. The permutation operation *P* yields a 32-bit result, wherein the bits of the result are 16, 7, and so on, of the 32-bit result of the set of selection functions.

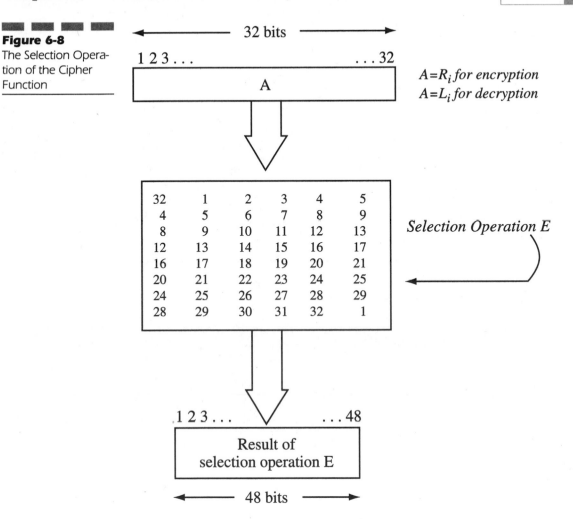

Figure 6-8
The Selection Opera-
tion of the Cipher
Function

Preoutput Block

The output of the last iteration in the product transformation goes through a block transformation, yielding a 64-bit result called the *pre-output block* (Figure 6-11). It is a simple exchange of R_{16} and L_{16}. The bits of R_{16} are followed by the bits of L_{16} and constitutes a 64-bit block, with bits numbered from 1–64, from left to right.

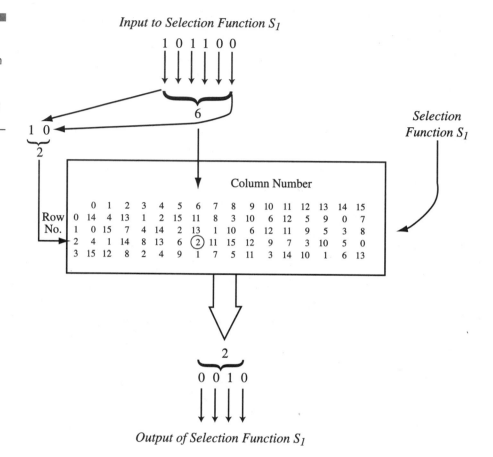

Input to Selection Function S_1

Output of Selection Function S_1

Initial Permutation (IP)

The *initial permutation* (IP) is the first step in the standard data encryption algorithm and is a key-independent permutation, as shown in Figure 6-12. The output of the IP are respectively, bits 58, 50,..., 2 and so on, of the plain-text input to the block. The result of the IP is a 64-bit block. The leftmost 32 bits constitute L_0 and the rightmost 32 bits constitute R_0. L_0 and R_0 are the initial input blocks to the product transformation.

TABLE 6-3

Matrices for the
Selection Functions
S_1 Through S_8

S_1

14	4	13	1	2	15	11	8	3	10	6	12	5	9	0	7
0	15	7	4	14	2	13	1	10	6	12	11	9	5	3	8
4	1	14	8	13	6	2	11	15	12	9	7	3	10	5	0
15	12	8	2	4	9	1	7	5	11	3	14	10	0	6	13

S_2

15	1	8	14	6	11	3	4	9	7	2	13	12	0	5	10
3	13	4	7	15	2	8	14	12	0	1	10	6	9	11	5
0	14	7	11	10	4	13	1	5	8	12	6	9	3	2	15
13	8	10	1	3	15	4	2	11	6	7	12	0	5	14	9

S_3

10	0	9	14	6	3	15	5	1	13	12	7	11	4	2	8
13	7	0	9	3	4	6	10	2	8	5	14	12	11	15	1
13	6	4	9	8	15	3	0	11	1	2	12	5	10	14	7
1	10	13	0	6	9	8	7	4	15	14	3	11	5	2	12

S_4

7	13	14	3	0	6	9	10	1	2	8	5	11	12	4	15
13	8	11	5	6	15	0	3	4	7	2	12	1	10	14	9
10	6	9	0	12	11	7	13	15	1	3	14	5	2	8	4
3	15	0	6	10	1	13	8	9	4	5	11	12	7	2	14

S_5

2	12	4	1	7	10	11	6	8	5	3	15	13	0	14	9
14	11	2	12	4	7	13	1	5	0	15	10	3	9	8	6
4	2	1	11	10	13	7	8	15	9	12	5	6	3	0	14
11	8	12	7	1	14	2	13	6	15	0	9	10	4	5	3

S_6

12	1	10	15	9	2	6	8	0	13	3	4	14	7	5	11
10	15	4	2	7	12	9	5	6	1	13	14	0	11	3	8
9	14	15	5	2	8	12	3	7	0	4	10	1	13	11	6
4	3	2	12	9	5	15	10	11	14	1	7	6	0	8	13

S_7

4	11	2	14	15	0	8	13	3	12	9	7	5	10	6	1
13	0	11	7	4	9	1	10	14	3	5	12	2	15	8	6
1	4	11	13	12	3	7	14	10	15	6	8	0	5	9	2
6	11	13	8	1	4	10	7	9	5	0	15	14	2	3	12

S_8

13	2	8	4	6	15	11	1	10	9	3	14	5	0	12	7
1	15	13	8	10	3	7	4	12	5	6	11	0	14	9	2
7	11	4	1	9	12	14	2	0	6	10	13	15	3	5	8
2	1	14	7	4	10	8	13	15	12	9	0	3	5	6	11

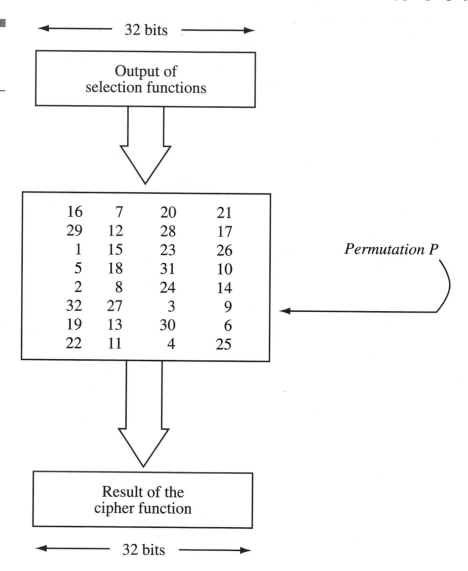

Figure 6-10
Permutation Operation *P* of the Cipher Function

Inverse Initial Permutation (IP⁻¹)

The output of the product transformation is the preoutput block, which is subjected to a permutation—the inverse of the IP. The IP⁻¹ is shown in Figure 6-13. The output of IP⁻¹, which is synonymously the cipher text output of the algorithm, is bits 40, 8, ..., to 25 of the preoutput block.

Figure 6-11
Block Transformation
Yielding the Preout-
put Block

Figure 6-11
Block Transformation
Yielding the Preout-
put Block

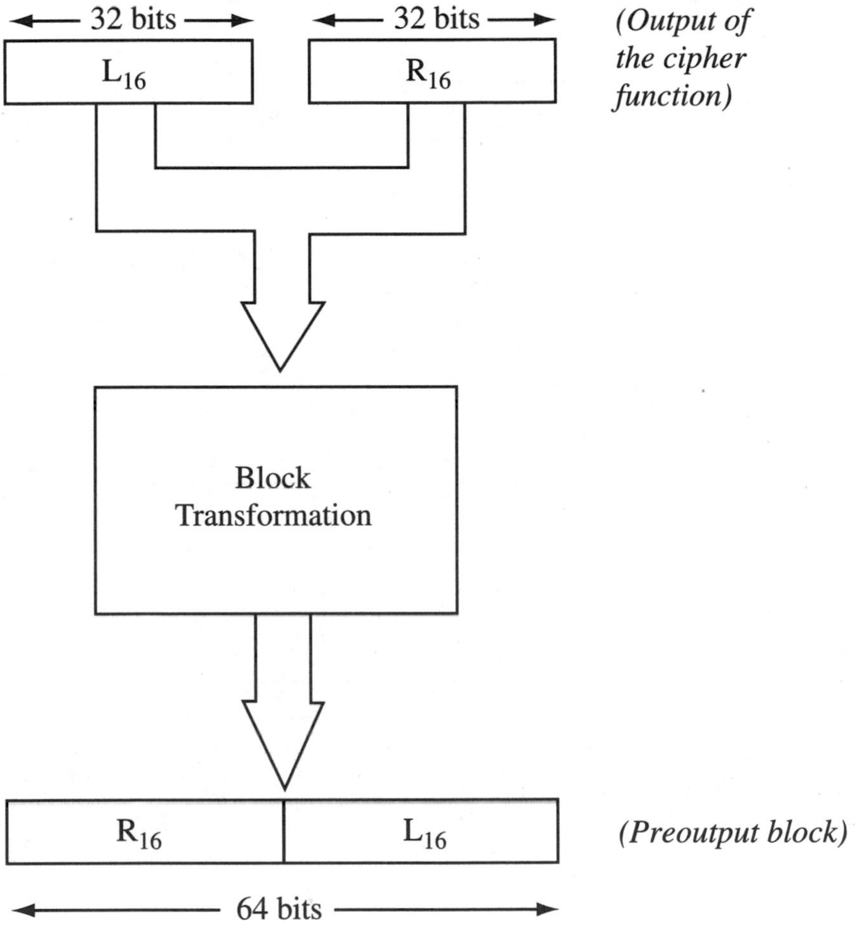

The 64-bit cipher text output of the DEA can be used as a string of data bits for transmission or storage, or may be converted back into BCD characters for further processing.

The Enciphering Process

The *enciphering process* can be summarized symbolically: Given two blocks L and R and using the convention that LR denotes the block consisting of bits of L followed by bits of R, the initial permutation (IP) is specified as:

Figure 6-12
The Initial Permutation (IP)

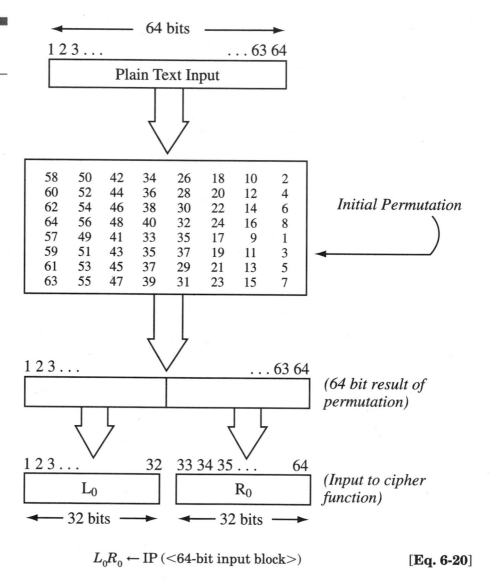

$$L_0R_0 \leftarrow \text{IP} (<\text{64-bit input block}>) \qquad \text{[Eq. 6-20]}$$

Let KS denote the key schedule calculations, where the function KS yields a 48-bit subkey K_n for input arguments n and KEY, where KEY is a 64-bit cipher key; it follows that:

$$K_n \leftarrow KS(n, \text{KEY}) \qquad \text{[Eq. 6-21]}$$

denotes the calculation of subkey K_n.

The 16 iterations in the product transformation that use the cipher function are then represented symbolically as:

Figure 6-13
The Inverse Initial Permutation (IP⁻¹)

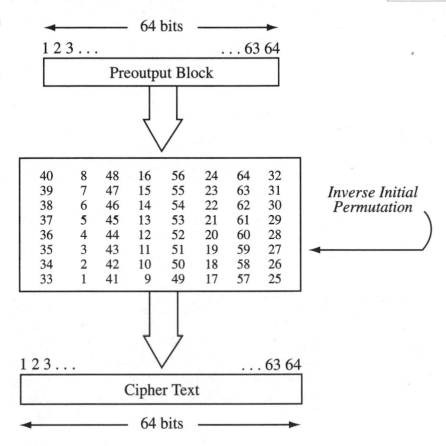

Figure 6-13
The Inverse Initial Permutation (IP⁻¹)

$$L_n \leftarrow R_{n-1} \qquad \text{[Eq. 6-22]}$$

$$R_n \leftarrow L_{n-1} \oplus f(R_{n-1}, K_n) \qquad \text{[Eq. 6-23]}$$

and f is the cipher function and $\oplus$ denotes bit-by-bit modulo-2 additions L_n and R_n are computed as n goes from 1 to 16. The preoutput block is $R_{16}L_{16}$ and the result of the DEA is specified as:

$$\text{<64-bit cipher text>} \leftarrow \text{IP}^{-1}\,(R_{16}L_{16}) \qquad \text{[Eq. 6-24]}$$

The enciphering equations are summarized in Table 6-4.

TABLE 6-4

Summarization of the Enciphering and Deciphering Equations

<table>
<tr><th colspan="2">Enciphering Equations</th></tr>
<tr><td>$L_0 R_0 \leftarrow$ IP (<64-bit input block>)</td><td>**[Eq. 6-25]**</td></tr>
<tr><td>$L_n \leftarrow R_{n-1}$</td><td>**[Eq. 6-26]**</td></tr>
<tr><td>$R_n \leftarrow L_{n-1} \oplus f(R_{n-1}, K_n)$</td><td>**[Eq. 6-27]**</td></tr>
<tr><td><64-bit cipher text> $\leftarrow$ IP^{-1} ($R_{16} L_{16}$)</td><td>**[Eq. 6-28]**</td></tr>
<tr><th colspan="2">Deciphering Equations</th></tr>
<tr><td>$R_{16} L_{16} \leftarrow$ IP (<64-bit cipher text>)</td><td>**[Eq. 6-29]**</td></tr>
<tr><td>$R_n \leftarrow L_n$</td><td>**[Eq. 6-30]**</td></tr>
<tr><td>$L_{n-1} \leftarrow R_n \oplus f(L_n, K_n)$</td><td>**[Eq. 6-31]**</td></tr>
<tr><td><64-bit plain text> $\leftarrow$ IP^{-1}($L_1 R_1$)</td><td>**[Eq. 6-32]**</td></tr>
</table>

The Deciphering Process

The process of deciphering a 64-bit cipher text message block involves the same algorithm as encipherment, as stated in FIPS publication 46 (Data Encryption Standard, U.S. Department of Commerce, National Bureau of Standards, FIPS publication 46, January 15, 1977, p. 10):

> ...to decipher it is only necessary to apply the very same algorithm to an enciphered message block, taking care that at each iteration of the computation the same block of key bits K is used during decipherment as was used during the encipherment of the block.

This is precisely the case because the IP and IP^{-1} are by definition inverses of each other.

Applying the notation given earlier, the result of the initial permutation (IP) is:

$$R_{16} L_{16} \leftarrow \text{IP}(<\text{64-bit cipher text}>) \qquad \textbf{[Eq. 6-33]}$$

where the expression takes the final block transformation into consideration. The 16 iterations in the product transformation are represented:

$$R_{n-1} \leftarrow L_n \qquad \textbf{[Eq. 6-34]}$$

$$L_{n-1} \leftarrow R_n \oplus f(L_n, K_n) \qquad \textbf{[Eq. 6-35]}$$

TABLE 6-5

Avalanche Effect in DES

	Change in Plain Text	Change in Key
Round	No. of Bits That Differ	No. of Bits That Differ
0	1	0
1	6	2
2	21	14
3	35	28
4	39	32
5	34	30
6	32	32
7	31	35
8	29	34
9	42	40
10	44	38
11	32	31
12	30	33
13	30	28
14	26	26
15	29	34
16	34	35

TABLE 6-6

DES Weak Keys in Hex

Weak Key Value (with parity bits)				Actual Key	
0101	0101	0101	0101	0 0 0 000 0	0 000 000
1F1F	1F1F	0E0E	0E0E	0 0 0 000 0	FFFFFFF
E0E0	E0E0	F1F1	F1F1	FF FFFFF	0 0 000 000
FEFE	FEFE	FEFE	FEFE	FF FFFFF	FFFFFFF

DES Semiweak Key Pairs

01FE	01FE	01FE	01FE	and	FE01	FE01	FE01	FE01
1FE0	1FE0	0EF1	0EF1	and	E01F	E01F	F10E	F10E
01E0	01E0	01F1	01F1	and	E001	E001	F101	F101
1FFE	1FFE	0EFE	0EFE	and	FE1F	FE1F	FE0E	FE0E
011F	011F	010E	010E	and	1F01	1F01	0E01	0E01
E0FE	E0FE	F1FE	F1FE	and	FEE0	FEE0	FEF1	FEF1

original DES key is split in half and each half is shifted independently, if all the bits are 0s or 1s, then the key used for any cycle is the same for all cycles: $K_1 = K_2 = K_2 = K_i = K_n$. Additionally, some pairs of keys encrypt plain text to the identical cipher text. This is due to the key generation mechanism in DES. Instead of generating 16 different subkeys, these keys generate only two different subkeys. Each of these subkeys is used eight times in the algorithm. We label these *semiweak keys*. A simi-

The XOR has the following properties:

$$[A \oplus B] \oplus C = A \oplus [B \oplus C] \qquad \textbf{[Eq.}$$

$$D \oplus D = 0 \qquad \textbf{[Eq.}$$

$$E \oplus 0 = E \qquad \textbf{[Eq.}$$

where the L_n and R_n are computed as n goes from 16 to 1. The res
the decipherment is then specified:

$$<\text{64-bit plain text}> \leftarrow IP^{-1}(L_0 R_0) \qquad \textbf{[Eq.}$$

Avalanche Effect

The key effect of the DEA is the *avalanche effect*. A desirable proper
any encryption algorithm is that a small change in the plain text sh
produce a large effect in the cipher text. A change in one bit of the
text or one bit of the key should produce a change in many bits o
cipher text. DES exhibits a strong avalanche effect. We have seen
in the E operation (expansion permutation) the right half of the da
is expanded from 32 bits to 48 bits. Because this operation changes
order of the bits as well as repeating certain bits, it is a true expan
permutation. This operation has two purposes: it makes the result
same size as the key for the XOR operation, and it provides a lo
result that can be compressed during the substitution operation.

Neither of these is its main cryptographic purpose, though. By al
ing one bit to affect two substitutions, the dependency of the output
on the input bits spreads faster. This is called the *avalanche crite
Much of DES's design revolves around reaching as quickly as poss
the condition of having every bit of the cipher text depend on every b
the plain text and every bit of the key. Meyer notes that statistical
put dependency is reached after just five rounds of DES. Konheim
Table 6-5) suggests eight rounds are required to reach full output de
dency of the data.

Weak Keys

Because of the way the initial key is modified to get a subkey for e
round of the algorithm, certain keys are *weak keys* (Table 6-6). Since

lar problem occurs when some keys produce only four subkeys and are used only four times in the algorithm. The total number of possibly weak keys is 64 out of 72,057,594,037,927,936 possible keys. Selecting a random key, the odds of picking 1 out of the 64 are worse than winning the Texas lottery twice in a month.

Modes of DES

FIPS Publication 74-81 defines four modes of operation that cover virtually all the possible applications of encryption for which DES could be used. Table 6-7 summarizes them.

TABLE 6-7

DES Modes of Operation

Mode	Description	Typical Application
Electronic Codebook (ECB)	Each block of 64 plain-text bits is encoded independently using the same key.	Secure transmission of single values (e.g., an encryption key)
Cipher Block Chaining (CBC)	The input to the encryption algorithm is the XOR of the next 64 bits of plain text and the preceding 64 bits of cipher text.	General-purpose block-oriented transmission
Cipher Feedback (CFB)	Input is processed J bits at a time. Preceding cipher text is used as input to the encryption algorithm to product pseudo-random output, which is XORed with plain text to produce next unit of cipher text.	Authentication
Output Feedback (OFB)	Similar to CFB, except that the input to the encryption algorithm is the preceding DES output.	Stream-oriented transmission over noisy channel (e.g., satellite communication)

ECB Mode

The *electronic codebook* (ECB) mode is relatively uncomplicated. The plain text is handled 64 bits at a time and each block is encrypted using the same key (Figure 6-14). The term *codebook* may be used because there is a unique cipher text for each 64-bit of plain text. Messages rarely

Figure 6-14
Electronic Codebook
(ECB) Mode

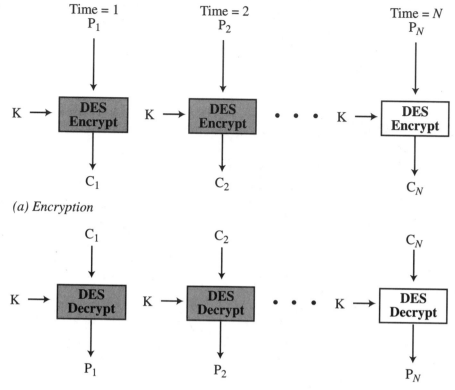

(a) Encryption

(b) Decryption

fit into 64 bits; longer messages are simply broken into 64-bit blocks, padding the last block if necessary. ECB has an exploitable flaw. Plain text repeats always are reproduced in the cipher-text form for the same 64-bit blocks. This particular flaw can be exploited using cryptanalysis. This author does not recommend using ECB because of this flaw.

CBC Mode

The *cipher block chaining* (CBC) mode (Figure 6-15) improves on the ECB mode by ensuring that same plain text blocks produce different cipher text blocks, enciphered by the same key. The input to the encryption algorithm is XORed with the preceding cipher text block; the same key is used for each block. We effectively chain together the processing of the plain-text blocks. Repeating 64-bit patterns are not exposed. Decryption is simply the reverse of encryption. To produce the first cipher text, an initialization vector (IV) is XORed with the first block of

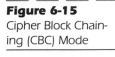
Figure 6-15
Cipher Block Chaining (CBC) Mode

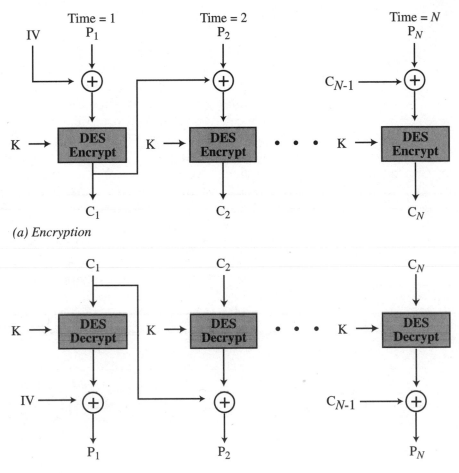

(a) Encryption

(b) Decryption

plain text. Both sender and receiver must know the IV. The IV may be the weak point in the CBC mode of operation. Stallings discusses spoof and inversion attacks on the IV. Lastly, CBC mode may be used for authentication. Descriptive equations for the CBC mode are as follows:

$$C_n = E_K[C_{n-1} \oplus P_n] \qquad \text{[Eq. 6-40]}$$

$$D_K[C_n] = D_K[E_K(C_{n-1} \oplus P_n)] \qquad \text{[Eq. 6-41]}$$

$$D_K[C_n] = C_{n-1} \oplus P_n \qquad \text{[Eq. 6-42]}$$

$$C_{n-1} \oplus D_K[C_n] = C_{n-1} \oplus C_{n-1} \oplus P_n = P_n \qquad \text{[Eq. 6-43]}$$

CFB Mode

The DES scheme is essentially a block cipher technique that uses 64-bit blocks. However, it is possible to convert DES into a stream cipher, using either the *cipher feedback* (CFB) or the *output feedback* (OFB) mode. A stream cipher eliminates the need to pad a message to be an integral number of blocks. It also can operate in real time. Thus, if a character stream is being transmitted, each character can be encrypted and transmitted immediately using a character-oriented stream cipher.

One desirable property of a stream cipher is that the cipher text be of the same length as the plain text. Thus, if 8-bit characters are being transmitted, each character should be encrypted using 8 bits. If more than 8 bits are used, transmission capacity is wasted.

Figure 6-16 depicts the CFB scheme. In the figure, it is assumed that the unit of transmission is j bits; a common value is $j = 8$. As with CBC, the units of plain text are chained together, so that the cipher text of any plain-text unit is a function of all the preceding plain text.

First, consider encryption. The input to the encryption function is a 64-bit shift register that is initially set to some initialization vector (IV). The leftmost (most significant) j bits of the output of the encryption function are XORed with the first unit of plain text P_1 to produce the first unit of cipher text C_1, which is then transmitted. In addition, the contents of the shift register are shifted left by j bits, and C_1 is placed in the rightmost (least significant) j bits of the shift register. This process continues until all plain-text units have been encrypted.

OFB Mode

The *output feedback* (OFB) mode is similar in structure to that of CFB, as illustrated in Figure 6-17. As can be seen, it is the output of the encryption function that is fed back to the shift register in OFB, whereas in CFB the cipher text unit is fed back to the shift register.

One advantage of the OFB method is that bit errors in transmission do not propagate. For example, if a bit error occurs in C_1, only the recovered value of P_1 is affected; subsequent plain-text units are not corrupted. With CFB, C_1 also serves as input to the shift register and therefore causes additional corruption downstream.

The disadvantage of OFB is that it is more vulnerable to a message-stream modification attack than is CFB. Consider that complementing a bit in the cipher text complements the corresponding bit in the recov-

Figure 6-16
J-Bit Cipher Feedback
(CFB) Mode

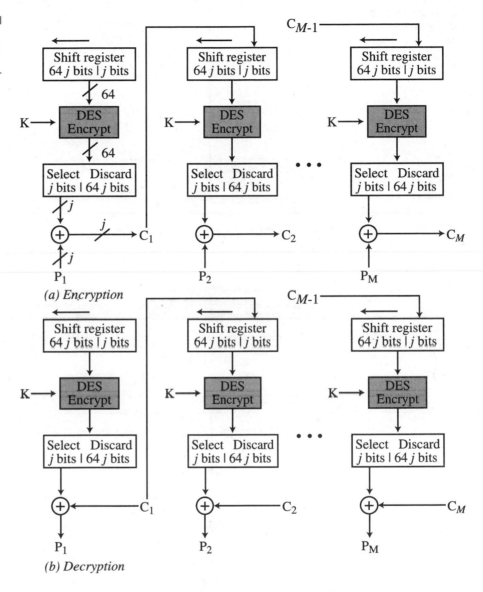

(a) Encryption

(b) Decryption

ered plain text. Thus, controlled changes to plain text can be made. However, most error-correction codes will pick up on such modifications.

Over the years, DES has been a very practical cryptosystem. Its 56-bit key potential vulnerability to brute force attack has forced many to look at multiple encryption schemes using DES to increase its cryptographic strength. Figure 6-18 shows multiple encryption schemes for DES.

Figure 6-17
J-Bit Output Feed-
back (OFB) Mode

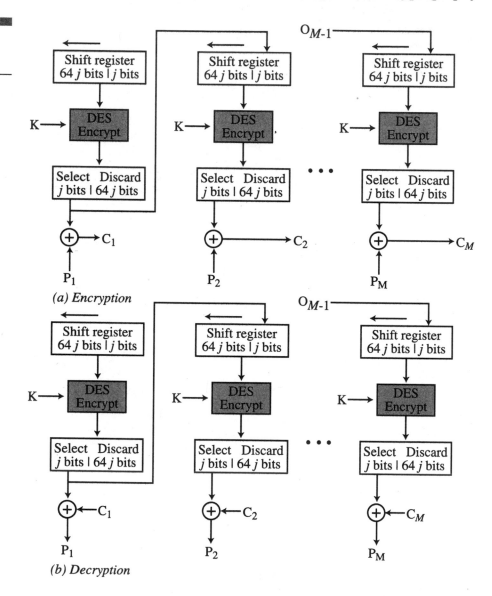

(a) Encryption

(b) Decryption

Double DES

Double DES has two encryption stages and uses two keys. Given a plain text P and keys K_1 and K_2, cipher text C is generated in this fashion:

$$C = E_{k2}[E_{k1}(P)]$$

[**Eq. 6-44**]

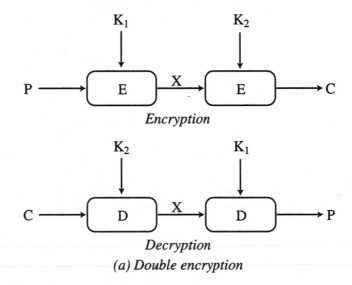

Encryption

Decryption

(a) Double encryption

Encryption

Decryption

(b) Triple encryption

Decryption is performed in reverse order:

$$P = D_{k1}[D_{k2}(P)] \qquad \qquad \textbf{[Eq. 6-45]}$$

Double DES is vulnerable to the famous man-in-the-middle (MIM) attack described by Winfield Diffie in 1977. His attack will work on almost any block cipher and is not dependent on any property of DES. The MIM was described as:

$$C = E_{k2}[E_{k1}(P)]$$ [Eq. 6-46]

and

$$X = E_{k1}(P) = D_{k2}(C)$$ [Eq. 6-47]

The MIM attack is a known plain-text attack. Given a known plain/cipher pair (P,C), P is enciphered for all 2^{56} possible values of K_1. The results are sorted and stored by values of X. Next C is decrypted using all 2^{56} possible values of K_2. As each decryption is produced, the results are checked against the first table for a match. If there is a match, a test is made against a new known plain/cipher text pair. If the two keys produce the correct cipher text, then accept the keys as the correct keys. Double DES in effect uses a 112-bit key and for any given plain text there are 2^{64} possible cipher text values that can be produced via double DES. Stallings shows that the probability that the correct keys are determined is $1-2^{-16}$. He feels that the MIM would succeed against double DES with an effort of the order of 2^{56}.

Triple DES

An obvious approach to defeat the MIM attack is to make it too costly to perform efficiently. One option is *triple DES,* with three keys with the effective key size at $56 \times 3 = 168$ bits and the cost of the plain text attack at about 2^{112}. Tuchman described a better alternative and just as effective—triple DES with two keys.

Triple DES with Two Keys (3DES)

The sequence of 3DES is EDE, or encrypt-decrypt-encrypt:

$$C = E_{k1}[D_{k2}[E_{k1}(P)]]$$ [Eq. 6-48]

3DES is very popular and has been adopted for use in the key management standards ANS X9.17 and ISO 8732, and for Privacy Enhanced Mail (PEM). 3DES is very strong and has survived the theoretical attacks designed by such researchers as Merkle and Oorshot. Both theoretical attacks set up plain-text pairs that reduce to either a zero alternative or the double DES problem.

Set of DES

DES is a secret-key, symmetric cryptosystem: when used for communication, both sender and receiver must know the same secret key, which is used both to encrypt and decrypt the message. DES can also be used for single-user encryption such as to store files on a hard disk in encrypted form. In a multiuser environment, secure key distribution may be difficult; public-key cryptography was invented to solve this problem. DES operates on 64-bit blocks with a 56-bit key, and works well for bulk encryption, that is, for encrypting a large set of data.

NIST has recertified DES as an official U.S. government encryption standard every five years; DES was last recertified in 1993, by default. NIST has indicated, however, that it will not recertify DES after 1997. NIST has asked for public submissions/comments on development of the Advanced Encryption Standard (AES). Submissions may be studied at *www.nist.aes.gov.*

In April 1998, Ron Rivest on behalf of RSA Laboratories submitted an advanced encryption system to NIST for evaluation. The future should be very interesting. DES has never *officially* been cracked, despite the efforts of many researchers over many years. The obvious method of attack is a brute-force exhaustive search of the key space; this takes 2^{55} steps on average. Early on it was suggested by cryptographer Michael Wiener of Bell-Northern Research that some country could build a special-purpose computer capable of breaking DES by exhaustive search in a reasonable amount of time. Later, Hellman demonstrated a time-memory trade-off that allowed improvement over exhaustive search if memory space was plentiful, after an exhaustive precomputation. These ideas fostered doubts about the security of DES. There were accusations that the NSA had intentionally weakened DES. Despite these suspicions, no feasible way to break DES faster than exhaustive search was discovered.

In 1991, the cost of a specialized computer to perform exhaustive search was estimated by Michael Wiener at $1 million and could find a DES key, on average, in about 3.5 hours. Michael Wiener updated his study in 1998 and published his results in RSA's *Cryptobytes* publication. In 1998 dollars and technology, today's version of Wiener's million-dollar machine could find a 56-bit DES key in about 35 minutes. It would use 57,600 specialized key search chips, each chip capable of testing 50 million keys per second.

The first attack on DES that was better than exhaustive search was announced by Eli Biham and Adi Shamir using a technique known as *differential cryptanalysis*. This attack required encryption of 2^{47} chosen plain texts, that is, plain texts chosen by the attacker. Although a theoretical breakthrough, this attack is not practical under normal circumstances because it requires the attacker to have easy access to the DES device in order to encrypt the chosen plain texts. Another attack, known as *linear cryptanalysis*, does not require chosen plain texts.

Differential Cryptanalysis and Linear Cryptanalysis

Both linear and differential analysis require obtaining enormous numbers of known-plain text pairs to be feasible. This is not practical in most environments. Linear cryptanalysis is possible in a cipher text-only environment if some of the underlying plain-text redundancy is known such as the parity or higher-order 0 bits in ASCII.

Differential cryptanalysis is, in this author's opinion, one of the most general cryptanalytic tools to date against modern iterated block ciphers such as DES or FEAL. However, it is a chosen-plain text attack. Menezes (Table 6-8) showed how DES strength fared against various attacks.

TABLE 6-8

DES Strength
Against Various
Attacks

Attack Method	Data Complexity		Storage Complexity	Processing Complexity
	Known	Chosen		
Exhaustive precomputation	—	1	2^{56}	1 (table lookup)
Exhaustive search	1	—	Negligible	2^{55}
Linear cryptanalysis	2^{43} (85%)	—	For texts	2^{43}
	2^{43} (10%)	—	For texts	2^{50}
Differential cryptanalysis	—	2^{47}	For texts	2^{47}
	2^{55}	—	For texts	2^{55}

To be meaningful, attack comparisons based on different models (e.g., Table 6-8) must appropriately weigh the feasibility of extracting (acquiring) enormous amounts of chosen (known) plain texts, which is considerably more difficult to arrange than a comparable number of computing cycles on an adversary's own machine. Exhaustive search with one known plain text–cipher text pair and 2^{55} DES operations is significantly more feasible in practice (e.g., using highly parallelized custom hardware) than linear cryptanalysis (LC) requiring 2^{43} known pairs.

Menezes suggested that although exhaustive search, linear, and differential cryptanalysis allow recovery of a DES key and, therefore, the entire plain text, the attacks which become feasible once in about 2^{32} cipher texts may be more efficient if the goal is to recover only part of the text.

The consensus is that DES, when used properly, is moderately secure against all but the most powerful players. In fact, triple encryption DES with three keys may be secure against anyone at all. DES is used extensively in a wide variety of cryptographic systems, and in fact, most vendor implementations of public-key cryptography include DES or 3DES at some product level.

How secure is DES today? *It is not.* Two commonly suggested ways to thwart key search attacks and enhance DES security are (1) avoiding known plain text and (2) making frequent key changes. The first may be difficult to achieve. At least three vendor products tested by ICSA leave fixed-byte known file headers. As little as 2 bits of redundancy can be used to reduce the number of overall key searches.

A commonly suggested way to avoid key search attacks is to change the DES key frequently. The assumption is that the encrypted information is stale after the key is changed. If it takes 35 minutes to find a DES key, why not change the keys every 5 minutes. The fallacy of logic that exists is that it does not take 35 minutes to find a key. The actual time is distributed between 0 and 70 minutes. The 5-minute window represents a $5/70 = 1/14$ probability of success. This turns out to be a factor of 2 in run time and a poor substitute for a strong algorithm with longer keys.

Winn Schwartau writes that the NSA built a massively parallel DES-cracking machine as early as the mid-1980s. Both contextual and statistical attacks might reduce the DES's effective key size. NSA has giant databanks of plain and cipher text to preperform the statistical calculations on and then go out to an array of optical disks and retrieve the key. If you believe the popular fictions of Chris Davis in *Death by Fire,* NSA's "Allo" group has already been busy cracking 56-bit DES by brute force for some time.

Diffie pointed out that many systems in use today have either 40-bit keys (which can be searched easily) or 56-bit keys (which can be searched with difficulty). *Dragging key* (looking through all possible keys) thus has a role to play in contemporary cryptanalysis. A far more subtle, but also universal, cryptanalytic method is the *Berlekamp-Massey algorithm*. It is a fact that any sequence of bits (keystream) whatsoever can be generated by a linear shift register of sufficient length. The Berlekamp-Massey algorithm automatically produces the right register. A major design criterion in modern cryptography is that the "right register" be too long for this approach to be practical. Diffie also feels that NSA's intercept equipment is quite effective. Under a deal between NSA and the Software Publisher's Association, some cryptographic systems with 40-bit keys can be rather freely exported when embodied in "mass-market software." Since modern computer workstations can execute 2^{40} instructions in an hour, 40-bit keys do not represent very much security from a commercial viewpoint. On the other hand, it is unlikely that intercept devices, which are comparable in price to high-end workstations, can do any better. Since decisions about intercept must be made not in hours, but in fractions of a second, it is prudent to presume that NSA knows how to break the ciphers in question with a work factor substantially less than 2^{40}.

Dan Ryan at SAIC provided some interesting data (Table 6-9). Incorporating specialized hardware, field programmable gate arrays (FPGA), and application-specific integrated circuits (ASIC), we can estimate that the effort to crack a 56-bit DES key by a government entity is measured in seconds.

TABLE 6-9

Key Strength

| | | | Time to Break | |
Threat	Budget	Technology	40 Bits	56 Bits
Hacker	Tiny	Scavenged time	1 week	Infeasible
Small Business	$10K	FPGA	12 min	556 days
Corporation	$300K	FPGA or ASIC	24 sec	19 days
Big Corp.	$10M	FPGA or ASIC	.7 sec	13 hours
Government	$300M	ASIC	.0002 sec	12 sec

FPGA = Field Programmable Gate Array
ASIC = Application Specific Integrated Circuits

EFF DES Cracker Machine

In July 1998. The Electronic Frontier Foundation (EFF) announced their DES Cracker project. EFF organized and funded a project to build a specialized DES Cracker for less than $250,000. The full story can be found at their site: *www.eff.org/pub/Privacy/Crypto_misc/DESCracker/HTML*

The actual machine has only 1500 specialized chips working in parallel to search all the DES key space. The EFF DES Cracker first solved the Matt Blaze (renowned cryptographer for AT&T Labs) problem of finding a key that permitted matching pairs of plain text and cipher text numbers consisting of nothing but repeated digits. It found that a hexadecimal key of 0E 32 92 32 EA 6D 0D 73 turns a plain text of 8787878787878787 into a cipher text 0000000000000000. The DES Cracker's second problem was to win the DES-cracking speed contest sponsored by RSA Laboratories in July 1998, beating out the combined efforts of massively parallel software from *www.distributed.net*. It found a 56-bit key in 56 hours by searching about 24.8 percent of the key space, or 88 billion keys tested per second.

This is impressive evidence that developers of cryptographic products should not design anything else that depends on single DES. It also suggests that developers should remove this option from cryptographic service. A stronger algorithm is three-key–3DES. It uses the same block size, the same hardware, three keys, and runs DES three times (encrypting each block with the first key, decrypting it with the second, and then encrypting it with the third). The 3DES effective key size is 168 bits. The strength of 3DES is substantially stronger and, looking at the profile in Chapter 21, is as close to white noise (random) as possible.

In June 1998, NSA released its most secret algorithm, SKIPJACK, to the public. It is an 80-bit algorithm. NSA has guarded this algorithm jealously, and it has been used in the secret Clipper chips. These signs cannot be ignored. DES is no longer secure and is at serious risk! EFF suggests minimum safe key sizes of 90 bits. This author suggests that 120 bits or more is more reasonable.

DES is being replaced at various levels. The financial community is about to deliver their #DES X9F1 standard. NIST has accepted 24 designs for the Advanced Encryption Standard. Half of these crypto-designs are from sources not in the United States. The IETF standards include 3DES and RC5. The IPSEC standards still specify DES, but optionally put 3DES in the forefront.

WRAP-UP

DES represents the turning point from classical to modern cryptographic systems. DES has its foundations in information theory and represents a complex combination of the mathematical operations available up to the 1950s. DES has survived for a long time but the fat lady is warming up her vocal chords. Modern attacks on single DES (such as the EFF DES Cracker) have invalidated its use for commercial purposes. Three-key 168-bit triple DES represents a more secure approach for commercial purposes.

DES is a natural randomizer. The avalanche criteria is perhaps the most important cryptographic effect of DES. DES modes of operation set the stage for all modern cipher operations and variants. The 56-bit key size is the DES weak link and multiple encryption methodologies have been suggested to improve the security of the DES cryptosystem. Modern day attacks have invalidated the 56-bit key length for DES but DES is still offered in most cryptographic products. The call for an AES by NIST, the NSA public announcements on SKIPJACK, and the EFF DES Cracker are flags that cannot be ignored. We should strive to use the best encryption available to us with the longest key.

Commercial Cryptographic Systems

CHAPTER 7

Public-Key (Asymmetric) Cryptography

When we think about the historical cryptosystems presented in Part 1, we find no difficulties in the decryption process for the cryptanalyst who has learned the encryption method. Knowing the encryption method provided us with a starting wedge for cracking the system. The primary goal of the symmetric (classical) cryptosystems was secrecy. The encryption and decryption keys coincide even in the sophisticated DES system. In one view, publicizing the encryption method essentially gives away the secrets being protected.

There are cryptosystems in which you can publicize the encryption method and still have security. The cryptanalyst has the system but is unable to crack it. This is what public-key cryptography is about—the encryption method can be made public. Another name for this form of cryptography is *asymmetric cryptography* because two different keys are employed—one by the sender and one by the receiver.

In 1974–1975, Whitfield Diffie and Martin Hellman, working at Stanford University, and Ralph Merkle, at the University of California at Berkeley, discovered the new concept in cryptography that was to have profound implications on the technology. They published their revolutionary idea to *safely* give away the encryption method. The idea was brilliant; we had the birth of a new cryptography. Giving "away" the encryption method essentially gives away the decryption method because they are mathematical inverses of each other. However, the difference for public-key methods is the *work factor* required to compute the decryption method. Suppose it takes hundreds of years for a cryptanalyst to compute the decryption method from the encryption method. We haven't compromised the cryptosystem even though we have released the system to the public—this is a measure of safety. Tables 6-8 and 6-9 in the previous chapter showed the relative work factors required to compromise 40- and 56-bit DES keys as a function of investment and technology.

Complexity theory is the branch of mathematics that deals with the complexity of various computations. It helps us understand how much time it will take to make those computations using state-of-the-art computer horsepower. Appendix C gives a short tutorial on complexity theory and is recommended reading prior to the next sections.

One-Way Functions

In mathematics, as in real life, there exist one-way streets. It is easy to go along the street from A to B, whereas it is practically impossible to go from B to A. Encryption is viewed as the direction of flow from A to B.

Although you are able to travel in this direction, this does not enable you to go in the opposite direction, that is, to decrypt.

As an example, take your local telephone book. It's easy to find the number of a friend. On the other hand, it is difficult, but not impossible to find your friend given the number. But now add all the telephone books in the United States to the pile. Two complications occur: (1) possible duplications yielding mixed decryptions and (2) lots of work to find the appropriate name–telephone number combination. If we look at this as a public-key system, we make the encryption context free and letter by letter. For each letter of the plain text, a name beginning with that letter is chosen at random from the directory. The corresponding telephone number constitutes the encryption of that occurrence of the letter in question.

The system is polyalphabetic and nondeterministic in nature. An enormous number of cipher texts may result from the same plain text. Table 7-1 shows an example of this simple scheme, which shows a possible encryption of COME AT ONCE. The entire cipher text is obtained by writing, one after the other, all the numbers (or a part of them), in the right column; they are written in the order indicated.

TABLE 7-1

Telephone Book
Encryption Scheme

Plain Text	Name Chosen	Cipher Text
C	Corning	5674564
O	Oldre	4509128
M	Murdock	7612345
E	Edwards	1098787
A	Arthur	6653458
T	Tomas	6690344
O	Oliviat	9912345
N	Nuberry	1245663
C	Calley	7740986
E	Everst	7858883

Cipher text starts: 5674564 4509128 7612345 ...

The legal receiver has CD ROMs or directories listed according to the increasing order of the number. Such a reverse directory facilitates the decryption process and represents a *secret trapdoor* known only to the legal users of the system. Without knowledge of the trapdoor—that is, possession of the reverse directory—the cryptanalyst has a difficult time. This is in spite of the fact that the cryptosystem has been publicized and he/she knows how to interpret the number sequences intercepted. Exhaustive search is likely to take too long and depends on the currency of the directories.

Intractability

The study of public key cryptography is closely related to the idea of one-way functions. Given argument of value x, it is easy to compute function value $f(x)$, whereas it is intractable to compute x from $f(x)$; $f(x)$ can be a function or any of a range of nondeterministic encryption methods such as the telephone directory hypothetical. *Intractability* is further defined in the section covering complexity theory in Appendix C. The situation is depicted in Figure 7-1.

Figure 7-1
Intractability

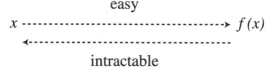

The computation of x from $f(x)$ should be intractable for the cryptanalyst only. The legal receiver should have a trapdoor available. This type of service is referred to as employing a cryptographic one-way function. In summary, cryptographic one-way functions $f(x)$ may exhibit two qualities:

1. It is easy to compute $f(x)$ from x.

2. Computations of x from $f(x)$ are likely to be intractable.

No proof is known for the intractability claimed for in 2. This reflects the fact that it is very hard to establish lower bounds in complexity theory. From the point of view of public-key cryptography, functions satisfying 1 and 2 are quite sufficient. In a typical public-key cryptosystem, only the straightforward cryptanalysis is based on computing x from $f(x)$. It is possible for the cryptanalyst to crack the system even if we show that the computation of x from $f(x)$ is intractable.

Salomaa, in his text *Public-Key Cryptography,* gives an excellent example defining one-way functions. A problem is termed intractable if there is no algorithm for the problem, operating in polynomial time (refer to Appendix C for a helpful tutorial). If there is such an algorithm, the problem is termed *tractable. Easy* refers to problems possessing an algorithm operating in low polynomial time. NP-complete problems are considered intractable. To say that $f(x)$ is one-way means that the transition from x to $f(x)$ is easy and the reverse transition from $f(x)$ to x is intractable. The second requirement is often replaced by a lesser condition: the reverse transition is likely to be intractable. A good illustration of mathematical intractability is found in an important class of problems known as *knapsack* problems. Understanding the knapsack problem helps us to understand the general principles underlying public-key cryptography.

Knapsack Problem

The knapsack problem may be defined as follows: Given the row vector (also called an n-tuple of distinct positive integers, and another positive integer k:

$$A = (a_1, a_2, \ldots, a_n) \qquad \text{[Eq. 7-1]}$$

The problem is to find, if possible, such integers a_i whose sum equals k. Intuitively, k indicates the size of the knapsack and each of the numbers a_i indicates the size of a particular item that can be packed into the knapsack (Figure 7-2). The problem is akin to an optimization problem. We must find the right items to make the knapsack full.

Figure 7-2
Knapsack Graphic

Filling the Knapsack

As an illustration, consider the row vector of length 10:

Let $A = (43, 129, 215, 473, 903, 302, 561, 1165, 697, 1523)$ **[Eq. 7-2]**

Let $k = 3231$ **[Eq. 7-3]**

We observe that a solution is:

$$3231 = 129 + 473 + 903 + 561 + 1165 \qquad \text{[Eq. 7-4]}$$

In principle, a solution can always be found by checking through all subsets of A and finding out whether one of them sums up to k. In the preceding example, this means $2^{10} = 1024$ subsets. This count includes even the empty subset. A more difficult problem would be, say, 300 a_i's. A search of 2^{300} subsets is definitely unmanageable. The knapsack problem is known to be NP-complete.

Our A vector defines a function $f(x)$ as follows. Any number x in the interval $1 \leq x \leq 2^n - 1$ can be given a binary representation consisting of n bits—we add leading zeros if necessary. Thus, 1, 2, and 3 are represented as 0...001, 0...010, and 0...011; 1...111 represents $2^n - 1$. We now define $f(x)$ to be the number obtained from A by summing up all the numbers a_i such that the corresponding bit in the binary representation of $x = 1$.

$$f(1) = f(0...001) = a_n \qquad \textbf{[Eq. 7-5]}$$

$$f(2) = f(0...010) = a_{n-1} \qquad \textbf{[Eq. 7-6]}$$

$$f(3) = f(0...011) = a_{n-1} + a_n \qquad \textbf{[Eq. 7-7]}$$

Using vector multiplication, we write

$$f(x) = AB_x \qquad \textbf{[Eq. 7-8]}$$

where B_x is the binary representation of x as a column vector.

Table 7-2 shows the natural encoding of the English alphabet.

Consider encrypting the phrase SAUNA AND HEALTH. We break the plain text into groups of 10 bits each, for a block division of our plain text:

SA UN Aspace AN Dspace HE AL TH

From Table 7-2 the corresponding eight sequences of bits are:

- 1001100001
- 1010101110
- 0000100000
- 0000101110
- 0010000000
- 0100000101
- 0000101100
- 1010001000

TABLE 7-2

Natural Encoding
of the English
Alphabet

Letter	Number	Binary Notation
Space	0	00000
A	1	00001
B	2	00010
C	3	00011
D	4	00100
E	5	00101
F	6	00110
G	7	00111
H	8	01000
I	9	01001
J	10	01010
K	11	01011
L	12	01100
M	13	01101
N	14	01110
O	15	01111
P	16	10000
Q	17	10001
R	18	10010
S	19	10011
T	20	10100
U	21	10101
V	22	10110
W	23	10111
X	24	11000
Y	25	11001
Z	26	11010

These sequences are the argument values of $f(x)$. The cipher text vector is:

$$(2942, 3584, 903, 3326, 215, 2817, 2629, 819)$$

Using Eq. 7-2, we derive the original k solution vector as:

$$f(364) = f(0101101100) = 129 + 473 + 903 + 561 \\ + 1165 = 3231 \qquad \text{[Eq. 7-9]}$$

and functions values related to the plain text:

$$f(609) = f(1001100001) = 43 + 473 + 903 + 1523 = 2942 \qquad \text{[Eq. 7-10]}$$

[first element in the cipher vector]

$$f(686) = f(1010101110) = 43 + 215 +$$
$$903 + 561 + 1165 + 697 = 3584 \qquad \text{[Eq. 7-11]}$$

$$f(32) = f(0000100000) = 903 \qquad \text{[Eq. 7-12]}$$

$$f(46) = f(0000101110) = 903 + 561 + 1165 + 697 = 3326 \qquad \text{[Eq. 7-13]}$$

$$f(128) = f(0010000000) = 215 \qquad \text{[Eq. 7-14]}$$

$$f(261) = f(0100000101) = 129 + 1165 + 1523 = 2817 \qquad \text{[Eq. 7-15]}$$

$$f(44) = f(0000101100) = 903 + 561 + 1165 = 2629 \qquad \text{[Eq. 7-16]}$$

$$f(648) = f(1010001000) = 43 + 215 + 561 = 819 \qquad \text{[Eq. 7-17]}$$

These knapsack vectors can be used for both a classical and public-key cryptosystem. The task of the cryptanalyst is to solve the basic A vector, and hence the knapsack problem. The goal of the system designer is to make illegal decryption immensely harder to solve than for the legal receiver. Furthermore, the decryption must be unique. This means, in our example, no two different sums formed from the entities of A should be equal. The number of elements may be the same but each entry can be used only once. The vector (17, 103, 50, 81, 33) does not have this property. The corresponding cipher-text vector (131, 33, 100, 234, 33) decrypts with some ambiguity to either SAUNA or FAUNA.

Our example can be improved by specifying that the knapsack be made up of superincreasing elements (or n-tuples). Vector A is superincreasing if each number exceeds the sum of the preceding numbers. So:

$$a_j \sum_{i=1}^{j-1} a_i \qquad for \ j = 2,\ldots, n \qquad \text{[Eq. 7-18]}$$

Exhaustive search is not required to solve this knapsack problem. It suffices to scan through A once from right to left. An algorithm might be: given k (the size of the knapsack) we find out if $k \geq a_n$. If yes, then we define:

$$k_1 = k \text{ if } k < a_n; \qquad k_1 = k - a_n \text{ if } k \geq a_n \qquad \text{[Eq. 7-19]}$$

The procedure is carried out for k_1 and a_{n-1} for all elements through a_1. The algorithm shows for k: the knapsack has one solution, providing A is superincreasing.

The level of difficulty of the knapsack may be transformed (scrambled) by modular multiplication. We choose an integer $m > \Sigma a_j$. Since we have defined A as superincreasing, m is large in comparisons with all numbers in knapsack vector A. Another integer t, with no common factors with m, is chosen; m and t are called the *modulus* and the *multiplier*, respectively. The choice of t guarantees that there exists another integer t^{-1} such that:

$$tt^{-1} \equiv 1(\text{mod } m) \qquad \text{[Eq. 7–20]}$$

The integer t^{-1} is regarded as the *multiplicative inverse*. It can be easily computed from t and m.

We form the products ta_i, $i = 1,..., n$ and reduce them modulo m. Let b_i be the least positive remainder of ta_i modulo m. The resulting vector is

$$B = (b_1, b_2,..., b_n) \qquad \text{[Eq. 7-21]}$$

and it is *publicized* as the encryption key. The encryption is performed on blocks of plain text consisting of n bits each.

The items t, t^{-1}, and m are kept as the *secret trapdoor*. Before comparing the situation from the point of legal receiver and cracker, let's finish the decryption details. The B vector (A renamed) is:

$$B = (43, 129, 215, 473, 903, 302, 561, 1165, 697, 1523) \qquad \text{[Eq. 7-22]}$$

It is obtained by modular multiplication with $m = 1590$ and $t = 43$ from the superincreasing knapsack vector:

$$A = (1, 3, 5, 11, 21, 44, 87, 175, 349, 701) \qquad \text{[Eq. 7-23]}$$

Verifying: the first five elements are obtained from the corresponding numbers in A by direct multiplication with 43—no reduction with respect to modulus is necessary. The next five elements are calculated:

$$43 * 44 = 1892 = 1590 + 302 \qquad \text{[Eq. 7-24]}$$

$$43 * 87 = 3741 = 2 * 1590 + 561 \qquad \text{[Eq. 7-25]}$$

$$43 * 175 = 7525 = 4 * 1590 + 1165 \qquad \text{[Eq. 7-26]}$$

$$43 * 349 = 15007 = 9 * 1590 + 697 \qquad \text{[Eq. 7-27]}$$

$$43 * 701 = 30143 = 1590 * + 1523 \qquad \text{[Eq. 7-28]}$$

Observe that t and m have no common factors.

$$43 * 37 = 1591 \equiv 1(\text{mod } 1590) \qquad \text{[Eq. 7-29]}$$

and

$$tt^{-1} \equiv 1(\text{mod } m) \qquad \textbf{[Eq. 7-30]}$$

Hence, the inverse

$$t^{-1} = 37 \qquad \textbf{[Eq. 7-31]}$$

The decryption method for the legal receiver must be easy as compared to the interloper (cryptanalyst) who must have an immensely more difficult job to decrypt the message. Since A was defined as an superincreasing vector and B is found from A by multiplying each number in A with $t(\text{mod } m)$. The legal receiver knows t^{-1} and m (the inverse and modulus); he or she is able to find the plain-text equivalents A from the public key B. This is done as follows.

After receiving a cipher text block c', which is an integer, the legal receiver calculates $(t^{-1})c'$ and its smallest positive remainder $c(\text{mod } m)$. To decrypt, he or she solves the easy knapsack problem defined by A and c. The solution is a unique sequence p of n bits. It is also a correct block of plain text because any solution p' of the knapsack problem defined by B and c' must equal p. Here's why:

$$c \equiv (t^{-1})c' \text{ [inversion for each cipher text element]} \qquad \textbf{[Eq. 7-32]}$$

and

$$c' = Bp' \qquad \textbf{[Eq. 7-33]}$$

So:

$$c \equiv (t^{-1})c' = (t^{-1})Bp' \qquad \textbf{[Eq. 7-34]}$$

The cipher-text block elements are computed from the public key and the claimed solution for the knapsack problem. The plain-text vector A and solution p' are congruent for the public key B and modulus t:

$$(t^{-1})Bp' \equiv (t^{-1})tAp' \qquad \textbf{[Eq. 7-35]}$$

By definition of an inverse, $(t^{-1})t = 1(\text{mod } m)$

$$(t^{-1})tAp' \equiv Ap'(\text{mod } m) \qquad \textbf{[Eq. 7-36]}$$

and finally,

$$c = Ap'(\text{mod } m)$$

provided:

$$m > a_1 + a_2 + a_3 + \ldots + a_n$$

Since the knapsack has only one solution, $p = p'$.

Let's complete the solution of our example. The c' vector defined from the bit representation was:

$$(2942, 3584, 903, 3326, 215, 2817, 2629, 819)$$

We multiply by $t^{-1} = 37$ and we obtain for the first element:

$$37 \times 2942 = 108854 = 68 \times 1590 + 734 \equiv 734 \ (\text{mod } 1590) \qquad \textbf{[Eq. 7-37]}$$

Continuing, we get the plain-text vector:

$$(734, 638, 21, 632, 5, 879, 283, 93)$$

From the plain-text vector and the superincreasing A, we can convert back into a binary sequence. The number 734 is 1001100001. Since 734 > 701, the last bit is 1. The numbers in A are now compared to the difference $734 - 701 = 33$. Going from right to left, the first number smaller than 33 is 21. The next number is 11 and is smaller than the difference $33 - 21 = 12$. The first number 1 equals the difference of $12 - 11$. The positions from right to left of 1, 11, 21, 701 in A are 1, 4, 5, 10 in the bit sequence and are represented by 1s. All other positions in the sequence are 0s. We do these calculations on the entire vector 638,..., 93. They yield the seven 10-bit sequences listed earlier. The legal receiver reads the plain text SAUNA and HEALTH.

▬ ▬ Caveat

The preceding example, based on an easy knapsack problem, is unreliable in practice. El Gamal designed a polynomial-time algorithm to crack it. The cracking algorithm was based on the fact that it is not necessary for the cryptanalyst to find the correct multiplier t and modulus m, the correct ones used by the system designer. It suffices to find any t' and m' such that the multiplication of the publicized vector by $t' - 1 \ (\text{mod } m')$ yields a superincreasing vector. The cryptanalyst breaks the system by preprocessing, after the encryption key has been publicized.

One-way functions (or streets) are prima facie to public-key cryptography. Think of the fish that goes into a snare cage or a turtle excluder device. Both allow their catch to go into the device without difficulty, but escape is nearly impossible. The legal receiver takes the turtle or fish out of the cage via an opening (trapdoor) on the top of the cage.

The cryptosystem based on the superincreasing knapsack vectors serves as a simple example of the principles that designers need to be concerned with when constructing a public-key cryptosystem.

General Principles

The simplest analogy for comparing classical and public-key cryptography is the lock box. In classical systems, the receiver would receive the lock box with one lock and the key sent by some trusted external channel. Key management represents an essential issue for classical systems. Since the knowledge of the encryption key E_k should not give away the decryption key D_k, the computation of D_k from E_k should be intractable for all keys. Public-key cryptography corresponds to having open padlocks on the box available to the public. A person who wants to send a message padlocks the box with *your* padlock and sends the box to you. You open it with your key.

There is a protocol modification that does not require the open padlocks to be sent in advance to the legal receiver. First, A sends the box to B locked with A's padlock. B sends the box to A with B's lock on it in addition. Next, A opens the A lock (decrypts it) and returns the box to B, who opens (decrypts) his or her B lock. The box is always protected with at least one lock and will stop passive eavesdropping.

We can now list general principles governing the construction of a *public-key cryptosystem*.

Step 1:
Choose a difficult mathematical problem P. P must be intractable according to complexity theory: there is no algorithm that solves all cases of P in polynomial time with regard to size of instance. The average complexity as well as the worst case complexity must be high.

Step 2:
Choose an easy subproblem P(easy) of P. P(easy) should be solvable in polynomial time, preferably linear.

Step 3:	Encrypt P(easy) in such a way that the resulting problem P(encrypted) does not resemble P(easy).
Step 4:	Publicize P(encrypted), describing how it is to be used as an encryption key. The information concerning how P(easy) can be recovered from P(encrypted) is kept as the secret trapdoor.
Step 5:	The details of the system must be such that decryption is different for the cryptanalyst and the legal receiver. The former must solve P(encrypted), while the latter may use the trapdoor to solve P(easy).
Step 6:	Test the system from all points of view. Don't be surprised when it fails a practical test.

Some lesser abstractions are determination of the process of encryption, the easiness of P, the specification of the trapdoor, and its resistance to preprocessing and similar issues. The previous example of the knapsack fits well into the preceding six steps.

Table 7-3 presents some of the fundamental number-theoretic problems used in public key systems. They have defied serious attempts to classify their complexities. They do not possess a deterministic polynomial time algorithm nor are they complete for any natural complexity class. Some mutual reductions among the problems have been made; some classification as to hard versus easy has been estimated. All have been very useful for public-key systems.

Work Factor

According to Whitfield Diffie, time is the essential element in measuring computation. The question is "How much will it cost me to get the answer when I need it?" Moore's Law states that computing power doubles every 18 months; thus a personal computer purchased for $1000 today will have twice the computing power of one purchased less than two years ago. Moore's Law has been remarkably accurate over the last decade. These improvements in speed have had profound implications for cryptographic systems.

TABLE 7-3

Number-Theoretic
Problems

FACTOR(n)	Find the factorization of n.
PRIMALITY(n)	Decide whether or not n is prime.
FIND-PRIME($>n$)	Find a prime number $>n$.
SQUARE-FREENESS(n)	Decide whether or not a square of a prime divides n.
QUAD-RESIDUE(a,n)	Decide whether or not $x^2 \equiv a(\mathrm{mod}\ n)$ holds for some x.
SQUARE ROOT(a,n)	Find, if possible, an x such that $x^2 \equiv a(\mathrm{mod}\ n)$.
DISCRETE-LOG(a,b,n)	Find, if possible, an x such that $ax \equiv b(\mathrm{mod}\ n)$.
ELLIPTIC CURVE DISCRETE-LOG (a,b,x,y,P,Q)	An elliptic curve, defined modulo a prime p, is the set of solutions (x,y) to an equation of the form: $y^2 = x^3 + ax + b(\mathrm{mod}\ p)$ for two numbers a and b. If (x,y) satisfies the preceding equation, then $P = (x,y)$ is a point on the elliptic curve. Fix a prime p and an elliptic curve, where xP represents the point P added to itself x times. Suppose Q is a multiple of P, so that $Q = xP$ for some x. Determine x given P and Q.

The number of operations required to break a cryptographic system is called its *work factor*. The form or complexity of the operations is not precisely stated. They might be encryptions, as they are when the analytic process is one of searching through the keys, or they might be something entirely different. In a spirit of oversimplification, we will assume that operations are always entirely parallelizable. If two processors can do a million operations in 5 seconds, then ten processors can do the same number of operations in 1 second. For our purposes, this assumption is conservative because, if it is false, the problem merely becomes harder. Another consideration is that specialized hardware is available (and specifically programmed for the application) to specifically work on finding a cryptographic solution.

If a system has a work factor of 2^{30}, it can be broken by a billion operations. These may not be elementary computer instructions; they may be complex operations requiring hundreds of instructions each. Even so, many specialized computers today can do a billion instructions in 5 seconds. If such a cryptosystem requires several hundred instructions per encryption, it can be searched in under an hour. In short, breaking a system with a work factor of 2^{30} is not trivial, but is attainable in reasonable time.

A work factor of 2^{60} means that a million processors, each doing a million operations a second, can solve the problem in a million seconds (between 11 and 12 days). It is clear that a system with a work factor of 2^{60} can be broken today if the analytic operations are such that processors capable of executing them are worth building or already available (Figure 6-9). If the operations are encryptions, the processors might be built from available encryption processors.

On this path, systems with work factors of 2^{90} are the first that seem beyond reach for the foreseeable future. A billion processors in parallel can certainly be imagined. A billion operations a second, even operations as complex as DES encryptions, have been achieved. A billion seconds, however, is 30 years long—enough to count as secure for most applications. Work factors 2^{120} seem beyond reach for the indefinite future. A trillionth of a second is less than one gate delay in the fastest experimental technologies; a trillion processors operating in parallel is beyond reach; and a trillion seconds is 30,000 years.

Estimating the cost of searching through keys and validating the estimates by actually doing it have become sports in the cryptographic community. In the fall of 1995, a group of cryptographers met and prepared an estimate of search costs, concluding that 40-bit keys (the largest that could be readily exported) could easily be searched and that keys at least 70 to 90 bits long were needed to provide security for commercial applications. The previous August, students at the Ecole Polytechnique in Paris had searched out a 40-bit key. The following January, students at MIT repeated the feat using an $83,000 graphics computer, which amounted to a cost of $584 per key. At its annual conference in January 1997, RSA Data Security offered prizes for searching key spaces of various sizes. The 40-bit prize was claimed before the conference ended and the 48-bit prize was claimed a week later. The 56-bit DES challenge lasted for only 5 months. Finally, the Electronic Frontier Foundation (EFF) announced the success of its "DES Cracker" project, with a shoestring budget of only $200,000, in May 1998.[1]

---

[1]Electronic Frontier Foundation, *Cracking DES: Secrets of Encryption Research, Wiretap Politics, and Chip Design*. O'Reilly: Sebastopol, CA, May 1998.

Lifetimes of Cryptosystems

Diffie and Landau present two lifetime design criteria for a cryptographic system: (1) how long the system will be in use and (2) how long the messages it encrypts will remain secret.

Cryptographic systems and cryptographic equipment often have very long lifetimes. The Sigaba system, introduced before World War II, was in use until the early 1960s. The KL-7, a later rotor machine, served from the 1950s to the 1980s. DES has been the U.S. standard for more than 20 years. Other systems that are neither formal standards nor under the tight control of organizations such as the American military probably have longer lifetimes still.

Secrets can also have very long lifetimes. The Venona messages were studied for nearly 40 years in hopes that they would reveal the identities of spies who had been young men in the 1930s and who might have been the senior intelligence officers of the 1970s. The principles of the Sigaba system were discovered in the mid-1930s and were not made public until 1996. Much of the "H-bomb secret" has been kept secret since its discovery in 1950, and the trade secrets of many industrial processes are much older. In the United States, census data, income tax returns, medical records, and other personal information are *supposed* to be kept secret for a lifetime.

If we set out to develop a piece of cryptographic equipment today, we might reasonably plan to have it in widespread use by the year 2000. We might also reasonably plan for the system to be in use for 20 or 25 years. No individual piece of equipment is likely to last that long; however, if the product is successful, the standards it implements will. If the equipment is intended for the protection of a broad range of business communications, some of the messages it encrypts may be intended to remain secret for decades. A cryptosystem designed today might thus encrypt its last message in 2025, and that message might be expected to remain secret 25 years later. It must therefore withstand attack by a cryptanalyst, whose mathematical and computing resources we have no way of predicting, to the year 2050.

Public-Key Cryptography Advantages—Key Management

The advantages of public-key cryptography are tremendous. The most far-reaching innovation due to public keys concerns how to manage and send keys.

Consider any classical (that is, symmetric) cryptosystem. The encryption key gives away the decryption key and, hence, the former cannot be publicized. This means that the two legal parties (sender and receiver) have to agree *in advance* upon the encryption method. This can happen either in a meeting between the two parties or else by sending the encryption key via some absolutely secure channel.

If a public-key cryptosystem is used, the two parties do not have to meet. They do not even have to know each other or be in any kind of previous communication! This is a huge advantage, for instance, in the case of a big data bank, where there are numerous users and some user wants to communicate only with a specific other user. Then he/she can do so just by applying the information in the data bank itself.

One can compare classical and public-key cryptosystems by the *length* of a key. Since every key had to be described somehow, the description being a sequence of letters of some alphabet (that is, a word), it is natural to talk about the length of a key. There is a remarkable difference between classical and public-key cryptosystems.

Consider first a classical cryptosystem. If the key is longer than the plain text, nothing has really been achieved. Since the key has to be transmitted securely, one could transmit the plain text instead of the key via this secure channel. Of course, in some situations the key is transmitted earlier to wait for the crucial moment.

Consider next a public-key cryptosystem. The length of the encryption key is largely irrelevant. The key is publicized anyway. This also means that the length of the decryption key is largely irrelevant; the receiver only has to store it in a secure place.

The easiness of key management can justly be regarded as the chief advantage of public-key cryptography. In Chapter 2 we introduced some of the requirements of cryptosystems in the commercial theater. Figure 7-3 shows some of the primary functions that cryptosystems are used for in commercial operations, as well as, their respective algorithms. The purview is indeed significant.

WRAP-UP

The discovery of public-key (PK) cryptography has greatly increased the options available to protect messages and reduce the management issues concerning cryptographic keys. A specific problem was used to illustrate some qualitative one-way functions, which are vital to the study of public-key cryptography. A generalized public-key cryptosystem design was introduced. Public-key cryptography expands the capabilities of commercial computer systems (refer to Figure 7-3).

Figure 7-3

Primary Functions and Their Respective Algorithms

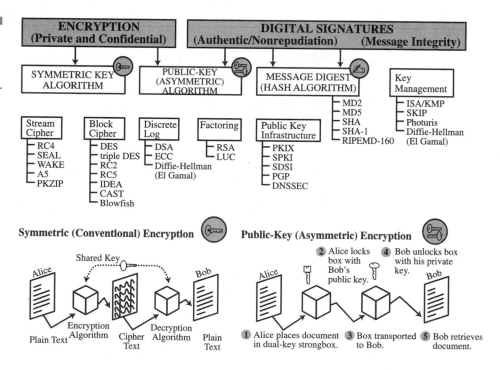

CHAPTER 8

Algorithms

When we peruse the literature of cryptography, we find many pages devoted to the practical and theoretical algorithms that are the bedrock of this science. Algorithms are the raison d'être for cryptography. What is needed is a scheme to put the mathematics into simple focus. The author suggests two practical ways to classify cryptographic algorithms. First, we can classify algorithms by their underlying difficulty of mathematical system and second, we can classify them by their cryptographic purpose.

In this chapter, we review both methods and focus on algorithms that support material, presented in Part 4, devoted to practical applications of cryptography. The interested reader is directed to the bibliography, which gives many references devoted to the mathematics and nuances of the various cryptographic algorithms. In addition, three appendices present refresher tutorials on the important principles of complexity theory, numerical theory, and elliptic curves, which are used to define practical public key cryptosystems. Cryptography algorithms span the mathematical gambit of number theory, complexity theory, elliptic curves, and set theory.

Difficulty of Mathematical Systems

In the first classification scheme, there are three types of mathematical problems considered both secure and efficient—that is, not "cracked"—found easier than postulated or impractical to calculate. The three mathematical problems on which practical cryptosystem security is based are:

1. *Integer factorization problem (IFP):*   RSA is the principal and best-known cryptosystem in this category.

2. *Discrete logarithm problem (DLP):*   Examples include the U.S. government's Digital Signature Algorithm (DSA), the Diffie-Hellman key agreement scheme, the El Gamal encryption and signature schemes, and the Schnorr signature scheme.

3. *Elliptic curve discrete logarithm problem (ECDLP):*   Examples of this type include the elliptic curve analog of the DSA (ECDSA), the elliptic curve analogs of the Diffie-Hellman key agreement scheme (ECDH), the El Gamal encryption and signature schemes (ECEG), and the Schnorr signature scheme (ECSS).

Cryptographic Functionality

The second classification method separates cryptographic algorithms by cryptographic purpose or functionality:

1. *Symmetric*

2. *Asymmetric*

3. *Authentication systems*

4. *Digital signatures / Hashes / Message digests*

Obviously, there is overlap between the proposed schemes of classification. We review three well-known symmetric algorithms: IDEA, Blowfish, and RC5. Another symmetric algorithm, DES, has already been dissected in a previous chapter. To illustrate asymmetric algorithms, we investigate the famous RSA algorithm by examining some of its computational and cryptanalytical implications. We then follow with three ECC systems: Diffie-Hellman, Key Transport, and the Menezes-Qu-Vanstone (MQV) key agreement scheme. The Raike Public Key (RPK) asymmetric system is based on the DLP problem and has interesting features worthy of review.

Authentication systems are of special interest in cryptography. They include message digests, cryptographic checksums, and hash functions. Hash functions have a significant authentication role in cryptography but are not immune from attack. A fascinating attack on hash systems, known as the Birthday Attack, is introduced. The Birthday Attack or one of its variants may be used in cryptanalysis of modern public-key systems.

Digital signatures are an upcoming technology. Their influence in the commercial theater of operations is growing. We introduce DSA and SHA-1 secure hash algorithm. The use of elliptic curve cryptography (ECC) digital signature systems in relation to the DLP problem is discussed. The two basic ECC encryption schemes are presented.

Finally, it is the author's considered opinion that perhaps *the* most powerful cryptotechnology is ECC because of its computational efficiencies as well as the security it offers. Elliptic curve cryptosystems have undergone a significant amount of theoretical research and authors internationally have supported its use.

Integer Factorization Systems

As covered in Chapter 7, Diffie and Hellman discovered the concept of public-key cryptography in 1976. Ron Rivest, Adi Shamir, and Len Adleman developed the first practical public-key cryptographic system at MIT, named RSA in honor of its inventors.

Security

RSA is the best known of a family of systems whose security relies on the difficulty of the *integer factorization problem* (IFP). The integer factorization problem is defined as follows.

Given an integer, a whole number p is *prime* if it is divisible only by 1 and p itself. Now, given an integer $n,$ which is the product of two large primes, determine those factors, that is, find primes p and q such that:

$$p \times q = n \qquad \text{[Eq. 8-1]}$$

An RSA public key consists of a pair (n,e), where e is a number between 1 and $n - 1$, and n is the product of two *large* primes p and q. It is widely believed that to break RSA in general, the integer factorization problem must be solved (hence factored) for the integer n. The factorization problem has been studied for over 300 years and no superefficient method of computation has been discovered. Since there is no efficient algorithm for the integer factorization problem, n can be chosen to be large enough to ensure that the system is secure. To provide even short-term security, given today's computing power, n should be at least 150 decimal digits long (150 decimal digits is approximately 500 bits). Hardware implementations in 1998 have become so effective that approximately 300 decimal digits or 1028 bits may be a better alternative.

Implementation

RSA, and other members of the integer factorization family, can be used both for encryption and for digital signatures (the digital equivalent of real signatures). To describe the operations used to perform these processes, modular arithmetic must first be defined. Modular addition and modular multiplication modulo n work just like ordinary addition and multiplication, except that the answer to the calculation is reduced to its remainder on division by n, so that the result always lies between 0 and $n - 1$. The phrase "mod n" is written after each calculation to denote modular arithmetic. Modular arithmetic plays a central role in the implementation of all three types of public-key cryptosystems.

When RSA is used either as an encryption scheme or as a digital signature scheme, exponentiation modulo n must be performed. Suppose m, a number between 0 and $n-1$, represents a message. Then the modular exponentiation

$$m^x \pmod{n} \qquad \text{[Eq. 8-2]}$$

must be calculated for some number x when m is transformed. This modular exponentiation dominates the time taken to perform the transformations involved in the RSA system, so that the time required to calculate modular exponentiation modulo n essentially determines the time required to perform RSA.

In short, the security of RSA, and the other members of the integer factorization family, rests on the difficulty of the integer factorization problem, and its efficiency rests on the speed of performing exponentiation modulo n.

Discrete Logarithm Systems

Security

Another mathematical problem defined in terms of modular arithmetic is the *discrete logarithm problem* modulo a prime p. Fix a prime number p; then, given an integer g between 0 and $p-1$, and y, which is the result of exponentiating g, we define the following relation between g and y:

$$y = g^x \pmod{p} \qquad \text{[Eq. 8-3]}$$

for some x. The discrete logarithm problem modulo p is to determine the integer x for a given pair g and y. The prime p used in discrete logarithm systems should also be at least 150 decimal digits (500 bits) in length to provide short-term security.

Like the integer factorization problem, no efficient algorithm is generally known to solve the discrete logarithm problem modulo p. Taher El Gamal was the first to propose a public-key cryptosystem based on this problem. In fact, El Gamal proposed two distinct systems: one to provide encryption, and one to perform digital signatures. In 1991, Claus Schnorr discovered a variant of the El-Gamal digital signature system, which offers added efficiency compared to the original system. The U.S. government's Digital Signature Algorithm (DSA) is also based on El Gamal's work. As a sidebar, the U.S. government may have chosen the DSA to be a direct refutation of the more popular RSA system. It may have been chosen to prevent RSA from being an accepted standard. The aforementioned systems are the best known of a large number of systems whose security is based on the discrete logarithm problem modulo p.

Implementation

As was the case with RSA, modular exponentiation must be performed to operate discrete logarithm systems. In every case, the dominant calculation in each of the transformations is:

$$g^x \ (\mathrm{mod}\ p) \hspace{5cm} \textbf{[Eq. 8-4]}$$

for some integer x, and a fixed number g between 0 and $p - 1$.

Therefore, discrete logarithm systems can be described as a member of the DLP family, which relies on the discrete logarithm problem modulo p, and the efficiency of the speed of performing modular exponentiation modulo p.

The Elliptic Curve Cryptosystem (ECC)

The discrete logarithm problem modulo p was described in terms of modular arithmetic on the remainders of division by p. This is not the only mathematical structure that forms the basis for discrete logarithm problems. In 1985, Neil Koblitz and Victor Miller independently proposed the *Elliptic Curve Cryptosystem* (ECC), the security of which rests on the discrete logarithm problem applied to the points on an elliptic curve and has some powerful and unique features available for use in cryptographic systems. ECC can be used to provide both a digital signature scheme and an encryption scheme. A simplified tutorial on ECC systems may be found in the appendices.

Security

An *elliptic curve*, defined modulo a prime p, is the set of solutions (x, y) to an equation of the form:

$$y^2 = x^3 + ax + b \pmod{p}$$ **[Eq. 8-5]**

for two numbers a and b. If (x, y) satisfies the preceding equation then $P = (x, y)$ is a *point* on the elliptic curve. An elliptic curve can also be defined over the *finite field* consisting of 2^m elements. Such a representation offers extra efficiency in the operation of the ECC. It is possible to define the "addition" of two points on the elliptic curve. Suppose P and Q are both points on the curve, then

$$P + Q$$

will always be another point on the curve.

The elliptic curve discrete logarithm problem can be stated as follows. Fix a prime p and an elliptic curve; xP represents the point P "added" to itself x times. Suppose Q is a multiple of P, so that

$$Q = xP$$ **[Eq. 8-6]**

for some x. Then the *elliptic curve discrete logarithm problem* is to determine x given P and Q.

The security of the ECC rests on the difficulty of the elliptic curve discrete logarithm problem. As was the case with the integer factorization problem and the discrete logarithm problem modulo p, no efficient algorithm is known at this time to solve the elliptic curve discrete logarithm problem.

One of the advantages of ECC is that the elliptic curve discrete logarithm problem *is believed to be harder* than both the integer factorization problem and the discrete logarithm problem modulo p. This extra difficulty implies that ECC is one of the strongest public-key cryptographic system known today. Moderate security can be achieved with ECC using an elliptic curve defined modulo a prime p that is several times shorter than 150 decimal digits. This is a real advantage from a computer hardware and software implementation viewpoint. Confirming research is still in progress with such brain trusts as the University of Waterloo's Centre for Applied Cryptographic Research. Such noted researchers as Neal Koblitz, Alfred Menezes, Simon Blake-Wilson, and

Scott VanStone, have joined to discover the secrets of ECC—ECC research is very exciting. As a side note, RSA Laboratories, in 1998, agreed to include a version of ECC in its BSAFE toolkit.

Implementation

Just as modular exponentiation determined the efficiency of integer factorization and discrete logarithm systems, so the calculation of

$$Q = xP \hspace{3cm} \text{[Eq. 8-7]}$$

for a point P on the elliptic curve and some integer x dominates the calculations involved in the operation of an ECC cryptosystem. The process of adding elliptic curve points requires a few modular calculations, so in the case of integer factorization, discrete logarithm systems, and elliptic curve cryptosystems, the operation of a public-key cryptographic system is dependent upon efficient modular arithmetic. What is very interesting is that the prime p used in an ECC system can be *smaller* than the numbers required in the other types of systems; so another advantage of ECC is that the modular calculations required in its operation are carried out over a smaller modulus. This may lead to a significant improvement in efficiency in the operation of ECC over both integer factorization and discrete logarithm systems.

In summarizing ECC, security rests on the elliptic curve discrete logarithm problem, and efficiency is dependent on the fast calculation of xP for some number x and a point P on the curve.

Comparison of Public-Key Cryptographic Systems

Security and *efficiency* are two important issues for comparing IFP, DLP, and ECDLP public-key cryptographic systems.

Security

When examining the theoretical security of a public-key cryptographic system, the prime consideration is solving the underlying mathematical problem. The concepts of complexity, Turing machines, polynomial time algorithms, and exponential time algorithms were introduced (refer to appendices) to show how the difficulty of solving a mathematical problem is relative to the fastest algorithm available and the problem input size. In Chapter 6, we looked for mathematical problems, which could form the basis for a public-key cryptographic system, and emphasized that the fastest algorithm takes exponential time. *The longer it takes to compute the best algorithm for the problem, the more secure a public-key cryptosystem based on that problem will be.*

It must be emphasized that none of the aforementioned problems—IFP, DLP, or ECDLP—has been *proven* to be intractable (i.e., difficult to solve in an efficient manner). Rather, they are *believed* to be intractable because years of intensive study by leading mathematicians and computer scientists have failed to yield efficient algorithms for solving them.

We might ask which is the hardest problem: the integer factorization problem (IFP), the discrete logarithm problem modulo p (DLP), or the elliptic curve discrete logarithm problem (ECDLP)? Unfortunately, there are no mathematical problems for which it can be proven that the best algorithm takes fully exponential time. Therefore, this discussion must focus on the best algorithms known today to solve these problems.

There are two types of algorithms: special-purpose and general-purpose. *Special-purpose* algorithms attempt to exploit special features of system under consideration, such as the number n being factored. A *general-purpose* algorithm solves *all* cases of the problem under consideration. The running time of a general-purpose algorithm is dependent on the *size* of the problem, for example, the size of n to be factored.

Special-Purpose Algorithms

With each of the three problems, there are good, special-purpose algorithms that solve the problem quickly in certain special (meaning reduced or easy) instances.

IFP For integer factorization, there is a fast algorithm for $n = p \times q$ provided $p-1$ or $q-1$ only has small prime factors.

One of the most powerful special-purpose factoring algorithms is the elliptic curve factoring method (ECM) that was invented in 1985 by Hendrik Lenstra, Jr. The running time of this method depends on the size of the prime factors of n, and hence the algorithm tends to find small factors first. On June 21, 1995, Andreas Mueller (Universitaet des Saarlandes, Germany) announced that he had found a 44-decimal digit (147-bit) factor of a 99-decimal digit (329-bit) composite integer using the ECM. The computation was carried out on a network of workstations and the speed was approximately 60 MIPS (million instructions per second). The largest prime factor found thus far by ECM is a 47-decimal digit (157-bit) prime factor of a 135-decimal digit (449-bit) number; the computation was carried out by Peter Montgomery and reported on November 27, 1995.

DLP For the discrete logarithm problem modulo p, there is a fast algorithm provided $p-1$ only has small prime factors. As with the integer factorization problem (IFP), there are two types of algorithms for solving the discrete logarithm problem. Special-purpose algorithms attempt to exploit special features of the prime p. In contrast, the running times of general-purpose algorithms depend only on the size of p.

ECDLP The elliptic curve discrete logarithm problem is relatively easy for a small class of elliptic curves, known as *supersingular elliptic curves* and also for certain *anomalous elliptic curves*. In both cases, the "weak" instances of the problem are easily identified, and implementation merely checks that the specific instance selected is not one of the class of easy problems.

General-Purpose Algorithms

General-purpose algorithms are those that *always* succeed in solving the problem. Of the three problems, the integer factorization problem and the discrete logarithm problem modulo p both admit general algorithms that run in *subexponential time,* which means that the problem should still be considered hard but not as hard as those problems, which admit only fully exponential time algorithms. Formally, the running time for the best general algorithm (subexponential running time) for both of these problems is of the form of algorithm A, whose inputs are elements of a finite field Fn or an integer n; the form of A is:

$$L_q \{\alpha, c\} = \Theta(\exp((c + o(1)))(\ln n)^\alpha (\ln \ln n)^{1-\alpha} \qquad \textbf{[Eq. 8-8]}$$

for a positive constant c, $0 \le \alpha \le 1$; α is usually of the order of $\frac{1}{3}$, so $(1 - \alpha)$ is $\frac{2}{3}$. When α satisfies the constraint $0 \le \alpha \le 1$, then A is a subexponential time algorithm. When $\alpha = 0$, $L_q \{0,c\}$ is a polynomial in $\ln n$, while for $\alpha = 1$, $L_q \{1,c\}$ is a polynomial in n, and thus fully exponential in $\ln n$.

IFP Prior to the development of the RSA cryptosystem, the best general-purpose factoring algorithm was the *continued fraction algorithm,* which could factor numbers up to 40 decimal digits (133 bits). This algorithm was based on the idea of using a factor base of primes and generating an associated set of linear equations whose solution ultimately led to a factorization. This is the same idea underlying the best general-purpose algorithms used today: the *quadratic sieve* (QS) and the *number field sieve* (NFS). Both these algorithms can be easily paralleled to permit factoring on distributed networks of workstations. Large mainframe computers or supercomputers are therefore not essential to factor large numbers.

Carl Pomerance developed the quadratic sieve in 1984. Initially, it was used to factor numbers in the 70-decimal digit (233-bit) range. In 1994, it was used by a group of researchers led by Arjen Lenstra to factor the 129-decimal digit (429-bit) RSA challenge number that was posed by Martin Gardner in 1977. Practically every modern advance in factoring technology has Lenstra's name associated with the development. The factorization was carried out in eight months by about 1600 computers around the world. The total running time for the factorization was estimated to be 5000 MIPS years.

The number field sieve was first developed in 1989 and works best on numbers of a special form. The algorithm was used to factor the 155-decimal digit (513-bit) number $2^{512} + 1$. It was subsequently extended to a general-purpose factorization algorithm. Although NFS was initially thought to be slower in practice than the quadratic sieve for factoring integers having fewer than 150 decimal digits (500 bits), recent experiments have suggested that the NFS is indeed the superior algorithm for factoring integers having at least 120 decimal digits (400 bits). In 1996, a group led again by Arjen Lenstra used the NFS to factor a 130-decimal digit (432-bit) number. This is the largest number factored to date. The factorization was estimated to take less than 15 percent of the 5000 MIPS years that was required for the factorization of the 129-decimal digit RSA challenge number. The authors concluded that factoring a 512-bit (155-decimal digit) number could take less than five times this effort. Table 8-1 contains some historical data on the progress of integer factorization.

Table 8-1 results indicate that a 512-bit modulus n provides only marginal security when used in the RSA cryptosystem. For long-term security, 1024-bit or larger moduli should be used. Computers took several technical jumps forward during 1994-1995. The effect was a reduction in work factor for solving the IFP problem.

DLP The fastest general-purpose algorithms known for solving the DLP are based on a method referred to as the *index-calculus*. In this method,

TABLE 8-1

Historical Data on the Integer Factorization Problem

Year	Number of Decimal Digits	Number of Bits	MIPS years
1984	71	236	0.1
1988	106	352	140
1993	120	399	825
1994	129	429	5000
1995	119	395	250
1996	130	432	750

a database of small primes and their corresponding logarithms is constructed, subsequent to which logarithms of arbitrary field elements can be easily obtained. This is reminiscent of the factor-base methods for integer factorization. For this reason, if an improvement in the algorithms for either the IFP or DLP is found, then shortly after a similar improved algorithm can be expected to be found for the other problem. As with the factoring methods, the index-calculus algorithms can be easily paralleled.

As in the case with factoring, the best current algorithm known for the DLP is the number field sieve. It has precisely the same asymptotic running time as the corresponding algorithm for integer factorization. This can be loosely interpreted as saying that finding logarithms in the case of a k-bit prime modulus p is roughly as difficult as factoring a k-bit composite number n.

The implementation of discrete logarithm algorithms has lagged behind the analogous efforts for factoring integers. In 1990, Brian LaMacchia and Andrew Odlyzko used a variant of the index-calculus method, called the *Gaussian integer method,* to compute discrete logarithms modulo a 191-bit prime. More recently, Weber, Denny, and Zayer computed discrete logarithms modulo a 248-bit prime using the number field sieve.

A project initiated in 1997 at the University of Waterloo, Canada, is attempting to refine this technology in both theory and practice with the goal of taking logarithms modulo a prime p of length in excess of 400 bits. It is likely safe to say that taking logarithms modulo a 512-bit prime p will remain intractable for the next three or four years. In comparison, a 512-bit RSA modulus will likely be factored before the end of this millennium.

The author believes that for long-term security, 1024-bit or larger moduli p should be used in discrete logarithm cryptosystems.

ECDLP The best general algorithm for the elliptic curve discrete logarithm problem is fully exponential time—its running time is:

$$\Theta(\sqrt{p})$$

In simple terms, this means that the elliptic curve discrete logarithm problem (ECDLP) may be considered harder with respect to time than either the integer factorization problem or the discrete logarithm problem modulo p.

Since 1985, the ECDLP has received considerable attention from leading mathematicians around the world. An algorithm developed by Pohlig and Hellman reduced the determination of l to the determination of l modulo for each of the prime factors of n. Hence, in order to achieve the maximum possible security level, n should be prime.

The best algorithm known to date for the ECDLP in general is the *Pollard rho-method*, which takes about $\sqrt{(\pi n/2)}$ steps, where a step is an elliptic curve point addition. In 1993, Paul van Oorschot and Michael Wiener showed how the Pollard rho-method can be paralleled so that if r processors are used, then the expected number of steps by each processor before a single discrete logarithm is obtained is $[\sqrt{(\pi n/2)}]/r$. Most significantly, no index-calculus-type algorithms are known for the ECDLP as for the DLP. This is the reason why the ECDLP is believed to be much harder than either the IFP or the DLP. No subexponential-time general-purpose algorithm is known for the ECDLP problem.

Table 8-2 shows the computing power required to compute a single discrete logarithm using the Pollard rho-method for various values of n. As an example, if 10,000 computers each rated at 1000 MIPS are available and $n \approx 2^{160}$, then an elliptic curve discrete logarithm can be computed in 96,000 years.

TABLE 8-2

Computing Power Required To Compute Elliptic Curve Logarithms with the Pollard Rho-Method

Field Size (in Bits)	Size of n (in Bits)	$\sqrt{\pi n/2}$	MIPS Years
163	160	2^{80}	9.6×10^{11}
191	186	2^{93}	7.9×10^{15}
239	234	2^{117}	1.6×10^{23}
359	354	2^{177}	1.5×10^{41}
431	426	2^{213}	1.0×10^{52}

TABLE 8-3

Computing Power Required to Factor Integers Using the General Number Field Sieve

Size of Integer to Be Factored (in Bits)	MIPS years
512	3×10^4
768	2×10^8
1024	3×10^{11}
1280	1×10^{14}
1536	3×10^{16}
2048	3×10^{20}

Table 8-3 (from Odlyzko) shows the estimated computing power required to factor integers with current versions of the number field sieve. This is also roughly equal to the time it takes to compute discrete logarithms modulo a prime p of the same bit length as n.

Menezes and Jurisic compared the time required to break the ECC with the time required to break RSA or DSA for various modulus sizes using the best general algorithm known. Values were computed in MIPS years, which represents a computing time of one year on a machine capable of performing one million instructions per second. As a benchmark, it is generally accepted that 10^{12} MIPS years represents reasonable security at this time, since this would require most of the computing power on the planet to work for a considerable amount of time.

Menezes and Jurisic found that to achieve reasonable security, RSA and DSA would need to employ a 1024-bit modulus, whereas a 160-bit modulus should be sufficient for the ECC. They found that ECC required a smaller modulus than RSA or DSA and that the security gap between the systems grew as the key size increased. For example, 300-bit ECC is significantly more secure than 2000-bit RSA or DSA. Recall that the ECDLP problem is judged to be the harder problem.

Another way to look at this security issue is to compare the equivalent strength of RSA/DSA keys and ECC keys for smartcard applications. Table 8-4 shows that in smartcard applications requiring higher

TABLE 8-4

Key Size: Equivalent Strength Comparison

Time to Break MIPS/Years	RSA/DSA Key Size	ECC Key Size	RSA/ECC Key Size Ratio
10^4	512	106	5:1
10^8	768	132	6:1
10^{11}	1,024	160	7:1
10^{20}	2,048	210	10:1
10^{78}	21,000	600	35:1

levels of security, ECC is able to offer security without a great deal of additional system resources.

Efficiency

When talking about the efficiency of a public-key cryptographic system, there are three distinct factors to take into account:

1. *Computational overheads:* How much computation is required to perform the public key and private key transformations.

2. *Key size:* How many bits are required to store the key pairs and associated system parameters.

3. *Bandwidth:* How many bits must be communicated to transfer an encrypted message or a signature.

Clearly the comparisons should be made between systems offering similar levels of security, so in order to make the comparisons as concrete as possible, 160-bit ECC is compared with 1024-bit RSA and DSA. These parameter sizes are believed to offer comparable levels of security.

Computational Overheads

In each of the three systems, considerable computational savings can be made. In RSA, a short public exponent can be employed (although this represents a trade-off and does incur some security risks) to speed up signature verification and encryption. In both DSA and ECC, a large proportion of the signature generation and encrypting transformations can be precomputed. Also, various special bases for the finite field $F_2{}^m$ can be employed to perform more quickly the modular arithmetic involved in ECC operation. State-of-the-art implementations of the systems show that with all of these efficiencies in place, ECC is an order of magnitude (roughly 10 times) faster than either RSA or DSA. The use of a short public exponent in RSA can make RSA encryption and signature verification timings (but not RSA decryption and signature generation timings) comparable with timings for these processes using the ECC.

Key Size

Table 8-5 compares the size of the system parameters and selected key pairs for the different systems, and presents evidence that the system parameters and key pairs are shorter for the ECC than for either RSA or DSA.

TABLE 8-5

Size of System Parameters and Key Pairs (Approx.)

	System Parameters (Bits)	Public Key (Bits)	Private Key (Bits)
RSA	n/a	1088	2048
DSA	2208	1024	160
ECC	481	161	160

Bandwidth

All three types of systems have similar bandwidth requirements when they are used to encrypt or sign long messages. However, the case when short messages are being transformed deserves particular attention because public-key cryptographic systems are often employed to transmit short messages, that is, to transport session keys for use in a symmetric-key cryptographic system. For comparison, suppose that each is being used to sign a 2000-bit message, or to encrypt a 100-bit message. Tables 8-6 and 8-7 compare the lengths of the signatures and encrypted messages, respectively. These tables suggest that ECC offers bandwidth savings over the other types of public-key cryptographic systems when being used to transform short messages.

TABLE 8-6

Signature Sizes on Long Messages (e.g., 2000-bit)

	Signature Size (Bits)
RSA	1024
DSA	320
ECC	320

TABLE 8-7

Size of Encrypted 100-Bit Messages

	Encrypted Message (Bits)
RSA	1024
El Gamal	2048
ECC	321

Comparison Summary

In summary, ECC provides greater efficiency than either integer factorization systems or discrete logarithm systems, in terms of computational overheads, key sizes, and bandwidth. In implementations, these savings mean higher speeds, lower power consumption, and code size reductions. However as of this writing, the RSA system (based on the IFP) is globally accepted in vendor offerings and may dominate the field until more research information about ECC becomes available. Times are changing, however, and recently in 1998, RSA, Inc. announced the inclusion of ECC technology in its basic cryptographic tool kit. The PKS 98 convention hosted by Certicom Corporation in Toronto, Canada, drew some of the best cryptographers and researchers in the world—and it was clear that their support for ECC was overwhelming.

ECC Standards

Other issues that affect the widespread employment of a cryptographic system are interoperability, public acceptance, and technical scrutiny. ECC and other cryptographic systems (RSA/DSA) have addressed these issues through *standardization.*

The international standardization of cryptographic systems, protocols, and interfaces is an important process and is actively supported by the ICSA consortium membership. Standardization has three main benefits.

1. It allows for interoperability among hardware and software systems from many different vendors.

2. It involves critical review of the security of the systems from a cryptographic standpoint.

3. It permits input into the design of cryptosystems from those who have to implement them in a wide range of environments.

Elliptic curves have been the subject of intensive scrutiny in the mathematical community for over ten years and have been scrutinized in standards organizations since 1995. This has given implementors the high degree of confidence in their security that could not be achieved through the support of only a few organizations.

The evolution of standards is a crucial part of the adoption of any cryptographic system. ECC standardization has encouraged its adoption by organizations worldwide. In addition, it has promoted the education of many cryptographers, developers, and engineers in the mathematical basis of ECC and in its importance in achieving practical, efficient public-key based systems. The following ECC standards initiatives have been initiated:

IEEE P1363:   ECC is included in the draft IEEE P1363 standard (Standard Specifications for Public Key Cryptography), which includes encryption, signature, and key-agreement mechanisms. Elliptic curves may be defined either modulo p or over $F_2{}^m$, the field with 2^m elements, for conformance with the standard. The latest drafts are available at: *http://stdsbbs.ieee.org/groups/1363/index.html.*

ANSI X9:   The ECC is being drafted into two work items by the American National Standards Institute (ANSI) ASC X9 Financial Services: ANSI X9.62, the Elliptic Curve Digital Signature Algorithm (ECDSA); and ANSI X9.63, Elliptic Curve Key Agreement (ECKA) and Transport Protocols (ECTP).

ISO/IEC: The draft document ISO/IEC 14888, *Digital signature with appendix—Part 3: Certificate-based mechanisms,* specifies elliptic curve analogues of some El Gamal-like signature algorithms.

IETF: The OAKLEY Key Determination Protocol of the Internet Engineering Task Force (IETF) describes a key agreement protocol that is a variant of the Diffie-Hellman protocol. It allows for a variety of groups to be used, including elliptic curves. The document makes specific mention of elliptic curve groups over the fields $F_2{}^{155}$ and $F_2{}^{210}$. A draft is available at: *http://www.ietf.cnri.reston.va.us/.*

ATM Forum: The ATM Forum Technical Committee's Phase I ATM Security Specification draft document aims to provide security mechanisms for ATM (Asynchronous Transfer Mode) networks. Security services provided include confidentiality, authentication, data integrity, and access control. ECC is one of the systems supported.

Numerous initiatives are under way for protocols that use public-key cryptography, public-key certificates, and other public-key management systems. Most of these standards are being written in an *algorithm-independent manner* so that any recognized public-key algorithm can be implemented. This will allow the use of algorithms, such as ECC, in environments where other public-key systems would be impractical.

Cryptographic Purpose/Functionality

We next consider the second classification scheme—cryptographic purpose or functionality. Algorithms commonly implemented by ICSA Cryptography Products Consortia (CPC) members are presented relative to their functionality. We start with three symmetric algorithms present by many CPC vendor products: IDEA, Blowfish, and RC5.

Symmetric Algorithms

IDEA

The *International Data Encryption Algorithm* (IDEA), authored by Xuejia Lai and James Massey, was introduced in 1990; strengthened in 1991 after Biham and Shamir's discovery of differential cryptanalysis; and reintroduced in 1992 as one of the stronger cryptanalytical engines on the market. Zimmerman introduced PGP with IDEA as its core engine.

IDEA is a symmetric block cipher that operates on 64-bit plain-text blocks. The key is 128 bits long. The design philosophy behind this algorithm is to use confusion and diffusion (substitution and transposition) in mixing operations of different algebraic groups. Three algebraic groups are employed:

1. XOR

2. Addition modulo 2^{16}

3. Multiplication modulo $2^{16}+1$

and work on 16-bit subblocks and are easy to implement in both hardware and software. IDEA is patented and registered by Swiss Ascom Tech AG, Solothurn. IDEA has been sold since 1993, without known commercial restrictions, as VSLI chip and as software. With a key space of 128 bits, IDEA measures up to the brute force attack and like DES, it may be vulnerable to other forms of attack. DES and IDEA both work on 8-byte plain-text blocks.

Description of the IDEA System

Figure 8-1 shows the computational path for the IDEA symmetric cipher. It is an iterated cryptosystem. The 64-bit data block is divided into four 16-bit subblocks: X_1, X_2, X_3, and X_4, and these four subblocks become the input to the first round of the algorithm. There are eight rounds total. In each round, the four subblocks are XORed, added, and multiplied with one another and with six 16-bit subkeys. Between rounds, the transposition step is accomplished and the second and third

Figure 8-1
IDEA Cipher Computational Path

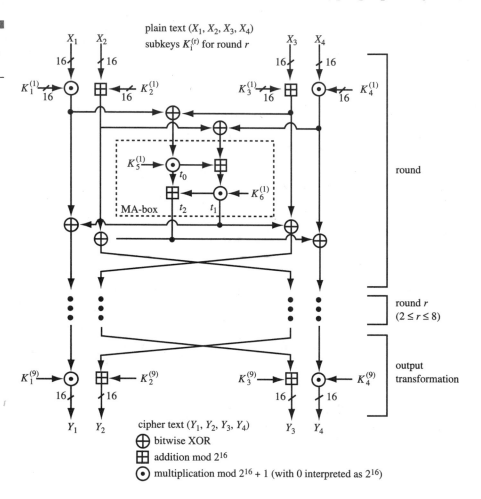

plain text (X_1, X_2, X_3, X_4)
subkeys $K_i^{(r)}$ for round r

cipher text (Y_1, Y_2, Y_3, Y_4)

⊕ bitwise XOR
⊞ addition mod 2^{16}
⊙ multiplication mod $2^{16} + 1$ (with 0 interpreted as 2^{16})

subblocks are swapped. The final step allows the four subblocks to be combined with four subkeys in an output transformation.

In each round, the sequence is:

1. Multiply X_1 and the first subkey.

2. Add X_2 and the second subkey.

3. Add X_3 and the third subkey.

4. Multiply X_4 and the fourth subkey.

5. XOR the results of Steps 1 and 3.

6. XOR the results of Steps 2 and 4.

7. Multiply the results of Step 5 with the fifth subkey.

8. Add the results of Steps 6 and 7.

9. Multiply the results of Step 8 with the sixth subkey.

10. Add the results of Steps 7 and 9.

11. XOR the results of Steps 1 and 9.

12. XOR the results of Steps 3 and 9.

13. XOR the results of Steps 2 and 10.

14. XOR the results of Steps 4 and 10.

The output of the round is the four subblocks that are the results of Steps 11-14. The two inner blocks are swapped and act as the input to the next round. The final output transformation, after the eighth round, completes the process:

1. Multiply X_1 and the first subkey.

2. Add X_2 and the second subkey.

3. Add X_3 and the third subkey.

4. Multiply X_4 and the fourth subkey.

The final four subblocks are concatenated to produce the cipher text.

The IDEA algorithm uses 52 subkeys sets (six for each round and four more for the output transformation) and the 128-bit key is divided into eight 16-bit subkeys, which are used to initiate the process. The key is rotated 25 bits to the left and again divided into eight subkeys. The first four are used in round 2 and the last four are used in round 3. The process continues, key rotation and division, until the end of the algorithm.

IDEA software implementations are at least twice as fast as DES. IDEA's key length of 128 bits is sufficiently long to resist brute force attacks: 2^{128} (10^{38}) encryptions to recover a key would require, even at a rate of a billion key calculations per second, well past the next millennium to solve for just one key. Eight-round IDEA has resisted differential cryptanalysis and linear cryptanalysis attacks. Although Daemen discovered a small set of weak IDEA keys, the chance of picking it is 1 in 2^{96}. A paper presented at Eurocrypt 98 suggests that another small class of weak keys have been found. The chance of accidentally generating them is greater than 2^{76}. Meier attacked the algebraic operations with limited success for a 2-3 round IDEA and no success for the normal 8-round IDEA calculations. Shamir, Zimmerman, Bauer, and Menezes have blessed this algorithm; the author definitely agrees with their collective wisdom.

A post to sci.crypt suggested that increasing the IDEA subblock size to 32-bit subblocks from the design of 16 bits would increase the security of the IDEA algorithm to a factor of 2^{32}. Lai answered that the strength of the algorithm was based on the fact that $2^{16} + 1$ is a prime, whereas $2^{32}+1$ is not. Lai suggests that the stronger properties of the algorithm would be compromised. The point is that small changes in structure can have adverse ripple effects on the cryptographic structure that can become serious implementation errors. We look at other implementation errors in Chapter 13.

Blowfish

Bruce Schneier is the author of Blowfish, a popular addition to file encryption packages. (Figure 8-2 shows the structure of the Blowfish algorithm.) Blowfish's key-length is variable and can be as long as 448 bits. Blowfish is not suitable for IPSEC or packet switching, with frequent key changes, or as a one-way hash function.

Description of Blowfish

Blowfish is a 64-bit block cipher with a variable key-length. The algorithm consists of a key-dependent permutation and data encryption. Key expansion converts a key of up to 448 bits into several subkey arrays totaling 4168 bytes.

The data encryption step consists of iteration of a function for 16 times. Each round consists of a key-dependent permutation coupled with a key and data-dependent substitution. All operations are additions and XORs on 32-bit words. Like DES, there are indexed array lookups per round.

Blowfish uses a large number of precomputed subkeys. Refer to Figure 8-2 to see how the P array is related to the process. It consists of eighteen 32-bit subkeys:

$$P_1, P_2, ..., P_{18}$$

Four 32-bit S-Boxes have 256 entries each:

$$S_{(1,0)}, S_{(1,1)}, ..., S_{(1,256)}$$
$$S_{(2,0)}, S_{(2,1)}, ..., S_{(2,256)}$$
$$S_{(3,0)}, S_{(3,1)}, ..., S_{(3,256)}$$

Figure 8-2
Blowfish Algorithm

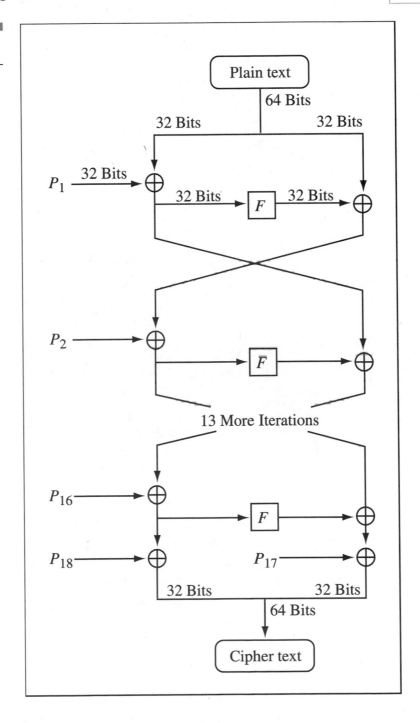

$$S_{(4,0)}, S_{(4,1)},..., S_{(4,256)}$$

Blowfish is actually a special kind of mathematical network, called a *Feistal network,* consisting of 16 rounds. The input is a 64-bit data element x. Encryption is performed by the following method:

1. Divide x into two 32-bit halves, x_L, x_R.

2. For $i = 1, 16$:

$$x_L = x_L \oplus P_i \qquad \text{[Eq. 8-9]}$$
$$x_R = F(x_L) \oplus x_R \qquad \text{[Eq. 8-10]}$$

3. Swap x_L and x_R.

4. Repeat step 2 for further iterations:

$$x_R = x_R \oplus P_{17} \qquad \text{[Eq. 8-11]}$$
$$x_L = x_L \oplus P_{18} \qquad \text{[Eq. 8-12]}$$

5. Recombine both halves.

6. Function F is as follows: Divide x_L into four 8-bit quarters: $a, b, c,$ and d

$$F(x_L) = ((S_{(1,a)} + S_{(2,b)} \bmod 2^{32}) \oplus S_{(3,c)} + S_{(4,d)} \bmod 2^{32} \qquad \text{[Eq. 8-13]}$$

Decryption is exactly the same as encryption, except that $P_1, P_2,...,$ P_{18} are used in the reverse order. The subkeys are calculated using the Blowfish algorithm. The exact method is:

1. First initialize the P-array and then the four S-boxes, in order, with a fixed string. This string consists of the hexadecimal digits of π.

2. XOR P_1 with the first 32 bits of the key, XOR P_2 with the second 32 bits of the key, and so on for all bits of the key (up to P_{18}). Repeatedly cycle through the key bits until the entire P-array has been XORed with key bits.

3. Encrypt the all-zero string with the Blowfish algorithm, using the subkeys described in Steps 1 and 2.

4. Replace P_1 and P_2 with the output of Step 3.

5. Encrypt the output of Step 3 using the Blowfish algorithm with the modified subkeys.

6. Replace P_3 and P_4 with the output of Step 5.

7. Continue the process, replacing all elements of the P-array and then all four S-boxes in order, with the output of the continuously changing Blowfish algorithm.

Cryptanalysis of Blowfish

Blowfish has resisted cryptanalytic attacks using differential cryptanalysis. Vaudenay has discovered weak keys but exploitation of them is impractical (1 in 2^{14}). The full 16-round Blowfish has been introduced in a number of vendor products examined by ICSA crypto laboratories. The full 16-round Blowfish appears to be a strong algorithm and meets its designers' goals. Unfortunately, several implementations of Blowfish that combine it with some other algorithm are not secure and have actually weakened the vendor cryptosystem delivery.

RC5

RC5 (Rivest Cipher Number 5), invented by Dr. Ronald Rivest, has been analyzed extensively by RSA laboratories. It is very strong block cipher with a variety of parameters: block size, key size, and number of rounds. The cipher is quite compact. Essentially three operations are employed: XOR; addition; and rotations, which are the heart of RC5. *Rotations* are constant-time operations on most processors and variable rotations are nonlinear functions, and depend on both the key and the data.

RC5 has a variable-length block. In fact, RC5 may be thought of as a family of algorithms. RC5 can have a 32-bit word size and a 64-bit input block. The same algorithm works well with a 64-bit word size and a 128 bit input block. Rivest designates the particular implementations of RC5 as $RC5\text{-}w/r/b$ where w is the word size, r is the number of rounds, and b is the length of the key in bytes.

For the 32-bit word size case encryption uses a $2r+2$ key-dependent 32-bit words—S_0, S_1, S_2,..., S_{2r+1}, where r is the number of rounds. The plain text is divided into two 32-bit words, A and B. Then:

$$A = A + S_0 \qquad \text{[Eq. 8-14]}$$

$$B = B + S_1 \qquad \text{[Eq. 8-15]}$$

For $i = 1$ to r:

$$A = ((A \oplus B) <<< B) + S_{2i} \qquad \text{[Eq. 8-16]}$$

$$B = ((B \oplus A) <<< A) + S_{2i+1} \qquad \text{[Eq. 8-17]}$$

The output is put in the registers A and B. The symbols $<<<$ and $>>>$ refer to a left or right circular shift, respectively. Addition and subtraction are performed mod 2^{32}.

Decryption is similar. For $i = r$ decremented to 1:

$$B = ((B - S_{2i+1}) >>> A) \oplus A \qquad \text{[Eq. 8-18]}$$

$$A = ((A - S_{2i}) >>> B) \oplus B \qquad \text{[Eq. 8-19]}$$

$$B = B - S_1 \qquad \text{[Eq. 8-20]}$$

$$A = A - S_0 \qquad \text{[Eq. 8-21]}$$

Keys

Copying the bytes of the symmetric key into an array L of c 32-bit words, padding the final word with zeros if necessary creates the key array. The array, called S, is initialized using a linear congruential generator mod 2^{32}. Two constants are used based on hexadecimal representation of natural log e and pi: $P = 0\text{xb7e15163}$ and $Q = 0\text{x9e3779b9}$. (For a word size of 64 bits, $P = 0\text{xb7e151628aed2a6b}$ and $Q = 0\text{x9e3779b97f4a7c15}$.)

$$S_0 = P \qquad \text{[Eq. 8-22]}$$

For $i = 1$ to $2(r+1)-1$:

$$S_i = (S_{i-1} + Q) \bmod 2^{32} \qquad \text{[Eq. 8-23]}$$

In the last step, we then mix L into S:

$$i = j = 0 \qquad \text{[Eq. 8-24]}$$

$$A = B = 0 \qquad \text{[Eq. 8-25]}$$

Do n times [where n is the maximum of $2(r + 1)$ and c]:

$$A = S_i + (S_i + A + B) <<< 3 \qquad \text{[Eq. 8-26]}$$

$$B = L_j = (L_j + A + B) <<< (A + B) \qquad \text{[Eq. 8-27]}$$

$$i = (i + 1) \bmod 2(r + 1) \qquad \text{[Eq. 8-28]}$$

$$j = (j + 1) \bmod c \qquad \text{[Eq. 8-29]}$$

RSA Laboratories has tested RC5 extensively and is satisfied with its results. Reported attacks against RC5 employ brute force or differential cryptanalysis on reduced rounds. They have been ineffective for the full 16-round version. ICSA cryptography lab tests have verified that RC5 is a very strong and resistant cipher.

Asymmetric Algorithms

We continue with three asymmetric algorithms: RSA, the ECC Diffie-Hellman (DH) analog, and the Raike Public Key (RPK) cryptosystem.

The RSA Algorithm

Whitfield Diffie and Martin Hellman of Stanford University gave birth to the new science of public-key cryptography, by challenging the scientific community to come up with a cryptographic algorithm that met the requirements of public-key systems. The extraordinary team of Ron Rivest, Adi Shamir, and Len Adleman (RSA) of MIT accepted the challenge in 1977 and developed what has become one of the world standards and one of the most widely accepted and implemented approaches to public-key encryption.

The RSA scheme makes use of an expression with exponentials. Plain text is encrypted in blocks. Each block has a binary value less than some value n. Encryption and decryption are of the following form, for some plain-text block M and cipher-text block C.

$$C = M^e \bmod n \qquad \text{[Eq. 8-30]}$$

$$M = C^d \bmod n = (M^e)^d \bmod n = M^{ed} \bmod n \qquad \text{[Eq. 8-31]}$$

Both sender and receiver must know the value of n. The sender knows the value of e, and only the lawful receiver knows the value of d. Note the similarity to the knapsack problem discussed in Chapter 7. This is a public-key encryption system with a public key of KU = $[e, n]$ and a private key KR = $[d,n]$. Three requirements for this system to be effective exist:

1. It must be possible to find values of e, d, and n, such that:

$$M^{ed} = M \bmod n \qquad \text{for all } M < n \qquad \text{[Eq. 8-32]}$$

2. It must be possible to easily calculate C^d and M^e for all values of $M < n$.

3. It must be computationally infeasible to determine d given e and n.

The first requirement is met using Euler's theorem and its corollary. Euler's theorem states that for every a and n that are relatively prime:

$$a\Phi^{(n)} \equiv 1 \bmod n \qquad \text{[Eq. 8-33]}$$

An important quantity in number theory, known as *Euler's Totient function,* is written as $\Phi^{(n)}$. It is defined as the number of positive integers less than n and relatively prime to n. For any prime number p,

$$\Phi^{(n)} = p - 1 \qquad \text{[Eq. 8-34]}$$

Two integers a and b are *relatively prime* if they have no prime factors in common, that is, if their only common factor is 1. This is equivalent to saying that a and b are relatively prime if $\gcd(a, b) = 1$, where gcd is defined as the *greatest common divisor.* For example, 8 and 15 are relatively prime because the divisors of 8 are 1, 2, 4, and 8 and the divisors of 15 are 1, 3, 5, and 15.

Fermat's theorem states:

$$a^{n-1} \equiv a \bmod n \qquad \text{if } a, n \text{ are relatively prime} \qquad \text{[Eq. 8-35]}$$

Note that

$$a^{n-1} \equiv 1 \bmod n \qquad \text{if } a, n \text{ are relatively prime} \qquad \text{[Eq. 8-36]}$$

Equation 8-35 holds if n is prime, because $\Phi^{(n)} = n-1$ and Fermat's theorem is valid. Actually, Eq. 8-35 holds for any integer n. The proof may be found in Stallings, who also presents a useful alternative form to Eq. 8-35:

$$a\Phi^{(n)+1} \equiv a \pmod{n} \qquad \text{[Eq. 8-37]}$$

A corollary to Euler's theorem that helps us understand the RSA algorithm is that given two prime numbers p and q and integers $n = p \times q$ and m, with $0 < m < n$, the following relationship holds:

$$m\Phi^{(n)} = m^{(p-1)(q-1)} \equiv 1 \bmod n \qquad \text{[Eq. 8-38]}$$

If gcd(m, n) = 1, that is, m and n are relatively prime, then the relationship holds true by virtue of Euler's theorem.

An alternative form of Eq. 8-38 is:

$$m^{k\Phi(n)+1} = m^{k(p-1)(q-1)+1} \equiv m \bmod n \qquad \textbf{[Eq. 8-39]}$$

Since p and q are prime we know that:

$$\Phi^{(n)} = \Phi^{(pq)} = \Phi^{(p)} \times \Phi^{(q)} = (p-1)(q-1) \qquad \textbf{[Eq. 8-40]}$$

We can satisfy the first requirement of the RSA system requirements by the following relationship:

$$ed = k\Phi^{(n)+1} \qquad \textbf{[Eq. 8-41]}$$

This is equivalent to saying:

$$ed \equiv 1 \bmod \Phi^{(n)} \qquad \textbf{[Eq. 8-42]}$$

And, most important, the inverse relationship exists:

$$e \equiv d^{-1} \bmod \Phi^{(n)} \qquad \textbf{[Eq. 8-43]}$$

That is, e and d are multiplicative inverses mod $\Phi^{(n)}$ because of the rules of modular arithmetic; this is true only if d and e are relatively prime to $\Phi^{(n)}$.

Equivalently,

$$\gcd(\Phi^{(n)}, d) = 1 \qquad \textbf{[Eq. 8-44]}$$

We have then a relationship of the form:

$$M^{ed} = M \bmod n \qquad \textbf{[Eq. 8-45]}$$

We also know that Eq. 8-39 is applicable, where $\Phi^{(n)}$ is Euler's Totient function.

$$m^{k\Phi(n)+1} = m^{k(p-1)(q-1)+1} \equiv m \bmod n \qquad \textbf{[Eq. 8-46]}$$

Modular arithmetic is the same as normal arithmetic in the sense that commutative, associative, distributive, and identity laws are the same. There is one peculiarity of modular arithmetic that sets it apart from ordinary arithmetic. The following statement is true:

$$\text{if } (a + b) \equiv (a + c) \bmod n, \text{ then } b \equiv c \bmod n \qquad \textbf{[Eq. 8-47]}$$

However, the following statement is true only with the attached condition:

$$\text{if } (a \times b) \equiv (a \times c) \bmod n, \text{ then } b \equiv c \bmod n, \text{ if } a$$
$$\text{is relatively prime to } n \qquad \textbf{[Eq. 8-48]}$$

The reason for this unusual result is that, for any general modulus n, the multiplier a, when applied in turn to the numbers 0 through $(n-1)$, will fail to produce a complete set of residues if a and n have any factors in common. Essentially when we have a many-to-one mapping, there is not a unique inverse to the multiply operation. For some prime number p, there may exist a multiplicative inverse (w^{-1}), which if drawn from a set of relatively prime numbers, and if it exists, there exists a z such that $w*z \equiv 1 \bmod p$.

Description of the RSA Algorithm

The RSA scheme has four essential ingredients:

1. p, q, two prime numbers   (private, chosen)

2. $n = pq$ (public, calculated)

3. d, with $\gcd(\Phi^{(n)}, d) = 1; 1 < d < \Phi^{(n)})$ (private, calculated)

4. $e \equiv d^{-1} \bmod \Phi^{(n)}$ (public, chosen)

The private key consists of $\{d, n\}$ and the public key consists of $\{e, n\}$. User A publishes his public key and user B wishes to use it to communicate, via message M, with user A. User B calculates the cipher text $C = M^e \pmod n$ and transmits C. Upon receipt of this cipher text, user A decrypts it by calculating $M = C^d \pmod n$.

Why does this work? We have chosen e and d such that

$$e \equiv d^{-1} \bmod \Phi^{(n)} \qquad \textbf{[Eq. 8-49]}$$

Therefore,

$$ed \equiv 1 \bmod \Phi^{(n)} \qquad \textbf{[Eq. 8-50]}$$

So in effect, ed is of the form $k\Phi^{(n)+1}$. But by Euler's theorem and its corollary, given two prime numbers p and q, and integers $n = pq$ and M, with $0 < M < n$:

$$M^{k\Phi^{(n)+1}} = M^{k(p-1)(q-1)+1} \equiv M \bmod n \qquad \textbf{[Eq. 8-51]}$$

So,

$$M^{ed} \equiv M \bmod n \qquad \text{[Eq. 8-52]}$$

Finally,

$$C = M^e \bmod n \qquad \text{[Eq. 8-53]}$$

$$M = C^d \bmod n \equiv (M^e)^d \bmod n \equiv M^{ed} \bmod n \equiv M \bmod n \qquad \text{[Eq. 8-54]}$$

Keys

RSA keys are generated via the following procedure:

1. Select p, q with p and q both prime
2. Calculate $n = p \times q$
3. Select integer d where $\gcd(\Phi^{(n)}, d) = 1; 1 < d < \Phi^{(n)})$
4. Calculate e where $e = d^{-1} \bmod \Phi^{(n)}$
5. Define the public key as $KU = \{e, n\}$
6. Define the private key as $KR = \{d, n\}$

Encryption

1. Plain text M must be $M < n$.
2. Cipher text is generated as $C = M^e \bmod n$.

Decryption

1. Cipher text is C.
2. We obtain the plain text M by calculating $M = C^d \bmod n$.

RSA Encryption/Decryption Calculations

The RSA encryption and decryption calculations involve raising an integer to an integer power, mod n. To reduce the possibility of working with superlarge numbers, we can use the property of modular arithmetic:

$$[(a \bmod n) \times (b \bmod n)] \bmod n = (a \times b) \bmod n \qquad \text{[Eq. 8-55]}$$

We can reduce intermediate results modulo n to make the calculation reasonable and practical.

The efficiency of exponentiation must be considered, since the RSA algorithm deals with quite large exponents. Compare the calculation of $x^{16} = x^1 * x^2 \cdots x^{16}$. This requires 15 multiplications. A better way involves only four multiplications: x^2, x^4, x^8, x^{16}. Essentially, we repeatedly take the square of each partial result. Key generation procedures require the determination of two prime numbers p and q and the selection of e or d. Having chosen e or d, we may calculate the other. Because $n = pq$ is known, to prevent brute force attacks, p and q must be chosen from a *very large set* and must be large numbers.

The one way to find an arbitrarily large prime number is to choose an odd number at random of order of magnitude required and test for primality. If found, continue; if not, choose another odd random number and test again. Most tests for primality are probabilistic and yield an integer that probably is prime. One of the most efficient algorithms for testing for primality is the Miller-Rabin algorithm (described in Stallings); the process looks like this:

1. Pick an odd integer n at random (using a PNRG).

2. Pick an integer $a < n$ at random.

3. Perform the probabilistic primality test. If n fails the test, reject the value n and start again.

4. If n has passed a sufficient number of tests, accept n; otherwise, return to Step 2.

5. This process is repeated each time a new public/private key pair is generated.

There will be a lot of numbers rejected in the process. The prime number theorem states that the primes near N are spaced, on the average, one every $(\ln N)$ integers. All even integers except 2 can be rejected since 2 is prime, so the real test involves only $[\frac{1}{2} \ln(N)]$ integers. If we want to calculate a prime on the order of 2^{200} we need to calculate $\ln(2^{200})/2 = 70$ trials to find the prime. With p and q determined as primes, the process of key generation requires the choosing of e and the calculation of d. We use Euclid's algorithm to generate a series of random numbers, testing each against $\Phi^{(n)}$ until a number relatively prime to $\Phi^{(n)}$ is found. The probability that two random numbers are relatively prime is about 0.6, so the number of tests required to find a suitable integer is reasonable.

Here is a simple example:

1. Let $M = 19$ (plain text).

2. Generate KU = public key = {5, 119}.

3. Generate KR = private key = {77, 119}.

4. Convert plain to cipher text: Calculate 19^5 = 2,476,099/n = 2,476,099/119 = 20,807 with a remainder of 66.

5. The cipher text C has been calculated to be 66.

6. Given the cipher text C = 66, we raise it to the power of 77 from the private key.

7. Calculate 66^{77} = 1.27×10^{140}.

8. Convert cipher text to plain text: Divide the intermediate result by 119, from the private key, to get 1.06×10^{138} with a remainder of 19.

9. The 19 is our original plain-text value = M.

Addressing the second and third requirements for the RSA algorithm, we see that both encryption and decryption involve raising an integer to a power. If exponentiation is done over integers and then reduces modulo n, the intermediate values would be extremely large and difficult to deal with. Modular arithmetic provides a useful property:

$$[(a \bmod n) \times (b \bmod n)] \bmod n = (a \times b) \bmod n \qquad \textbf{[Eq. 8-56]}$$

Therefore intermediate results are reduced modulo n.

RSA Cryptanalytic Considerations

Researchers have attacked the RSA cryptosystem extensively. Four possible approaches have been identified:

1. Brute force: try all possible private keys.

2. Factor p into its two prime factors. This enables the calculation of $\Phi^{(n)} = (p - 1)(q - 1)$, which in turn enables determination of $d = e^{-1} \pmod{\Phi^{(n)}}$.

3. Determine $\Phi^{(n)}$ directly, without first determining p and q. Again, this enables determination of $d = e^{-1} \bmod \Phi(n)$.

4. Determine d directly, without first determining $\Phi^{(n)}$.

The defense against brute force attacks is to enhance the key space. The larger the number of bits in e and d, the better the defense. However, with larger key generation size, the complexity of the calculations reduces the system speed.

Much effort has been focused on factoring p into its two prime factors. No algorithm published can reasonably factor the product of two primes for very large values (e.g., several hundred decimal digits). Hence, the success of the RSA system.

The best known algorithms factor an integer n in a time proportional to Eq. 8-57:

$$L^{(n)} = e\sqrt{\{\ln n \times \ln(\ln n)\}} \qquad \text{[Eq. 8-57]}$$

When we use order of magnitude analysis on Eq. 8-57, for a key of 150 in length, $e^{150} = 10^{65}$ and this equals about 10^{12} operations per hour on a fast machine. It is suggested that a magnitude of $n = 150$ to 200 digits will be secure for some time.

With presently known algorithms, determining $\Phi^{(n)}$ directly given n or determining d given e and n, appear to be just as time-consuming as the factoring problems. Factoring performance is the benchmark from which we measure the cryptosecurity of RSA.

Rivest made the following suggestions:

1. n should be very large, on the order of 10^{150} to 10^{200}.

2. p and q should differ in length by only a few digits.

3. Both p and q should be on the order of 10^{75} to 10^{100}. In addition, both $(p - 1)$ and $(q - 1)$ should contain a large prime factor.

4. $\gcd(p - 1, q - 1)$ should be small.

Wiener describes a rather contrived attack where $e < n$ and d is set at $< n^{1/4}$.

Diffie-Hellman Key Agreement Algorithm (DH)

Key agreement is a protocol by which a pair of users, communicating over an insecure channel, can independently calculate the same secret key from publicly communicated numbers. In 1976, Whitfield Diffie and Martin Hellman developed the first key-exchange protocol. The DH protocol is:

1. Alice and Bob agree on a large prime n, and g, such that g is primitive mod n. *Primitive* means that the various powers of g will generate all nonzero integers mod n or all the integers in the set between 1 and $n-1$. (Alice and Bob are part of a politically correct set of fictional characters that seem to have permeated recent literature.)

2. Alice chooses a random large integer x and sends it to Bob in the form:

$$X = g^x \bmod n \qquad \text{[Eq. 8-58]}$$

3. Bob chooses a random large integer y and sends it to Alice in the form:

$$Y = g^y \bmod n \qquad \text{[Eq. 8-59]}$$

4. Clever Alice computes

$$k = Y^x \bmod n \qquad \text{[Eq. 8-60]}$$

5. And Bob, not to be outdone, computes

$$k'' = X^y \bmod n \qquad \text{[Eq. 8-61]}$$

Both k and k'' are equal to $g^{xy} \bmod n$, because $k = (g^y)^x \bmod n = g^{yx} \bmod n = g^{xy} \bmod n$; and k'' is equal to $g^{xy} \bmod n$, because $k'' = (g^x)^y \bmod n = g^{xy} \bmod n$. Note that x and y cannot be recovered without computing the discrete logarithms of X and Y. Computing a discrete logarithm in certain finite groups is computationally difficult, so the secret values x and y are effectively hidden in the quantities transmitted. The resulting key is k (or k'') and is known only to Bob and Alice.

These values could also be public/private key pairs. Instead of Alice generating an integer and sending it to Bob, Bob need only look up Alice's public key $X = g^x \bmod n$ in a common database and use it to generate their shared secret key. Bob could encrypt a message with that key and send it to Alice. To decrypt the message, Alice would look up Bob's key in the database and use it to generate their shared secret key, which could be used to decrypt the message. This approach eliminates the need for prior communication between users. Note that the unauthenticated protocol could be vulnerable to a MIM or "man-in-the-middle" attack.

ECDH Key Agreement

ECDH is the elliptic curve analog of the traditional DH key-agreement algorithm. The DH method requires no prior contact between two parties. Each party generates a remote key and a local key and they exchange the remote keys. Each party then combines its local key with

Figure 8-3
ECDH Key
Agreement

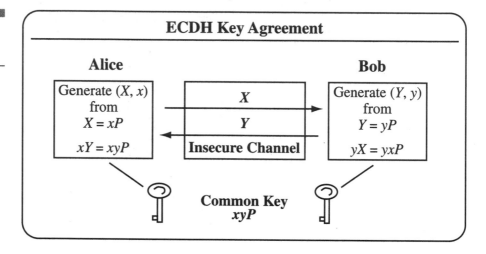

the other party's remote key to form a *shared secret*. This method is also known as carrying out an ECDH key agreement and is shown in Figure 8-3.

ECDH works as follows: Alice and Bob agree to use ECDH to obtain a shared secret.

1. Alice generates a session key pair (X, x) by randomly generating x and calculating $X = xG$, where x is an integer and G is a point on an elliptic curve. (Refer to Appendix D for a discussion of the Fields F_p and $F_2{}^m$ used to define elliptic curves from which point G is taken.)

2. Bob generates a session pair (Y, y) by randomly generating y and calculating $Y = yG$.

3. Alice sends X to Bob; Bob sends Y to Alice.

4. Alice receives Y from Bob and calculates $xY = xyG$. Bob receives X from Alice and calculates $yX = yxG$. Both Bob and Alice now have the same shared secret xyG.

Key Transport

Symmetric-key cryptography is efficient for bulk encryption and decryption of files and data. Public-key cryptography is more efficient for key management than symmetric-key but usually is much slower to encrypt and decrypt data. It is best to combine the two solutions. Two parties, who want to establish a link for the transfer of encrypted data, employ a public-key cryptosystem to transfer a one-time symmetric key, which is

Figure 8-4
Key Transport

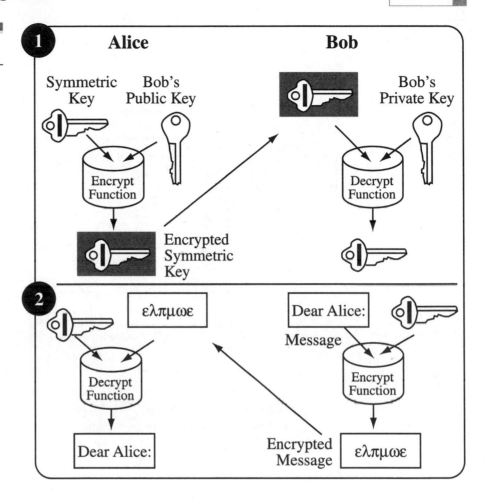

then used for the remainder of the session. The process of transferring a key via a public-key cryptosystem is known as *key-transport,* also known as *wrapping* the key to be transported. The process operates as shown in Figure 8-4.

MQV Key Agreement—Implicit Signatures

There is another ECC public-key agreement scheme, which thwarts the MIM attack. Named after its inventors Menezes, Qu, and Vanstone (MQV), it is used to share secrets between parties who already possess trusted copies of each other's public keys. As shown in Figure 8-5, both parties still generate remote and local keys and then exchange remote keys. However, upon receipt of the other party's remote key, each party

Figure 8-5
MQV Key Agreement

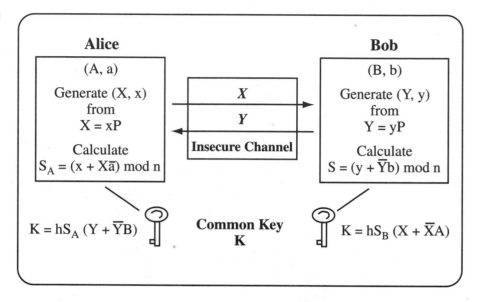

calculates a quantity called an *implicit signature,* using its own private key and the other party's public key. The shared secret is then generated from the implicit signature. What is interesting about an implicit signature is that the secrets do not agree if the other party's public key is not employed, thus, giving implicit verification that the remote secret is generated by the remote party. The MIM attack will fail; the shared secrets are not the same shared secrets because the adversary's private key is not linked to the trusted public key.

The implicit signature capability of MQV results in a computational advantage over authenticated versions of ECDH, since authentication is built into the protocol and does not require additional steps to compute.

MQV works as follows: Alice possesses a key pair (A, a), where A is her public key and a is her private key. Similarly, Bob possesses a key pair (B, b), where B is his public key and b is his private key.

1. Alice generates a session key pair (X, x) by randomly generating x and calculating $X = xG$, where x is an integer and G is a point on an elliptic curve.

2. Bob generates a session pair (Y, y) by randomly generating y and calculating $Y = yG$.

3. Alice sends X to Bob and Bob sends Y to Alice. It is assumed that Alice already has Bob's public key B and that Bob already has Alice's public key A. The public keys have been received in some trusted manner.

4. Alice calculates the implicit signature S_A:

$$S_A = (x + X'a) \bmod n \qquad \text{[Eq. 8-62]}$$

5. Bob calculates S_B in a similar manner:

$$S_B = (y + Y'b) \bmod n \qquad \text{[Eq. 8-63]}$$

6. Both Alice and Bob calculate a shared secret K:

$$K = hS_A (Y + Y'B) \qquad \text{[Eq. 8-64]}$$

$$K = hS_B (X + X'A) \qquad \text{[Eq. 8-65]}$$

where h is the cofactor defined in the August 1996 version of P1363, the draft IEEE industry standard for public-key cryptography designed by the Institute of Electrical and Electronics Engineers; and X' and Y' represent the first L bits of the first component of the point X (or Y) where:

$$L = [(\log_2 n + 1)/2] \qquad \text{[Eq. 8-66]}$$

Raike Public-Key (RPK) Cryptosystem

The RPK system, invented by Dr. William Raike, of the University of New Zealand, is based upon the discrete logarithm problem, the same mathematical basis as Diffie-Hellman Key Exchange. In this system, a public key is calculated from a private key using operations mathematically equivalent to exponentiation in finite fields. Consequently, breaking the system in the sense of computing a private key from its public key, using the best known algorithm, requires an attacker to compute logarithms over finite fields. For reasons of computational efficiency, simplicity, speed, and security, the finite fields underlying the RPK system are the Galois fields GF[2^p], where, in addition, p is selected so that 2^p-1 is a large prime, specifically a "Mersenne" prime.

Mixture Generator

The central concept, the unifying thread and the essential distinguishing feature of RPK is the concept of a *mixture generator*, which is an abstract finite state machine that starts out in a given initial state and is then able to be "clocked" or stepped through an extremely long fixed sequence of different states. Then, if there were enough time to "clock" it a sufficiently large number of times (its "period"), that sequence would repeat. After each such step, it also produces an "output" consisting of a single bit, 0 or 1. The state sequence is so long that it could never be physically stepped through its entire period, since this would require more time than the remaining lifetime of the universe. The state sequence can be imagined as a very large number of points on a circle, with a particular initial state marked to identify it as a starting point. The successive states can then be referred to according to their "distance" from the initial state, measured in numbers of steps or clock pulses.

The mixture generator's internal structure gives it interesting abilities. Viewed as an "object" in the sense of object-oriented analysis, it "knows" how to do more than simply move from one state to the next, one step (or "clock" pulse) at a time. First, it can move ahead in the state sequence by any fixed number of steps, and this operation requires not much more time than moving a single step. Second, if it is forcibly placed in a particular state that occurs some unknown number of steps D after the initial state, it is able to "jump" ahead to another state—additional D steps ahead without needing to "know" the number D. This operation requires not much more time than moving a small number of steps, unrelated to however large D might be! Finally, suppose we are interested in repeating such a jump some fixed number of times R, where we specify R but don't know D, only our jumping off state. The mixture generator can do this as well, and requires not much more than a small multiple of the time required for a single such jump, regardless of how large the multiple R might be.

Despite the fact that making such jumps is easy for the mixture generator, it is extremely difficult (in the case of large mixture generators) to answer the inverse question: If we forcibly set the mixture generator into a particular state (say, E), where is E located in the state sequence? That is, even using very powerful computers, it is quite difficult to compute how many single steps would be required to get from the fixed initial state to the state E. The precise level of difficulty of this kind of computation is the *source of security* of RPK private keys.

Another essential property of the mixture generator, viewed as a simple finite state machine, is that it has no "memory" of its "history." That is, if we place it into any particular one of its states and then clock it through successive states one step at a time while observing its outputs, the sequence of outputs will be the same regardless of how the mixture generator happened to arrive at that state. Critically, the output sequence is complex and unpredictable in a well-defined sense. As a result, it is extremely difficult for an observer to measure only the output sequence of a mixture generator to determine the details of its internal state in an effort to predict future outputs.

In the RPK system, *a public key corresponds to a state of a mixture generator, whereas a private key corresponds to the number of steps in the mixture generator's state sequence leading from the initial state to the public key.*

Within this conceptual framework, the RPK encryption and decryption algorithms can be viewed as methods by which a message sender (who possesses only a public key but not its private key) and a recipient (who knows the private key) can independently "match" the states of their own mixture generators in order to make use of the output sequences (keystreams) of the generators to respectively encrypt and decrypt an arbitrary message.

To see how this matching can work when the sender and recipient know the structure of each other's mixture generator but also each have information that is unknown to the other, refer to conceptual Figures 8-6 to 8-8. In all three, the circle represents the long sequence of mixture generator states. Letters on the insides of the circles denote mixture generator states, while letters next to arrows on the outsides of the circles denote the numbers of states between two points. The state that is twice as far along the state sequence as E is correctly denoted as "E squared" since jumping corresponds to an exponentiation process whose definition can be made precise. E is a state, not a distance or a number of steps.

Figures 8-6 and 8-7 depict the sender's steps during the start of encryption. In Figure 8-6, the sender first obtains a true random number R (not a pseudorandom number). The figure depicts using the mixture generator to "get to" the state Q, which is R steps away from the initial state. The sender then inserts Q at the start of the encrypted data to be sent to the recipient.

In Figure 8-7, the sender then resets the mixture generator, loading it with the state E represented by the recipient's public key. Despite the fact that the number of steps needed to get to E from the initial state is unknown—in fact, this number is the recipient's private key—the sender is able to use the mixture generator to jump to a state R times further along in the state sequence than E is. The sender's mixture generator has now arrived at a state K, mathematically represented by E to the power R, that is $R \times D$ steps away from the initial state. This completes the RPK initialization phase and the sender is ready to begin encrypting data to be sent by combining it with the mixture generator's output sequence.

Figure 8-6
The Sender Obtains a
True Random
Number

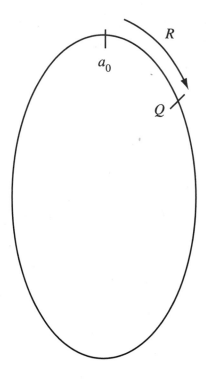

Figure 8-7
The Sender Resets
the Mixture
Generator

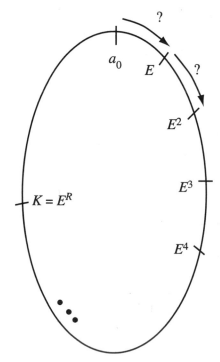

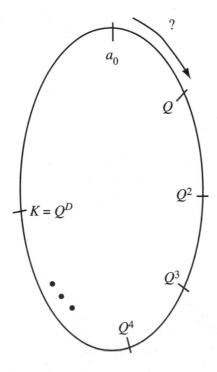

Figure 8-8
The Initialization
Process

Figure 8-8 represents the initialization process performed by the recipient. The recipient first extracts Q from the start of the encrypted data that has been received, setting the mixture generator to the state represented by Q. Then, using the same special abilities of the mixture generator, the recipient jumps to a state D times further along the state sequence than Q. Here the recipient knows Q and D, but does not know R (the random number selected by the sender specifically for this message). Nevertheless, the recipient's mixture generator has now arrived at a state mathematically represented by Q to the power D, that is also $R \times D$ steps away from the initial state. It has managed to arrive at the same state K. Having completed the initialization phase, the recipient is now ready to begin decrypting the rest of the received data by using the mixture generator's output sequence to reverse the combining process performed by the sender during encryption.

One of the central concepts underlying the RPK system is a pseudo-random binary keystream generator called a mixture generator, taken from probability theory, of a mixture (not a sum) of independent and identically distributed random variables. The probability distribution of the mixture, in the case when there are a finite number of random variables being mixed, is a *convex combination* of the distributions of the components. A mixture of independent identically uniformly distributed random variables is itself uniform. A mixture generator consists of a single pseudorandom binary generator, called the *mixer,* whose outputs or states are used to successively select, in a memoryless fashion, outputs from members of a set of other component pseudorandom binary generators.

One example of such a configuration is shown in Figure 8-9, where the mixer generator G_m is a *maximal-period linear shift register generator* (MLSRG), whose last three stages at time T are used to select one of eight other MLSRGs ($G_0,...,G_i,...,G_7$), whose output is to be used at time T. The clock rate of the mixer generator G_m in this case can be taken as three times the clock rate of the component generators G_i. A simpler example, shown in Figure 8-10, is a special case of this and is known as a *Geffe generator.* In Figure 8-10, the last stage of the mixer generator G_m selects the output of the top generator G_t if the mixer output at time T is a 1, or the output of the bottom generator G_b if the mixer output at time T is a 0. The mixer and both components in this case are all clocked at the same rate. When using MLSRGs as component generators, it is essential to use generators with the mathematical property that their generator polynomials are primitive polynomials. In addition, such gen-

Figure 8-9
Mixture Generator with MLSRG Component Generators

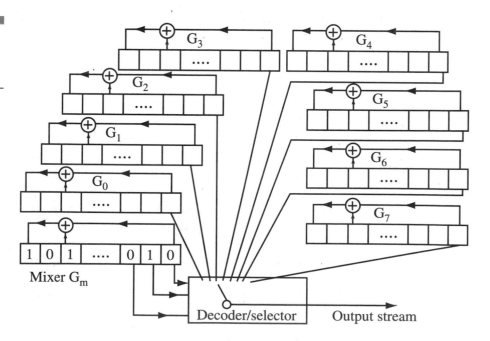

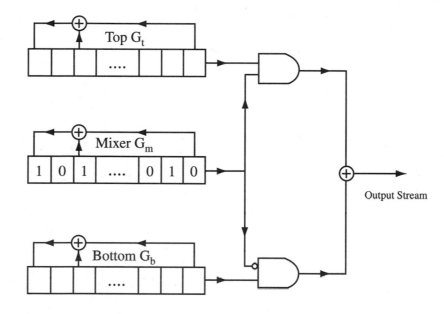

Figure 8-10
Geffe-Type Generator

⊕   Denotes mod-2 adder (XOR gate)

o   Denotes complemented (inverted) input

Denotes logical AND gate (multiplication)

erators may have the additional property that they have a prime number of stages, so that the lengths of their periods are Mersenne primes.

Since it is a finite-state device, starting from any particular state of its mixer and other component generators, a mixture generator can be used to generate a periodic binary sequence (i.e., a sequence of 0s and 1s that will eventually repeat). The state of the generator is described by a collection of binary values specifying the state of each stage of each of its components.

The advantages of mixer generator configurations are that their periods are very long, their complexity is very high, their distribution of 0s and 1s is well-balanced, and successive outputs are substantially uncorrelated. Their outputs also have excellent statistical properties in terms of their n-tuple distribution and runs statistics. Some of these properties can be demonstrated mathematically, whereas others have been verified statistically (for example, using chi-square and runs tests).

Any periodic binary sequence is capable of being generated by some MLSRG, and one critical factor in assessing the suitability of a sequence for cryptographic purposes is the length of the *shortest* linear feedback shift register required to generate the sequence. A strong advantage of mixture generator configurations is that it is often easy to precisely characterize this length as a function of the mixer and component generator lengths and that the length (the *Berlekamp complexity*)—which is a good measure of the complexity of the generator and consequently its usefulness for *some* cryptographic purposes—is very high.

The RPK system mechanics may be discussed using the Geffe-type mixture generator shown earlier in Figure 8-10 as an example. We denote the numbers of stages in the MLSRGs forming the mixer, top, and bottom generators by n_m, n_t, and n_b, and the initial states (at time $T = 0$) of the respective generators by a_{m0}, a_{t0}, and a_{b0}, respectively. Each of the initial states is fixed and publicly known, although it is possible to use the initial states as part of a key known only to a particular group of users in order to permit secure and authenticated transmission of messages among members of this group.

The period (i.e., the number of clock cycles after which the generator output repeats itself) of a Geffe-type generator is the product of the periods of the component generators. Its complexity, as measured by the number of stages in the shortest equivalent linear shift register generator that is able to produce the same output sequence, is $n_m n_t + (1 + n_m)n_b$.

Using a Mixture Generator to Implement a One-Way Function

The very long binary sequence generated by a mixture generator has a number of useful properties. It is of course possible to actually run or "clock" the generator to obtain its output stream and its sequence of internal states. Since the generator's period is so long, of course, it is not possible to generate more than a tiny segment of the entire output stream in any reasonable period of time no matter how fast the generator can be clocked. Even for the smaller of the example generators mentioned previously, the period length is on the order of 2^{303}!

It is possible to use the mixture generator to rapidly and efficiently "calculate" what its final internal state would be if its individual components were clocked any given numbers of times, no matter how huge, starting from a known starting state.

It is, however, not computationally feasible to answer the inverse question. That is, given known final states for each component, it is extremely difficult to determine the numbers of times each of them would need to be clocked in order to reach such final states from known starting states. Answering this question is tantamount to solving a so-called "discrete logarithm" problem. One of the better algorithms for solving such problems is the one due to D. Coppersmith, which is highly efficient. The time required to execute it on any conceivable computer can be quantitatively estimated. Although it is practical to carry out the necessary calculations in a modest length of time on very fast computers in the case when the longest component generator is of length, say, 127, this is not the case when the longest component generator length is above 600 or so. Given the most recent work done at Sandia Labs, it appears that the only way to distribute the discrete log problem for $GF(2^n)$ is on a massively parallel computer with a specially tuned operating system designed to leverage the various processors to speed up intermediate calculations. The best progress to date has been on a field of size 503. Given the lack of progress in the area of massively parallel computing and the enormous storage requirements of solving discrete logs for fields of 600 bits or larger, it is believed that a mixture generator configured with one element of 607 bits or larger will be cryptographically secure through the end of the century.

Mixture generators incorporating components with lengths considerably higher than 600 are still efficient and practical to implement. One current implementation, for example, allows component generators of length 1279 or even 2281. Solving such problems will remain computationally infeasible even under the most optimistic predictions concerning available computing power. Moreover, the difficulty of obtaining solutions can be accurately engineered by selecting generator lengths appropriately.

RPK Private and Public Keys

- In the RPK system, a private key is equivalent to a set of (binary) numbers that specify arbitrary numbers of times the components of the mixer generator are to be imagined to be clocked. These can be interpreted as "distances" (measured in units of numbers of clock ticks) within the periodic output stream of each component, starting from a fixed and known starting point.

- The public key corresponding to a private key is the final state of the mixture generator that would result if each component were to be clocked a number of times given by the corresponding part of the private key.

It is important here to draw attention to an important characteristic of the pairs of private keys and public keys used in the RPK system. In some systems, the key pairs must be selected together, according to specific requirements and limitations, or are required to be randomly generated. In the RPK system, the selection of a private key is free and unrestricted. It may even be selected arbitrarily by its user.

The preferred implementation of RPK now specifies that the user need only choose a single value for the longest generator. The initialization phase performs only the necessary exponentiations on the longest generator as well. The resultant state of that generator is then distributed to the other two generators. This preferred approach is more efficient since the other component generators require no exponentiations and it is also believed to add a measure of enhanced security.

In the context of the Geffe generator mentioned, for purposes of selecting a *private key* a user A selects three numbers D_m, D_t, and D_b, where D_m is in the range from 1 to $2^{(n^m-1)}$, D_t is in the range from 1 to $2^{(n^t-1)}$, and D_b is in the range from 1 to $2^{(n^b-1)}$. It should be noted that each of these ranges include the extreme values mentioned, although strictly speaking the high end of the range (all ones in binary) should be excluded since it is equal to the period. The *public key* for user A will consist of the states E_m, E_t, and E_b of the three component generators after D_m, D_t, and D_b clock cycles (shifts), respectively. For a mixture generator with, say, N component generators, the private and public keys will have N, rather than 3, such component states. The number of bits required to form either a private or public key is $n_m + n_t + n_b$.

Encryption Using a Public Key

The private key D for user A, say, consists of three numbers (D_m, D_t, D_b) while user A's public key E consists of the three numbers (E_m, E_t, E_b), which are assumed to be publicly known, perhaps posted in a public directory file. The public key represents the states of the corresponding generators after D_m, D_t, and D_b clock ticks, respectively, starting from given and known initial states $a_0 = (a_{m0}, a_{t0}, a_{b0})$. Note that corresponding components of D and E are represented by the same number of bits.

When user B wishes to encrypt a plain-text message P so that it can be decrypted only by user A (using A's private key), user B first generates a true random initialization key $R = (R_m, R_t, R_b)$ that is to be used solely during the encryption of P. R is analogous to D in that it represents "exponents" for the component generators, and the three components of R must fall in the same ranges as those of D. User B next computes an "open key" $Q = (Q_m, Q_t, Q_b)$ from R in the same way that a public key E is computed from a private key D. That is, Q represents the states of the component generators at time R, starting from the initial state a_0. User B then includes Q in the cipher-text message header, to be transmitted or stored in the clear and which may also contain other information useful for communication purposes.

To continue the encryption process, user B loads the component generators with an initial state consisting of E (user A's public key) and then again uses the same random initialization key $R = (R_m, R_t, R_b)$ to compute a final generator initialization state $K = (K_m, K_t, K_b)$ by "exponentiating" A's public key E, taking R as the exponent. In polynomial notation, this can be written as $K_j(x) = [E_j(x)]R_j \bmod p(x)$, for $j = m, t, b$. User B does this "exponentiation" of A's public key by using the mixture generator's component shift registers, interpreted as computing products of binary powers E^{2^k}, $[k = 0,1,...,n - 1]$, analogous to the way that a public key is computed from a private key.

Note that user B has used both the random initialization key R and user A's public key E in computing K, as well as publicly available knowledge of the initial state a_0 and the structure of the underlying mixture generator. The total computational effort, accomplished using the mixture generator's component generators, has amounted only to the polynomial exponentiations required to advance the states of the component generators twice—that is, once to compute Q and once to compute K.

The essential property of K for purposes of the RPK encryption system is that K describes the state resulting from advancing the generators first by D and then exponentiating the resulting state by R. This represents the state that would be the result if the generator could be advanced by a number of clock ticks equal to R multiplied by D, despite the fact that user B has been able to compute K without knowing D.

The state K is used as a final generator initialization state with which to begin creating the cipher text. User B generates the body of the cipher text C by using the keystream obtained by clocking (running) the mixture generator starting from the state K, operating with it and combining it with the plain-text bit stream P. This *combining process* must be invertible (that is, it must be possible to recover the plain text P given K and C) and can be done in a variety of ways.

Decryption

To decrypt the received cipher text, user A first uses the state given by the open key Q contained in the message header to compute the generator state corresponding to Q^D, where the exponent is his private key D. This process of exponentiating Q by D is done using the same kind of process used to exponentiate E by R during encryption. We observe that the resulting generator state is K, since Q represents the generator state after R clock ticks starting from the base state a_0 and the state after $R \cdot D$ clock ticks is just K, as noted earlier. In polynomial notation this fact can be expressed as

$$E^R = (x^D)^R = K = (x^R)^D = Q^D \qquad \textbf{[Eq. 8-67]}$$

This mathematical relationship is the same one underlying the Diffie-Hellman key exchange previously discussed. Note that the recipient has been able to compute K without the need to know the random initialization key R generated for encryption. User A is then able to run the mixture generator starting from the final initialization state K (that is, clock it through successive states) to obtain the keystream bits needed to invert the combining process performed during encryption. Since the mixture generator is started from the state K for both encryption and decryption, the keystream output will be identical in both cases.

Authentication Systems

Many of today's messages travel via the Internet or through corporate or military network systems. One of the more confusing areas of network security is *authentication* and its sister, *digital signatures*. The bibliography gives several references that cover this topic in detail. We look first at the goals of authentication, then the three classes of authentication functions: message encryption, cryptographic checksums, and finally we consider hash functions. Authentication protocols are discussed further relative to the Internet in Chapter 9.

There are several cryptanalytic attacks on hash functions. The most fascinating of these attacks on hash functions is affectionately known as the *Birthday Attack,* which is the underlying justification for a generalized theory of duplications and can be used to defeat hash codes with lengths less than approximately 64 bits (like DES if it was used to produce the hash code).

 **Authentication Goals**

A modern cryptosystem must be able to provide authentication of its users. The Internet and the digital revolution have made the security goal of authentication as important as secrecy. There are at least seven goals for cryptographic authentication depending on computer environment:

1. To prevent unauthorized disclosure

2. To thwart traffic analysis of messages

3. To thwart masquerade attacks, where fraudulent messages may be inserted between parties communicating

4. To prevent content modification, deletion, revision, or reordering

5. To prevent any sequence modification, transposition, deletion, or such

6. To prevent timing modifications, that is, delay or replay of messages or DOS (denial of service) attacks

7. To prevent message repudiation (user denial of agreement)

The first two goals may be addressed by cryptographic countermeasures. Goals 3 through 6 are achieved by message authentication mechanisms. The last goal can be dealt with using digital signatures. Digital signatures can be used as a broad spectrum countermeasure against many of the previously listed attacks.

Both message authentication and digital signature mechanisms include an authentication value and a protocol to enable the receiver to verify the authenticity of the message.

There are three basic authentication functions:

1. *Message encryption:* The cipher text of the entire message acts as its own authenticator.

2. *Cryptographic checksum:* A known function of the message M and a secret key that produces a fixed-length value that serves as an authenticator.

3. *Hash function:* A known function that maps a message of any length into a fixed-length hash value, which serves as an authenticator.

Message Encryption

Message encryption by itself offers a measure of authentication and confidentiality. Given a conventional (symmetric) encryption:

$$A \rightarrow B: E_k\,[M] \qquad\qquad \textbf{[Eq. 8-68]}$$

Since A and B share key K, message encryption provides confidentiality. It also provides a degree of authenticity because the message that could only come from A has not been altered in transit but requires some formatting and redundancy. What is not provided is a digital signature; the receiver B could forge the message. The sender A can deny (repudiate) the message.

Let me reiterate that conventional encryption provides limited authentication. The receiver B has a decryption function D and a secret key K and will accept any input X such that the output $Y = D_k\,(X)$. If X is the cipher text of the legitimate message M produced by the encryption function, then Y is some plain-text message M. Otherwise, Y will be a meaningless sequence of bits. The problem occurs when there is no automated means of determining whether Y is legitimate plain text coming from A.

One solution to this problem is to add structure to the plain text but that cannot be replicated without using the encryption function. An example of such structure is the communication architecture consisting of layered protocols. Consider Figure 8-11, which shows the structure of messages using the TCP/IP protocol architecture.

If two hosts using this protocol share a unique secret key and all exchanges between a pair of hosts used the same key, regardless of application, then one could simply encrypt all the datagram except the IP header (see Figure 8-11). If the opponent substituted some arbitrary bit pattern for the encrypted TCP segment, the resulting plain text would not include a meaningful header because the header includes both a checksum and sequence information. Successive TCP segments on a given connection are numbered sequentially and encryption ensures that the opponent does not delay, misorder, or delete any segments.

By itself, public-key encryption provides confidentiality but not authentication. The source A uses public key KU_b of the destination B to encrypt M. Because only B can decrypt M using his private key KR_b, confidentiality is assured. Any opponent could also use B's public key to encrypt a message M', claiming to be A. Hence no authentication is available for the communication.

Figure 8-11
TCP/IP Protocol Architecture

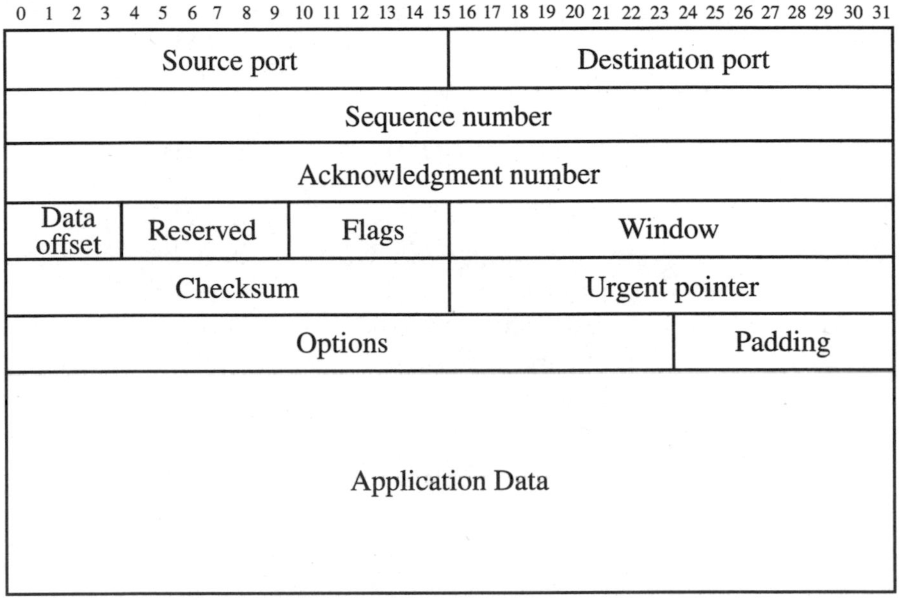

0 1 2 3 4 5 6 7 8 9 10 11 12 13 14 15	16 17 18 19 20 21 22 23 24 25 26 27 28 29 30 31
Source port	Destination port
Sequence number	
Acknowledgment number	

Data offset	Reserved	Flags	Window

Checksum	Urgent pointer

Options	Padding

Application Data

TCP Segment

$$A \rightarrow B: E_{KUb}\,[M] \qquad \textbf{[Eq. 8-69]}$$

To provide authentication, A uses his private key to encrypt the message, and B uses A's public key to decrypt the message M. This provides a measure of authentication but, similar to conventional cryptography, there must be an internal structure to the plain text so that B can distinguish between real plain text and random bits.

$$A \rightarrow B: E_{KRa}\,[M] \qquad \textbf{[Eq. 8-70]}$$

In the previous equation, since only A has the key KR_a to encrypt, we are assured that the message has not been altered in transit, the message M requires a level of formatting and redundancy, and any party can use KU_b to verify the signature.

To provide both confidentiality and authentication, A can encrypt M with his private key, which provides digital signature, then use B's public key to encrypt for confidentiality. The algorithm must be executed four times between A and B. This might be a complex transaction from a processing point of view.

$$A \rightarrow B: E_{KUb}\,[E_{KRa}\,[M]] \qquad \textbf{[Eq. 8-71]}$$

So, confidentiality is provided because of KU_b, and authentication and signature are provided because of KR_a.

Cryptographic Checksums

A second method of authentication is known as the *cryptographic checksum,* a technique that uses a secret key to generate a small fixed-size block of data, known as a cryptographic checksum or MAC (message authentication code) that is appended to the message M. The basic reason to use a MAC is to provide authentication. Both A and B share a common secret key. A calculates the MAC as a function of the message and sends it along to B as part of the message M. B decrypts the message and performs the same calculation (or inverse) on the message using the shared secret key and verifies the sender A.

$$A \rightarrow B: M \parallel C_K(M)] \hspace{2cm} \textbf{[Eq. 8-72]}$$

where $\parallel$ means concatenated with.

This also ensures that the message M has not been altered. Confidentiality can be added to the information transfer by encrypting M either before or after the cryptographic checksum operation. In both cases two separate keys are needed, each of which is shared by the sender and the receiver.

$$A \rightarrow B: E_{K_2}[M \parallel C_{K_1}(M)]] \hspace{2cm} \textbf{[Eq. 8-73]}$$

In the preceding case, authentication is provided to A and B because they share K_1; Confidentiality is established because A and B share K_2.

$$A \rightarrow B: E_{K_2}[M] \parallel C_{K_1}(E_{K_2}[M]) \hspace{2cm} \textbf{[Eq. 8-74]}$$

In this last case, authentication is provided via K_1 and confidentiality is included because of K_2.

The question is when would we use a MAC? Stallings presents six cases where a MAC is effective:

1. *Broadcast messages:* Applications where the same message is broadcast to many destinations at the same approximate time. Generally the message will be broadcast in the clear with the associated MAC attached. General alarms on a ship fall into this class. Only one destination may monitor the message for authenticity.

2. *Heavy traffic:* When lots of messages are sent, authentication may be done on a random or selected basis.

3. *Authentication of raw code:* Done in a computer program without the need to decrypt it each time the code is executed. This is typical with some file encryptor software.

4. *SNMP traffic:* The Simple Network Management Protocol v2.0 separates the functions of confidentiality and authenticity. It is important to know when parameter changes are requested by remote command.

5. *OSI layers:* Some systems require separation of authentication at one level and confidentiality at another level of design.

6. *Time:* User may want to prolong the period of protection beyond the time of reception and still process the contents. Encryption protection is lost when the message M is decrypted. This is not the case with the MAC.

Hash Functions

The goal of *hash functions,* introduced in the early 1950s, was to have functions that uniformly map a large collection of messages into a smaller set of message digests known as *hash values,* the original purpose for which was error detection. The message digest or hash value was appended to cipher text or plain text to allow detection of errors in transmission. At the receiving end, the hash value of the received message is recalculated and compared with the received value. If they do not match, an error has occurred. This detection was only for random errors. An active "spoofer" may intercept the message, modify it as he/she wishes and resend it appended with the digest or hash value recalculated for the modified message.

Public-key cryptography changed the picture. With the invention of digital signature schemes, cryptographic hash functions gained a new start. Using hash functions, it is possible to produce a fixed-length digital signature that depends on the whole message and ensures authenticity of the message. To produce a digital signature for a message x, the hash value of x, given by $H(x)$, is calculated and then encrypted with a secret key of the sender. Encryption may be by using either a public-key or private-key (symmetric) algorithm. Encryption of the hash value thwarts a replay attack or modification of the message and recalculation of the checksum or hash value accordingly. One either has the key access or doesn't—those that do can unlock the correct checksums. It should be clear that with a public key algorithm, only one person has the private key to uniquely identify the sender. With symmetric cryptography, both the sender and receiver have the key to produce a valid hashed message—hence, uniqueness is not available but alteration of the message or digest is not plausible.

There are a variety of ways in which a hash code can be used to provide message authentication, as follows:

1. The message plus concatenated code is encrypted using conventional encryption. This method provides confidentiality and internal error control because only A and B share K. It provides authentication because $H(M)$ is cryptographically protected.

$$A \rightarrow B: E_k[M \parallel H(M)] \qquad \textbf{[Eq. 8-75]}$$

where $\parallel$ means concatenated with.

2. Only the hash code is encrypted, using conventional encryption. This reduces the burden for those applications that do not require confidentiality. The combination of hashing and encryption results in an overall function that is in essence a cryptographic checksum. Case 2 provides authentication and $H(M)$ is cryptographically protected.

$$A \rightarrow B: M \parallel E_k[H(M)] \qquad \textbf{[Eq. 8-76]}$$

3. Only the hash code is encrypted, using public-key encryption and using the sender's private key. Case 3 provides authentication and a digital signature, because only the sender could have produced the encrypted hash code.

$$A \rightarrow B: M \parallel E_{KRa}[H(M)] \qquad \textbf{[Eq. 8-77]}$$

4. If confidentiality as well as a digital signature is desired, then the message plus the public-key-encrypted hash code can be encrypted using a conventional secret key.

$$A \rightarrow B: E_k\{M \parallel E_{KRa}[H(M)]\} \qquad \textbf{[Eq. 8-78]}$$

5. Case 5 uses the hash function but no encryption for message authentication. A and B share a common secret value S. A computes the hash value over the concatenation of M and S and appends the resulting hash value M. Because B possesses S, he can recompute the hash value to verify. Because the secret value itself is not sent, an opponent cannot modify an intercepted message and cannot generate a false message.

$$A \to B: [M \parallel H(M \parallel S)] \qquad \text{[Eq. 8-79]}$$

Case 5 provides authentication because only A and B share S.

6. In Case 6, confidentiality can be added to Case 5 by encrypting the entire message plus hash code.

$$A \to B: E_k [M \parallel H(M \parallel S)] \qquad \text{[Eq. 8-80]}$$

Case 6 provides authentication because only A and B share S. It also provides confidentiality because only A and B share K.

The Birthday Attack

A hash value is generated by a function H of the form

$$H = H(M) \qquad \text{[Eq. 8-81]}$$

where M is a variable length message and $H(M)$ is the fixed-length hash value. The hash value is appended to the message at the source at a time when the message is assumed or known to be correct. The receiver authenticates the message by recomputing the hash value. The hash value is by itself not secret and generally must be protected from tampering.

A general problem relating to hash values is the following. Given a hash function H, with n possible outputs and a specific value $H(x)$, if H is applied to k random inputs, what must be the value of k so that the probability that at least one input y satisfies:

$$H(y) = H(x) = 0.5 \qquad \text{[Eq. 8-82]}$$

or 50 percent chance of a hit?

For any value of y, the probability that $H(y) = H(x)$ is $1/n$. The probability that $H(y) \neq H(x)$ is $1 - 1/n$. For k random values of y, the probability that none of them matches is a multiplicative function of individual probabilities or $[1 - (1/n)]^k$. So the probability that there is at least one match is $1 - [1 - (1/n)]^k$. The well known binomial theorem applies to this problem:

$$(1 - a)^k = 1 - ka + k(k - 1)/2!(a^2) - k(k - 1)(k - 2)/3!(a^3) + \cdots \quad \textbf{[Eq. 8-83]}$$

For small values of a, this can be approximated at the first order as $(1 - ka)$. The probability of at least one match ("hit") is approximately k/n. For a probability to be even at 0.50, we must have $k = n/2$. Translated to an m-bit hash code, the number of possible codes is 2^m and the value of k that produces a probability of $\frac{1}{2}$ is $2^{(m-1)}$.

The Birthday Paradox is a problem that gives one thought. What is the minimum value k such that the probability is greater than 0.50 that at least two people in a group of k people have the same birthday? We designate this probability as $P(n, k) = Pr$. That is, Pr is the probability that at least one item in k is a duplicate, out of n equally likely items. We are looking for the smallest value k that $p(365, k) \geq 0.50$. The number of different ways N that we can have no duplicates is:

$$N = 365 \times 364 \times \cdots \times (365 - k + 1) = 365!/(365 - k!) \quad \textbf{[Eq. 8-84]}$$

The total number of possibilities without restrictions is 365!

The probability of no duplicates is a portion of the total number of possibilities, or

$$Q(365, k) = 365!/(365 - k!)/365! \quad \textbf{[Eq. 8-85]}$$

So recycling our reasoning, we find that the probability of finding a duplicate is

$$P(365,k) = 1 - Q(365,k) = 1 - [365!/(365 - k!)/365!] \quad \textbf{[Eq. 8-86]}$$

A plot of $P(365, k)$ versus k for Eq. 8-86 shows that only 23 people in a group are required to yield a probability of 0.5073, or about equal chances. At $k = 100$, the probability is 0.9999997 that at least one duplicate will be found. The probability result is explained by the fact that we are interested in pairs of people, not individual birthdays. For 23 people there are $[23(23-1)]/2 = 253$ pairs of people, hence the high probability.

Equation 8-86 is a special case of a more general problem. What is the probability of at least one duplicate when $k \leq n$, given a random variable that is an integer with a uniform distribution between 1 and n, and k is the number of instances selected? Equation 8-87 shows the answer to this question:

$$P(n, k) = 1 - n!/[(n - k)!\, n^k] \quad \textbf{[Eq. 8-87]}$$

With a little help from differential calculus, we can reorganize this equation to yield:

$$P(n,k) < 1 - e^{-[k \times (k-1)]/2n} \qquad \textbf{[Eq. 8-88]}$$

Solving for the value of k such that $P(n, k) > 0.50$, we find that

$$\tfrac{1}{2} = 1 - e^{-[k \times (k-1)]/2n} \qquad \textbf{[Eq. 8-89]}$$

and

$$\ln(2) = k \times (k - 1)/2n \qquad \textbf{[Eq. 8-90]}$$

For large n, we can estimate the right hand side of Eq. 8-90 by k^2 and get

$$k = \sqrt{[2 \ln(2)n]} = 1.18 \sqrt{n} \approx \sqrt{n} \qquad \textbf{[Eq. 8-91]}$$

As a reality check, we test the people problem at $k = 365$; $k = 1.18 \sqrt{365} \cong 22.54$, which is close enough to 23 for this estimation.

Bringing this section to a peak, we realize that in terms of hash functions, the Birthday Attack is quite important. Suppose we have a function H, with 2^m possible outputs (i.e., an m-bit output). If H is applied to k random inputs, what must be the value of k so that there is the probability of at least one duplicate [i.e., $H(x) = H(y)$ for some inputs x, y]?

Using the approximation Eq. 8-91, we find:

$$k = \sqrt{2^m} = 2^{m/2} \qquad \textbf{[Eq. 8-92]}$$

Suppose that a 64-bit hash code is used. Is this secure? If the encrypted hash code C is sent along with the corresponding unencrypted message M, then the opponent would need to find an M' such that $H(M') = H(M)$ in order to substitute another message and to fool the receiver. On average he would have to try 2^{63} messages to find one that matches the hash code of the intercepted message. Or would he? Equation 8-92 implies another type of attack, the Birthday Attack.

Yuval proposed the following strategy:

1. A signs a message by appending the appropriate m-bit checksum and encrypting that checksum with A's private key.

2. The opponent generates $2^{m/2}$ variations on the message, all of which convey the same meaning. The opponent prepares an equal number of fraudulent messages to be substituted for the real one.

3. Compare the sets of messages until we find one pair that produces a duplicate hash code. The probability is >0.50 that we will be successful. If not, add additional fraudulent messages until a hit is found.

4. The opponent offers the valid variation to A for signature, which is subsequently attached to the fraudulent variation for transmission to B. The opponent is assured of success even though the encryption key is not known. Both versions have the same hash code.

Thus if a 64-bit hash code is used, the level of effort required to fake it is only on the order of about 2^{32} values. The generation of duplicate messages is easier than expected. Davies and Price give good examples of the process. The conclusion is clear. A length of only 64 bits is not secure. Something in excess of 100 bits would be more preferable.

SHA-1

The *Secure Hash Algorithm version 1* (SHA-1) was developed by the National Institute of Standards and Technology and published as FIPS PUB 180 in 1993. SHA is based on Ron Rivest's MD4 and sister MD5 algorithms. The hash function is used extensively in vendor products as well as the IPSEC criteria for the auto industry. SHA-1 has five steps to produce a digest from a message:

1. Append Padding Bits so that the message length is congruent to 448 mod 512. Padding is always added. The number of bits is 1 to 512. Padding is all 0s except the leading bit.

2. A block of 64 bits is appended to the message and is treated like an unsigned 64-bit integer and contains the length of the original message before padding. The total length of the message is $L\times512$ bits. The resulting message digest is a multiple of sixteen 32-bit words.

3. Initialize the Message Digest Buffer with five hexadecimal values.

4. Process the Message in 512-bit (16-Word) Blocks. The heart of the algorithm is a module that consists of 80 steps of processing and reusing four different hexadecimal constants and additions modulo 2^{32}.

5. Process the output block as a 160-bit message.

Both FIPS 160 and Stallings give a detailed discussion of SHA-1. Both MD5 (message digest 5) and SHA-1 are derived from Rivest's MD4 algorithm. All of these algorithms offer strong security, speed, and compactness of design. MD5 offers a 128-bit digest compared to SHA-1's 160 bits. They both work on a 512-bit unit. They differ in the number of steps. MD5 uses 64 steps in 16 rounds and SHA-1 uses 80 steps. MD5 is not limited by message length, whereas SHA-1 is limited to 2^{64} bits.

The Digital Signature Algorithm (DSA)

The *DSA* was proposed in August 1991 by the U.S. National Institute of Standards and Technology (NIST) and became a U.S. Federal Information Processing Standard (FIPS 186) in 1993. It was the first digital signature scheme to be accepted as legally binding by a government. The algorithm is a variant of the El Gamal signature scheme. It exploits small subgroups in Z_p^* in order to decrease the size of signatures. The key generation, signature generation, and signature verification procedures for DSA are given next.

DSA Key Generation

Each entity A does the following:

1. Select a prime divisor $(p - 1)$, q such that $2^{159} < q < 2^{160}$ (i.e., bit length of 160 bits).

2. Select a 1024-bit prime number p with the property that $q \mid p - 1$. (The DSS mandates that p be a prime such that $2^{511 + 64t} < p < 2^{512 + 64t}$ where $0 \leq t \leq 8$. If $t = 8$, then p is a 1024-bit prime.)

3. Select an element $h \in Z_p^*$ and compute $g = h^{(p-1)/q} \bmod p$; repeat until $g \neq 1$. (g is a generator of the unique cyclic group of order q in Z_p^*.)

4. Select a random integer x for user's private key in the interval $0 < x < q$.

5. Compute user's public key $y = g^x \bmod p$.

A's public key is (p, q, g, y); A's private key is x.

DSA Signature Generation

To sign a message m, A does the following:

1. Select a random integer k in the interval $[1, q - 1]$.

2. Compute $r = (g^k \bmod p) \bmod q$.

3. Compute $k^{-1} \bmod q$.

4. Compute $s = k^{-1}\{H(m) + xr\} \bmod q$, where H is the Secure Hash Algorithm (SHA-1).

5. If $s = 0$, then go back to Step 1. (If $s = 0$, then $s^{-1} \bmod q$ does not exist; s^{-1} is required in Step 2 of signature verification.)

The signature for the message m is the pair of integers (r, s).

DSA Signature Verification

To verify A's signature (r, s) on m, B should do the following:

1. Obtain an authentic copy of A's public key (p, q, g, y).

2. Compute $w = s^{-1} \bmod q$ and $H(m)$.

3. Compute $u_1 = H(m)w \bmod q$ and $u_2 = rw \bmod q$.

4. Compute $v = [(g^{u_1}y^{u_2}) \bmod p] \bmod q$.

5. Accept the signature if and only if $v = r$.

Since r and s are each integers less than q, DSA signatures are 320 bits in length. The security of the DSA relies on two distinct (but related) discrete logarithm problems. One is the discrete logarithm problem in Z_p^*, where the number field sieve algorithm applies. Since p is a 1024-bit prime, the DSA is currently not vulnerable to this attack. The second discrete logarithm problem works to the base g: given p, q, g, and y, find x such that $y \equiv g^x \pmod{p}$. For large p (e.g., 1024 bits), the best algorithm known for this problem is the Pollard rho-method, and takes about $\sqrt{\pi q/2}$ steps. Since $q \approx 2^{160}$, the DSA is not vulnerable to this attack.

Elliptic Curve Digital Signature Algorithm (ECDSA)

ECDSA is the elliptic curve analogy of the Digital Signature Algorithm (DSA). With this scheme, a hash value is created from the message using the hash function SHA-1, and the hash value is then signed with the signer's key. The verification portion of this scheme validates a signature on data with the signer's public key, given the signature and the data. The recipient verifies the message by creating a hash value using the same hash function and processing it with the signer's public key. The verification output is compared with the signature received to determine its validity.

Alice possesses a key pair (A, a), where A is her public key and a is her private key. To sign a message, Alice employs her private key and the message in the ECDSA signing operation:

1. The message is passed through SHA-1 to obtain a hash H. Alice is not really signing a message; she is signing the hash of a message.

2. A session key pair (X, x) is produced by randomly generating x and calculating $X = xG$.

3. The two pieces of the ECDSA signature are two integers (r, s), where $r = X \bmod n$, and

$$s = 1/x(H + ar) \bmod n \qquad \textbf{[Eq. 8-93]}$$

If either integer is zero then the entire process is repeated.

4. The message and the signature (r, s) are sent to Bob.

To verify the signature, Bob uses Alice's public key and the message in the ECDSA verification operation:

1. First an elliptic curve point is calculated:

$$Q = 1/s\, HG + r/sA \qquad \textbf{[Eq 8-94]}$$

2. The signature is true if the equality s true:

$$r = Q \bmod n \qquad \textbf{[Eq. 8-95]}$$

WRAP-UP ▬ ▬ ▬ ▬ ▬ ▬ ▬

Public-key cryptography (PK) was introduced with the RSA PK algorithm. The RSA algorithm has gained wide acceptance and exhibits substantial cryptographic utility. Confidentiality is not the only goal of message security; authentication and digital signatures are two equally important security goals. Authentication systems include message encryption, cryptographic checksums, MACs, and one-way hash functions. The latter method is the most useful for security enhancement and verification of user authenticity. The hash function under certain conditions may be subject to the Birthday Attack. ICSA's approved list of algorithms was introduced.

Public-key cryptographic systems have proven to be effective and more manageable than symmetric key systems in a large number of scenarios. Implementers today are faced with a choice between three types of public-key systems: integer factorization systems, discrete logarithm systems, and elliptic curve cryptosystems (ECC). Each of these systems is capable of providing confidentiality, authentication, data integrity, and nonrepudiation.

In the author's opinion, of the three fundamental cryptosystems, ECC cryptosystems offer significant efficiency savings due to added strength-per-bit of the system. These savings are advantageous in many commercial applications, particularly when computational power, bandwidth, or storage spaces are limited.

CHAPTER 9

Identification, Authentication, and Authorization on the World Wide Web

The buying public is leery of engaging in electronic commerce largely because they worry that their electronic transactions will be insecure. Observers of the growing field of e-commerce concur that lack of consumer confidence is the essential obstacle to continued growth of business on the World Wide Web (WWW).

Both merchants and clients need to be confident of the identity of the people and institutions with which they are doing business. At a technical level, these concerns focus on identification, authentication, and authorization. *Identification* consists of providing a unique identifier for automated systems; *authentication* consists of correlating this electronic identity to a real-world, legally binding, identity; and *authorization* consists of assigning rights to the authenticated identifier.

Encryption technologies play a crucial role in protecting confidentiality, integrity, and authenticity in cyberspace. Standards for labeling Web sites' compliance with privacy policies help consumers judge where to do business. Digital certificates and electronic cash of various kinds allow authorization for purchases with varying degrees of assurance for customer privacy. Single sign-on systems allow clients to establish and prove their identity once and then shop at several electronic locations without further inconvenience. Systems for extending the content and flexibility of digital certificates allow Web sites to tailor their services more closely to the needs and demands of their clientele.

When users communicate securely with an online merchant on the Web, they may establish a *session* using any of a variety of authentication procedures such as giving a password, using a physical device (a *token*), or providing other evidence of their identity (e.g., *biometric* authentication). During the session that they establish, it is assumed that only the authorized person will transact business with the merchant. One practical problem for customers is that buying more than one object or service may require communications with many Web sites, each of which currently requires a separate identification, authentication, and authorization cycle. This chapter discusses several approaches to providing a secure and convenient shopping experience for consumers on the Web.

Internet commerce is a strategic tool for business today and all evidence indicates that it will grow rapidly in the coming years if potential customers can gain confidence in the safety of electronic commerce. E-commerce is widely seen as threatening the privacy of the individual.

Several surveys indicate considerable concern by users about their online privacy. For example, in March 1997, the Boston Consulting Group (BCG) surveyed 9300 people about privacy concerns. The Boston Consulting Group found 76 percent of respondents expressed concern about sites monitoring browsing on the Net; 78 percent said privacy assurance would increase their willingness to disclose private information on the Net. Without privacy assurance, the Boston Consulting Group expects $6 billion of Web business compared with $12 billion if privacy were assured. The Lou Harris organization surveyed 1009 computer users in a national sample; more than 50 percent of users are concerned about the release of their email address by those responsible for the Web sites they visit.

In general, observers feel that lack of consumer confidence is seriously limiting growth of e-commerce. In one large survey, 70 percent of respondents were worried about safety of buying things online; 71 percent were more worried about Internet transfer of information than phone communications; and 42 percent said they refused to transmit registration information via the Internet. Several other observers report that lack of perceived privacy is a major block to the growth of e-commerce and that security is essential for e-commerce. Barriers to more effective e-commerce include poor security standards.

Indeed, the lack of confidence may be measurably slowing the progress of e-commerce: the percentage of online purchases was roughly the same in 1996 as in 1995 according to a study by Dataquest and consumers seem to think the Internet is not secure enough to give their credit-card information to a Web site.

One of the vexing problems faced by consumers is the "cookies.txt" file, in which browsers such as Internet Explorer and Netscape Navigator store information sent from Web servers to the client. These records of client activity can be abused. For example, a Web server offering clothing might determine that a particular client had previously visited a Web site dealing with new car sales and accordingly pipe the user's name to a service sending junk mail or junk email offering cars for sale. According to an independent group that monitors government activities, U.S. federal Web sites are failing to protect user privacy. OMB Watch said, "There is no government-wide policy regarding privacy concerns on federal Web sites....Agencies collect personal information about visitors to their Web sites, but fail to tell them why that information is being collected and what it is being used for." After the report, three agencies that were collecting cookies files stopped doing so.

As for the economic consequences of this general lack of confidence, the evidence warrants serious investment in whatever is required to improve public confidence. According to a report by JCP Computer Services that summarizes several other studies, by the year 2000 the top 100 United Kingdom companies will have 20 percent of their revenue from e-commerce. Killen & Associates say in another report that by the year 2005 worldwide Internet e-commerce will be approximately US$27B (billion), about 50 percent of the revenue from credit-card sales at that time. JCP Computing Services studied the average online transactions per household and by the year 2000 they expect the average number of online transactions per household will rise from 9 per year in 1997 to 120 per year. A report published in *PC Magazine* estimates that one of every three Internet users already buys goods over the World Wide Web and predicts that e-commerce revenues will double between 1997 and 2001.

In addition, micropayments mediated by secure electronic forms of payment may help Web-based businesses, such as magazines, become profitable; currently they are experiencing customer resistance to paying for annual subscriptions, but micropayments are expected to help users by allowing small fees for use of individual articles. Similar micropayments may revolutionize the music and video business.

Identification, Authentication, and Authorization

Whether users know it or not, their concerns about e-commerce security are fundamentally those of *remote access controls*. Any time someone needs to transact business, whether online or face-to-face, the client and the merchant must both provide identification, authentication, and authorization. Users need to be sure that they know exactly who is running the Web server with which they intend to transact business. Merchants need identification of their clients to be sure they get paid for their products and services.

In a startling case of breach of identification, authentication, and authorization in 1996 and 1997, viewers of pictures on several Web sites were in for a surprise when they got their next phone bills. Victims who downloaded a "special viewer" were actually installing a Trojan program that silently disconnected their connection to their normal ISP and reconnected them (with the modem speaker turned off) to a number in Moldavia in central Europe. The phone call was then forwarded to an ISP in North America, which continued the session. The long-distance charges then ratcheted up until the user disconnected the session— sometimes hours later, even when the victims switched to other, perhaps less prurient, sites. In New York City, a federal judge ordered the scam shut down; however, the site persists on the Web and includes warnings that law enforcement officials and those intending to bring legal action against the owners are not to log in (we do *not* recommend that you risk connecting to it). Later in 1997, the FCC ordered $2.6 million in fraudulently obtained charges to be refunded to the embarrassed victims.

Identification

Identification, according to a current compilation of information security terms, is "the process that enables recognition of a user described to an automated data processing system. This is generally by the use of unique machine-readable names." In human terms, client and merchant engage in mutual identification when, for example, they tell each other their names over the phone. In the Moldavian Trojan case, the violation of identification occurred when there was no provision at all for ascertaining the identity of the company running the fraud.

Authentication

Authentication is "a positive identification, with a degree of certainty sufficient for permitting certain rights or privileges to the person or thing positively identified." In simpler terms, it is "the act of verifying the claimed identity of an individual, station or originator." In a human contact by phone, the client and merchant might recognize (authenticate) each other by their familiar voices. The Moldavian Trojan fraudulently violated the principle of authentication by claiming that its software was a file-viewer, when it was actually an ISP-switcher as well. The classic methods for correlating virtual and physical identities in cyberspace are parallel to methods used for authenticating human beings in the physical world.

The four categories of authenticating information are:

1. *What you know:* The password or passphrase
2. *What you do:* How one signs one's name or speaks
3. *What you are:* One's face or other biometric attributes such as fingerprints
4. *What you have:* A token such as a key or a certificate such as a driver's license

All of these categories of authentication are used in cyberspace. The last example is particularly interesting: certificates play a crucial role in authenticating people (or programs or machines) in the world of e-commerce. The driver's license, for example, if assumed to be real, tells a merchant that at some time in the past, a certification authority—the issuing department of motor vehicles—had undertaken some measures to ensure that the information on the license is (or was) correct. In cyberspace, verifying the legitimacy of a certificate can be easier than in real space.

Authentication leads to a related concept, that of *nonrepudiation*, formally defined as a "method by which the sender of data is provided with proof of delivery and the recipient is assured of the sender's identity, so that neither can later deny having processed the data." Nonrepudiation, as we see in a later section on encryption, depends on asserting that authenticity has not been violated when identifying the source of that transaction or message.

Authorization

Authorization is "the granting to a user, program, or process the right of access." In the real world, we experience authorization every time a merchant queries our VISA or MasterCard service to see if we are authorized to spend a certain amount of money at their establishment.

The Moldavian Trojan violated authorization by fraudulently appropriating the right to disconnect a phone call and initiate an expensive long-distance call without notification to or permission from the victim.

In the mainframe environment, authorization depends on the operating system and the level of security that system administrators have imposed. Identification and authentication (I&A) begin when a session is initiated. A *session* is "an activity for a period of time; the activity is access to a computer/network resource by a user; a period of time is bounded by session initiation (a form of logon) and session termination (a form of logoff)." On the Web, however, most interactions are *sessionless*; for example, there is no identification and authentication when an *anonymous* user accesses a *public* page on a Web site. There is no logon and no logoff under such circumstances. Web interactions require I&A only when the user and the Web owner agree to establish a secure session. Typically, secure Web transactions do require some form of logon and logoff even if these steps are not explicitly labeled as such.

Session integrity and authenticity can be violated in a number of ways. *Piggybacking* is the unauthorized use of an existing session by unauthorized personnel. This problem is difficult to imagine in the real world, where it would be unlikely that someone could, say, cut into the middle of a phone conversation to order goods and services using someone else's good name and credit card. In cyberspace, though, it is quite commonplace for users to initiate a transaction on a terminal or workstation and then to walk away from their unprotected session to go do something else. If a dishonest person sits at their place, it is possible to misuse the absent person's session. A common problem of piggybacking is the misuse of someone else's email program to send fraudulent messages in the absent person's name. Another example might have the thief stepping into a session to change an order or to have goods sent to a different address but be paid for by the session initiator's credit card. Such examples of fraud can have disastrous consequences for the victims; in general, every news story about this kind of abuse reduces confidence in the security of e-commerce.

A more technical attack is called session *hijacking,* which allows an attacker to take over an open terminal or login session from a user who has been authenticated by the system. Hijacking attacks generally take place on a remote computer, although it is sometimes possible to hijack a connection from a computer on the route between the remote computer and your local computer. Hijacking occurs when an intruder uses ill-gotten privileges to tap into a system's software that accesses or controls the behavior of the local TCP (Transmission Control Protocol).

A successful hijack enables an attacker to borrow or steal an open connection (say, a telnet session) to a remote host for his own purposes. In the likely event that the genuine user has already (been) authenticated to the remote host, any key strokes sent by the attacker are received and processed as if typed by the user.

In summary, identification, authentication, and authorization are normal components of any business transaction and must be guaranteed by the communications systems and software mediating the relationship between supplier and customer.

The Role of Encryption

All of the technologies being proposed by competing companies and consortia, including tokens, secure protocols for data transmission, digital certificates, and standards for trusting Web sites involve some form of encryption. Chapters 1 to 8 have addressed both classical and modern encryption methodology. Let's glean the salient features that we can apply to the identification/authentication/authorization challenge. With respect to cryptography for e-commerce, here are two major classes of encryption: *symmetrical* and *asymmetrical*. It is the asymmetrical class that has helped e-commerce the most in recent years.

Figure 9-1

Symmetric Encryption
and Decryption

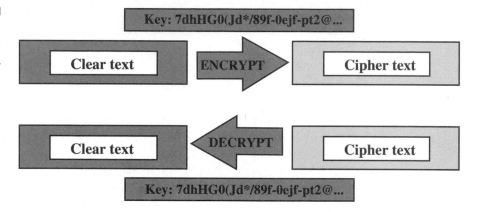

Symmetrical Encryption Algorithms

Figure 9-1 illustrates a simple *symmetric* encryption technique such as the Digital Encryption Standard (DES). In this figure, the original text (or *clear text*) is run through an *encryption algorithm* using a specific *encryption key*. This *encryption* process generates a form of the text called *cipher text,* which is unreadable by anyone who does not possess the appropriate key. To retrieve the original clear text after encryption using a symmetric algorithm, one uses the same key and algorithm to *decrypt* the cipher text.

The symmetric encryption algorithms—and there are many—are usually very fast and they play an important role in securing information against detection. However, symmetric algorithms do require both sides of a transaction to know the same key, leading to risks if either sender or recipient compromise the secrecy of the key. In addition, every pair of correspondents that want to have purely confidential transactions has to generate a unique key known by no one else. This requirement for secret keys for each pair of correspondents leads to a *combinatorial explosion* because the number of pairs climbs approximately as the square of the number of correspondents. For example, three people need $(3 \times 2)/2 = 3$ unique keys for the three possible pairs of people (AB, AC, and BC). Four people need $(4 \times 3)/2 = 6$ unique keys to protect the confidentiality of all possible pairs of correspondents (AB, AC, AD, BC, BD, and CD). But a thousand people need $(1000 \times 999)/2 = 499,500$ or almost half a million unique pairs for all the possible combinations of correspondent pairs.

Asymmetrical Encryption Algorithms: The Public-Key Cryptosystem

One of the most powerful tools invented to help protect information is the asymmetric encryption algorithms used in the *Public-Key Cryptosystem* (PKC), first developed by Rivest, Shamir, and Adleman in the 1970s. *Asymmetric encryption algorithms,* unlike symmetrical encryption algorithms, use different keys for encryption and decryption. Instead of creating a single key that handles both encryption and decryption, the key generation function creates two different keys at once that are peculiarly complementary. One key is used to encrypt the clear text and a different key is used to decrypt the cipher text. Whatever is encrypted by one of the asymmetric keys can be decrypted only by the *other* key—and vice versa, since one can encrypt with either key and then decrypt successfully with the other key. Figure 9-2 shows this principle.

Figure 9-2
Asymmetrical Encryption and Decryption

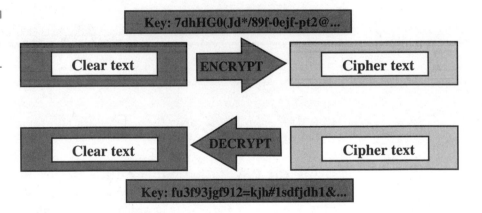

The PKC uses the fact that complementary keys can decrypt only what each key's complement encrypted. One of the pair is declared as a *public key* (known to anyone who wishes to use it) and the other is kept as a *secret* (or *private*) *key.*

Using the PKC to Protect Confidentiality   To send messages that can be read only by a specific holder of a public key, one encrypts the clear text using the recipient's public key to produce a cipher text; only the corresponding private key (known only, one hopes, to the recipient) can decrypt the cipher text. Decrypting the message with any key other

Figure 9-3
How the PKC Protects
Confidentiality

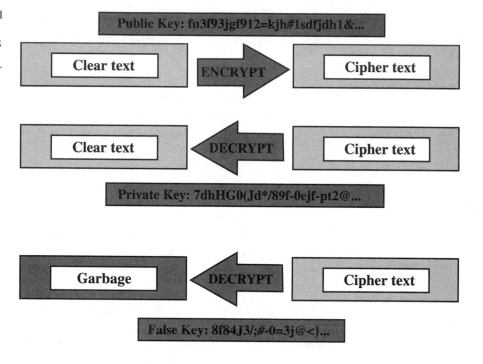

than the appropriate private key results in unusable garbage text, as shown in Figure 9-3.

Using the PKC to Establish Authenticity   Similarly, to prove the authenticity and integrity of a message, the sender can encrypt the clear text using the sender's *private* key; any recipient can verify both the integrity and authenticity of the clear text by decrypting the cipher text using the sender's *public* key. If the cipher text can successfully be decrypted using the sender's public key, then only the user of the corresponding private key could have created the cipher text. Figure 9-4 illustrates the demonstration of authenticity using the PKC.

Using the PKC to Establish Integrity   In addition, if the cipher text has been successfully deciphered, then the received text must be identical to what was originally sent. Figure 9-5 shows how the PKC (or any encryption method) helps ensure integrity of transmitted information.

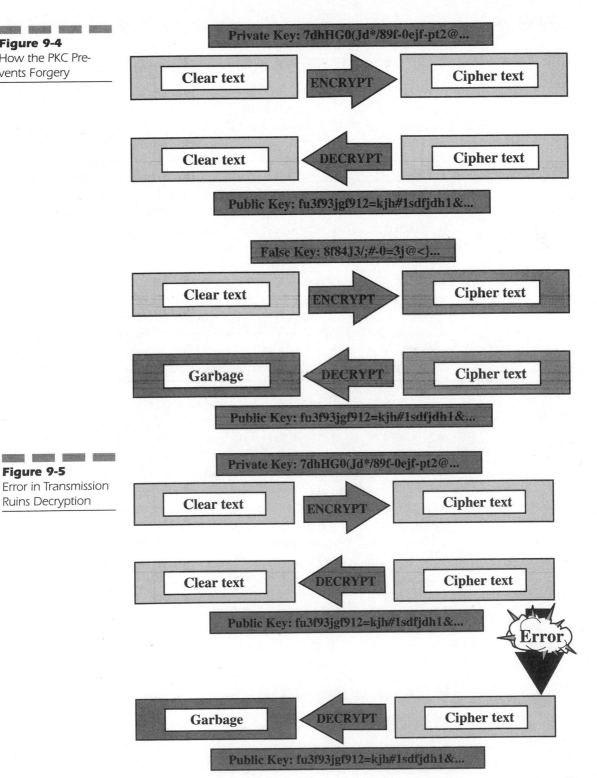

Figure 9-4
How the PKC Prevents Forgery

Private Key: 7dhHG0(Jd*/89f-0ejf-pt2@...

Clear text

ENCRYPT

Cipher text

Clear text

DECRYPT

Cipher text

Public Key: fu3f93jgf912=kjh#1sdfjdh1&...

False Key: 8f84J3/;#-0=3j@<}...

Clear text

ENCRYPT

Cipher text

Garbage

DECRYPT

Cipher text

Public Key: fu3f93jgf912=kjh#1sdfjdh1&...

Figure 9-4
How the PKC Prevents Forgery

Figure 9-5
Error in Transmission Ruins Decryption

Private Key: 7dhHG0(Jd*/89f-0ejf-pt2@...

Clear text

ENCRYPT

Cipher text

Clear text

DECRYPT

Cipher text

Public Key: fu3f93jgf912=kjh#1sdfjdh1&...

Error

Garbage

DECRYPT

Cipher text

Public Key: fu3f93jgf912=kjh#1sdfjdh1&...

309

Use of Both Symmetric and Asymmetric Algorithms in the PKC

Typically, the asymmetric algorithms used in the PKC take a long time for encryption and decryption. In addition, longer messages naturally take longer to encrypt than short ones. To reduce the time required for tedious asymmetric encryption and decryption, one creates a *digital signature* under the PKC by generating a mathematical *hash* of the clear text.

A *hash function* is any method that creates a short sequence of data to be used in verifying the integrity of its source; a *checksum* is an example of a hash total. For instance, the last four digits of most credit cards are a checksum. The algorithms for generating a hash are selected to generate a very different value for the clear text modified by even so little as a single character. For example, if someone makes a mistake in reading his or her credit card number out over the phone so that one of the digits is wrong, it is very unlikely that the original four-digit checksum will be correct; when the incorrect card number is checked by the credit card company, the erroneous checksum instantly identifies the mistake.

To shorten the time required for systems to check message integrity, the PKC usually does not encrypt the entire message. Instead, the PKC implementations create a hash total and it is the hash that is encrypted using the sender's private key. The recipient can decrypt the hash using the sender's public key and then independently calculate the hash value; if the recalculated hash matches the decrypted hash, then the message is unchanged and it has been authenticated to have originated with the holder of the corresponding private key.

Figure 9-6 illustrates how the PKC uses hashes to check for authenticity and integrity. The PKC does not usually encrypt the entire message; it normally creates an encrypted hash total that authenticates the origin. The hash itself is based on the complete encrypted form of the message and when the hash has been authenticated, the message would then be decrypted.

Frameworks for Secure E-Commerce

E-commerce security is currently under rapid and uncoordinated development. Many manufacturers, industry associations, and standards bod-

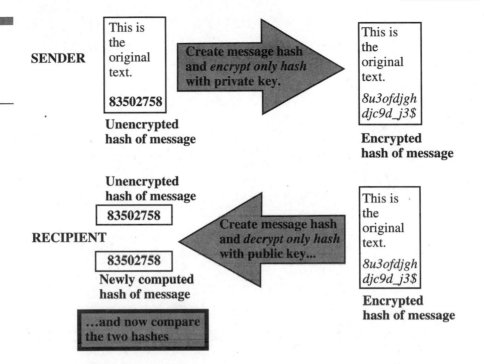

Figure 9-6
How the PKC Uses Hashes to Check Authenticity and Integrity

ies have proposed and implemented different solutions for the problems of ensuring confidentiality, identification, authentication, and authorization for e-commerce. This section summarizes some of the key initiatives and provides pointers for further details.

The frameworks discussed below emphasize various aspects of e-commerce security. Table 9-1 shows how these frameworks fit together in meeting the needs of users and businesses seeking to establish secure business relations through the Internet and the Web.

Privacy

P3 The Platform for Privacy Principles (P3) is backed by the World Wide Web Consortium, the Direct Marketing Association, and (originally) Microsoft. This standard helps describe and define limitations on the collection and use of private information from users of Web sites.

TRUSTe TRUSTe (formerly known as eTRUST) is a nonprofit initiative that certifies the respect for users' privacy by Web sites. Users are empowered to control how much information about themselves will be

TABLE 9-1

Frameworks for Privacy, Identification, Authentication, Authorization, and Single Sign-On

Framework	Privacy	Identification	Authentication	Authorization	Single Sign-On
P3	Y				
TRUSTe	Y				
SSL	Y	Y	Y		
Tokens		Y	Y		
FIPS 196		Y	Y		
VCard		Y			
Digital certificates		Y	Y		
X.509v3		Y	Y		
SESAME		Y	Y	Y	
Certification authorities		Y	Y	Y	
SET		Y	Y	Y	
OFX		Y	Y	Y	
Gold Standard		Y	Y	Y	
Kerberos		Y	Y	Y	Y
OPS	Y	Y	Y	Y	Y

revealed while they are online. The TRUSTe Trustmark indicates that a Web site is committed to protecting user privacy; its privacy assurance program is backed by periodic reviews by TRUSTe, which also seeds the site with personal user information to see if it is misused. In addition, Coopers & Lybrand and KPMG Peat Marwick audit sites randomly. TRUSTe also receives feedback from users about trustmarked sites. The Trustmark from TRUSTe helps users feel confident about their personal privacy. There are three levels of Trustmark:

1. *Third-party exchange:*   The lowest TRUSTe level; the vendor shares information with other vendors.

2. *One-to-one exchange:*   The vendor keeps information at the Web server but uses it only for interactions with that specific client.

3. *No-exchange warranty:*   The highest TRUSTe level; the vendor does not capture or keep client data at all.

SSL   Netscape Communications Corporation, creators of the widely used Netscape Navigator browser, created the Secure Sockets Layer

(SSL) protocol to protect information being transmitted through the Internet. In addition, the SSL provides for authentication of Web servers.

Identification

Tokens Many identification and authentication methods rely on *tokens,* devices that are encapsulated microprocessors in a tamper-resistant package usually the size of a thick credit card. One-time password generators have an LCD panel to display an alphanumeric string that consists of their own serial number combined with the time and date and encrypted appropriately so that only the host software can deduce the serial number of the token that generated that particular string. Such devices currently cost about $30 or so.

Smartcards are similar to the handheld one-time password generators and can also be used for authentication; however, they require specialized readers. Some tokens have been created to interact with the common floppy drive apparatus. PC-card (formerly "PCMCIA") based authentication is available, but these devices are more expensive than smartcards, costing about $60 not counting the readers. Tokens are usually owned by issuing organizations; however, a new approach involves smartcards owned by user. Such user-owned devices can function as electronic purses and play a role in anonymous payment schemes designed to protect user privacy.

FIPS 196 The U.S. government's Federal Information Processing Standard (FIPS) 196 defines how the PKC is to be used for user authentication with challenge-response systems. Suppliers aiming at government procurement will have to take FIPS 196 into account in their system designs.

vCard The vCard specification is managed by the Internet Mail Consortium; it allows "electronic business cards" to be exchanged. The vCard protocol has been submitted to IETF for approval as an open standard.

Authentication

Digital Certificates Digital certificates are growing in importance for Internet commerce. Basically, to generate digital certificates, users and merchants use secret keys in concert to establish trust.

Devices can authenticate each other using *digital certificates,* which are being used to authenticate email and other electronic messages. In addition, corporations can issue digital certificates to employees, obviating the need for user IDs and passwords to gain access to intranets and other corporate networks. However, using certificates outside a single business can be complicated because digital certificates issued under different protocols are in general still not interoperable.

CCITT (ITU) X.509v3 Standard for Digital Certificates   Most digital certificates are based on the CCITT (ITU) X.509v3 standard. Groupware vendors are agreed that X.509 is the best way to secure information for Internet transfer; Lotus, Microsoft, and Novell agreed to support X.509 (used by VeriSign and GTE Service Corp.) and X.509 compliance is believed to enhance interoperability and simplification of security protocols. Other supporters of X.509 include Lotus (Domino 4.6 will support X.509 certificates) and Microsoft (the next version of MS Exchange will support X.509 certificates). Novell's NDS directory services will support X.509 by 1998. The X.509-compliant Public Key Infrastructure is sometimes known as the PKIX.

SESAME—European Standard for Digital Certificate Authentication   In Europe, BULL, ICL, and Siemens Nixdorf are pushing the SESAME standard for digital certificates. SESAME certificates expire after minutes or days to control access to system privileges. SESAME may eventually incorporate X.509 protocols.

Third-Party Certification Authorities

The authenticity of digital certificates can be displayed by having each certificate signed by an entity (or person) that is trusted by both parties in the transaction. In one popular model of authentication of certificates, a web of trust among people and organizations ensures that every public key is signed by someone who knows that the public key is authentic. In a more hierarchical model, public keys used to sign certificates are authenticated by certification authorities (CAs) that are themselves authenticated by higher levels of CA. Organizations needing their own certification infrastructure can buy software from vendors; linking certificates to a directory structure facilitates single-logon systems, where users need to identify and authenticate themselves to a system only once to gain access to all authorized system services.

However, CAs have failed to take into account the importance and history of bilateral trading relations; today's CA products are "complex, hard to manage, and scare the hell out of people."

Perhaps as a result of this complexity, a survey in December 1996 by Netcraft and O'Reilly & Associates which examined 648,613 sites on the WWW found less than 1 percent of WWW sites offering both SSL and third-party authentication.

SET—Authorization and Nonrepudiation

The Secure Electronic Transactions (SET) protocol requires digital certificates for each use of a credit card by a user trying to pay a merchant. MasterCard and VISA announced the SET standard in February 1996; SET is also supported by GTE, IBM, Microsoft, Netscape, SAIC, Terisa, and VeriSign.

SET-compliant sites protect merchants from unauthorized payments and repudiation by clients; banks using SET are protected against unauthorized purchases using their cards; and consumers are protected from merchant imposters and theft of credit card numbers. Supporters say SET will allow consumers to relax about security on the Web.

OFX—Open Financial Exchange

The Open Financial Exchange (OFX) is supported by Microsoft, Intuit, Checkfree, and others. The standard governs digital certificates to be exchanged among financial institutions to authenticate transactions. VeriSign, currently the most important third-party CA, has issued a new type of digital ID called the Financial Service ID that is usable by institutions supporting the OFX specification. The Financial Service ID will secure transactions such as home banking applications.

Gold Standard

In direct competition with OFX, Integrion (a joint venture of IBM, VISA, and 17 North American banks) is creating a separate financial certificate protocol called "The Gold Standard."

Authorization and Single Sign-On

Kerberos

Kerberos was developed at MIT in the 1980s as part of an extended scheme for user identification, authentication, and authorization. The system's security depends strongly on protection of a Kerberos server that talks to both users and computer services such as printers and file servers. Once a user has been securely enrolled in the Kerberos server, the user's passwords never travel the Kerberos authentication server. Each subsequent request for a bilateral relation with a service by an authenticated user is itself authenticated by the Kerberos server, which issues digital certificates (called *tickets*) to allow use of specific services by specific users. Kerberos requires applications and servers to be *Kerberized*—modified for use with Kerberos; most off-the-shelf software does not support Kerberos. However, Microsoft defines Kerberos as its Windows NT v5 default authentication mechanism and there is considerable interest in extending Kerberos to other applications as part of the Distributed Computing Environment (DCE) supported by a consortium of computer manufacturers.

Open Profiling Standard (OPS)

The Open Profiling Standard (OPS), backed by Netscape, Firefly, and VeriSign, removes the need for users to reenter their identifying information more than once on Web sites. It is also designed to allow Web sites to tailor their presentation to a user by reading personal information that has been authorized by that user and is transmitted to the server via vCards and digital certificates. The OPS is supported by privacy activists such as the EFF, EPIC, and also eTRUST/CommerceNet (now TRUSTe).

Interoperability

Competing standards make it difficult for users and corporations to communicate effectively; many observers hope that the field will develop standards for interoperability of the different certificates and protocols. Most of the directory/certificate linkage schemes that relate certificates to specific users and servers generally use LDAP (Lightweight Directory

Access Protocol) and there is some talk of merging OFX and the Gold Standard, but as of October 1997 there had been no progress reported.

Application Programming Interfaces (APIs) allow different programs to interoperate. It is frustrating that several API frameworks are under development by competing vendor groups and that the proposed standards do not spell out how to progress from authentication to authorization. Gradient Technologies, a Kerberizing specialist, supports integration of the Public Key Infrastructure (PKI) with Kerberos/DCE. The SecureOne framework integrates APIs for antivirus programs, authentication, encryption, and digital certificates; RSA, VeriSign, McAfee, and Security Dynamics support SecureOne.

Products

This section includes a few products thought to be particularly significant in the developing field of Web commerce security. Inclusion does not imply endorsement by the ICSA, nor does exclusion imply criticism. See Table 9-2.

TABLE 9-2

Functionality of Some E-Commerce Security Products

Products	Privacy	Identity	Authen-ticity	Authori-zation	Single Sign-On	Extended Information
VeriSign Digital IDs		Y	Y			
DigiCash	Y			Y		
CyberCash	Y			Y		
Xcert Sentry CA			Y			
Auric Systems ASA	Y	Y	Y	Y		
Security Dynamics Secur ID		Y	Y	Y		
Bellcore S/KEY		Y	Y	Y	Y	
Internet Mall		Y	Y	Y	Y	
VeriSign Private Label Digital ID Services		Y	Y	Y	Y	Y
NCR Smart EC TrustedPASS		Y	Y	Y	Y	Y

VeriSign Digital IDs

VeriSign has established itself as the supplier of digital certificates with the largest base of commercial and individual customers among the third-party CAs. The Digital IDs use RSA cryptography with 1024-bit key length and are being used by more than 16,000 Web servers and over 500,000 individuals. VeriSign's Server Digital IDs enable organizations to establish secure sessions with visitors; the Server Digital IDs authenticate the Web site and ensure that customers will not be fooled by unauthenticated Web sites of unscrupulous con artists who make their sites look as convincing as those of real businesses.

Digital IDs dispense with the need for users to memorize individual user IDs and passwords for different Web sites. Digital IDs are issued by CAs and securely exchanged using SSL. VeriSign verifies a server operator's identity using Dun & Bradstreet, InterNIC, and others authenticating information such as articles of incorporation, partnership papers, and tax records. VeriSign (or other CA) signs a Digital ID only after verifying the site's authenticity in these ways.

AOL offers VeriSign Digital IDs to let customers and merchants authenticate each other. In use for a specific transaction between user and Web site, *the server generates a random session key that is encrypted by the secret key from the server's Digital ID; this session key expires in 24 hours and each session uses a different session key, making it impossible for a captured certificate to be misused.*

From the user's perspective, Digital IDs are easy to use. The Web user clicks on a credit-card icon on the Web site. The user then fills out a form that automatically provides the merchant's Web server with the user's public key, a list of desired purchases, and the user's digital certificate. The merchant's software decodes the user authentication and corresponding bank identification to process the order.

Generally, Digital IDs are implemented for automatic use by Web browsers and email software. However, currently, the VeriSign smart-card system requires a card reader on the client system. VeriSign announced plans for SET compliance in its digital authentication certificates in July 1996.

VeriSign has been working on new digital certificates including new attributes to extend personalization of Web sites; the current version of Digital IDs have limited fields for user information that can be used to personalize Web site responses. One of the limitations of the VeriSign scheme is that each Web site visited by a user must request the client Digital ID for reauthentication. If access control lists (ACLs) are to be linked to Digital IDs, every authorized user for a specific site must be entered into a database for ACL implementation.

DigiCash

DigiCash provides smartcard payments and software ecash using the PKC. This system is designed to enhance user privacy; for example, a user can use a different digital pseudonym (account identifier) for every organization. These tokens may contain personal information about the user, but the user can exert control over which data are sent to which server. Traditional security measures necessarily trace individual identity but the DigiCash approach ensures anonymity of each user while simultaneously ensuring data integrity and nonrepudiation of transactions. Certificates of receipt are digitally signed to prevent repudiation of the transaction. The DigiCash system allows purchases to be subject to "cooling-off periods" during which they can be reversed. DigiCash protocols require a secret authorizing number (PIN) that would make use of a stolen or lost smartcard difficult.

DigiCash is open to implementation on any device and hopes that this open system can allow merchants to take advantage of the best solutions available rather than be tied to a single supplier.

Merchants can lock out individuals who abuse their relationship; this locking function would allow the new system to be extended to polling and voting with security and anonymity.

DigiCash's ecash is a software-based payment system for use on any computer and network. The ecash system requires DigiCash software to be installed on each user's workstation. Such a system makes micropayments for services and products delivered via the Web economically feasible.

CyberCash

CyberCash customer information is sent encrypted to a merchant Web server, which signs and forwards it to CyberCash as a secure intermediary. The merchant never sees the customer's credit card number because it remains encrypted while on the merchant's server. CyberCash securely decrypts and reformats the transaction and sends the information securely to the merchant's bank. The merchant's bank securely forwards a request for authorization of the purchase to the customer's bank. The customer's bank sends a digitally signed authorization back to Cyber-Cash, which then securely returns the authorization (or denial) to the merchant. The merchant in turn notifies the customer of the acceptance or rejection of the purchase.

The secure exchange depends on non-Internet communications between CyberCash and the financial institutions. CyberCash is integrating its electronic cash system with the SET protocol.

AOL is an example of a large vendor that offers CyberCash authentication for its Web-hosting services.

Xcert Sentry CA

Xcert, a Canadian company, provides a CA proxy to retrofit legacy systems so they can generate and interpret digital certificates. Xcert's Sentry CA allows cross-authentication between CAs, although the current implementation requires Sentry CA 1.1 on all servers for cross-authentication. Later versions of Sentry CA will cross-authenticate to other types of CAs. In initial evaluations Netscape Navigator used Sentry CA certificates flawlessly but Microsoft Explorer 3.02 did not.

Auric Systems ASA

Auric Web Systems has announced Automatic and Secure Authentication (ASA). ASA allows any Web site to identify and authenticate a customer browsing its site; Web surfers do not need to type in any data for I&A by the Web server.

To authorize a purchase, the server queries an ASA server where customer and server are registered; the ASA server authenticates both sides of transaction and communicates with banks/credit services. Interestingly, customers need no special software or hardware; any browser works with ASA. ASA essentially creates a Virtual Proprietary Network (VPN, usually called a Virtual Private Network) over the Internet. The Web site needs only to add a single plug-in software module to its dial-up user authentication to use ASA. Several ISPs are interested in ASA.

Security Dynamics SecurID and ACE/Server

Security Dynamics is the leading provider of token-based authentication using the SecurID and ACE/Server.

These systems are widely used for I&A within corporations. However, penetration of the wider commercial market is problematic because of the capital cost of the hardware. It remains to be seen how the public will accept having to pay for and carry such tokens.

Bellcore's S/KEY

The S/KEY v2.6 from Bellcore is a system for one-time password authentication via software only. S/KEY uses a challenge-response system and the one-time password is never stored on the client or on the server and it never crosses the network. S/KEY complies with the Internet Engineering Task Force (IETF) standard RFC 1938 on One-Time Passwords.

Internet Mall

How can a customer buy things from a number of vendors without repeatedly having to reauthenticate? Internet Mall Inc. provides for a single validation for all purchases in a series among any of the vendors signed up at the Mall.

Extending the Usefulness of Certificates

Since customers and vendors are exchanging digital certificates, there has been considerable interest in extending the format of the certificates to allow additional information to be carried. Currently, digital certificates are being extended by developers to include more information; certificates with extended fields could help users by carrying personal details or preferences that would allow Web software to adjust the content presented so as better to suit each customer. For example, extended fields including an authenticated birth date could easily limit access to certain Web pages to adults, thus helping to reduce the problem of exposing children to pornography or other dangers on the Web.

VeriSign Digital Certificates

VeriSign's Digital IDs are currently rigidly defined following the CCITT (ITU) X.509 standard. Digital IDs include the owner's public key, name, expiration date, CA name, serial number, and CA signature.

VeriSign says that attribute extensions to certificates will have to enter the PKIX eventually. Some analysts believe that privilege and policy attributes will migrate from certificates to the LDAP. However, an auto industry expert argues that it is unacceptable to put privileges in a certificate because changing privileges would require revoking the certificate and such a computationally- and I/O-intensive process would not be scalable.

Netscape's CA already attaches some privileges to its certificates and Consensus Development Corp. is building privilege/authority plug-ins for Netscape and Microsoft servers. Entrust also puts nonidentity attributes in its certificates.

Recent news suggests that VeriSign's Digital Certificates will include any type of data that can be programmed on servers. Corporations will customize VeriSign's Digital Certificates to their own specifications. Customers using the "Private Label Digital ID services" will be able to add their own customized fields at will. Such new expandable certificates could replace cookies (the text records stored in the cookies.txt file by browsers).

VeriSign will offer free upgrades to its Private Label Digital Certificates to its 500,000 current customers using the older, fixed-format certificates; corporate users will also be able to upgrade their server software easily to be able to use the expandable certificates.

NCR TrustedPASS

Another interesting new product is NCR's SmartEC TrustedPASS, originally developed as part of a system designed to allow telecommunications companies to control access by their customers to their own billing records. This software features an extendible certificate (called the *TrustedPASS*) format that includes fields for issuer, server port, originating IP address, time of expiration for the TrustedPASS, a flexible area for additional data, and a digital signature for the whole Trusted-PASS. This design requires no software changes on the user side and there are no plug-ins for the client browser.

A TrustedPASS authentication server on the server side uses whatever I&A the merchant chooses to impose. However, once the user is authenticated in compliance with the Web site's criteria, the Trusted-PASS authentication server sends the client a TrustedPASS. If the customer repeatedly fails the authentication phase (e.g., by giving the wrong password too many times) the authentication server can invalidate the customer record in its public-key database and the customer can be instructed to call for help.

The TrustedPASS is described as extendible because there are no limits to how much information can precede the digital signature field. Such information could easily include personal details and permission fields controlling which data should be used for which purposes. The system would fit very well into many other frameworks and could help solve the problem of tailoring authorization privileges to a user's characteristics or displaying different views of Web site information.

The TrustedPASS system explicitly allows configuration of an expected lifetime for the TrustedPASS. If the authentication server notices that the current TrustedPASS being used for a specific session is reaching its limit, it issues another TrustedPASS. This feature allows an active user to continue to access a Web site without manual reauthentication. In addition, if the user holding a valid TrustedPASS accesses a different Web site that also has TrustedPASS software running, the new server can accept a valid TrustedPASS from a trusted site that it explicitly knows because of entries in its public-key database. If the user reaches expiration of the valid TrustedPASS from the first site, the second site can issue a new TrustedPASS that will in turn be respected by any other Web site that is running TrustedPASS and has a trust relationship with the second Web site. This is an unusual feature that permits a user to browse among many Web sites without reauthentication and without requiring a visit to a limited electronic mall where the vendors are required to pay a service fee to the mall owner.

Web Sites

The following Web sites have further information about the systems discussed in this chapter:

BCG: *http://www.etrust.org/
                         webpublishers/studies_BCG.html*

Privacy: *http://www.etrust.org/
                         webpublishers/privacypays_
                         studiesresearch.html*

E-commerce: *http://www.digicash.com/news/
                         archive/bigbro.html*

Gartner: *http://www.digicash.com/news/
                         room/art/gartners01.html*

VeriSign: *http://www.verisign.com/products/
                         sites/serverauth.html*

JCP: *http://www.jcp.co.uk/research.html*

E-commerce: *http://www.zdnet.com/pcmag/
                         news/trends/t970221a.htm*

Privacy: *http://www.epic.org/privacy/
                         internet/cookies/default.htm l*

Fed Privacy: *http://www.techweb.com/se/
                         linkthru.cgi?WIR1997082713*

Trends: *http://www.zdnet.com/pcmag/
                         news/trends/t970221a.htm*

DigiCcash: *http://www.digicash.com/news/
                         room/art/gartners01.html*

Risk: *http://www.businessknowhow.com/
                         newlong.htm*

RSA: *http://www.rsa.com/rsalabs/
                         newfaq/*

Ethics: *http://www.zdnet.com/intweek/
                         print/970609/inwk0040.html*

Entrust: *http://www.etrust.org/*

Privacy: *http://www.zdnet.com/intweek/
                         print/970609/inwk0040.html*

Entrust: *http://www.etrust.org/users/
                         program.html*

Issues: *http://www.zdnet.com/pcmag/
                         issues/1612/pcmg0022.htm*

SSL: *http://search.netscape.com/newsref/
                         std/SSL_old.html*

TrustedPASS: *http://www.ncr.com/press_release/pr101497.html*

Authentication: *http://www.zdnet.com/pcmag/features/inetsecurity/authentication.htm*

Smartcards: *http://www.digicash.com/news/archive/bigbro.html*

Vcard: *http://www.zdnet.com/pcweek/news/0526/26apro.html*

Digital CA: *http://www.zdnet.com/pcweek/reviews/0428/28cert.html*

CCITT: *http://www.zdnet.com/pcweek/news/0526/26apro.html*

X.509: *http://www.zdnet.com/pcweek/news/0804/04cert.html*

PKIX: *http://pubsys.cmp.com/nc/813/813hrb.html*

SESAME: *http://pubsys.cmp.com/nc/813/813hrb.html*

CA: *http://www.zdnet.com/pcweek/reviews/0428/28cert.html*

CA: *http://pubsys.cmp.com/nc/813/813hrb.html*

Trends: *http://www.zdnet.com/pcmag/news/trends/t961220a.htm*

SET: *http://www.zdnet.com/pcweek/reviews/0428/28cert.html*

SET: *http://www.zdnet.com/pcmag/news/trends/t960201d.htm*

SET: *http://www.cybercash.com/cybercash/about/set.html*

SET: *http://www.zdnet.com/pcmag/news/trends/t970221a.htm*

OFX: *http://www.news.com/News/Item/0,4,15222,00.html*

Gold: *http://www.news.com/News/Item/0,4,15222,00.html*

in coming to agreements on interoperability as a minimum requirement for the good of the buying public and of vendors.

With the technologies described in previous sections, it should be increasingly acceptable for consumers and business people to do business securely on the Internet. Methods for evaluating each Web site's adherence to different levels of privacy policy will allow the marketplace, rather than governments and bureaucrats, to define the importance of protecting consumers' private information. Those wishing to protect their privacy to the utmost will favor electronic cash solutions, where funds will be expended without having to convey details of any kind about the identity of the purchaser. Such anonymous transactions may be especially useful for those businesses looking at micropayments as a method for selling access to publications, music, films, and other services where long-term subscriptions have so far remained unattractive to the public. Other developments such as single sign-on systems and customized contents in digital certificates will contribute to the ease with which ordinary consumers will be able to shop online.

CHAPTER **10**

Digital Signatures

Digital signatures are a result of the computer and its influence in our daily lives. Digital signatures can be generated very quickly and can bind a document to its owner to help authenticate the message. The National Institute of Standards and Technology (NIST) defines the *Digital Signature Standard* (DSS) as a cryptographic method for authenticating the identity of the sender of an electronic communication and for authenticating the integrity of the data contained in that communication. The public-key system was intended for all federal departments and agencies in the protection of unclassified information. NIST had intended to use the de facto international standard RSA algorithm as its standard for digital signatures. The RSA algorithm is a public-key algorithm that supports a variable key length and variable block size of the text to be encrypted. Public-Key Cryptography Standard (PKCS) and PKCS #1-12 was RSA's attempt to provide a standard interface for public-eye cryptography. *PKCS #1* is the RSA public-key cryptography standard, which defines the method of encrypting and signing data using RSA's public-key cryptosystem. PKCS #1 describes syntax identical to that of PEM and X.509 for RSA public/private keys and three signature algorithms for signing certificates.

The ability to "crack" an encrypted message is a function of the key length. The National Security Agency (NSA), insisting on a weaker algorithm, opposed NIST on its RSA choice and along with the FBI put NIST under intense pressure to accept the NSA proposal. The NSA-proposed algorithm did not meet the NIST request for secure key exchange in confidential unclassified communications. When all was said and done, NIST publicly proposed the DSS developed by the NSA in August 1991 for unclassified information. DSS approval was announced by the Department of Commerce (DOC) on May 19, 1994, as Federal Information Processing Standard (FIPS) 186, effective December 1, 1994.

What Is a Digital Signature?

A *digital signature* is an electronic method of signing an electronic document that is reliable, convenient, and secure. An electronic document includes any instrument created or stored on a computer. These include email, letters, contracts, and images. Many states are enacting legislation concerning the use of digital signatures. The most widely used type of electronic signature relies on public/private-key encryption. This asymmetric cryptosystem key pair technology has been available for nearly 20 years. A public/private-key encryption system involves two mathematically related keys that are like large passwords for each user. The private key, known only by the "signer," can encrypt a message that only his or her public key can decrypt. Once the private/public keys are generated using a valid Certificate Authority (CA), they remain associated with the person who generates the two keys. The *certificate authority* is a trusted entity that issues certificates to end entities and other CAs. CAs also issue Certificate Revocation Lists (CRLs) periodically, and post certificates and CRLs to a database or repository.

Figure 10-1 shows the components of ordinary digital signature schemes; in this figure, components in the strict sense are the algorithms *gen, sign,* and *test. Gen* and *sign* are probabilistic. The main security requirement on an ordinary digital signature scheme is that one cannot forge signatures although one knows the public key. A necessary but not sufficient condition for this is that one cannot compute the secret key from the public key. Such a scheme can never be information-theoretically (i.e., perfectly) secure. For practicality, there must be an upper bound on the length of the signatures produced with signing keys and messages of a certain length. The security of such digital signature schemes is computational. A consequence of computational security is that signature schemes usually depend on a so-called *security parameter,* which determines the length of the problem instances that are supposed to be infeasible. Choosing a larger security parameter usually makes keys and signatures longer, and signing and testing more time-consuming. One hopes that it also makes forging signatures significantly more difficult even more quickly, so that the gap between the complexities of the legal algorithms (*gen, sign,* and *test*) and of forging widens.

Figure 10-1

Components of Ordinary Digital Signatures

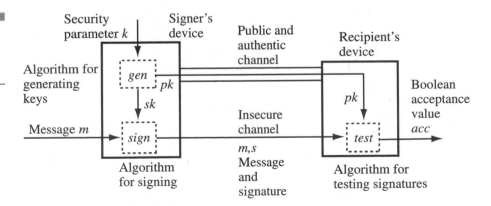

The public key can be distributed freely to anyone the public-key owner wishes to communicate with securely. The public key cannot derive the attributes of the private key although they are related. The private key is derived using the asymmetric encryption algorithm, providing message origination authentication and nonrepudiation. One of the not commonly known features of the private and public key is that data encrypted by one key can be decrypted by the other.

Why Do We Need Digital Signatures?

Digital signatures become more important each day as we slowly change the way business is conducted. Contracts that were once only signed by both parties in person with a witness have transpired to agreements that are signed and then faxed with a hard copy placed in the mail. Not only is the current method time-consuming, slow, and inefficient, it is a somewhat costly way to conduct business in today's frenetic world. Secure digital signatures sent over the Internet can be a quick and inexpensive way to conduct global commerce, with the correct security measures in place.

There are three basic assumptions we unconsciously make when we sign a document:

1. Your signature binds you to whatever the document states.

2. The document will not be charged after you sign it.

3. Your signature will not be transferred to another document.

There are laws and conventions that make these assumptions valid, but how is this carried into the networked world? We need to ensure that the message hasn't changed (data integrity) as well as prevent someone from simply moving our signature to another document we never intended to sign.

How Does a Document Get Signed?

Signing a document is a unique two-step process. First, the message is hashed using a message digest function. This is done because the cryptographic algorithms used to encrypt messages are slow. In order to speed up the process, a short representation of the message (*message digest*) can be created using a cryptographic algorithm, known as a *one-*

Figure 10-2
Digital Signature with
MD5

How Digital Signatures Work

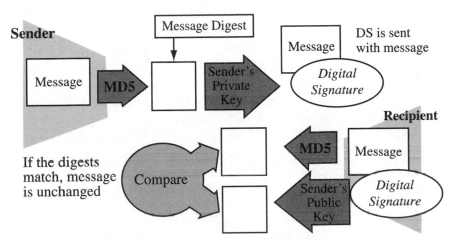

way hash function. The hash function is a function that maps strings of bits to fixed-length strings of bits that make it computationally infeasible to find a given input or output that maps to a particular output or input. Figure 10-2 shows a typical digital signature created using *MD5* (Message Digest 5, a strong algorithm that reduces a document of any size and creates a digest or unique "thumbprint" that is always the same length. An MD5 message digest cannot be reversed.)

The message digest function is an algorithm that maps the sequence of bits comprising an electronic record into a smaller set of bits without requiring the use of a key or any secret information. Each electronic record yields the exact same message digest every time the algorithm is executed. This method makes it computationally unfeasible for any two electronic records to produce identical results unless they are exactly alike. The digest is simply a smaller extrapolated version of the original message. Digesting a message is a necessary way to speed transmission and assists in verification.

Second, the sender signs the message using his/her private key. This digitally signed message is then sent to the recipient. The recipient generates the message hash from the message itself and then the message is verified using the sender's public key, which was in the recipient's possession before the message transmission. If the two message hashes are the same, the message can be viewed as genuine and authentic. If the hashes do not match, the message is either corrupted or a forgery. An important thing to remember is that the message can still be in clear text. Digital certificates only validate the message origination and integrity.

Signing denotes the process of applying a digital signature to some message or data. This works by appending organizational data to the message and optionally transforming the message so that it will pass mail transfer agents unmodified. Any further change to the contents of the message results in the digital signature being corrupted. The recipient can detect this using the sender's public key. Although the message data may look unreadable after the transfer encoding, there is actually no protection against eavesdropping at this point. The message is just encoded and not encrypted.

When the message is intended for recipients who might not have a compatible system available, any recipient can actually look at the message and read it, although he/she will not be able to properly verify the signature. The recipient should treat the message with the same caution normally extended to any nonsigned messages.

Encryption renders the message unreadable to anyone but the intended recipients. This means that in order to create an encrypted message a set of recipients must be chosen. This works by selecting a number of aliases from the user's database. Based on the alias, the program looks up the corresponding certificate in the database and uses the public key to encrypt the message session key.

Decryption is the reception of a message and the removal of security features, a process also called the *de-enhancement* of a message. Where a message is not actually encrypted and only signed, the process is usually just called *signature verification*. A message should be considered untrustworthy should any steps fail.

Automatic addition of new certificates to the user's database can be a good feature. Whenever a message is received from an unknown sender, the certificate (which must be embedded in the message for this to work) is checked in the context of the user's certification hierarchy. If the check is successful, then the message is considered trustworthy and the new certificate can be automatically added to the database.

An alias name can be determined automatically or it can be specified explicitly before the decryption operation is run. When the alias name is determined automatically, a certain subcomponent of the distinguished name of the owner of the new certificate is taken.

Once the sender of the message has been put into the user's database with an alias, messages can be encrypted to this user by selecting the alias. To distribute one's own certificate, it is appropriate to distribute signed (but not encrypted) messages.

After a message has been decrypted successfully (i.e., its digital signature has been verified), the so-called *certification path* is displayed.

This certification path, starting with the details of the sender's certificate, up to and including the root self-signed certificate, can be used to further check the trustworthiness of the message by inspection.

A digital signature should be time-stamped to allow the recipient to see when the transaction transpired and to allow the signer the ability to invalidate and terminate the digital signature if it were to be compromised.

Certificates

A *certificate* is a digitally signed data structure defined in the X.509 standard that binds the identity of a certificate holder to his or her public key. X.509 is the X.500 directory service standard relevant to public-key infrastructures describing two authentication methods: (1) *simple* authentication based on password usage and (2) *strong* authentication based on public-key cryptography. Version 3 added certificate extensions to the X.509 standard.

This standard is relevant to public-key cryptographic infrastructures defining two methods of authentication: (1) standard authentication relies on password usage and (2) strong authentication is based on public-key cryptography. The operational period of a certificate should be directly linked to the confidentiality and security required. We can look at the use and rules applied to passwords to draw a comparison. The life expectancy of a password is defined in the organization's security policy. As a simple rule of thumb, the more security that is required, the more often it will need to be changed. This will probably be the same for a digital signature certificate. Administrators have learned to expect the worst case when it comes to their users. They will expect that the user may compromise his or her private key and as a precaution use key expiration dates to maintain a tight control on security.

The public-key certificate must be obtained to verify a digital signature. A public key has no identifier with a private key or person; it is only a string of numbers, which adds to the complexity of the transaction. Each recipient must obtain the signer's public key in order to verify the message. To ensure that each recipient is identified with a particular key pair, a third party that is trusted by both recipients must associate a person to a key pair. This trusted third party is called the *certification authority*.

Before users can actually sign documents or to encrypt messages, they must create their key database. When creating this database: an asymmetric key pair is created; the public key is put in a self-signed certificate; and the certificate and Certificate Revocation List are initialized.

From a cryptographic point of view, the key-pair generation is the most important step in this process. Once the database has been created, the user name cannot be changed anymore. If a new database is required, it must be done with a new key.

The public-key component of the user's key pair is stored as a special certificate in the database. Messages are usually encrypted in such a way that the sender can read them. The status and values of the current user's certificate should include a distinguished user name, an actual public key, an algorithm used to compute the digital signature inside the certificate, and a certificate validity period.

The user's certificate will become a properly signed certificate after the import of the certification reply message. Before this stage, it is a nontrusted, self-signed certificate.

Symmetric algorithms include the Data Encryption Standard (DES) and Triple-DES, which processes the data three times with DES, thereby using a session key of double the length of a single DES key. Triple-DES is stronger than single DES, but it takes proportionally longer to process data with Triple-DES than with single DES.

To generate a digital signature, an asymmetric signature algorithm is needed. Currently, only the PEM and MailTrusT standards support the RSA algorithm. Privacy Enhanced Mail (PEM) is an enhanced electronic mail system that includes privacy for use on the Internet, defined by four RFCs (1421-1424) that specify message encipherment and authentication procedures, a key management infrastructure, relevant algorithms and information, and specific details on the electronic formats for key management.

In a strong cryptosystem, each newly encrypted message is encrypted with a pseudorandomly generated key, the length of which depends on the selected symmetric encryption algorithm. The randomness of a session key generation is the center of a cryptographically strong one-way hash function.

Certification hierarchies, certificate chains, and the certificate revocation list are what make the asymmetric cryptosystems so powerful. In order to participate in such a hierarchy, any user must obtain a certificate for his or her public key. This is achieved by creating and sending a certification request to the user's certification authority, which in turn creates a proper certificate that is embedded in a certification reply message, which is sent back. This reply is then loaded by the user. The user then becomes a member of the certification hierarchy. The certification process has to be executed only once after the key pair has been generated. A certification request is like a message that bears only a digital signature. The difference is that the message is signed with the user's newly created private key, which is not yet certified. To all other users in the system this would be a nontrusted message (since the user's key is not properly certified yet), but the certification authority detects this as the intended means to forward certification requests. The contents of the certification request's text data is irrelevant; it can be empty. It is not possible for the user who creates the request to check the signature him/herself. This check will be possible only after the certification process has been completed.

The protection of the private key can be achieved by using a password-derived symmetric key to encrypt the asymmetric private key. In fact, the password does not need to be a single word; it can be a passphrase. It is desirable to use a longer sequence of words, containing uppercase and lowercase letters, as well as digits, symbols, punctuation marks, and so forth. Simply speaking, the longer the passphrase and the more unique characters it contains, the more difficult it is to break. Good security procedures still require that the password be changed at regular intervals. This limits the chance of an attacker or intruder getting the private-key file and the matching passphrase at the same time. The password should not be stored on the hard disk or in the Windows registry.

For each enrolled user, a separate database is maintained. In this database, the (protected) user's key pair is stored along with the certificates from other users that the user has loaded over time. A database view lets a user look at the database. It lists all certificates stored in the database that have an alias. It is these certificates that are used to send encrypted messages to the respective certificate owners. Certificates can be stored in a database without an alias. These certificates may belong to intermediate certification authorities. These certificates are used only to verify certificate chains, but not to encrypt messages intended for the certification authority. A display of the trust status of the certificates may be misleading. Certificates can be stored in the database as nontrusted, with the trust established only on demand when sending a message to this recipient or when verifying a signature, which was done with the appropriate public key. Any certificate in the database that has an alias can be deleted. Certificates should be deleted one by one. There will be certificates in the database that do not have an alias. Generally, these certificates should not be removed from the database.

The input data selected (file or clipboard contents) are hashed with the hash algorithm and the result is displayed. Since access is not required either to the private-key, the public-key, or the user's database, this function can be executed freely. A hash value can be used to check the unmodified transmission of otherwise unprotected data. This is especially suitable to check the correct reception of the certification reply message. This message must not have been tampered with during transit. This is a suitable means to verify that the hash value computed at the sender's side is identical to the one computed on the recipient's side. The reference hash value must be transmitted via a different communication method and should be well protected against manipulation. It does not need to be secret. These values are small and it could be read over the telephone or faxed. The exact method by which the certification reply is protected against manipulation should be defined in the security policy.

Cryptographic hash functions originally required for email were MD2 and MD5. MD5 is a hashing technique that creates a 128-bit message digit. SHA-1 is the Secure Hash Algorithm designed by NIST and NSA to be used with the DSS to ensure the security of the Digital Signature Algorithm (DSA).

More advanced hashing methods are SHA-1 and RIPEMD-160; using one of the latter two algorithms is recommended. The security of these algorithms is much better than that of MD2 and MD5. A hash function is used to: specify which hash algorithm is used when signing messages; specify which hash is used inside the certificate when creating the user's self-signed certificate; specify which hash is used inside the certificate when creating a certification reply; specify which hash is used inside the Certificate Revocation List (CRL); and compute the hash value of data. The certificate revocation list is a list of revoked but unexpired certificates issued by a CA.

Institutional overhead includes the costs associated with establishing and maintaining a Certificate Authority service center whether it is kept in-house or outsourced. This cost includes professional accreditation, government compliance, auditing, and any legal and financial liabilities that may arise from any errors, omissions, or negligence. Distributed Key Administration is one way to spread the costs, control, and work load of the key distribution and management system back into the organization. Establishing subordinate certificate authorities throughout an organization may be viewed as a weak point in the security policy.

Attacks on Digital Signatures

Implicitly, one assumes the following problem: Given the public key and a message, find the corresponding signature. Is it possible that some schemes that seem infeasible to break are vulnerable if one allows stronger attacks and weaker forms of success?

The most important types of attacks, in order of increasing strength, are:

1. *Key-only attack:*   The only information the attacker has to work on is the public key.

2. *Known-message attack or a general passive attack:*   The attacker is given the public key and some signed messages.

3. *Chosen plain text or active attack:*   The attacker can choose some messages that the signer will sign for him or her before forging a signature on another message on his/her own. In the general case of this attack, the attacker can choose those messages at any time, in effect adapting or applying an adaptive chosen-message attack.

The most important types of success, in decreasing order, are:

1. *Total break:*   The attacker has found the secret key, or the equivalent way of constructing signatures on arbitrary messages efficiently.

2. *Selective forgery:*   The attacker has forged the signature on a message that he/she could select independently of the public key and before a possible active attack.

3. *Existential forgery:*   The attacker has forged the signature on a message that the signer has not signed, but the attacker could choose what message (or plain text).

Problems

The Rabin and Williams' schemes were both examples of weaker forms of breaking. Both are similar to RSA, but constructed so that selective forgery with a passive attack was as hard as the integer factorization problem (IFP). An active attack on these schemes was shown to yield a total break. Rabin devised a signature-like scheme that an attacker with limited resources could find two messages with the same signature, so that by asking the signer to sign one of them, he/she also obtained a signature on the other.

These attacks were not really noticed until similar attacks were made on RSA. The first attack used the secret RSA operation as a homomorphism. By multiplying the signatures on two messages m_1 and m_2, one obtains the signature on the product $m_1 \times m_2$. Thus, if the attacker breaks his/her message into two factors and gets the signer to sign those, the attacker can derive the signature on the chosen message (plain text). Another researcher used a little trickery and reduced the attacker's requirement for two sets of chosen plain text for signature. These are selective forgeries after chosen plain text attacks, or alternatively, existential forgeries after known plain text attacks.

Existential forgery is possible with a key-only attack in all signature schemes built from the trapdoor one-way permutations described in Chapter 7. The attacker chooses a value and calls it a signature, computes the permutation with a public key, and calls the result a message. The El Gamal scheme was introduced in Chapter 8. Although similar to RSA, it is not directly constructed from trapdoor one-way permutations. Existential forgery is possible with key-only attack. However, the author knows of no method for selective forgery with an active attack.

Assessment of Attacks and Success

A known plain text attack is perfectly realistic. Historically, it has been one of the more successful forms on all types of ciphers. A completely unrestricted adaptive chosen message attack is not. If the signer signed arbitrary messages, there would be no need for forgery. It is reasonable to consider restricted forms of active attacks in practice. Every recipient will have some influence on what messages are signed, and perhaps determines the message almost completely. An example is a notary public who signs almost everything.

As to types of success, a scheme where selective forgery is possible cannot be used in practice. Existential forgery may not always be harmful, because the signed message may have no practical value to the attacker. Many of the PGP signed email messages qualify. One does not know what will be of practical value in all applications of digital signature schemes. This is particularly true if data without inherent redundancy are signed. Hence to be on the safe side, every signed message is assumed to be valuable.

Countermeasures

There are two ad hoc measures against the aforementioned problems. One is to add redundancy to messages before signing. In this case, only messages that fulfill a certain predicate are signed; this makes the chosen plain text attacks more complicated. Furthermore, a signature is valid only if the message fulfills the predicate; thus, existential forgery in the original scheme seems unlikely (highly improbable) to yield a valid message.

The second measure is to apply a one-way hash function to the messages before they are signed. In this case, it is unlikely that an attacker can find messages for a chosen plain text attack where the hash values actually signed are useful to him. An existential forgery in the original scheme should yield a message whose preimage under the hash function is not known. Applying a hash function has the additional advantage that it makes the complete scheme more efficient, if the hash function is fast (which is one of the original system design parameters).

The choice of good redundancy predicates or hash functions is not easy, especially if one wants to execute a fast hash algorithm. There are significant differences in symmetrical cryptologic schemes like DES and an IFP.

Provably Secure Digital Signature Schemes

Research on proving the security of signature schemes has centered on two steps in the process. The first step was to recognize that redundancy or hash functions are not some protocol around a real signature scheme. Instead, the signature scheme must comprise everything that happens within a message, and security must be proved for the complete scheme. A second step was to formalize the infeasibility of computing the inverse of a function. Instead, the definition must comprise an active attack and exclude existential forgery. Goldwasser accomplished this in his research in 1988. The result was known as the GMR definition. Basically a signature scheme such as that portrayed in Figure 10-1 is defined as a collection of algorithms *gen, sign,* and *test,* such that, when the keys are correctly generated with *gen,* two properties hold:

1. Signatures correctly generated with *sign* pass the corresponding test.

2. If any polynomial-time attacker first communicates with a signer for a while, and then tries to compute a pair of new message and a signature, the success probability is very small. During the key generation, the maximum number of messages to be signed must be fixed, and *sign* takes the number of messages as input.

Both properties portend cryptographically strong schemes. GMR is discussed in the literature and reference to it can be found in the resources section.

Trusting Digital Signed Documents

A digital signature is reliable when it has been issued by a trusted Certificate Authority (CA), authenticates the sender, guarantees the message integrity, and provides nonrepudiation of the message. A weakness and major concern of using digital signatures involves the notion that digital signatures can properly ensure a person's identification over the Internet or some other nonpresent situation. Digital signatures alone cannot identify people. Digital signatures can only assure the recipient that a particular identification process was completed. Likewise, a manual signature not witnessed or notarized cannot assure the recipient that the sender was truly the person who signed the document. In fact, a digital signature may have been stolen, or compromised in some way, without the owner's even being aware of its theft. Security experts have been essential in defining and detecting the security system holes that digital signatures have created.

Fraud can take place in many ways. On site, a thief can simply use your computer and send a signed message, with your digital signature, without your even being present. They need only to access your computer, maybe an ability to bypass your password, create and send the email, delete the item from the outbox, and power the unit down with no one the wiser. Digital signatures require strong security policies in order to be used as a viable method of conducting electronic business.

Other Methods

Biometrics includes fingerprints, iris scans, retinal scans, digitally captured handwriting, speech, DNA, or any digital information, which can be linked to a specific person's biological information. These items have the ability to scientifically separate them from anyone else and are considered the most secure mechanism for authentication. The next method is two-factor authentication. *Two-factor authentication* involves something I have in my possession in conjunction with something I know. These can be smartcards with encrypted data on the chip and personal identification numbers (PINs), proximity badges that require PINs, or tokens with PINs to unlock them in order to operate. The least secure are the single-factor authentication devices we use today, the most common of which is the everyday credit card we use to make purchases from a variety of merchants.

The U.S. Government Position

Politicians have added their mark on digital signatures with the Electronic Financial Services Efficiency Act (EFSEA) of 1997 and H.R. 2937. The EFSEA promotes industry to establish a uniform digital signature system and other forms of authentication that will be an alternative to existing paper-based methods. A popular position is that "the federal government encourage the private sector development of uniform standards for electronic authentication, while not imposing rigid rules that may stifle innovation." H.R. 2937 establishes a self-regulatory agency and a mandatory registration of all certificate authorities (CAs) providing that service with the National Association of Certification Authorities (NACA). Registration with the NACA will not automatically connect the trusted roots of each CA.

WRAP-UP

The challenge for the implementation and use of digital signatures in our daily lives boils down to the perceived service it can provide coupled with its ease of use. Here we are a number of years after the Department of Commerce's approval announcement of the Digital Signature Standard and we are just starting to see its implementation become a reality. We still have many problems to solve. One of the most important issues is that all public-key exchange mechanisms can be subject to what is commonly termed a "Man in the Middle Attack." We have commercial Certificate Authorities providing a service for banks and financial institutions in order to facilitate Internet transactions without having a common trusted root. We are deploying systems worldwide with different types of certificates and algorithms. We have not fully identified transaction relationships and the legal aspects. Individual states are enacting legislation concerning digital signatures, which could lead to a significant number of different legal standards across the United States. The general public is terrified of "Big Brother" and the ability to track each person by following the digital trails of electronic commerce and the seemingly encrypted contents of email by simply tapping into the Internet.

CHAPTER 11

Hardware
Implementations

Cryptographic systems can be implemented in software or hardware, or a combination of the two. Hardware implementations have traditionally been more secure and faster, but also more expensive. This chapter quantifies and explores the benefits of cryptographic hardware. We evaluate commercial market needs for these benefits and consider integration issues with common Internet security architectures.

Definitions

In this chapter, *hardware,* means any physical device that implements cryptographic math primitives or stores cryptographic keys. See Table 11-1.

TABLE 11-1

Categories of Cryptographic Hardware

Token	A personal, portable device for storing and exercising cryptographic keys, for example:
Smartcard	Described in Chapter 17
PC Card	aka the form-factor formerly known as PCMCIA
Antipiracy device	Client side hardware meant to enforce digital property use rights, for example:
Set top box	A cable TV, satellite, DVD, or other player required to reproduce copyrighted material that enforces use rights.
Dongle	Software antipiracy devices, typically employing a weak or proprietary algorithm.
Security processors	Server-side, security-oriented devices for banking, government, or network security, for example:
Link encryptor	Layer 2, or point-to-point, security devices, usually using a proprietary security protocol.
VPN box	Virtual Private Network (Layer 3) device, usually employing the IPSec standard (Chapter 18).
Accelerator	Performance-oriented hardware algorithm implementations.

Some products attempt to fit into more than one category, often sacrificing excellence in one area to offer this flexibility. Tokens and antipiracy devices are both client-side devices. Security processors and accelerators are most commonly used on servers. There is a spectrum of products from security processor to accelerator, with the two extremes being characterized by a focus on high security and high performance, respectively.

Layers shown in Figure 11-1 above the two core elements, key storage

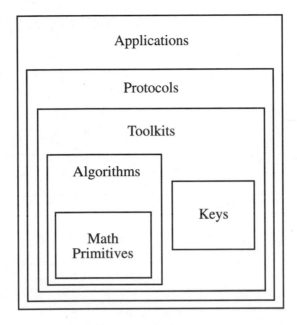

Figure 11-1
What Elements Are in Hardware?

Applications

Protocols

Toolkits

Algorithms

Keys

Math Primitives

and math primitives, may also be included in hardware. The hardware may be an entire slave computer, with its own operating system, or it may implement only fundamental low-level algorithms. If all layers, including an application, are included in a hardware device then one might argue that we have made a full circle back to software cryptography!

The most common scenario for commercial hardware is for math primitives, algorithms, key storage, and a primitive toolkit to be included.

Trade-offs: Performance, Security, Economics, and Ergonomics

Implementing the math primitives for cryptographic algorithms can offer tremendous performance benefits over software implementations. Cryptographic accelerators exploit this performance to deliver lower system cost—resulting in better economics.

Storing keys in hardware is one basis of higher security. Personal, portable tokens, such as smartcards, derive an ergonomic benefit from key storage as well. Inexpensive tokens are generally slower than a host CPU and only add to system cost; their benefits are security and ergonomics.

TABLE 11-2

Trade-offs in
Cryptographic
Hardware

	Security	Performance	Ergonomics	Economics
Antipiracy device	Better than software	As required	High	More expensive
Token	High	Low	High	More expensive
Accelerator	Same	Very high	High	Less expensive
Security processor	Very high	As required	Low	Very expensive, depending on security level

Some of these objectives are at odds. For instance, the higher security of hardware generally comes only at additional cost, offering poorer economics than a software equivalent. High-security hardware design also imposes rigorous procedures and use constraints on the user. Table 11-2 summarizes the benefits sought by different kinds of hardware.

Security

The original reason for cryptographic hardware was to increase the overall security of a system. This higher security comes largely from the isolation of sensitive security functions from complex—thus less trustworthy—host systems. Modern operating systems, the applications we use, and the hardware they run on have security holes and bugs.

The most common threat, one which hardware effectively guards against, is an adversary who gains control (i.e., *root access*) to your server, then attempts to steal a copy of your cryptographic keys. This allows the successful adversary to masquerade as your service without your knowledge—a catastrophic security breach.

Secure Storage

The first objective of secure hardware is to keep secrets secret. Even if the host operating system has bugs, which allows a hacker to break into it, the cryptographic subsystem will not reveal its secrets. This capability is called *secure storage*.

Secure storage can be useful for any case where bits have value. In particular this is true with electronic money. Because cryptography transfers all of the value of information being secured or signed to a key, keys often have very high value.

Biometric identification is another example of information that must not be revealed, else the possessor could easily masquerade as you (Chapter 22).

Antipiracy devices also store a secret necessary to access their associated copyrighted material. *Dongles* either store "critical values" or calculate them from challenge values presented by the application. Execution of the software thus requires the existence of a valid dongle, providing an effective deterrent against piracy. Set top and other rights management boxes use the same strategy to control access to copyrighted video and services.

Secure Key Storage

When the secret being protected is a cryptographic key, we call the capability *secure key storage*. Secure key storage is employed for secret, private, and public keys, although the benefits differ. Higher-value keys, such as root keys, benefit the most from secure storage. In modern cryptographic systems, root keys are often private keys. Session keys are more often secret keys—those that have a short life span. The value of these keys is lower, and so it is often common to store root keys in hardware, but not session keys.

Public keys do not have a requirement for secrecy—they are public. Why then would one benefit from storing public keys in hardware? The answer lies in a user's need to be certain that public keys are authentic. Storing public keys—and indeed entire certificate chains—in hardware ensures that a rogue cannot circumvent chains of trust.

Secure Execution

Having secrets securely stored in hardware means that we must next move any software that needs to manipulate these secrets in with them. Failure to do so would require bringing the keys out of hardware to exercise them, defeating the goal.

For this reason, smartcards not only store a private key, but also implement the algorithms (such as RSA, DSA, or EC-DSA) that use the keys.

The PIN pad at your local grocery store is another example of a secure execution unit. It encrypts your PIN number with a DES-based scheme called *Derived Unique Key Per Transaction* (DUKPT). DUKPT ensures that a high school hacker working as a grocery store clerk cannot connect his laptop under the checkout counter to collect debit card account and PIN numbers.

Secure execution also ensures that the software is run with integrity—that an adversary cannot alter its behavior. Hardware with this property is said to provide a *trusted execution environment*. A trusted execution environment may have one of several applications, depending upon who benefits from the assurance. Three common scenarios are shown in Table 11-3.

TABLE 11-3

Applications of Secure Execution

Trusting Entity	Application
Administrator	Secure key management
Jurisdictional authorities	Policy enforcement
Content provider	Digital rights management

Secure Key Management

Now that keys may be stored in hardware and used by algorithms also stored and executed in hardware, we are much closer to a secure system. However, keys must come from somewhere, may need to be backed up, and must be destroyed when their life has ended—in other words, key management.

Secure key management is secure key storage plus the secure execution of all key management functions. Secure key management architectures vary greatly, but generally include:

- Key generation
- Key backup
- Key destruction

In the most secure systems, keys used by a hardware device can only be generated in that secure environment and they cannot be removed. This may seem reasonable at first, but the constraints are rarely reasonable in a real-world commercial application. Consider the following examples:

- You operate a secure Web server with a valid server certificate, then purchase hardware as an add-on. Do you really want to throw out your existing certificate and start over?

- You decide to set up a second server for higher capacity or redundancy. Do you really want to have the second system operate with a separate certificate?

- Your hardware fails and the keys are lost.

Some architecture allows keys to be generated by existing software and backed up in conventional manners. The keys are then installed in the hardware in a secure offline mode, solving these problems. This installation process must be done carefully, when the machine configuring the hardware is not connected to a network and is certain to be free of any malicious software. The key backups must be afforded reasonable safeguards, such as a floppy disk in a safety deposit box. Upper-layer software is given a reference number for each key. Because there is a finite storage capacity to any hardware device, some means to destroy a key is generally included. The limited space, or slots, results in this technique being known as *key slots*.

For higher-assurance applications, where keys are generated in hardware, some means to export the keys is also required. Exported keys can then be backed up or installed in other hardware to scale performance or provide high availability. This may sound like a direct contradiction to our objective, but in fact exported keys are first encrypted.

The Red/Black Boundary

You may think the red/black boundary is a financial line that all crypto-hardware companies aspire to cross, but it's more than that. We call encrypted keys *black keys* and unencrypted ones *red keys*. Red keys are never stored outside of the hardware's secure boundary, the *red/black boundary*. The red/black boundary is sometimes also known as the *cryptographic boundary*.

Black keys are those encrypted with a *key encrypting key* (KEK). The KEK will be derived from some secret, often a PIN, specified at initialization time. If another device is initialized with the same PIN, the black keys from the first unit can be installed in it. While outside hardware, black keys are of no value unless you disclose the PIN.

Isn't it funny how all the security in the world seems to end up with a four-digit PIN? Rather than enter the PIN into the host, which malicious software may have infested, ultrasecure hardware has a keypad built in. The PIN may also be a longer passphrase, and may be split among several trustees.

The use of KEKs allows applications to generate, back up, and destroy keys without ever exposing them to the host.

Protocol Integration Issues

Secure key management requires protocol awareness because it changes the way in which keys are handled. The traditional design solution in banking security processors was to run the entire protocol in hardware. In the Internet world, however, consumers expect hardware to support many and varied protocols, such as Secure Sockets Layer (SSL), Secure Electronic Transactions (SET), and IP Security (IPSec). To meet this goal, several standards have emerged for plugging in cryptographic hardware that supports secure key management. These include:

- Intel® Common Data Security Architecture™ (CDSA)
- Cryptoki (RSA® PKCS#11)
- Microsoft® CryptoAPI™ (CAPI)

By choosing software and hardware that conforms to one of these standards, you can be assured vendor choice and product interoperability. Intel's CDSA is the most sophisticated; Cryptoki is the most widely supported; and CryptAPI comes as standard equipment with all Microsoft operating systems.

Policy Enforcement

When the integrity of software executing in secure hardware is assured to a third party, that software could enforce the third-party's policy. The third party may be a government or other stakeholder in the operation of the device.

The HP® Versecure™ initiative is one such example. Versecure is a system wherein hardware is shipped in a disabled mode, then a policy activation token must be obtained from the local government and installed. The *policy activation token* is a digital certificate-like structure that tells the hardware what use of cryptography is legal in that jurisdiction. In this example, secure execution enables exportability by assuring governments that their rules will be observed and obeyed.

The U.S. government's ill-fated Clipper chip initiative is another example of secure execution applied for purposes of policy enforcement. In this case, chips implementing strong cryptography (stronger than DES) were hard-wired to attach a government key recovery field to every message stream. The federal government was willing to allow Clipper to be exported—had anyone other than the government itself been interested in using it!

Physical Security

The secure hardware described thus far provides effective protection against hackers; it makes up for security holes and bugs in modern operating systems and applications. An adversary who has physical access to the hardware is another matter, however, and for this we must add *physical security*. Although other related attacks are possible, two examples allow us to divide attacks into two useful categories, given in Table 11-4.

TABLE 11-4

Categories of Physical Security Attacks

Category	Example
Detectable breach	Steal the hardware
Nondetectable breach	Open the hardware, connect leads, and read the keys

Either category of attack allows the adversary to masquerade as you on the network, but a nondetectable breach is a much graver threat because it can happen *without your knowledge*. An adversary who breaches the cryptographic boundary may also modify the workings of the device to their benefit or mount other attacks. In any event, a breach is much less of a problem if it is quickly detected because it can be dealt with by revoking certificates, notifying interested parties, and taking other appropriate remedial actions.

Physical removal of hardware can be detected. Although a mission-critical server will have redundancy—such that the service may not fail when one cryptographic hardware device is stolen—electronic and physical audit practices should alert a site security officer to the theft in short order. Notice that if the hardware is an embedded form factor, such as a PCI card, good security practice must include inspection on a regular basis.

A high-value server is usually stored in a physically secure room, a locked area which may even be guarded. These measures are reasonably effective at limiting access, creating accountability among those who have access, and stopping theft. Physical security of hardware complements physical security that your application requires at the server, room, and building level. For a balanced system, real-world *procedural* security must augment cryptographic and physical security.

The goal of *tamper evidence* is to make attacks detectable. Tamper evidence is one of three physical security properties of common interest, introduced in Table 11-5. These three properties can be applied at the chip (ASIC), multichip module (MCM), or device (cryptographic module) level. Whatever level is chosen, an important principle in physical security is that it be applied at the red/black key boundary. Only black-key material is ever permitted outside of the physical security boundary.

TABLE 11-5

Physical Security Properties

Property	Benefit
Tamper resistant	Difficult to open the hardware
Tamper evident	It is obvious when someone has attempted to open hardware
Tamper detection	Hardware detects attempts at opening or manipulating device

Many people speak of "tamper-proof" hardware, but in fact nothing can be perfectly tamper proof. Tamper resistance comes in a wide range of strengths: from simple screws with beveled slots so that they can be tightened but not loosened, opaque potting material common on printed circuit boards, up to cast titanium cases.

A "warranty void if seal broken" sticker is the simplest form of tamper evidence, however low tech it may seem! All imaginable varieties of colored dyes, trip wires, films, coatings, and other materials are used on government cryptographic hardware. For example, the Government Fortezza™ PC Cards (the form factor previously known as PCMCIA) are tamper resistant and tamper evident, using a unibody welded case. Although manufactured for well under US$100 in high volume, this design makes them not only very hard to open, but also virtually impossible to open without the attempt being noticeable.

Tamper Detection

There are an infinite variety of sensors and switches designed to detect violation of a security boundary. Black arts to some extent, these techniques often rely in part on the adversary's lack of knowledge about their design. Tamper detection systems trigger some response, which may be simply making a log entry, activating an alarm, disabling functionality, or causing memory to be lost.

For example, a U.S. government cryptographic token for classified information is tamper responsive, using a proprietary technology to envelop the entire device. Any attempt to violate the cryptographic boundary closes a circuit, causing a tamper responsive system to zero key material. Temperature, pressure, voltage, and other environment sensors are also common on such highly secure devices.

Tamper-detection systems can trigger active zeroing or passive zeroing of key material. In an active zeroize system, a battery-driven circuit overwrites, or erases, the memory containing the keys as a response to tampering. Less secure systems have a passive zeroize system, wherein a battery maintains the key memory, so that a break in the circuit causes the memory to be lost.

Zeroing memory is not appropriate in all applications, however. Consider cases where the module contains stored value, perhaps as a secure repository for large sums of money or other irreplaceable "bits of value." Zeroing memory in these cases is an absolute last resort!

Tempest Devices

Electronic devices generate emissions that can be read at a distance with appropriate surveillance equipment. The FCC enforces rudimentary standards to ensure that emissions don't disrupt your television viewing enjoyment, but we are interested in much more than this. *Tempest devices* have adequate shielding to stop electromagnetic impulse (emi) or radio frequency impulse (rfi) signals from escaping the compartment containing red keys. Not just for small modules, entire tempest rooms also exist, where classified work is performed. Other physical security properties, such as radiation hardening, are common in satellite security module construction, but offer little benefit in commercial applications.

To sum up, physical security is meant to deter potential entry, then detect the undeterred adversary.

Random Generation

A special class of math primitive included in almost any cryptographic hardware is the *random number generator* (RNG). Almost always the Achilles' heel of security systems, an RNG provides basic security relied upon by virtually every protocol. In addition to gambling, random numbers are used to generate keys, pad messages, and as inputs to many other common functions. As reported in the *New York Times,* Berkeley graduate students broke Netscape Navigator's security by predicting the "random" numbers it would generate. Because they are deterministic by definition, general-purpose computers are simply incapable of producing truly random numbers; they must be obtained from some analog source. Netscape's products now allow the addition of hardware to provide true analog random numbers.

Analog noise sources suitable for secure random number generation are notoriously difficult to design. The National Security Agency (NSA) has endorsed some implementations as acceptable for use with classified data and other high-security applications, but the market is filled with ad hoc systems that are routinely broken. Because most good noise sources may generate only a few kilobits of true random information per second, this is often fed into a pseudo-RNG (PRNG) when a higher performance is required. Hardware will often include the PRNG as well to ensure that it runs with the integrity of secure execution.

Digital Rights Management

Set-top boxes and other rights management devices are an interesting category of cryptographic hardware because they are agents of the content provider, in the physical possession of an end user. In a sense, they use secure execution to put a "cop in the box." Due to this unusual situation wherein the end user is the adversary, they must have good physical security but because the security provides no direct value to the end user, they must also be low in cost.

How to Defeat Hardware Security

We have now covered the basics of hardware security. Hardware can securely generate, safeguard, and exercise keys from both electronic and physical attackers, even while allowing them to be backed up in case of failure. Where is the gotcha?

A cryptographic hardware device needs to accept calls from the hosts that access its functionality. For instance, hardware will sign or encrypt a message with its keys. How does the hardware know if the command is coming from your application or malicious software that has broken into the host? It can't.

This means that it may still be possible for an attacker to install software on your system that applies your cryptographic hardware to its ill purposes. Hardware systems that maintain audit records of operations performed and attempt to authenticate the calling application can help, but the bottom line is the same: host system security is the weak link in the chain.

Performance

The IETF Internet-Draft describing SSL says, "Cryptographic operations tend to be highly CPU intensive, particularly public key operations." Indeed, cryptographic algorithms are often very inefficient when implemented on general-purpose processors. Just as with video or math coprocessors, custom silicon can perform cryptographic algorithms more efficiently than a CISC (i.e., Intel Pentium™), RISC (i.e., DEC Strong-ARM™) or DSP (i.e., AMD 79Cxx) processor. This efficiency can be taken as some combination of lower cost, higher performance, and lower power consumption. The performance of common algorithms implemented in software and currently available hardware is given in Table 11-6. No currently available cryptoprocessor implements both the public-key and bulk-data cryptographic algorithms in common use today.

Notice that RC4 and hash functions (MD5, SHA-1) run quickly enough on a Pentium to satisfy most network applications. In a server environment, dedicated hardware can offload the processor in these cases, but does not accelerate the operations.

The algorithms given in Table 11-6 form the core set for today's Internet security protocols, including SSL, SET, and IPSec. Although not

TABLE 11-6

Hardware vs. Soft-
ware Performance
for Common
Algorithms

	Pentium II™ at 266 mHz	Hi/fn 7711	Rainbow FastMAP
Published Q1000 price	$250	$50	$125
Power consumption	37 watts	<1 watt	2 watts
Source, http://	www.eskimo.com/~weidai	www.hifn.com	www.rainbow.com
RSA (1024 bit)	46 ms	—	4.9 ms
DSA Sign	24 ms	—	7.0 ms
DSA Verify	30 ms	—	7.0 ms
DH (1024^160 bit)	24 ms	—	3.9 ms
1024 × 1024 bit raw exponentiation	154 ms	—	22 ms
Analogue RNG	—	—	1.0 Mbps
DES	33 Mbps	225 Mbps	—
3DES	11 Mbps	80 Mbps	—
RC4	135 Mbps (est.)	120 Mbps	—
MD5	260 Mbps	115 Mbps	—
SHA-1	115 Mbps	95 Mbps	—

included in this table, Certicom's ECC (elliptic curve cryptosystem) algorithms are beginning to come into use due to their performance advantages. Dedicated low-power and low-cost client-side hardware has been
developed, but high-performance specialized ASICs are not yet available
for ECC.

Metrics

Performance is primarily of interest on a machine acting as server. Performance metrics of interest for servers include those shown in Table
11-7.

Expect cryptographic hardware vendors to provide real-world performance numbers on and for your application on each of these metrics.

SSL is most frequently used under Web transactions (http) or directory lookups (ldap). SGI's WebStone metric has been a popular way to
measure server performance for years. More recently, HP's WebSpec

queues lengthen. Many slow processors do not yield the same result as one fast one.

SSL performs one RSA operation per connection and busy Web servers and many secure Web servers spend 90 percent of their CPU time on this operation. SSL-based servers benefit dramatically from the addition of a public-key accelerator. SET performs several public key operations per transaction, so SET merchant servers and payment gateways can also benefit from public-key hardware. A device running the IPSec protocol may or may not benefit from the added performance of hardware, depending on its application. Routers, firewalls, and servers, which need to admit large bursts of clients, say hundreds at a time, will most certainly be public-key bound.

Impact of Hardware on Bulk-Data Cryptography

Bulk-data algorithms are those that process the data stream, including DES, 3DES, RC4, MD5, and SHA-1. Bulk data cryptohardware does not offer a performance benefit to SET because it encrypts only small packets of data. The protocol processing overhead far outweighs bulk-data operations. SSL is almost always used with an RC4/MD5 algorithm suite, which is optimized for use on a general-purpose processor. Unless SSL is used to secure a 100-Mbps or greater connection, bulk data cryptographic hardware is not necessary.

IPSec requires DES or 3DES and is commonly implemented on smaller network devices that need bulk data cryptographic hardware. Even high-end servers can benefit from bulk data hardware when supporting a 10-Mbps connection or greater and it is prerequisite to supporting 100-Mbps and greater connections. DES, SHA-1, and other bulk-data cryptographic algorithms not only burden the host processor, but also consume memory and bus bandwidth. If data needs to be transferred from memory to the coprocessor and back to be encrypted then to the coprocessor again to compute a hash, then three times the quantity of data is consumed in memory and bus bandwidth. For a 100-Mbps stream, this consumes 30 percent of a PCI bandwidth and even more of the memory bandwidth (depending on RAM type in the system). If the driver architecture is such that the host processor needs to feed data to the device and get it back then this will again double the local bus bandwidth consumption, as well as add significant processing load. The bottom line is

TABLE 11-7

Performance Metrics and Bottlenecks

Protocol	Metric	B
SSL	Capacity, TPS (transactions per second) Response time, milliseconds Maximum burst, number of visitors	Pu
SET	Capacity, TPS	Pu
IPSec	Capacity, CPS (connections per second) Throughput, Mbps (megabits per second) Throughput, PPS (packets per second)	Bu Pu

metric has also been developed to the same end. Both of these m
an excellent job of contemplating the impact of traffic pattern
width constraints, content variables, and CGI use, and provide
basis to measure the performance of SSL. Good industry metric
yet exist for SET and IPSec.

To understand the impact of hardware on common protocols,
to look separately at public-key and bulk-data cryptography.

Impact of Hardware on Public-Key Cryptography

The performance advantage of public-key hardware is particula
pelling because large integer math is so inefficient on a 32-bit m
Further, the times given for a Pentium assume dedicated p
attention wherein the processor is not interrupted and the L1
not flushed. These ideals are rarely achieved in a real-world ser
ronment. Public-key processors contain 128-, 256-, or even 512-
multipliers. The 1024-bit RSA private key is considered the "re
public-key operation and is widely used for performance compa
is computed taking the average of many tests with random inpu
the Chinese remainder theorem and a full modulus. A public-ke
sor must be able to perform 2048-bit operations as well if it is to
emerging security requirements.

Some cryptographic accelerators use arrays of RISC processo
than a public-key processor. Each operation takes longer than
on a host processor—slowing it down under nominal load but in
response time and capacity under heavy load. This strategy
work well on all operating systems, however, as efficiency

that offloading bulk-data cryptography often has a negative rather than positive effect, unless it is done correctly. If you are choosing a system for performance reasons, be sure to understand the system architecture in addition to looking at the raw data rates.

WRAP-UP

Cryptographic hardware comes in many forms, each offering its own mix of advantages in performance, security, economics, and ergonomics. The right mix depends upon the application. It is certain that as Internet security becomes more and more ubiquitous, so will the hardware to support it.

CHAPTER 12

Certificate Authorities

Certificate Authorities play a fundamental role in key management for products and systems using asymmetric encryption technology. This chapter provides a system-level view of the role a Certificate Authority (CA) plays in the security of asymmetric cryptographic systems. Public-key certificates are described, then examined as to why they are important, and once created, how they should be managed. This basic preliminary information on certificates is necessary to fully appreciate the importance of a CA.

Concept/Purpose of Public-Key Certificates

The increase in popularity and use of public/private (asymmetric) key cryptography has brought with it the need to manage the public/private key pair required to uniquely and correctly encrypt and decrypt data. A public/private key pair is created for a specific purpose such as representing an individual, an organization, a physical or network entity location, and so forth. The possibilities are nearly endless. The essential point is that a public/private key pair is created to represent some entity. The unique association of the key pair with a specific identified entity is absolutely critical for this technology to perform its intended function—apply a unique cryptographic transformation to a field of data. The binding between the key pair and the unique entity assigned that key pair must be unbreakable if the key pair is to provide meaningful security.

The most fundamental components of a certificate are a *public key* and the *identity associated* with that key. Other common fields found in a certificate are an expiration date, the name of the certifying authority that issued the certificate, certificate serial number, and the digital signature of the certificate issuer. This last element is probably the most critical. It creates the strong union or binding between the elements of the certificate and provides a mechanism for verifying the authenticity of a certificate after issuance. See Figure 12-1.

As the name implies, a public key is not sensitive information. It does not provide any advantage to figuring out what private key is paired with a particular public key. The challenge with a public key is not guarding the content of the key, but in making it broadly available and easily accessible to others while ensuring that the correct identity is maintained with a given public key. Public keys are packaged in certifi-

Figure 12-1
Fields in a Version 1
X.509 Certificate

Version
Serial Number
Issuer's Signature Algorithm
Issuer Distinguished Name
Validity Period
Subject Distinguished Name
Subject Public Key Information
Issuer's Signature

cates to aid in meeting this second challenge—insuring the correct association of a particular public key with its proper owner or assignee.

Public-key certificates are required to encrypt or decrypt information, which then requires the companion private key (which only the owner has knowledge of) to perform the inverse encryption or decryption operation. These certificates play a major role in verifying digital signatures, securing session key exchanges, and authenticating a user's identity.

The most prevalent certificate structure is based on the International Telegraph and Telephone Consultative Committee (CCITT) X.509 Recommendation. To date, this standard has evolved through three stages of definition and refinement. Each version has built upon the preceding ones and now offers a great deal of functional capability and flexibility.

Version 1 Certificates

As the version number suggests, *Version 1* was the initial standardization effort for public key certificates and was published in 1988. The basic essential elements for a certificate are covered in the Version 1 standard. The following fields are included in a Version 1 certificate.

Version

The *version* field specifies the format of the certificate to enable parsing of information contained in the certificate. The implementation of this field in Version 1 allows for future modifications of the certificate format as they were developed.

Serial Number

The X.500 Recommendation requires that the certificate *serial number* be a unique integer assigned to each certificate issued by a given CA. However, the X.500 Recommendation does not specify how this serial number is generated. The certificate issuer's distinguished name along with the certificate serial number uniquely identifies that certificate among all domains.

Issuer's Signature Algorithm

The *issuer's signature algorithm* field specifies the digital signature algorithm used to bind the information contained in the certificate. This field may contain any parameters required by the signature algorithm.

Issuer's Distinguished Name

The *issuer's distinguished name* field specifies the issuer of the certificate.

Validity Period

The *validity period* specifies the time period for which the certificate is valid. The validity period is expressed in the Coordinated Universal Time (UCT) format which is year, month, day, hours, and minutes terminated by a Z (YYMMDDHHMMZ). Since the year is specified without a century designator, care must be taken when comparing UCT times of different centuries. The Year 2000 (Y2K) problem for X.509 is currently being addressed. It is not clear yet whether X.509 itself will be modified or the certificate encoding process (ASN-1) will be modified. The issuer sets the validity period for a certificate. If the certificate validity period has expired, it can be revalidated without issuing new keys.

Subject Distinguished Name

The *subject's distinguished name* field specifies the identity of the user of the certificate. The issuer of the certificate is responsible for guaranteeing the uniqueness of the subject distinguished names in the certificates within a given certificate domain. If certificate identities were duplicated, this would mean that two entities would be operating with the same electronic identity bound to distinctly different public keys. Untold confusion would result when requesting, retrieving, and processing certificates. Duplication in IDs must be avoided to prevent false rejection of signatures and undecipherable encryption of session keys.

Subject Public Key Information

The *subject's public key information* field contains the certificate's public key information and identifies the algorithm being used. Optionally, this field can include parameters associated with the keys, followed by a "subject public key" field which contains information concerning the clearances and other privileges associated with the subject, as well as the subject's public key. If there are no parameters present, the certificate inherits the parameters of its issuer's certificate. Only the top-level issuer's (the Policy Approving Authority defined later in this chapter) certificate is required to contain parameters associated with the public keys.

Issuer's Signature

The *issuer's signature* is the digital signature, which spans the encoded fields of the certificate. This electronic signature affixes the issuer's seal to the certificate and provides the means for any user of a certificate to later verify its authenticity.

Version 2 Certificates

Version 2 of X.509 was drafted but never officially published as a standard. Version 2 appeared in the 1993 time frame and served primarily as a transitional step to Version 3 certificates. The major contribution made by Version 2 was the definition of the Certification Revocation List mechanism.

Version 3 Certificates

Version 3 was established in the 1994-95 time frame. Version 3 built upon the foundation created by earlier versions and greatly expanded the power and versatility of certificates. The following functionality was added in Version 3:

- A flexible framework for extending the functionality of Versions 1 and 2
- Subject and user attributes
- Key use restrictions
- Security policy information
- Certification path constraints
- Enhanced certificate revocation lists

As new and upgraded security products implement the extensions created by the X.509 Version 3 standard, the real power of these extensions will be apparent. Along with this added sophistication, of course, will come the need to manage this increased set of potential security functionality now made possible. This flexibility can become a real problem for a standard that seeks to establish a common approach everyone will use to achieve compatibility. In order to manage the options provided by Version 3, user groups will most certainly be driven to develop certificate implementation conventions for classes of applications to ensure certificate extensions are properly interpreted for that class of users. This still begs the point of compatibility beyond some specific group of users unless the extensions are simply ignored by others outside the special user's group. The certificate issuers will be faced with the dilemma of how much of this certificate extension functionality should it have to verify and vouch for when it signs a certificate. Whatever fields of a certificate an issuer places his/her signature over can become a responsibility for the issuer to stand behind with potential liability ramifications if a mistake is made. As long as the certificate subject will take responsibility for the content of this extension information, the issuer will only vouch for correct replication of subject provided extension information. This approach protects the content of this information in the certificate and avoids the burden of verification for the certificate issuer.

Association Between a Public Key and Its Assigned Owner

All cryptographic mechanisms depend on some form of security management support to provide the intended strength of mechanism. In the case of public/private-key cryptography, the private key must be known only to the owner and protected from disclosure to others, while the companion public key must be freely shared with the public.

The need to protect a private key is intuitive. Failure or inability to protect one's private key implies that other parties can gain a copy of this key. Whoever possesses a given private key can perform cryptographic actions in place of the true owner of that private key. Since the primary uses of a private key are to create a digital signature or decrypt a symmetric session key, a second party possessing an owner's private key can (1) forge that owner's digital signature and (2) decrypt a session key and thereby decrypt a confidential message intended only for the owner. Mismanagement of a receiving party's private key can improperly expose the sending party's confidential data. Therefore the sender can hold the true owner of the compromised private key legally and financially liable for any losses associated with the improper disclosure of confidential data protected by that key. To avoid or limit liability, the true owner of the private key would need to show due diligence was used to protect the lost or stolen private key. Therefore protection of an individual's private key is a critical element of any cryptographic product.

What is less intuitive, however, is how misapplication of a public key can be equally problematic as loss of a private key. The critical security issue with a public key is creating and maintaining the proper association of a given public key to its true owner. This association or binding between a public key and its true owner must be correctly established at the start and maintained during the life of that public key. Furthermore, this user/key association should be verifiable by third parties that use this public key and should be traceable to a trusted agent that will vouch for the correctness of this user/key association. This set of conditions then provides a third party with a logical basis for trusting the relationship between a public key and its asserted owner; otherwise, false identities can be attached to legitimately issued public keys or completely counterfeit public/private key pairs can be created and bogus identities assigned to the public keys. This can lead to various forms of data spoofing, loss of privacy, and deception that may not be easily detected.

The Role of Certificates in Establishing Trust

Use of public-key certificates, issued by trusted agents called *certificate authorities,* are the mechanisms that have evolved for providing sound management and control of public keys and maintaining the correct identities assigned to them. The certificate creates a very strong association or binding between the public key and its assignee through a verifiable electronic signature affixed by a trusted certification authority. The ability for a third party to independently verify the authenticity of a certificate by verifying the CA's signature allows immediate detection of attempts to tamper with or counterfeit a certificate. This gives the user of the certificate confidence that, when used, the certificate will perform its intended function.

Verification of Requestor's Information

Two levels of verification are needed for certificates. First, when the certificate is created, the trusted agent creating the certificate must verify the identity of the person or entity whose identifying information and public key will be joined in the certificate. Verification at creation can be done by requiring the certificate requestor to positively identify him/herself much like the U.S. Post Office requires a person to appear with his/her birth certificate to apply for a passport. This type of representation between the certificate requestor and certificate creator does not require a physical appearance as is the custom for a passport, but can be done remotely through a Registration Authority (defined later in this chapter) that has established a trusted relationship with the certificate creator. Other possibilities include use of a trusted path between the requestor and the certificate creator. Whatever the mechanism for identification and interaction, an unbroken chain of trust should exist between the certificate requestor and certificate issuer. Once the certificate issuer verifies the identity to be included in the certificate, the certificate is completed and signed by the issuer. This is equivalent to a Notary Public witnessing the signing of a document and then putting his/her own seal on that document to attest to the validity of the identity of the signer of the document. In most cases, the trusted agent who creates and signs a certificate will be an officially recognized Certificate Authority (CA).

The second level of verification needed for certificates is use based. Good security practice for a user of an asymmetric key encryption system will involve performing certificate verification checks on second-party certificates prior to their use. An important part of the certificate validation process is to determine that the distinguished name contained in the certificate issuer's field of the certificate represents a valid issuer in the certification path hierarchy for the certificate domain.

A *certification hierarchy* is a set of two or more certificates concatenated together, forming a hierarchical chain, wherein one certificate testifies to the authenticity of the previous certificate. At the end of a certificate hierarchy is a top-level certifying authority, which is trusted without a certificate from any other certifying authority. The public key of the top-level certifying authority is often referred to as the *root certificate,* which is a self-generated and signed certificate that is inherently trustworthy, independently known, and widely available. See Figure 12-2.

Figure 12-2
Certificate Hierarchy

Certificate ID	Signed By
PAA (Root)	Self Signed
PCA	PAA
CA	PCA
RA/User	CA

An example of possible steps that can be used to validate a second party's certificate is as follows, starting with the Policy Approving Authority's signature and continuing until the user's certificate is processed:

1. Verify the issuer's signature on the target certificate.

2. Ensure that the certificate is valid by comparing the current time with the validity period.

3. Ensure that the subject distinguished name in the issuer certificate matches the issuer distinguished name in the target certificate.

4. Ensure that the subject distinguished name is subordinate to the issuer distinguished name by ensuring that the initial portion of the subject distinguished name matches the corresponding portion of the issuer distinguished name.

5. Check the current Certificate Revocation List to make sure the signer's certificate has not been revoked.

Verifying certificate authenticity requires tracing its origin back to a trusted entity. The certification path hierarchy should permit verification up to the root level for a particular domain when maximum confidence is needed. However, it may be possible to establish sufficient verification trust by tracing to a lower level in the path such as the Certificate Authority level. The receiver of a message could verify a certificate using the certifying authority's public key and based on a high degree of trust in that certifying authority, confidently accept the public key of the sender. This will reduce the overhead needed to implement the verification procedure. If certificates are locally stored for future use, trade-offs also exist regarding the frequency of verification for a given certificate. A time period or number of times used could trigger verification as an alternative to per use verification. These trade-offs for reduced frequency of verification should be made only if there is a compelling reason to take the added security risk associated with use of an altered or counterfeit certificate.

When issued by a Certificate Authority, a public-key certificate is relied upon by a potentially large number of users to verify another party's digital signature and to encrypt session keys used for data encryption. The security provided by a cryptographic system can be circumvented if the public-key certificates can be tampered with or counterfeited. The quality of a cryptographic algorithm and the length of its key can be circumvented if the public-key certificates supporting them can be forged or manipulated without detection. Therefore it is critically important to have a sound basis to assign trust to another party's public-key certificate.

What Certificate Authorities Do

A *Certificate Authority* (CA) is an agent that is trusted by its constituents to issue public-key certificates and vouch for the accuracy of critical data elements contained in the certificates it issues. The closest analogy in the United States to a CA is the familiar notary public. Similar to a notary public, a CA applies its signature to verified information fields contained within a document (in this case, an electronic file called a *certificate*) and in so doing vouches for the identity of the person and/ or organization being affixed to that original document.

A CA establishes one or more communities or certificate domains for the constituents it serves. A given certificate domain can be small or large, open or closed, based on a constituent's needs. Since one of the primary advantages of asymmetric encryption is the ability to widely distribute users' public keys, the norm would be for a certificate domain to be quite large. A certificate generation process can be a centralized or distributed function and therefore may be part of a hierarchical certificate generation structure. Each certificate domain begins with the top-level point of origin commonly referred to as a *root authority*. One of the early models for a scalable certificate hierarchy consists of the following functional roles:

- Policy Approving Authority (PAA)
- Policy Creation Authority (PCA)
- Certification Authority (CA)
- Registration Authority (RA)
- User represented by certificate

The functional roles of the infrastructure are hierarchical and collectively make up a *domain certification path*. Each point in the certification path, working from the certificate user up to the PAA, must have a means of authenticating itself to the next higher element in the certification path. From the CA upward, this authentication is provided using digital signatures. Up to CA level, the element above will normally establish the authentication mechanism used between those two levels.

The purpose for the certificate hierarchy is to allow a single domain to scale to whatever size it needs to be. Multiple PCAs can serve under one PAA, and in turn multiple CAs can serve under one PCA and so on. The size and geographical diversity of the user population in a single domain will dictate the number of RAs, CAs, and so forth, that will be needed to efficiently serve all users. For small or highly centralized domains, a CA can also serve as the Policy Control Authority and the Policy Administration Authority for that domain. If a domain is large, then a true distributed certificate issuance hierarchy may become necessary for logistical reasons. However, if a CA can provide high capacity automated remote service while maintaining an adequate level of quality and assurance, then a single CA could serve a very extensive population.

Certification Hierarchy

Policy Approving Authority (PAA)

The PAA resides at the top of the certification path hierarchy. The PAA is responsible for generating and signing PCA certificates as well as generating and signing its own certificates. The PAA is also responsible for establishing communications with other PAA domains. A PAA domain consists of a defined user community, and can establish communications with other PAAs by generating a cross-certificate such that users in its domain can now communicate with users in the other domain. Additionally, a PAA generates and distributes Certificate Revocation Lists (CRLs) for users in its domain. A CRL contains a listing of certificates whose associated private keys have been declared invalid for a variety of possible reasons. CRLs are used to inform users within a particular domain which certificates issued by that domain should no longer be used.

Policy Creation Authority (PCA)

The next level in the certification path hierarchy is the PCA. The PCA is responsible for generating and signing CAs' certificates in its domain. The number of PCAs is primarily a function of the number of CAs required.

Certification Authority (CA)

The CA is responsible for generating and signing user certificates. Before processing any requests for certificates for users in its domain, the CA must verify that an authorized registration authority (RA) sent the request. If the RA is authorized to request services from the CA on behalf of the user, the CA will process the request. A certificate is considered invalid if any data on the certificate changes, if the certificate is no longer needed, or if the certificate has expired.

Registration Authority (RA)

At the next level in the certification path hierarchy is the RA. The RA acts as an intermediary between the CA and the user. Any user requiring certificate services will be directed to the RA. The RA will be responsible for verifying the authenticity of critical information requested for inclusion on a given certificate, ensuring user IDs are not duplicated, and sending certificate requests to the CA. A trust relationship must be established between the CA and RA because the CA must rely on the RA to perform certificate requestor ID verification.

User

The users consist of those entities that employ public/private-key cryptography to protect their business or private interests. The user is responsible for requesting certificates directly from the CA or from a designated RA. The user is also responsible for reporting compromise or suspected compromise of his/her private key to the RA or CA.

Who Can Be a CA?

There are no real limitations on who can be a CA. There are two generic groups, however, that would naturally gravitate toward being a CA. First there is the company whose business mission is to provide professional CA services to the general public for profit. This is a significant commitment due to the liability issues associated with the potential impact of improper public key certificates being issued. A significant investment in physical and electronic emanation security is required due to the very sensitive nature of their business.

The second general category of CA is companies, organizations, government entities, and so forth, that for security, cost, control, or other reasons want to perform this function for themselves. This type of CA can operate its own certificate domain or become a part of another domain. This allows a particular company, organization, or government entity to control its own keys and set up an optimum internal process for requesting, generating and distributing certificates.

Building Trust in a CA

The trust that should be placed in a public-key certificate is heavily affected by the operating practices the associated CA adopts. This degree of trust should be a function of the rigor the CA applies in the process of binding an entity's identity with its associated public key. This in turn is primarily a function of the certification practices employed. A CA can establish trust by publishing its operating procedures and security controls. By publishing and adhering to these self-imposed standards, the CA will define the level of trust a user should expect as well as criteria for due diligence that a constituent should use to hold the CA accountable.

Certificate Policy

A *certificate policy* should indicate to both the certificate issuer and user the suitability of use for a particular application. In X.509 terminology, a certificate policy is "a named set of rules that indicates the applicability of a certificate to a particular community and/or class of application with common security requirements." Every certificate user should be cognizant of the certificate policy governing that certificate. For a certificate to perform its intended function, it should be applied consistently with the policy under which it was generated. This implies that a computer application using a certificate must be aware and capable of responding to the policy contained in a given certificate. Misapplication of a certificate policy therefore can result in a loss of protection. This is why the issuer, user, and user application should be cognizant of the policy being implemented with a particular certificate.

Certification Practice Statement

A *certification practice standard* is a statement of the practices that a certification authority employs in issuing certificates. A CA that has adopted and published its own certification practice standard will be more likely to win the trust of its customers. This statement allows the certificate user to set reasonable expectations for the level of security inherent in its certificates. A certification practice statement should be structured well enough to be legally clear to a CA's constituent what is and is not to be expected from the CA. The American Bar Association's guidelines for a certification practice statement is as follows:

> A certification practice statement may take the form of a declaration by the certification authority of the details of its trustworthy system and the practices it employs in its operations and in support of issuance of a certificate, or it may be a statute or regulation applicable to the certification authority and covering similar subject matter. It may also be part of the contract between the certification authority and the subscriber. A certification practice statement may also be comprised of multiple documents, a combination of public law, private contract, and/or declaration. A certification practice statement is useful in helping subscribers and relying parties

distinguish which certification authorities provide more reliable representations in the certificates they issue.

Certain forms of legally implementing certification practice statements lend themselves to particular relationships. For example, when the legal relationship between a certification authority and subscriber is consensual, a contract would ordinarily be the means of giving effect to a certification practice statement. The duties a certification authority owes to a relying person are generally based on the certification authority's representations, which may include a certification practice statement.

Whether a certification practice statement is binding on a relying person (who would not usually be a party to the certification practice statement) depends on whether the relying person has knowledge or notice of the certification practice statement. A relying person has knowledge or at least notice of the contents of the certificate used by the relying person to verify a digital signature, including documents incorporated into the certificate by reference. Documents considered incorporated by reference should be available through the same channel or repository through which the incorporating document is accessible. It is therefore advisable to incorporate a certification practice statement into a certificate by reference.

As much as possible, a certification practice statement should indicate any of the widely recognized standards to which the certification authority's practices conform. Reference to widely recognized standards may indicate concisely the suitability of the certification authority's practices for another person's purposes, as well as the potential technological compatibility of the certificates issued by the certification authority with repositories and other systems.

Potential Liability

Due to the potential damage that can occur if a flawed certificate is issued and used, a CA assumes a level of liability for mistakes and lack of due diligence in creating these public key certificates. In order to minimize this potential liability and instill confidence in their constituents, a CA may choose to publish or make available its certification practice statement. This helps both the certificate owner and the CA. The practice statement will inform the user of the level of diligence that will be applied by the CA while creating certificates, while providing a standard of due diligence for the CA to follow. If the certificate policy and practice statements are credible, the CA's liability can be minimized if the policy and statement are in fact followed.

Trust Level Between the CA and Certificate Requestor

A CA should establish standards for the level of confidence or assurance that it must have in the information contained in a certificate before signing that certificate. Once the certificate is signed, the CA shares in responsibility for the validity of the information it contains. The critical item that must be validated is the subject's distinguished name that is combined with that subject's public key in a certificate. The CA must establish the degree of positive identification or assurance that will be required to acquire a certificate from that CA. The CA has to be concerned about creating certificates that bear a false or incorrect identity since the CA is "certifying" this information. Whatever standards of identification the CA adopts, it should be clear to all certificate users in that domain, what level of assurance or reliance should be afforded to any given certificate.

If a CA offers certificates with varying levels of assurance, then each certificate needs to be clearly identified as to its level of assurance and all certificate users need to be informed of the risks and implications of each different level of certificate assurance present within their domain. CAs that require very little identification and offer certificates with very low assurance have an obligation to holders and owners of higher-assurance certificates, to alert them to the risks associated with accepting and using lower-assurance certificates. Therefore every CA should publicly disclose its identification requirements and policies so that certificate users can establish their own policy of accepting certificates that vary in level of assurance.

Expiration Policy for Certificates

One of the fundamentals of good key management is to change keys periodically to limit losses if your key has been compromised without your knowledge. Otherwise, the damage due to unknown key compromise would be unbounded. Therefore all well-managed keys are assigned a useful life and need to be replaced before that useful life is exceeded. Certificates fall is this category. A public/private key pair should be changed at some interval. If a private key is stored on media accessible by hackers and unauthorized insiders, then a more frequent key change is very prudent. When a certificate is created, a reasonable expiration date should be assigned. Prior to expiration, the certificate should be superseded as a new key pair is installed.

Certificate Revocation

There will always be reasons why public/private key pairs will need to be deactivated before their expiration date. The most common reasons are:

- There is a suspected or confirmed compromise of the private key.
- The user specified in the certificate may no longer have authority to use the key due to a change in job assignment or employment status.
- The information in a certificate is no longer accurate due to a change in name or authority granted to a particular individual.

It is the certificate owner's or Registration Authority's responsibility to initiate action for revocation of a certificate. The PAA is responsible for processing that request and creating a new entry on a certificate revocation list.

Certificate Revocation Lists (CRLs)

A *certificate revocation list* (CRL) is a list of certificates that have been revoked by their PAA before their scheduled expiration date. CRLs are created, maintained, and made available by the PAA responsible for the certificate domains they operate. CRLs only list current certificates since expired certificates should already be treated as invalid for any new use after the expiration date. When a revoked certificate is past its original expiration date, it is removed from the CRL. CRLs should be distributed to all certificate holders in a given domain and are usually posted at a central distribution point by the PAA.

Protection Against Attack

Since a PAA, PCA, and CA (the certificate creation hierarchy) provide an essential element of trust in the management of public key certificates, that trust could be eroded if exploitable security vulnerabilities are present within any of these functions. The question then naturally arises regarding whether elements of the certificate creation hierarchy (CCH) are vulnerable to attack. The CCH should address the following threats and defensive strategies should be employed where vulnerabilities are discovered before attempts are made to exploit them.

1. Break into a CCH facility and steal or copy a CCH's private key.

2. Acquire a CCH's private key through cryptanalysis.

3. Bribe a CCH staff member to create a false certificate.

4. Social engineer the CA into issuing a certificate with a false identity.

5. If the CA accepts remote certificate request over a network, then a hacker has an opportunity to create certificates with false identities and possibly copy the CA's private key.

The first scenario requires physical penetration of the CA's facility and can be adequately defended against by employing layers of physical and personnel security including locks, alarms, badges, cameras, access control monitoring and auditing, and so forth.

The second scenario can also be easily countered by selecting an adequately long key length that would make cryptanalysis infeasible. The impact of having to change a CA's (or PCA's or PAA's) key pair could be very disruptive if a large user population is supported and a mechanism for smoothly performing this key change is not in place. Therefore it is preferable for CCH elements to avoid unnecessary key changes. Due to the possible archiving of digitally signed documents for some significant time period (7-25 years), the key length selection should be very conservative (longer is better) and the physical protection of these special keys should be extraordinary to provide very long term protection.

The third and fourth scenarios involve exploitation of a CCH employee. Insider human weaknesses that can be exploited within a CCH element are clearly a possibility that cannot be easily argued away in today's world. Good training, good policies and procedures, use of a two-person operation, independent checks and balances, and employee tracking and monitoring can all work together to provide a strong controlled environment that should discourage and detect dishonest behavior by CCH employees.

The fifth scenario applies only to cases where RAs remotely submit certificate requests and receive a completed certificate in return. Remote access to a CA should be via a trusted path that cannot be breached by a hacker.

Optional CA Services

In addition to the basic functions already addressed, there are several other services that a CA can offer to users who have special requirements. The need for these extra services will vary significantly between users. Some users will not want to bother learning and performing certain key management functions such as archiving certificates. Others will require an exportable security solution that can be greatly facilitated by a CA performing certain centralized key management functions. The most common of these additional services are:

- Generation of the public/private key pair for the user
- Archiving of public and private key pairs for users
- Data recovery services for users desiring this service
- Programming of hardware security tokens
- Cross-certification with other certificate domains

Each of these optional services is briefly explained along with possible motivations for these added services.

Generation of the Public/Private Key Pair

The physical location where the public/private key pair is generated for a particular user is not a concern. What is critical though is (1) the integrity of the key generation process, (2) the protection of the private key so only the intended user has access to it, and (3) the proper incorporation of the public key into a certificate. If an application performs these functions transparently, the integrity of these processes must be maintained over the life of the application. This may be difficult to ensure if these key management processes are implemented in software on a networked computer. A network intrusion will put this software at risk with little chance of detection. If key generation requires too much user involvement or if the generation process is unprotected, then outsourcing this function may make sense. A CA can perform this function with high integrity over a prolonged period of time because it will use trained people and a reliable process in a safe environment. Having a CA perform asymmetric key-pair generation positions it to provide other important key management services which, for some users, will make outsourcing increasingly attractive.

Archiving of Keys

If a user has a data archival requirement, and if the archived data bears a digital signature or is encrypted, access to a specific user's public/private key pairs will become a long-term requirement that will most likely extend beyond the expiration date of a single public/private pair. In order to ensure that digital signature verification and decryption on archived data can be performed indefinitely into the future, the supporting keys must be archived as well.

In order to verify a digital signature on an archived file, the public-key certificate of the signer must be retained in addition to the archived data. This certificate can be archived with the file or kept in a separate certificate archive to avoid duplicate storage of the same certificate; however, the certificate hierarchy verification path needed for checking the authenticity of an archived certificate must also be archived. Performing these security-related archiving steps properly will guard the long-term integrity of important electronic files and will ensure that these documents retain their legal status. Relying on the CA to archive the certificate verification path information has a significant benefit in that a third party can now obtain the information required to verify a signature from a neutral party. This allows independent validation of a signature, which in litigation situations allows the holder of a signed file to convincingly show an unbroken chain of data integrity and nonrepudiation of origin. This will give the archived electronic file in your computer the legal weight of a hand-signed paper document filed in your office file cabinet. If the chain of integrity and nonrepudiation is not maintained and is not verifiable by a neutral third party, there is no objective proof that an electronic file you have archived is authentic.

For users that archive files in encrypted form, retention of the corresponding private key for later decryption is needed. Like digital signatures, secure distribution of the symmetric encryption keys requires use of a public/private key pair. Common practice is to append the encrypted session key with the encrypted file. After decrypting the session key with the recipient's private key, the encrypted file is then decrypted using this recovered session key. Since only the user will have a need or right to access his/her private key, this part of the key archival process must be very secure and very competently managed. If a private key is ever permanently lost, erased, or destroyed, any data encrypted in that key will be permanently scrambled and useless. Having a CA professionally archive and protect your private key is a prudent choice if you want to ensure long-term access to encrypted data.

Data Recovery Services

In its most elementary form, *data recovery* is no more than archiving keys for a user, as just described in the previous section. This section outlines how a CA might add value and play a positive role in an area that has become rather complex and politically driven.

First, a brief background on the controversy that has surrounded this topic: Data recovery (or *key escrow*) has been the subject of a high-profile public debate over the past few years. A highly publicized negative aspect of key escrow has been the specter of governments (with the United States taking the lead) making key escrow mandatory and then abusing the service by improperly acquiring a user's private key and subsequently decrypting his/her private information.

On the other hand, those who object to the government mandating key escrow will also agree that key recovery is necessary for a business to sustain its operations. If an employee secures sensitive company information using his/her public/private key pair, then loses or accidentally destroys that key pair, then there must be a way to recover the secured data. There are no apparent objective arguments against this form of self-protection. The issue then boils down to what role the government should play and whether the government will abuse whatever system of key recovery is adopted.

The middle ground that seems to be emerging is that users can select how, by whom, and even whether they will do key recovery. However, for a cryptographic product using strong encryption (greater-than-40-bit symmetric key) to be approved for export, there must be a credible escrow system in place. The deal between private citizens and their government then becomes:

1. Let the owner of the key decide the details of how and by whom key recovery will be performed.

2. The government will rely on court orders to gain access to keys when law enforcement or national security events dictate.

3. Strong cryptographic products can be approved for export if a satisfactory key recovery system is backing up the product.

The details are obviously much more complex, but that is the deal in a conceptual nutshell. If this type of agreement is not brokered, then the issue will likely remain unresolved and the debate will continue.

A CA can serve as a credible key recovery agent since its users already trusted it to create certificates. If it also generates asymmetric key pairs for its users, then the data recovery task becomes natural and efficient for it to perform. Since CAs are legally accountable to their users, it is in the CA's best interest to perform a data recovery task honestly and diligently.

Programming of Hardware Security Tokens

Some security products use *hardware tokens* to increase the level of security offered. Smartcards and PC cards are two common types of security tokens in use today. Both of these types of tokens implement asymmetric encryption on the token and store the user's private key and public certificate on the token. It is also common for these tokens to use a stored PIN to authenticate the user to the token. From the factory, these tokens are unprogrammed with respect to keys, certificates, and PINs. Since in most cases a CA will be used to create the user's certificate, there will be some minimum level of interaction between the user and the CA to get the certificate needed for placement on the token. This opens the question of whether it is desirable for the CA to play a broader role in the programming of the security token. Trade-offs can be made regarding where the public/private key pair is generated, and where the PIN is generated. The user, the RA, or the CA can perform these last two functions. If the CA is performing the data recovery function, this heavily tips the trade-off in the direction of the CA generating the public/private key pair as well. In turn, this makes programming of the token a natural function for the CA to perform.

If no data recovery service is being provided, then the balance shifts toward generating the public/private key pair on the token at a location most convenient to the user. This minimizes exposure of the private key (no one ever sees it) at the expense of data recovery. The public key would then be read off the token, forwarded to the CA with the user's identification information, and the certificate returned by the CA to the device programming the token. The token programming would be performed by a special PC located anywhere network access to the CA is available, and the programming could take place at the location of either the user, RA, or CA.

Cross-Certification

Currently there are a number of CAs operating commercially, each supporting one or more certificate domains. Each CA has its set of customers using certificates that should be verifiable back to the issuing CA. When a certificate is received from a user in another domain, its authenticity cannot be verified unless the two domains operate from a common root authority or an accommodation is made to recognize certificates across CA domain boundaries. One such accommodation would have a CA from one domain append its signature to the certificate verification paths for another CA's domain. If both CAs sign the other domain's certification path, then the two domains have "interoperable" certificates. Now the verification path will work across agreed domains. This process is sometimes referred to as *CA cross-certification.*

When negotiating a cross-certification agreement, certification authorities will need to examine and compare each other's Certification Practice Statements and certificate policies supported to determine the risk to their own certificate holders of accepting and vouching for certificates issued under another CA. Certificate holders will expect any cross-certified certificates to provide approximately the same level of assurance offered by their own CA. If this is not the case, then the CA with the stronger practice statement should make disclosure to its certificate holders calling attention to the added risks assumed by accepting a certificate of lower assurance—this can easily become a management, configuration, and liability headache. A CA that issues high-assurance certificates must be very careful in gauging the impact on its own customers before agreeing to cross-certify a domain that issues lower-assurance certificates.

Alternatives to Cross-Certification

If cross-certification turns out to be too hard or too risky for groups of CAs to arrange, then other approaches need to be explored to allow users in different certificate domains to interoperate. Certificate users will demand this from their CAs and will probably be the forcing function needed to cause CAs to hammer out a workable certificate interoperability scheme that protects all users' security interests. Until CAs work out such a scheme, users will be left to their own devices to interoperate in the interim.

It is not likely that two CAs will agree to subordinate themselves to a common PAA or root authority to avoid the need for cross-certification. This would probably be as difficult as working out a sound cross-certification agreement, which would require the involved CAs to level their certification practice statements. If adopting a common root authority is not likely, then the next most workable scheme would seem to be equipping users with certification hierarchy paths for multiple domains. This is something that users could implement without the CAs' having to change. Since the user would now be cognizant of which domains it would accept certificates from, the user can now manage the risks associated with difference in assurance between domains.

Need for Certificate Distribution

In order for asymmetric key encryption and decryption to occur between two parties, one party must obtain the other's public-key certificate. If the sending party encrypts with a private key (for digital signing), the receiving party must obtain the sending party's public key certificate for signature verification. If the sending party encrypts with a public key (for secure session key exchange), it must be with the public key of the intended recipient. In this case, the sending party must obtain the receiving party's certificate prior to encryption. This is as fundamental in cryptography as gravity is in physics. In order to perform this movement of certificates, a means of publicly publishing and disseminating certificates is required. The task of sharing certificates to support asymmetric cryptography is similar to the problem the phone companies have of broadly publishing phone numbers to support their customers making phone calls. There are several useful analogies between certificate distribution and telephone number distribution.

Certificate Directories

The most common method for making certificates widely available is to post them on a bulletin board, Web page, or directory and provide network access to these centralized repositories. X.500 is by far the dominant standard and model for directory services today. This model provides the name spaces and protocols needed to query and update a certificate directory. A major feature of X.500 is that it defines a global directory structure and offers the potential for global retrieval of certificates. Anyone with an X.500 or TCP/IP-based client can take advantage of certificate directory services, as they become available. X.500 provides standardization in the following functional areas:

■ The form and character of the information in the directory

- How the directory information is referenced and organized

- Operations that can be performed on the information in the directory

- An authentication framework that allows information in the directory to be secured

- How data is distributed and how related operations are carried out

X.500 directory entries are arranged in a hierarchical structure and can be divided among Directory System Agent (DSA) servers based on geographical and/or organizational distribution. Users will access certificates using a Directory User Agent (DUA). Entries are named according to their position in this hierarchy by a unique identifier called a *Distinguished Name* (DN). Each component of the DN is called a *Relative Distinguished Name* (RDN). See Figure 12-3.

Figure 12-3
X.500 Directory
Structure

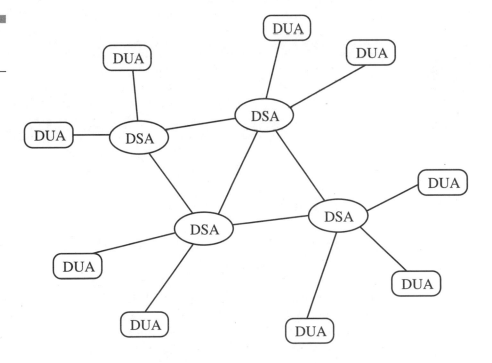

X.500 defines three basic categories of directory operations: (1) search and read, (2) modify, and (3) authenticate. The search operation selects entries from a defined area of the directory tree based on some user-provided selection criteria using a search filter. For each matching entry, a requested set of attributes is returned according to the search criteria supplied. The read operation retrieves the attributes of a directory entry whose name has been provided in the user's request. The modify operation can be used to change existing entries, insert new entries, and remove old entries. The final operation, authenticate, defines a set of options that allow a user to initiate, cancel, or terminate a session on the directory. The bind operation allows a client to initiate a session and prove its identity to the directory. Several user-authentication methods are supported, from a simple fixed unprotected password to strong public key-based authentication. The unbind operation is used to terminate a directory session. An abandon operation is also defined, allowing an operation in progress to be canceled.

Each X.500 operation and result can be signed to ensure its integrity. Digital signing is done using the originating party's private key. The signed request or result is carried end-to-end in the protocol, allowing integrity to be checked at every step. This allows detection of connection hijacking or modification by intermediate servers.

In X.500, the directory can be distributed among many servers (called *DSAs* for Directory System Agents). No matter which server a client connects to, it sees the same view of the directory. If a server is unable to answer a client's request, it can either chain the request to another server, or refer the client to the server. A user with access to a DSA and connectivity to a directory can request or search for certificates electronically across the X.500 directory. The DSA software also allows users to retrieve Certificate Revocation Lists kept in the directory.

Directory Access Protocol (DAP)

The *Directory Access Protocol* (DAP) provides users a means to use the full functionality and features of an X.500 directory. DAP is a full OSI protocol that contains extensive functionality that will serve the most demanding and sophisticated high-end user population. DAP provides a rich set of directory services but has acquired the tag of being a heavyweight solution because a number of its more complex features are not widely needed. Running and administering a full-featured X.500 DAP client and having it "fit" on smaller computer systems has proved to be difficult. For this reason a simpler protocol was developed—the Lightweight Directory Access Protocol (LDAP).

Lightweight Directory Access Protocol (LDAP)

LDAP specifies a protocol, which allows low-overhead access to a X.500 directory using a reduced set of services offered by the full X.500 directory service. It is an access protocol and does not specify how the directory service itself operates. It runs directly with the TCP network protocol and simplifies directory access to the extent that LDAP clients can be smaller, faster, and easier to implement than full X.500 clients—that is, LDAP makes modifications to the search, read, and modify operations of X.500 with only minor loss of basic functionality. The changes to the authentication operations are also relatively minor, except for user authentication that is limited to simple fixed passwords and Kerberos Version 4 functionality.

Certificate Sharing Between Users (Directory-less)

Rather than rely on a third-party directory, users can share certificates if they can agree on a protocol for sharing. By implication, a user that needs another party's certificate will already have some form of connectivity with that other party. The only prerequisite for sharing is that the parties sharing must have a means of communication with each other independent of the certificate exchange protocol used. The sharing protocol can be as simple as attaching your certificate to signed messages to aid signature verification during the initial exchange with that party. The protocol could be more sophisticated and provide a mechanism for requesting and responding to requests for certificates on demand. The sharing protocol should be standards-based to avoid proprietary implementations and a natural extension to the protocols already being used to communicate with others.

An example of such a sharing method is use of the ANSI ASC X12.815 cryptographic service message within the X12 EDI community. The 815 message provides the functionality for users to request certificates, transmit certificates, and exchange certificate revocation lists. It is part of the X12 body of standards and is just one more type of EDI transaction that can be exchanged between trading partners.

When sharing is used, there is no dependence on external directories, no prior directory access arrangements need be arranged, and loss of directory service will not deny operation to users that would otherwise be dependent on the directory. Of course, the need to construct or participate in a certificate directory goes away for groups that find certificate sharing a viable approach. Another subtle advantage of sharing is that the users are basically in control. If a certificate directory is used, then the directory will dictate and change the access rules according to their best interests. As long as the users' best interests and the directory's best interests are congruent there is no problem, but this will not always be the case. Then there is the issue of cost: someone must bear the cost of establishing and operating a certificate directory. If that cost is passed on to the user on a recurring usage or per access basis, then certificate sharing may provide cost savings. If directories are preferred and used, sharing can be viewed as a backup alternative to avoid denial of service if a directory becomes inaccessible or ceases to operate for a period of time.

Local Caching by User

Regardless of how a user obtains needed certificates, it is prudent in most cases to locally retain those certificate for future use. This eliminates the need to repeatedly access a certificate directory or continually swap certificates between the same users. With certificate requests or searches minimized, the primary task now becomes local management of the certificate cache. These tasks include processing certificate revocation lists, acting on certificates that have been revoked or expired, and periodically verifying the authenticity of stored certificates. These tasks can be automated and therefore be transparent to the user.

WRAP UP

Public-key certificates perform a fundamental role in the secure use of public/private-key cryptography. The ability to accurately verify digital signatures and properly encrypt session keys depends on the underlying integrity of the public-key certificates used to perform these security operations. The integrity of these certificates is to a large extent the responsibility of trusted agents called certificate authorities (CAs). The

CA creates and vouches for the content of the certificates it create key part of the creation process is checking the authenticity of the i tity, which is combined with the public key associated with that iden

There are two basic categories of CA: those that perform the fun for profit and those that perform the function for their own organiz or closed community. All CAs do not necessarily operate the same. CAs will practice and apply more rigorous verification procedures others and therefore will issue certificates with varying levels of a ance.

Certificates are intended for distribution, much like phone nu are published for the benefit of others. Certificate distribution accomplished through centrally managed directories or through sl between certificate holders. Certificates contain no private inforr per se but represent a very critical binding between the ID and th lic key associated with that ID. If this association can be modi forged, then the underlying security function it supports will be c mised. Therefore, certificate authenticity should be independentl fied by a second party prior to use. The CA's signature over the cate is the mechanism for this verification of authenticity. To m their security utility, certificates are given a prudent useful life assigning an expiration date. The CA's root authority will revoke cates that must be deactivated prior to expiration. Notice of this tion will be broadcast via a certificate revocation list to all p holders of this certificate.

Finally, CAs can provide other value-added services for th stituents other than certificate issuance. They can generate asy key pairs, archive certificates and keys, perform data recovery, hardware security tokens, and cross-certify certificates wi domains.

PART 3

Implementation and Product Certification

CHAPTER 13

Implementation
Mistakes

This chapter characterizes the types of mistakes that occur during implementation of practical cryptographic systems. We look at various attacks that can be made against a crypto-product because of errors in product implementation. ICSA has developed guidelines and tests to reduce risk in digital security systems by eliminating implementation mistakes and by ensuring that cryptographic products perform as claimed.

The Puzzle

Stallings presents a clear conceptual framework for a general cryptosystem in Figures 13-1 to 13-3. Figure 13-1 shows a simplified model of a conventional cryptosystem. Note the position that the cryptanalyst plays in the conventional model versus the one he or she plays in the public-key models for secrecy and authentication shown in Figures 13-2 and 13-3; in the latter figure, the amount of cryptanalytic work is more, but the number of potential attack points is also higher.

Plain text, transformation algorithms, governing keys, random number generation, initialization vectors, cipher text, hardware kernel, pro-

Figure 13-1
Model of Conventional Cryptosystem

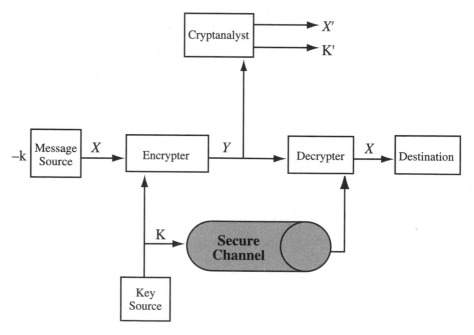

Figure 13-2
Public-Key Cryptosys-
tem: Secrecy

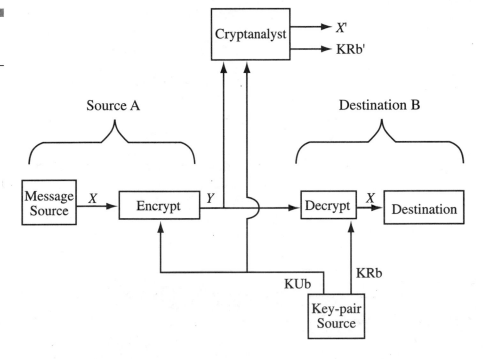

Figure 13-3
Public-Key Cryptosys-
tem: Authentication

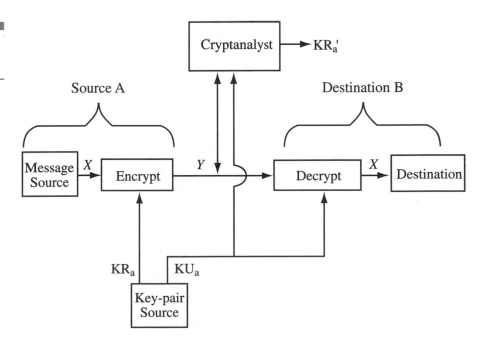

tocols, and communications software—these are the basic blocks of a cryptographic system. These blocks may be coordinated in four general types of products:

1. File/disk encryptors

2. Virtual private networks (VPNs)

3. Smartcards

4. Toolkits

The diversity of applications these products cover draws from the widest possible purview: from protecting privacy to financial transactions; from corporate intranets to biometric defenses; from defense to space communications; from automotive, health care, research, heavy metal, DvD, manufacturing, law enforcement, business services, telephone communications to surfing the Internet—ICSA has tested and certified cryptographic products in all of these applications.

Strong cryptographic algorithms do not guarantee a secure system. Longer keys help, but do not guarantee a secure system. Adding proprietary algorithms or special randomization functions may reduce rather than improve the practical security of the cryptosystem. ICSA certifies vendor products: about two-thirds of the errors found by ICSA are errors of implementation; the remaining one-third is split between errors of installation and fundamental design. When errors are found, the vendor is notified and certification is withheld until the error is corrected, generally by a software patch or a specific change in protocol. Hardware is rarely an issue, but it is not immune to attack.

ICSA maintains a crypto-intel group, which spends its waking hours (and many not so waking) getting leads on new system attacks both reported and theoretical. ICSA's labs then proceed to add these new attacks or variations of old ones to a continuously evolving battery of tests that they apply to all consortium membership products.

In reviewing Figures 13-1 to 13-3, it is clear that the conceptual basis for both symmetric and asymmetric systems is not faulted; however, potential implementation of these systems may be. Every input, output, or transformation for these systems may become the weak link in the cryptosecurity for a product. ICSA endeavors to look at each area of crypto-service with the intent to ascertain any apparent weaknesses. Once any weaknesses are found, the vendor is notified to correct them, during which time product certification is suspended. ICSA's product investigation usually starts with questions about its implementation.

Attacks on Product Connections and Installation

The first place to look for problems is the installation procedures. Usually, vendor-supplied documentation (specification sheets, user documentation, technical reference files, marketing literature) covers three areas of interest:

1. *Platforms:* What platform will the product run on and what other components are required for the product to operate effectively? These include hardware, network type and components, operating system, and competing applications. Installation of a cryptosystem on a platform only marginally supported is looking for compromise.

2. *Connections:* What kind of physical connections are required in addition to power? For example, what ports are used for the management console, which I/O ports are excluded, and what type are acceptable to connect to? What other devices are connected and why? Can these additional devices interact with the security kernel? By design? Is information left on the disk in the clear as a result of this interaction?

3. *Upgrades.* Is the product upgradable either by hardware or software? Are keys that are created under a previous version usable in the upgrade? Does the software upgrade wipe out the previous version in total? What trails are left and can they be retrieved from the media?

Attacks on Random Number Generation and Seed Values

A fundamental area of concern is the generation of random numbers. The use of random numbers for generation of keys and seed values is of paramount importance to a cryptographically secure system. Random values are easy to generate incorrectly. Many designs do not produce cryptographically random, that is, secure numbers. Vendor products use either a hardware random number generator or a PRNG (Pseudo-Random Number Generator, based on assessment of computer state functions—which are anything but random.) Remember that a computer is a state machine, hence its function is to be deterministic, not chaotic. The cryptography may be strong but the keys generated by a poor random number generator may be weak and, therefore, the total system is weakened. A second design error occurs when random numbers are generated that do not carry enough information (entropy) with them. A third implementation error may arise when random number generators are intentionally cascaded. ICSA found that such a design seems to work in one application but not in others. The connection between the PRNGs is critical to the design. A fourth error occurs when random numbers are reused.

The latter can have unusual consequences. The Venona project was partially successful against the one-time pads used by the Soviets in the late 1940s and 1950s, when the Soviets had such a key distribution problem that they reused a small portion of their keys. The NSA kept an enormous amount of traffic (cipher text) and was able to catalogue, isolate, and decrypt important traffic during the period.

Random numbers are prima facie to the generation of strong keys. The more random the key, the harder it will be to guess. Attackers will have the hardest time guessing your key if they can make no assumptions about its form or content. Shortcuts taken in generating keys, like using poor random number generators or limiting them to alphanumeric characters or readable words, help the attacker. Compare the 56-bit long text password with the 56-bit DES key in Table 13-1. There are ten times as many binary DES keys as there are text strings with the same number of bits. The effect of key length is more pronounced with longer keys, as in Table 13-2.

Computers are essentially deterministic machines. They are designed to act in the same way every time. Variations are rarely in the extreme. The yield from many PRNGs leads to predictable values and to predictable keys. A practical and secure cryptosystem requires that the keys not be easily guessed. The attacker should not be able to guess or predict anything about the keys.

TABLE 13-1

Properties of Some Secret Key Block Cipher Algorithms

Secret Key Block Ciphers	Data Block Size (bits)	Crypto Key Size (bits)	In Use?
DES	64	56	Yes
International data encryption algorithm (IDEA)	64	128	Yes
Modular multiplication block cipher (MMB)	128	128	No
Cellular automata cipher CA-1.1	384	1088	No
SKIPJACK	64	80	Yes

TABLE 13-2

Brute Force Attacks on Shorter Key Lengths

Type of Key	No. of bits	No. of Keys	Time to Test One*	No. of Parallel Tests	Average Search Time
3-digit luggage lock	10	1,000	2 sec	1	17 min
4-digit cash card PIN†	14	10,000	60 sec	1	3.5 d
Short-text password	28	81,450,625	50 μsec	1	34 min
Netscape export crypto	40	1,099,511,627,776	50 μsec	1	10 mo
Netscape export crypto	40	1,099,511,627,776	50 μsec	50	6 d
Long-text password	56	6,634,204,312,890,620	50 μsec	1	5,274 yr
DES key	56	72,057,594,037,927,900	50 μsec	1	57,280 yr
DES key	56	72,057,594,037,927,900	0.02 μsec	57,600	3.5 hr

*One microsecond (μsec) is a millionth of a second (0.000001 second).
†PIN = personal identification number.

A good key generator will produce keys that cannot be guessed even if the attacker knows how the generator works. Numbers must be practically impossible to predict. PRNG can generate hard-to-predict sequences but they depend on a seed as an initializer to ensure randomness; the seed itself is random. See Figure 13-4.

Attackers who make a close guess on the seed can compromise the PRNG. This is exactly what happened with the 1995 famous crack of Netscape's early release of the SSL protocol for encrypting data being passed on a TCP connection. The seed sampling program was based only on the system clock, which was not effective. There is a difference between PRNG-generated statistically random numbers and cryptographically random numbers: the former reflects a known distribution of values, and the latter reflects a uniformly equal probability distribution—all equally probable. A statistical PRNG is unbiased. A cryptographic PRNG must be completely unpredictable and secure. PRNGs produce sequences. Can an attacker gain the advantage because he or she recognizes the repeatable sequences? This led to the first of four classes of attacks that ICSA uses to test the PRNG; ICSA tests for repeatable sequences. Two properties are laboratory checked:

Figure 13-4
Good Keys Come
from a Random Seed
and a Good Pseudo-
Random Number
Generator

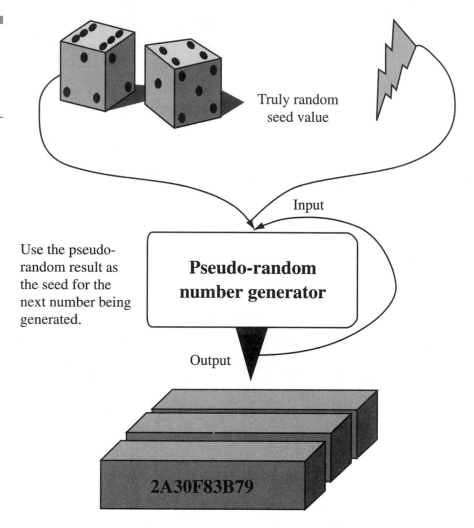

We use part of the output sequence to produce
keys that are practically impossible to guess.

1. There should not be any obvious mathematical relations between
   numbers in the sequence, like common multiples, ordering of values, or pattern of values.
2. Any given key may be generated as part of a variety of different
   key sequences.

DES is an excellent randomizer. ANSI X9.17 describes a procedure
that has been effective for financial institutions (see Figure 13-5).

Figure 13-5
Banker's Key Genera-
tion Using DES with
a Secret Key and a
Unique Seed Value

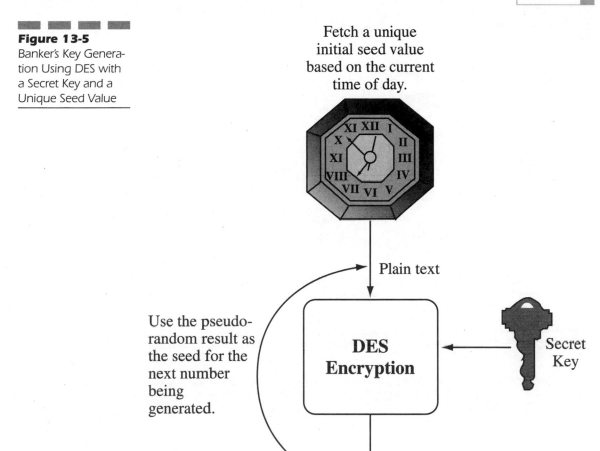

Figure 13-5
Banker's Key Generation Using DES with a Secret Key and a Unique Seed Value

Fetch a unique initial seed value based on the current time of day.

Plain text

Use the pseudo-random result as the seed for the next number being generated.

DES Encryption

Secret Key

Output (cipher text)

Sequence of keys that are practically impossible to guess.

Schneier describes an autoclave (autokey) procedure that will produce good random numbers (see Figure 13-6).

In addition, ICSA's crypto labs test for three conditions (if possible):

1. *That the entire key is constructed from random data.* (If we use 16 bits of randomness to produce an 80-bit SKIPJACK key, the attack-

Figure 13-6
Using DES in Autokey
Mode to Produce
Good Random Num-
bers

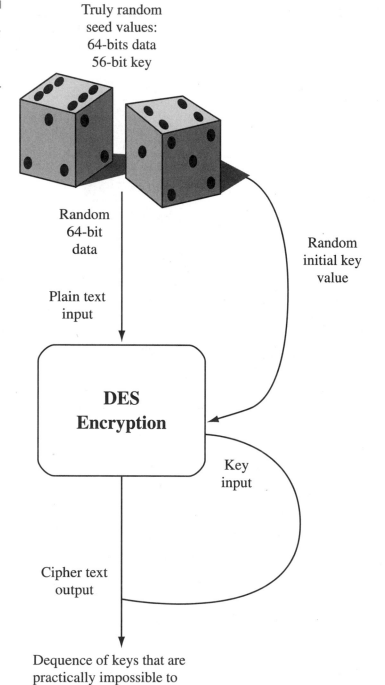

Truly random
seed values:
64-bits data
56-bit key

Random
64-bit
data

Random
initial key
value

Plain text
input

**DES
Encryption**

Key
input

Cipher text
output

Dequence of keys that are
practically impossible to
guess.

er only has to search 2^{16} or 65,536 keys to find the one we chose. The other 64 key bits are junk.)

2. *That the seed is unpredictable.* The number of bits of randomness in the seed determines the randomness of the keys.

3. *That the product uses a cryptographically secure PRNG.* The output must meet the classical tests of randomness and the sequence of generated numbers must be unpredictable. The latter tests may be augmented by procedures developed by Dr. Metzger at the University of North Dakota.

Most CPC products use PRNGs. ICSA starts inquiries by listing all the functions and parts affected by the PRNG. They check to see if the size of the seed value is at least as large as the largest key supported by the system. They confirm the number of bits and range generated for the seed or initial value. If available, code regarding the derivation of the seed value is reviewed. The product is reviewed and checked to see that random numbers are derived from a compilation of a large number of machine states (20 or more). Furthermore, the implementation is checked to see if it uses the least-significant data from at least 20 different states, the sum of which provides at least as large a data element as the largest key supported and none of which dominates the resulting seed value by more than two times their percentage participation. This is a difficult criterion for many vendor products tested.

ICSA has catalogued or tested the following PRNG techniques. Each has its advantages and disadvantages.

- *Additive RNG or Lagged-Fibonacci Generator,* which is an improved GFSR, produces longer sequences than a GFSR of similar size.

- *Cebysev Mixing,* derived from computational physics.

- *Cellular Automata,* a model of one dimensional "Life."

- *Chaos,* or nonlinear dynamically aligned equations.

- *Clock-Controlled Shift Registers,* using multiple shift registers with clock enable or disable signals and combined output.

- *Generalized Feedback Shift Register (GFSR),* which allows customized element width, shift-register height, and polynomial output.

- *Linear Congruential,* the common computer RNG.

- *Linear Feedback Shift Register (LFSR).*

- *Nonlinear Shift Register (NLSR).*

■ $X^2 \bmod N$, generator of Blum, Blum, and Shub.

ICSA also has developed some reasonable tests for the following Multiple Mechanism PRNGs:

■ One-Way Hash Functions, Checksum Algorithms, such as CRC

■ Randomizers, such as CRC-32 used in PKZIP

■ Isolators, mechanisms designed to complicate external analysis of the RNG

■ Primitive Polynomial checks

■ Combined RNGs to increase complexity

■ Diagnostics/Checks on Minimum Length Cycles

■ Cycle Detection, to detect the repeated use of short RNG sequences

Attacks on Algorithms

Appendix E shows the algorithms accepted by the cryptography products consortium (CPC). ICSA certifies products using these algorithms, and has run proprietary algorithms through its labs, although reporting is restricted to ICSA-defined and published standards.

A cryptographic system is only as strong as the weakest link and can only be as strong as the encryption algorithm, key generation, digital signature system, one-way hash functions, or MAC (message authentication codes) that the cryptosystem is built on. ICSA ascertains the strength of the symmetric and asymmetric algorithms used in the product by testing them against known profiles; its cryptography lab uses a series of automated tests to classify these algorithms with respect to compression, entropy, statistical properties, and repeated sequences. There are several important questions that can be asked to investigate implementation of the encryption algorithm, key generation, digital signature system, one-way hash functions, or MACs in a vendor product:

1. Was the algorithm used in its natural form or was the source code modified in any way during the implementation into the product?

2. Does the user or system manager have any influence over the cryptography function of the product?

3. Can the user choose a PIN or password or similar user-key that reduces the "effective key length" to one shorter than that which the product was configured to operate?

4. If a standard source-code library was used for any algorithm, was the source code modified in any way during the product implementation?

5. What key length(s) does the product normally use? What is the shortest key length that is possible to configure the product to use? What is the longest? What control does the user have over this parameter?

6. What algorithmic elements are add-ons? Is the functionality improvement at the expense of cryptosecurity?

7. What key exchange protocols or algorithms(s) are provided with the product or available as add-on functionality? What is the source for the code or library used for each algorithm (vendor, product, version and library, function, or call)?

8. If the product uses a cryptography-specific toolkit, was the supplied code modified in any way or was it used in its natural form?

One of the surprising areas ICSA has found during testing was in those products using key recovery protocol(s) or TTP (trusted third-party implementations). It is clear that products that add key recovery systems may be at the expense of the overall security of the product. Additional questions come to mind:

9. If key recovery protocols are used in the product, was the source code for any of the fundamental algorithms modified in any way that might negatively impact the security requirements for the product? This question is especially true if key recovery protocols are add-ons to an existing, working cryptosystem.

Reviewing cryptosystems with the preceding questions in mind helps reduce the mistakes incorporated in the final product design.

Properties of "Good" Crypto Algorithms

Another question comes to mind: If the final product design is dependent on the cryptosecurity of the algorithm, how is a strong crypto algorithm recognized?

Smith presents four properties that strong crypto algorithms should possess:

1. It should not be necessary to keep the algorithm secret. Good crypto algorithms rely exclusively on the keys to protect the data. Revealing the algorithm (Kerchoffs' law) should not significantly improve an attacker's success factors.

2. The algorithm should be designed specifically for encryption and to resist cryptanalysis. Playing "tinker toys" with encryption algorithms can have disastrous effects on the security of the system.

3. A strong crypto algorithm should be available for analysis. DES has been scrutinized by the best mathematicians and cryptographers in the world for more than three decades. Scrutiny by the scientific community tends to flesh out the snake oil. Algorithms offered for analysis under the protection of nondisclosure agreements restrict efforts to understand the security claimed.

4. A strong algorithm has been subjected to proper analysis. Algorithms that exhibit "legs" have much published about their effectiveness. Many of the modern algorithms are discussed on the Internet, by the various task forces investigating standards and by scientists in technical journals. Algorithms recognized by the CPC have been subjected to years of analysis and are generally accepted by authorities worldwide.

A strong crypto algorithm exhibits no practical weaknesses. Custombuilt algorithms embedded in commercial software tend to have serious weaknesses. Products that use proprietary wraps and embedded algorithms exhibit weaknesses in entropy or sequence repeatability when subjected to "ICSA automated attacks" in their laboratory.

Attacks on Cryptodesigns

In a strong cryptosystem, a hacker's attacking and recovering a key should not mean that the entire system becomes compromised or readable. Breaking into a smartcard should not permit the entry or reengineering of other smartcards supported by the system. In a system where secrets are shared, compromise of one set of keys should not permit compromise of everyone's shared keys. Systems should be designed with the principle of "reduction of loss" in mind.

Many cryptosystems have a default mode or default settings. Some of these settings establish fallback modes to less secure settings to permit backward compatibility of products. In the case of one major vendor, this preference actually reduced the strength of the main cryptosystem. Some designs have no established procedures for recovery when a system loses power or when the security module is threatened. Hardware and software disaster recovery procedures must be in place, too.

Many products have installation settings that are created for designers to service the system or perform routine maintenance functions. When a user installs the product, he or she may leave the "backdoor" settings in place, rather than disable them. Serious problems can arise when these back doors are not closed.

Red/Black Separation

The phrase *black secret* has one set of roots that refers to the red/black separation principle for cryptographic machinery. The red/black electrical leads were attached to separate plain-text and cipher-text connections (Figure 13-7). Good design warrants the complete and unequivocal separation of *red* plain text from *black* cipher text.

Figure 13-7
Inside an In-Line Encryptor

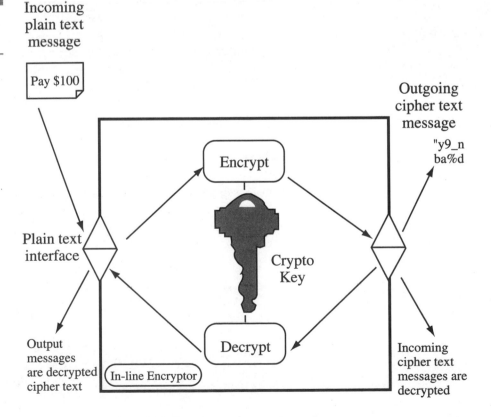

Incoming plain text message

Pay $100

Outgoing cipher text message

"y9_n ba%d

Encrypt

Crypto Key

Plain text interface

Decrypt

In-line Encryptor

Output messages are decrypted cipher text

Incoming cipher text messages are decrypted

Figure 13-7 shows the principle applied to an in-line network encryptor. The safest encryptors provide no way to bypass the encryption; crypto is applied to everything passing through it. In high-end military systems this is taken to the logical extreme. Every part of a circuit is specifically identified according to the red/black properties that it carries. Some devices have separate power sources for plain-text and cipher-text carriers. The point is that when you design a transfer of plain text and cipher text through the same interface, you run the risk of sending plain-text data in the wrong direction.

Attacks Against Keys

The most secret part of a cryptosystem is its *key structure*. It follows that, when effective, attacks against the private, public, master, session keys, or key generation will essentially compromise the entire security system.

Brute force attacks are interesting, require enormous computer resources, and have limited effectiveness in terms of either key recovery or information recovery when the lifetime of session keys is short. It is much easier and eminently more damaging to a cryptosystem to plan and capitalize on a poor implementation (see Table 13-2).

Any trade-off that compromises the key structure can be fatal to the security. Some electronic commerce systems record keys for backup purposes—*en clair!* Others encrypt the same data with two different keys. A variant of this is to encrypt the same data with one strong key and a substantially weaker key; still another variant (see Chapter 21 on cryptanalysis for a detailed example) is the *stagger,* which is a retransmit and reencryption of the same message with the same key at an offset—the offset caused by an omission in the original plain text.

Creating a master key and shared session keys may be a potential problem, if any of the information is left available to unfriendly eyes.

Attacks Against Passwords

Password and dictionary-based attacks are covered in detail in a later chapter. Many systems defenses fold quickly because they are protected by user-generated passwords. Users are for the most part not interested in the security aspect of the cryptosystem; they want the system to be easy to work with. As a matter of practical experience, users do not choose strong passwords—if they must use them, they tend to forget them, forcing them to write the passwords down or post them for easy reference. If a password translates to be a key, it is easier to guess the password than the key. Automated dictionary attacks are prevalent on the Net. Dictionaries of about 45,000 words, phrases, and symbols have been created to crack the user passwords. Two forms of these dictionaries are available. The first uses plain text with anagrams to test the system passwords. The second uses preencrypted entries by various strong ciphers DES, 3DES, RC4, RC5, IDEA, CAST, and so forth, and then runs a compare file on an intercepted cipher-text password file. Hit rates higher than 40 percent have been reported using limited resources and specialized dictionaries. Several of these dictionaries are available on the Net. Franklin makes a small anagramming password (used for crossword puzzles) calculator and sells it for about $25.00. Hit rates using this little demon (as an assistant) have been reported at 10 percent.

Good cryptosecurity permits the generation of new keys regularly. Systems that allow old keys to be recovered in an emergency provide a fertile area for attack. Strong systems are designed to allow keys to exist for as short a period of time as possible. Key recovery often negates any security benefit by forcing keys to exist for longer periods than designed as well as to be kept in some location that is further subject to scrutiny. The trusted third party (TTP) fails to be useful for this reason. TTP key recovery databases are a prime target of concern. The current wave of "same face fraud" at retail stores costs millions of dollars to users and owners. (BEST's in Corpus Christi, Texas, went bankrupt because of this problem.) What was actually being fraudulently used was the good credit of legitimate customers. The keys that support social security numbers and credit information were compromised. Challenge-response schemes were introduced to confirm the request for credit information.

Leakage

We could add an egress line from the encryptor box labeled "leakage." Many hardware devices leak information; they leave it in temporary files and in storage files. It is feasible for some crypto-hardware to develop side channels allowing for the measurement of power consumption, Van Eck emissions, or tangential measurement of timing in the kernel operations. Another way that hardware may not respond as expected is when an attacker purposely introduces faults into the cryptosystem. Cryptographic processors may have difficulty in securing their secret keys; leakage is possible to a side channel. Electronic commerce products such as dongles and smartcards use tamper-resistant hardware to shut down leakage. ICSA uses specialized software to test for leakage.

Attacks on Protocol Service

In trying to determine the root cause for an implementation problem, we sometimes find that the security of the hardware and software is strong but it uses incongruent protocols. Several questions are asked by the technicians:

1. Are any cryptographic protocols, file formats, data formats, or protocols used in any way that the resulting data is likely to be interoperable with another product using the same algorithms and protocols?

2. Is the product intended to be used in a mixed-vendor environment, where similar products from different vendors interoperate with encrypted information? This question is very important in IPSEC (Internet Protocol Security) "bake-offs" for the automobile industry. Vendors share information very freely and generally pick choices that allow for maximum interoperability as a trade-off to maximum security.

3. Does the product include/provide for any master-key, management key, or supervisory hierarchical key structure such that a person, company, or organization with the proper knowledge, data, and tools could gain access to a given user's encrypted data?

4. Does the product include/provide for any master-key or similar ability for the manufacturer, vendor, or technical support function to provide a user with a mechanism to recover data in the event that the user forgets, misplaces, or otherwise loses his/her key or password?

If either of the last two questions is affirmative for a vendor, then what information is available that documents the function, and the measures taken to avoid exploitation of this function?

███ ███ **Test Bench Information**

Security awareness varies among users. Apart from users posting their passwords on the PC or giving their passwords to coworkers, users tend to subvert computer security directly. Because of this maxim, lab technicians check whether any of the following items in the principal encryption operation can be directly manipulated/monitored on the test bench:

Key

Plain-text data

Cipher-text data

Initialization vector

Random-number generator

Random-number seed

Random number itself

Hash data

Hash result

Key recovery

Protocol

File formats for any of the preceding items

IP addresses or server addresses for network

WRAP-UP ███ ███ ███ ███ ███ ███ ███

Strong cryptography, when implemented correctly, is one of the most powerful security tools available for digital systems. It helps designers meet the goals of security, authentication, and data integrity in an increasingly more intrusive digital environment. It should be apparent from the previous checklists and questions that for every design variable in a cryptosystem, there are many ways to subvert what is meant to be a secure implementation. However, the use of cryptography, by itself, is not a panacea.

Crypto-locks alone will not deter the motivated attacker, who will use the backdoor, steal the keys, social-engineer the user, measure the leakage, introduce faults into the system, search for the defaults, or maybe reengineer the code. There are four types of errors that designers and security professionals need to consider when using a cryptosystem: (1) errors in implementation, (2) errors in design, (3) errors in installation, and (4) side channels or bypass architecture. These four categories of error are orders of magnitude easier to exploit than mounting a brute force attack against the crypto algorithm.

14

ICSA Product Certification

In the previous chapter, we characterized the types of mistakes that occur during implementation of cryptographic systems. ICSA has developed guidelines to reduce risk in digital security systems by eliminating implementation mistakes and ensuring that cryptographic products perform as claimed. This chapter is divided into two general subjects. First, we explore the ICSA general framework for certification and second, we apply these guidelines to the ICSA's cryptographic certification process. Further details of the process are found in the appendix. ICSA's process is not a static one—improvements such as new cryptographic attacks on established algorithms or protocols are incorporated into the review process on a quarterly basis or as valid information becomes known.

ICSA Generic Certification Framework

In today's complex business world, managers should recognize a fundamental premise: it is not possible to have a risk-free information technology environment. Risks therefore must be managed, which means that they must be reduced to an acceptable level—in other words, security products and information technology systems security should be good enough within the context of the realities of the "now," which refers to how a user or business can obtain some level of confidence about the trustworthiness of systems upon which they depend. The reality is that most of us have to live with whatever commercial off-the-shelf (COTS) technology, to include security solutions, is available to solve our problem of the moment. Technology, the speed of business, and competition are such that we assume some level of risk and take care of business. It can be argued that consumers accept a "just-in-time security" approach to fix problems. Furthermore, the time frame for strategic, tactical, and operational business decisions relating to security has been compressed because of the technology available to solve our problem of the moment and which contains security solutions. ICSA has developed a certification approach for products and systems based on the "Secure Enough" paradigm. This chapter incorporates Fred Tompkins' brilliant work at ICSA and presents a description of a risk-based *Generic Certification Framework* that defines the ICSA approach for assisting users in reducing the security risks associated with the operation of information technology systems in the evolving digital world.

The "trusted system" paradigm poses the following questions:

■ Knowing that we must live with technology as it is and not necessarily what we would like it to be, how can we find some level of comfort that we can live with and reduce risks to an acceptable level?

■ How can we become significantly better off in the short term than we are at the moment?

A level of *comfort* implies there is also some level of *discomfort,* which comes from uncertainty. *Risk* has been defined as uncertainty regarding the occurrence of an undesirable event. Use of *risk management* is one of the more accepted approaches for addressing issues of uncertainty associated with the use of information technology systems. The objective of information security risk management is to attempt to reduce the degrees of uncertainty concerning:

■ Past undesirable events that have affected the system under consideration

■ The present environment and actions taken to reduce the potential for the occurrence of an undesirable event affecting the system under consideration

■ The effect of proposed actions that can be taken to reduce the likelihood of undesirable events affecting the future of the system under consideration

The risk analysis phase of risk management is a systematic process for collecting information that will reduce degrees of uncertainty concerning past events and the present environment. The risk reduction analysis phase is a systematic process for reducing degrees of uncertainty about the effect of proposed actions.

When applied to systems, ICSA's risk-based Generic Certification Framework is designed to address uncertainty within present environments. When applied to products, the Framework is designed to address the uncertainty associated with the effect of proposed actions. The purpose of the Generic Certification Framework is to define *what* the ICSA's approach to certification is, not *how* certification is performed. The Framework is based on a set of assertions and a set of fundamental principles.

Framework Assertions

Information security as we understand it today includes the following assertions:

- Risk avoidance is not possible; reduction of risks is possible.
- Perfect security is unattainable (and may not be desirable).
- As an industry, we must simultaneously pursue improvements in security technology while implementing security that is secure enough for practical reduction of real risks.
- The process of security technology improvement should be collaborative and iterative.
- Competition drives the speed of acceptance of technological changes.
- Vulnerability is a function of the complexity of technology.

Framework Principles

ICSA's Generic Certification Framework is based on the following fundamental principles:

- Certification should be oriented toward results and not processes.
- Certification processes for security products and systems must be flexible and dynamic. (Criteria should be based on de facto standards that dynamically respond to changing technology.)
- Products should provide security functions to reduce risks consistent with a set of industry-accepted standards.
- Over time, we should be able to improve the "trustworthiness" of security of systems on which we depend.
- System certification should provide assurance that sites have a verified implementation of security in accordance with industry-accepted security standards.
- Certification criteria should be simply stated and understandable.
- Certification criteria should be public and include a notice of proposed rule making.
- Certification criteria should be objective and fair so that a variety of implementation approaches can be certified.

■ Certification criteria should be based on a pass-fail system (resistant to ranking or levels of acceptability) and not be based primarily on fundamental design or engineering principles or on an assessment of underlying technology.

■ Certification criteria should be results, not process, oriented (demonstrate resistance to threats and risks or unsuccessful outcomes).

■ We should become significantly better off (be susceptible to less risk) in the short term than we are at the moment (risk reduction, not risk elimination).

The Framework

ICSA's Generic Certification Framework approaches risk reduction at the general, specific, and unique level of information technologies and systems. At the *general* level, risk-reduction measures are based on the fundamental actions (industry-accepted standards) that should be accomplished by a product or a system without regard to the specific business functions being protected. At the *specific* level, risk-reduction measures are those additive security functions that are pertinent to a specific business sector such as the financial, insurance, or manufacturing industries. At the *unique* level, risk-reduction measures are those needed to reduce the security concerns at a particular organization.

Framework Components

The Framework is comprised of five components:

1. Environment
2. Connectivity (communication, etc.)
3. Platform (hosting hardware and operating systems software)
4. Services (including application) that run on the platform
5. Human factors

The *environment* component is defined as the physical site and supporting elements to include the land, structures, power, water; and heating, ventilation, and air conditioning (HVAC). Certification is concerned with such items as adherence to building codes and OSHA requirements, integrity of power supplies, ability to recover from physical damage, and physical protection of the site against unauthorized access.

The *connectivity* component is concerned with communications technology such as routers, firewalls, hubs, and so forth, and the associated interfaces. Certification is concerned primarily with ensuring that security services can provide resistance to electronic intrusion attempts. Also included are detection and auditing functions.

The *platform* component is defined as the information technology systems and the associated operating systems. Certification is concerned with the known vulnerabilities in computing systems and devices and operating system maintenance to include version control. Also included is the major area of system administration to include password policies and administration.

The *services* component includes application and network, logging and auditing, and security service. Certification is concerned with ensuring that known vulnerabilities have been patched and that basic security services are functioning.

The *human factors* component addresses such areas as policy, management plans for security of information and awareness, training, and education. Certification is concerned with policies and procedures for personnel activities for emergency responses, protection of sensitive data, and assignment of security responsibilities. Figure 14-1 provides a graphic representation of the components of the Framework.

Figure 14-1
Framework Components

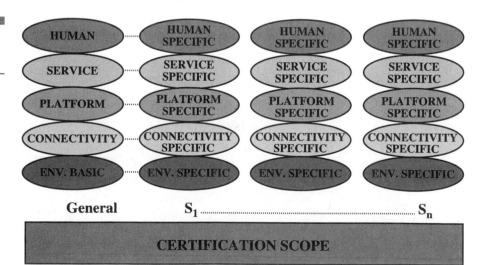

Framework Characteristics

We live in a dynamic business environment in which the technology changes rapidly as do the risks associated with use of products and systems. It is therefore necessary that the Framework be dynamic and readily adaptable to a change in the most significant risks. Within each of the components are several modules that address specific risks. The process underlying the Framework is designed so that the modules within each component can be modified in response to changes in our understanding of security risks.

The most significant characteristics of the Framework that contributes to flexibility is that certification is a *process and not an event*. ICSA's Generic Certification Framework is also designed to provide an initial reasonable reduction of the most prevalent risks at a point in time. The Framework is sufficiently flexible to adjust to the changing nature of risks.

Initial reduction of risk is achieved by defining safeguards for each of the following risk categories:

- Physical attempts to gain control (physical intrusion)
- Electronic attempts to gain control (malicious hacking)
- Execution of arbitrary codes (viruses, Trojans, Active-X, Java, etc.)
- Spoofing (lying about who you are as an authorized user, site, or device)
- Eavesdropping (sniffing, wiretapping of data, passwords, etc.)
- Lack of awareness/knowledge (systems administrator, users, etc.)
- Lack of trust or confidence (in the information system, users, disgruntled employees, etc.)
- Denial of service (cripple the system by physical means, natural disasters, loss of reliability, automated saturation of resources, etc.)
- Exploitation of a user by a site (loss of privacy, fraud, swindles, etc.)
- Exploitation of a data subject (privacy, confidentiality, nonuser)
- Lack of interoperability (between security products and hosting system, between security products)

Figure 14-2
Safeguards Matrix

Objective of the Safeguard

Category		Protect	Detect	Recover
	Administrative			
	Physical			
	Technical			

Risk Reduction

The safeguards for each category of risk are defined using the matrix in Figure 14-2. The categories or types of safeguards are administrative, physical, and technical. Safeguards are also distinguished based on the security objective; that is, protection, detection, or recovery.

Administrative safeguards are procedural in nature and tend to be manual, for example, company policies that generally instruct personnel in the proper way to interact with other personnel, equipment, facilities, or system functions. Administrative safeguards also include procedures such as separation of duties and assignment of responsibilities for specific functions.

Physical safeguards include such measures as locks, badges, alarms, or similar devices, to protect personnel and property from damage by accident, fire and loss of utilities, environmental hazards, and unauthorized access. *Technical safeguards* that are used are based on communications equipment or operating systems, applications software, or maybe additive COTS products, and are normally used to assist in controlling electronic access, limit user privileges, maintain data and software integrity, and provide tools for detecting security intrusions and auditing system activities.

Safeguards can also be viewed in terms of their security objective. *Preventive type safeguards* attempt to eliminate vulnerabilities by denying a path for a threat agent to attack. If complete prevention is not possible, and it usually is not, the vulnerability should be controlled or monitored and, as a threat agent attempts to exploit the vulnerability, an alarm is sounded. Safeguards designed to alert personnel to an attempted or actual security breach are referred to as *detection safeguards*. *Recovery safeguards* are designed to minimize the impacts associated with short- or long-term unavailability of resources and functions by permitting the return to normalcy.

Validation of Risk Measures

The process for determining whether or not a product or system meets the criteria for a particular component includes one of the following (see Figure 14-3):

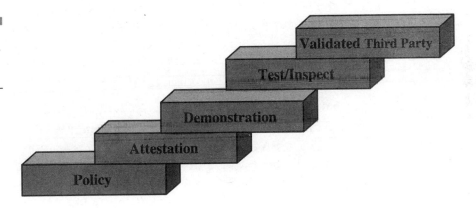

Figure 14-3
Approaches for Verification of Satisfying Criteria

- Policy
- Attestation
- Demonstration
- Test or Inspection
- Third-Party Validation

If the vendor or the organization has a policy that requires that a specific security or security-related practice will be followed, this may be sufficient evidence that the organization meets the criteria. If a senior official of the organization is willing to sign a statement that a policy or a set of practices is adhered to by the organization, this may also be further evidence that the criteria have been met.

The more frequent, and most desirable, evidence that an organization meets particular criteria is through demonstration or by virtue of a successful test or inspection. The organization could also provide evidence that the criteria have been met and validated by a third party.

The ICSA Approach to Certification: A New Paradigm for Information Security

ICSA has spent a significant amount of time developing a certification approach that is appropriate for the need to reduce information security risks in the commercial sector. In addition, ICSA has developed several prototypes of certification models that are responsive to technology change, COTS, and the need to move at the speed of business.

The ICSA risk-based Generic Certification Framework presented in this chapter represents an understanding of the information security field at the moment, a set of fundamental principles to support that understanding, and an approach for increasing the level of comfort based on a reduction of the most prevalent risks to an acceptable level. The approach is designed to be sufficiently flexible and dynamic to adapt to an ever-changing risk environment.

The ICSA system certification criteria generally attempt to attain a substantial reduction of risk for each of the 11 categories of risk described in the "ICSA Risk Framework." ICSA performs or seeks out research to identify and categorize the prevalence and cost of various threats in each of these 11 risk categories, and to identify the most effective, available, and cost-efficient safeguards and controls that are generally applicable to prevent, detect, or recover from the threats.

New Paradigm

The information security community over the last 25 years, primarily driven by the defense interests of the U.S. government, has attempted to design and develop secure computer systems, although there is probably no general agreement on what constitutes a secure system. Many will contend that the attempt to define the secure system has been based on the "trusted computer" model; some will contend that perhaps we are using the wrong or a faulty paradigm. The reality for most of us in the commercial sector is that we live with off-the-shelf technology and will for some years to come. We must understand that we are going to be dealing with security in the "now" for some time to come.

In *The Emperor's Old Armor** Bob Blakley states:

> The traditional computer security model is built around a *reference monitor,* supported by hardware protection mechanisms, which enforces administratively defined security policies. The reference monitor's software is assumed to be of high reliability and integrity. The reference monitor is supplemented by strong cryptography for those unfortunate occasions when our data must venture outside the cozy confines of its safe haven.
>
> This model's analogies are mostly military: the image is that of an *information fortress,* with walls, guards, interior compartments, and a defending army....

In his concluding remarks, Blakley writes:

> If today's security epicycles now seem too ugly to live with, the next steps look like these:
>
> **1.** Enumerate new principles of the security worldview. Here are a few nominations:
>
> - Assume low integrity.
> - You can't keep a secret.
> - Security should be inherent, not imposed.
> - Policy is evidence that security is imposed.
> - Identity is a side-effect of policy (don't depend on it, don't authenticate it).
> - Trust is evidence that security is imposed (trust nothing and no one).
> - Ease of use should be proportional to the probability that use is harmless.
> - Make the user ask forgiveness, not permission.
> - Plan for emergency.
> - Secrecy is not privacy.
> - Control is not protection.
> - "Confidentiality, integrity, availability" is not security.
> - Good enough is good enough. Perfect is too good.
> - Evolve!
>
> **2.** Identify primitives required to build the new-model word.
>
> **3.** Map out an infrastructure development program for the new-model world.

---

*Blakley, Bob, *The Emperor's Old Armor,* Proceedings: New Security Paradigms Workshop, September 17-20, 1996, Association for Computing Machinery Special Interest Group on Security and Privacy, New York, 1996, p. 2.

4. Set out the research agenda for the new-model world.

Dr. Dixie Baker in her paper from the ACM New Paradigms Workshop, *Fortress Built Upon Sand**, observed:

> The current "trusted system" paradigm is built upon the notion of a Reference Monitor that assumes the existence of a well-defined security policy, a bounded system entity, and centralized reference validation mechanism with knowledge of control over the system entity. The "trusted system" paradigm is hierarchical: management defines the policy, the hardware and software that comprise the trusted computing base enforce the policy, and applications must conform to the policy. This paradigm acknowledges that applications depend upon the hardware and operating system on which they run, and that *assurance that they will execute safely is derived from the strength of the "trusted computing base.*

Several observations have prompted computer scientists to reexamine and question the relevance of this hierarchical "trusted system" paradigm:

- Individuals, businesses, government, and social services are increasing their dependence upon computer systems and networks for both routine and critical functions, including electronic commerce, communications, education, medical collaboration, and entertainment.

- The information systems upon which society is becoming increasingly dependent (e.g., power grids, telephone, Internet) are highly complex and nonhierarchical, often lacking a clear boundary and common set of security objectives.

- Attacks on networks and computer systems are becoming more frequent, virulent, global, and broadly publicized.

Initiating the Process

In 1997, the ICSA senior management directed a review of the computer market—vendors, developers, and users to determine the potential threats and required safeguards for reducing the digital risks to the

---

*Baker, Dixie B., *Fortress Built Upon Sand,* Proceedings: New Security Paradigms Workshop, September 17–20, 1996, Association for Computing Machinery Special Interest Group on Security and Privacy, New York; 1996, pp. 148–9, 152.

public. What they found was a need to develop specific standards and criteria, a need to evaluate vendor products in light of those criteria, and to establish a certification program to verify that products were implemented correctly within the purview of "generally accepted criteria." Product certification lifetimes were another issue. Standard quality systems like ISO 9002 could not meet the time frames for product delivery to the market or the increasing implementation requirements of a dynamic product certification process.

Furthermore, the digital world moves far too quickly to certify only a particular version of a product or particular incarnation of a system. Therefore, the ICSA certification criteria and processes were designed so that once a product or system was certified, all future versions of the product (or updates of the system) were also inherently certified. In practice, this is accomplished by three means:

1. ICSA gains a contractual commitment from the product vendor or the organization that owns or runs the certified system that the product or system will be maintained at current, published ICSA certification standards. ICSA expects that the organization's own quality assurance programs will incorporate current ICSA certification criteria as a part of their continuous product or system development processes. This means that a significant part of the ICSA certification process involves self-checking, against the ICSA-published criteria, by the organization whose product or system is certified.

2. The ICSA or its authorized agents normally perform random spot checking of the current product (or system) against current ICSA criteria for that certification category. Products or systems are typically spot checked for current compliance at regular intervals during a calendar year. The interval may vary depending on the product or system category. If a product or system fails a spot check, the responsible party is given a reasonable time to rectify the problem(s). If the shipping version product or production system still does not meet current certification criteria by the end of this grace period, then the ICSA certification is explicitly and publicly revoked.

3. ICSA certification is renewed annually. At renewal time, the full certification process is usually repeated for the current production system or shipping product against the current criteria.

Collectively, these steps ensure that ICSA certification is a continuous process through product or system updates and version changes.

Process for Development of Certification Criteria

In order to develop and evolve appropriate and meaningful certification criteria, ICSA uses a "notice or proposed certification criteria" system. ICSA questions a variety of people and organizations potentially including affected vendors, developers, and users; the security expert community; the nonvendor specialists and experts; the Fortune 500 and vertical user consortia; unrelated or minimally related vendor consortia, academia, and other consumer and industry groups. They draft proposed criteria and then request review from appropriate people and groups before making the criteria final. Finally, the ICSA certification criteria and processes are overseen by a Certification Oversight Board. The Board is comprised of several recognized experts who provide a broad representation of the computer security and user communities.

As a design goal, testing is automated where possible. Checklists are provided when automation is not applicable or appropriate. The test protocols are reproducible, objective, and not open to interpretation. There is minimal or no judgment by the testing personnel or authorized laboratories. The testing personnel or authorized labs have a help desk to resolve questions. An escalation procedure is used to resolve any potential conflicts or judgment questions. To be appropriate to meet the needs of the commercial sector, certification testing is inexpensive and provides for a rapid turnaround.

Motivation for Becoming ICSA Certified

The fundamental motivation for a company to get its product or system certified is to reduce both the real and perceived risk. Customers of the certified product or users of the certified system can gain assurance that the product/system, at the least, meets minimum standards and that the organization has taken due care, having addressed the security issue, at least to an established minimum level. Therefore, certification serves to reassure customers and other users. Certification may also decrease liability in the inevitable event of a security breach or failure.

Certification allows the organization with its product or system certified to point to a recognized publicly available standard of care and show that they meet or exceed that standard. Certification makes insurance possible where it was not before, or makes it less expensive. Other motivations for a company to get its product or system certified derive from commercial, market, and competitive forces. A vendor will seek product certification partly because competitive products are certified. Similarly, a site will seek system-level certification partly because other similar sites in their industry sector have been certified.

The most important motive for certification is that certification will improve the *safety* and *security* in computing, which will lead to improved confidence in computing, and which will, in turn, inevitably lead to more constructive and pervasive uses of computing and of the very products or systems that are certified.

Providers of security products and services and organizations that implement and operate systems need to provide assurances to management, users, customers, and stockholders that due care in addressing security has been exercised. The inherent complexity of information technology, the interconnectivity of systems and networks, and the constantly changing nature of business relationships increase security risks—the risks cannot be avoided, but they can be reduced to acceptable levels. Certification is one of the tools that assist in reducing uncertainty about security solutions and the implementation of those solutions.

The Cryptography Product Certification (CPCe) Process

Criteria Essentials

Cryptography products are examined and tested to verify that:

1. The vendor completes the ICSA Product Testing Guide, which requires the vendor to provide company contact data, product marketing and characterization data, and product cryptography implementation data. The latest version of the Product Testing Guide is included in the CPCe section at the ICSA Web site: *http://www.icsa.net*

2. The product uses an initialization vector generator that produces

random, statistically independent initialization vectors over the useful life of the product.

3. The product does not store accessible, unencrypted key(s) or secrets in memory or in storage media or does not send accessible, unencrypted keys or secrets across a network.

4. The product uses a cryptographic algorithm from the list of the ICSA Adopted Algorithms. ICSA will not test or certify the algorithms per se. The ICSA list of Adopted Algorithms is a continually evolving list of algorithms accepted by the cryptographic community (see the later section "Vetting"). The most current list is applied in each version of the Cryptographic Product Certification Criteria.

5. The algorithms are implemented without fatal or security-degrading mistakes. (Ideas for implementation mistakes to be applied in the criteria are received from any credible source in the international cryptography community. All ideas submitted will be refined to a set of workable, yes/no criteria useful for Certification testing.)

Vendor product implementation is evaluated in seven critical areas:

1. Random-number generation/seed values

2. PRNG initiation

3. Available testing parameters

4. User influence

5. Compatible algorithms

6. Compatible protocols

7. Third-party evaluations

Part C of the Product Testing Guide provides data to help the ICSA evaluate product implementation.

1. Cryptographic Toolkits must have their source code evaluated by an independent third-party evaluator recognized by the community as competent to perform such evaluations.

2. The product must pass input-output "Black Box" testing. The ICSA has developed a cryptographic "Black Box" test suite that is used to classify, evaluate, and certify cryptography products. Black Box testing includes automated attacks and quantitative measures of repetition, coincidences, entropy, and randomness as well as graphical depictions of the cipher-test output. Attacks are made against

the Initialization Vector (IV) and the Random-Number Generator (RNG or PRNG).

Black Box Testing

The Black Box test suite is used to determine whether cryptography products are vulnerable to trivial-to-easy cryptanalytical attack or easy-to-moderate cryptanalytical attack. If significant implementation errors occur, these can also be seen through black box testing. The ICSA Black Box Suite consists of five consistent classification tests:

1. Repetitions

2. Entropy

3. Degree of randomness/approach to monoalphabeticity/polyalpha-beticity

4. Graphical

5. PRGN effectiveness

Each test measures a different dimension of the tested cryptographic algorithm. Viewed as a group, the preceding attributes can be used to effectively characterize a cryptosystem and suggest its vulnerability to cryptanalytic attack.

Cipher-text *repetitions* provide a distinctive wedge into a cryptogram. Repetition represents an inherent weakness in the basis encryption algorithm. In theory, a perfect algorithm produces no "fingerprints" or repetitions. In general, the lower repetition factor, the better the scrambling of data that results in fewer repetitions being available as a wedge for the cryptanalyst to break into the system. The *entropy* calculation is an important measure of predictability and organization. The higher the entropy, the more chaotic and disorganized the information, hence the more unpredictable the cryptographic shifts and more difficult the cipher is to break without significant work factor. If entropy is low, the data is well organized and orderly. A higher entropy indicates a stronger level of obfuscation of data. Calculations of *randomness* and *IC* (incidence of coincidence of two letters) help to classify the subject cryptosystem based on probability and language bonds. The closer the observed cipher text is to random text, the more difficult it will be to recover the original plain text. The lower the IC, the closer the cipher text approximates random text. Similarly, the closer the *graphical* depiction of a cipher text approaches that of a random text (flat graph), the more difficult it will be to find a cryptanalytic wedge. Strong cryptography uses cryptographically based random numbers. ICSA uses a series of attacks on the vendor's *PRNG* to determine if random number or initialization vector generation is effective.

Common Scenarios

1. The ICSA will certify (a) generic security products that use cryptography and (b) specific products such as VPNs (virtual private networks), tokens, toolkits, and so forth.

2. The ICSA-certified cryptography products can contain algorithms not on the ICSA list of adopted algorithms as long as the product can provide its cryptographic security functions using algorithms that *are* on the list. The ICSA will post on its Web page the specific configurations or conditions that are certified.

3. Some cryptographic standards specify different padding schemes (e.g., RSA padding in PKCS, ISO 9796, OAEP). The padding scheme that applies to each product would be a part of that product's makeup and be examined and tested as such in the Certification process. If a single product contained several padding schemes for several security functions provided by that product, then each scheme would have to be examined for its effects on the security functions.

4. Among the methods used to determine whether a product's implementation doesn't degrade the security of the algorithm are demonstration, testing, and verification. For example, if the vendor can demonstrate that the use of a weak-key generator (or other feature) does not degrade the security, or the ICSA's testing shows that it doesn't, or that some qualified evaluator has shown that it doesn't, then the implementation or use of a weak-key generation scheme (or other feature) would prevent Certification.

5. Specific-product testing is performed on a case-by-case basis. It is possible that the ICSA could certify a product for use only under certain configurations or conditions. The ICSA will post on its Web page that these products, specific configurations, or conditions are certified.

6. Generally, Certification of software products is platform-specific. Each product must be evaluated within its own operating environment. However, when the number of products and platforms is

large, then, on a case-by-case basis, the ICSA will work with the vendor concerning multiple-product Certification.

Vetting

In order to develop appropriate and meaningful Certification criteria, the ICSA uses a notice of proposed Certification Criteria. In the *vetting* process of appraisal and evaluation, the ICSA may query numerous people and organizations that will eventually include affected vendors, independent consultants, the ICSA Cryptography Products Certification Advisory Board (CPCAB), academia, and other consumer groups and industry groups—input from all sources impacts the draft criteria. Finally, the ICSA Certification Criteria and the Certification process are reviewed by a Certification Oversight Board (COB). The CPCAB consists of internationally recognized leaders in the field of cryptography; the COB members have broad representation in the general fields of computer science and information security.

Testing

The actual testing of security products is implemented by skilled testing technicians with expert supervision and oversight. Certification testing is performed by ICSA personnel or by third-party laboratories and personnel authorized and overseen by ICSA. Testing is automated where possible and checklist-driven where not automated. The test protocols are reproducible and objective. Testing personnel and authorized labs have a help desk to resolve questions and mediation procedures to resolve conflicts.

The Certification testing process has two phases:

Phase 1, *Familiarization*

- Familiarize the ICSA or third-party laboratory personnel with the vendor, the product, the technology, and specific product components.

- Review the Product Testing Guide provided by the product vendor.

- Resolve technical issues such as operability, interface to test equipment, and setup considerations.

- Establish procedures and guidelines for training on product.

- Establish debugging procedures.
- Test and debug the specific testing setup.

Phase 2, *Certification Testing*

- Verify that the algorithm used is on the ICSA Adopted Algorithm list.
- Verify that implementation mistakes are not made.
- Verify that the product passes black box data testing.
- Verify that the product passes any specific-product testing requirements.

Vendor Involvement

1. At ICSA's discretion, vendors may be asked to participate in the Phase 1, *Familiarization* portion of the test, which is designed to familiarize test personnel with the products, resolve problem/concerns/questions about the product's operation, and ensure proper training of the testing personnel.
2. Vendors will be on standby for Phase 2, *Certification Testing,* and although vendors will not be present during the testing, they will have spare products/equipment readily available and a technical liaison for problem resolution, usually via email or phone.

Required from Vendor

A vendor who wants to have a product certified under the ICSA Cryptography Product Certification Program should follow the procedure outlined below:

- Documentation—a signed Terms and Conditions for Cryptography Product Certification Program, which includes the ICSA Logo and Certification Seal Usage Guidelines, a completed and signed Product Testing Guide, and a signed Certification Purchase Order Form
- Every version of the product hardware/software suite—turnkey
- Related/peripheral computer or communications equipment, as required
- Instructional manual, cards, tapes, or other media

- On-site setup and/or training if requested by ICSA
- Any special product operating instructions

The Certification Year

The ICSA Cryptography Product Certification is valid for one full year. Vendors submitting payment to the ICSA for testing will receive services for one product for one year from the effective date of the contract. This might include retesting a product that failed Certification or that has undergone a revision. Periodic or random spot checks of the product will be conducted by the ICSA labs throughout the Certification year to ensure continual compliance with the evolving criteria and with product revisions. No additional charges will be levied for product Certification during the contract year. Certification includes all activities surrounding the testing process, including promotion, logo use, and other services.

Criteria Changes

ICSA anticipates quarterly or near quarterly iterative updates of the Certification Criteria (Version 1.1, 1.2, etc.). These are meant to adopt new algorithms, new testing tools and controls, and so forth.

ICSA usually increases the difficulty of the Certification as the ICSA Cryptography Products Consortium members and end users see a need for more stringent testing. For example, an entirely new cycle and Certification window will occur to yield 2.x Criteria. Vendors and other shareholders have ample input as to the criteria and timing.

Reporting Certification Results

Four requirements of reporting are:

1. Certification is pass/fail.
2. Only the list of products passing Certification will be released to the press.
3. Products participating in the test are not reported.
4. Products failing the test are not reported.

WRAP-UP

The fundamental motivation for a company to get its product or system certified is to reduce risk. Reducing the degree of uncertainty about security solutions is an important step in determining what can be done to reduce the degree of risk or harm from undesirable events. Reducing the degree of uncertainty occurs for customers of security solutions or users of systems when they can be assured that the product or system at least meets minimum standards. Certifications provide a level of minimum standards. Certification allows the organization with its product or system certified to point to a recognized minimum standard and demonstrate that they meet or exceed that standard. Certification is an important step in reducing the degree of uncertainty about security solutions and therefore provides one approach for reducing risk exposures. Certification is an important step in improving the safety and security of computing, which will lead to improved confidence in computing, and which, in turn, will inevitably lead to more constructive and pervasive uses of computing and of the very products or systems that are certified.

ICSA is keenly aware that there is no silver bullet for resolving the many issues associated with the security of the digital world. ICSA's certification and testing programs are a significant step in the evolutionary process of achieving a level of acceptable trust in digital technology.

The ICSA's Cryptography Certification Program can be found at *http://www.icsa.net*.

PART 4

Practical Cryptography

CHAPTER 15

Internet
Cryptography

Although the Internet is notorious for its security risks, there are a variety of cryptographic products available to protect Internet users. Any of these products can protect Internet traffic against a variety of threats. The challenge is to pick the right product for a given purpose. Cryptography can provide strong, foolproof protection, but easy protection can interfere with easy communication. A proper choice depends on the practical goals of Internet access and what types of threats might interfere with those goals.

This chapter examines the selection of Internet cryptographic products in the following sections.

- How network software products are structured and how that relates to types of crypto products

- Administrative and policy issues that will affect the choice of crypto products .

- Key management alternatives

- Products that protect Internet traffic automatically without user intervention

- Application layer products, like secure Web browsers and email packages.

Protocol Layers and Network Products

Several decades of experience with computer networking has led to a well-understood architecture for mixing and matching among different networking products. No single, universal solution solves every possible problem. Instead, each user must select and customize components according to the particular application. This approach is called the *network protocol stack,* a strategy for organizing networking hardware and software products into a set of known layers.

The best-known definition of protocol stack architecture is the *Open System Interconnection (OSI) Reference Model,* which defines an idealized set of communications protocol components organized into seven distinct layers. In the commercial world, however, these seven layers are usually organized into three specific packages: application software, network software, and peripheral devices (Figure 15-1). Commercial crypto software is provided as a feature incorporated into these various packages.

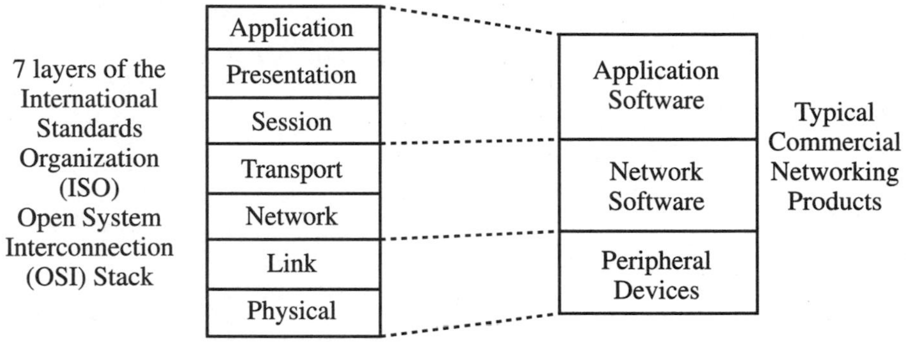

■■ ■■ ■■ ■■
Figure 15-1
Mapping of 7 OSI
Layers to 3 Product
Packages

7 layers of the International Standards Organization (ISO) Open System Interconnection (OSI) Stack		
Application		
Presentation	Application Software	Typical Commercial Networking Products
Session		
Transport	Network Software	
Network		
Link	Peripheral Devices	
Physical		

Application software packages provide capabilities like word processing, Web browsing, graphical design, or electronic mail. These packages are the ones people feel most comfortable with: they are designed to be easy to buy, install, and use on typical desktop workstations. Network-oriented applications use the workstation's existing network software via the *socket interface,* a well-understood programming interface. The application uses this interface to identify the networking service being provided or used, and to establish connections with other, identified hosts on the network.

The *network software* refers to the software that implements the socket interface on a particular workstation. It is packaged as part of the workstation's operating system: Windows, Unix, or Mac OS. The network software allows a variety of network applications to share an equally diverse variety of peripheral devices connecting to a large variety of networks. Typical workstations today include Internet networking software, but some may also provide software for Appletalk, Novell, IBM, or other networking protocols.

The *peripheral device* provides the interface hardware and software that connects to particular networks. The link layer is selected to match the network being connected to. The network protocol software communicates with the data link via a *device driver* installed in the system. To install a particular data link into a host system requires both hardware and software. The hardware consists of an interface device to physically connect the host to the network. The software consists of a device driver to allow the host's network software to talk to the device.

Cryptographic products fall into four categories according to how they fit into the protocol stack (shown in Figure 15-2). Starting from the bottom, there is *link encryption* and *network encryption*. Link encryption is applied to data on the network link itself. Network encryption is applied to data carried within packets, leaving additional network control infor-

Figure 15-2
Categories of Cryp-
tography Products for
Internet Security

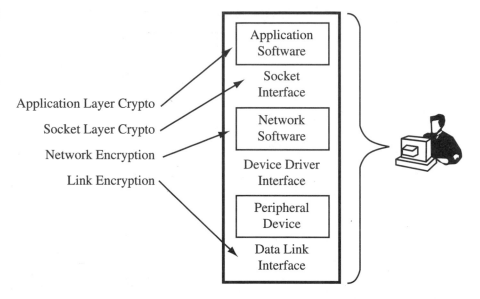

mation in a readable form. This allows other networking devices (like Internet routers) to deliver encrypted packets without having to decrypt them first. Link and network encryption both provide *automatic encryption,* because users have no choice in applying the encryption: if it is enabled, then it is automatically applied to the data.

The remaining two types of products are packaged and sold as applications. Socket layer crypto provides both secrecy and integrity protection to data passing through the application's socket layer interface. Web browsers like Netscape Navigator and Microsoft Internet Explorer are the most common examples of socket layer crypto products. Application layer crypto is integrated into the application, so that crypto protections are applied directly to application data items. The most common products of this type are electronic mail crypto packages, like Pretty Good Privacy (PGP).

Administrative and Policy Issues

There are four essential administrative and policy issues that will help decide what crypto products will best fit a particular situation: secrecy, accountability, public access, and connection topology. Before choosing crypto products and technologies, you should review these issues and establish priorities for each. These issues often present important trade-offs between security and an enterprise's operational needs.

Secrecy Risks

When typical employees are required to keep information secret in the course of their professional duties, most will follow the necessary rules to do so. They will occasionally make a mistake when following these rules but individual mistakes don't generally cause a damaging leak of information. Such occasional lapses are considered an acceptable risk in most working environments since the risk of real damage from individual errors is small. However, some environments face stronger risks from leaking information or their employees have more trouble applying secrecy rules for one reason or another. Different crypto products rely on correct user operation to different degrees. If computer users are sensitive to the importance of secrecy and are well trained in using crypto software, then they can probably be relied on to apply crypto when necessary. If the users are less familiar with the secrecy issues or less reliable at following security procedures, then you should consider products that apply encryption automatically. This is also true if the information is particularly sensitive so that even rare mistakes could cause serious damage.

Individual Accountability

In some enterprises it is essential to keep track of who does what. If these critical activities are computer-based and distributed geographically, then individually assigned cryptographic keys can be used to associate network message traffic with specific individuals. The enterprise can assign secret cryptographic keys to pairs of users, and then each pair has strong confidence that messages originate and are readable only by the two of them. Even better, the enterprise can assign public/private key pairs to each user, and trace each authenticated message back to the user whose private key has authenticated it (Figure 15-3).

Unfortunately, per-user cryptography is costly. Each user must have a personal copy of the crypto software and/or hardware. Keys must be generated and assigned to each user and be correctly cataloged and distributed to other users. Administrators must keep up to date all hardware and software that is used by these individuals and must revoke and/or reissue keying material as people leave or as keys are compromised.

Many enterprises need per-user accountability but do not need the level of certainty provided by per-user crypto. In such cases, it is enough to share crypto capabilities on a per-site basis. Messages traveling

Figure 15-3
Per-User Encryption

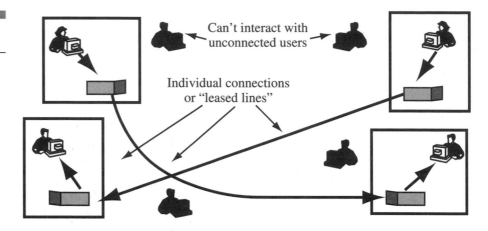

Figure 15-4
Proxy Encryption:
Sharing the Crypto
Facilities Among
Users

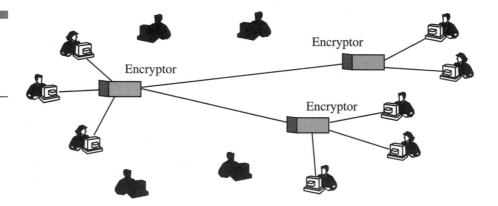

among computers within a single geographical site will travel as plain text and messages traveling between sites over public networks will be cryptographically protected. This notion of sharing a crypto device among multiple users is usually called *proxy encryption* (Figure 15-4) and is often used to implement cryptographic *virtual private networks* (VPNs).

Access to Public Sites

Many enterprises have a network that connects their geographically remote sites together and many have a connection to the Internet; some have both. Internet access is common in organizations that need rapid and timely communications with a large customer community. The Internet connection allows the enterprise to publish up-to-date product information on Web sites that customers can easily visit. It also supports email messaging that gives customers another method of expressing their needs to the enterprise. If a site has an Internet connection and uses it only to make encrypted connections to associated sites, then new customers and other members of the general public will have no way to communicate with the enterprise via the Internet (Figure 15-5).

Figure 15-5
Encrypted Access
Can Block Public
Access

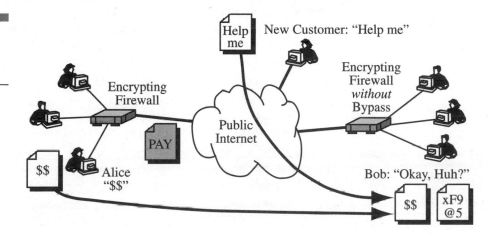

Internet access is less common when secrecy is a very, very important enterprise requirement. There are two reasons for this. First, modern commercial computing systems are not very strong in the face of sophisticated attacks from the Internet. Fortunately, most attackers are relatively unsophisticated and rely on automated attack techniques that trained system managers can protect against. However, this does not change the fact that typical computer security is like typical physical security: good enough to block most attacks, but not particularly clever.

The second reason why enterprises with high security requirements shun the Internet is because it is risky for the same network to be communicating to trustworthy sites via encrypted connections and to arbitrary public sites without encryption. This arrangement makes it possible for the crypto equipment to accidentally send unprotected information between sites when the information should have been protected. This type of failure is difficult to detect and can occur due to configuration errors in the VPN crypto devices.

Connection Topology

Another consideration is the general topology of the remote connections required among associated computers. In particular, it is important to recognize whether or not the topology consists primarily of connections to a central site. Many organizations have a central site, and all connections tend to be between remote sites and the central site. This is common when everyone generally uses a particular server system that resides at a single location or when employees often connect portable systems to a single, central site. Other organizations have several sites that tend to establish connections between themselves in an arbitrary manner. This is more common in enterprises with longer experience in Internet technology. Internet-savvy organizations often have a variety of servers and applications that are distributed geographically among the enterprise's sites. Centralized access has an advantage over distributed access because there are a larger variety of products that support it. Centralized access can be supported safely and efficiently using secret-key technology. Distributed access is possible using secret keys but it gets unwieldy as the number of sites increases. Public-key techniques are much more efficient at supporting distributed communications but there are not as many products that support them.

Key Management Alternatives

There are essentially four techniques commonly seen in key management for Internet cryptographic products:

- Shared manual secret key
- Automatic rekeying with preshared secret keys
- Key distribution centers
- Public keys

Each of these techniques has its own set of strengths and weaknesses, along with distinct impacts on the administrative and policy issues noted earlier. These can interact to make security administration easy, difficult, or nearly impossible in different situations. Unfortunately, most products choose to support only one key management technique, so it is essential to understand which alternative a given product provides and how the choice affects the product's capabilities.

Shared Manual Key

This is the classic technique for establishing crypto keys. If a group of crypto devices must be able to intercommunicate, a single crypto key is generated and distributed manually to every crypto device that needs it. If the key is stolen or accidentally disclosed by any of the users, then it is necessary to generate and distribute a new key to all devices.

This technique is best used under the following circumstances:

- *Small number of easy-to-reach crypto devices:* Since this technique relies on routine distribution of secret keys, the distribution process should be as painless as possible. The expense of rekeying will go up as the number of devices goes up, and as the difficulty of visiting the devices goes up.

- *All crypto devices reside in physically secure locations:* A major risk of this approach is that the shared key might be stolen or accidentally disclosed. We reduce this risk if the crypto devices are physically safe.

- *All communicating devices are identified beforehand:* Keys must be distributed before communications can take place. It is not practical to momentarily decide to communicate to another user or site. The site must share a key with the other sites first.

- *The crypto devices use computationally secure cryptography:* The cryptographic techniques should be immune to systematic attacks that might disclose the secret key. Changing keys will be relatively costly, so keys will probably not be changed very often. This gives attackers more time to try to guess a given key, and more encrypted data to analyze when seeking the key.

- *Turnkey, off-the-shelf availability:* Numerous working products have been developed that use this technique. The products are relatively mature and easy to use subject to the essential limitations of manual keying. Vendors may provide systems that interoperate based on secret keys even if they don't interoperate based on more sophisticated key management mechanisms.

The technique of shared manual keys is relatively common because it is easy to implement in products and permits easy interoperation between different vendor implementations. However, it has a variety of shortcomings that limit its value except when the network traffic isn't subject to serious attack. As the size of the network goes up, it becomes difficult and then impossible to efficiently change crypto keys. At some point, it becomes easier for the organization to face the increasing risk of an attack than to change the key and prevent possible attacks.

Preshared Keys with Rekeying

This technique evolved as a response to the shortcomings of manual secret keys. In particular, the banking industry developed ANSI Standard X9.17 to solve the problems faced with rekeying large, international networks using the Data Encryption Standard in the late 1970s. This technique differs from manual secret keys in two important ways. First, each secret key is used only to encrypt data between a single pair of devices or users; every pair of devices that must communicate is assigned its own key. Second, the keys that are distributed manually are never used to encrypt actual data; instead, they are used as *key encrypting keys* (KEKs). Each time a pair of devices starts to communicate, one of the devices generates a random *session key* that is used to encrypt the actual data being exchanged. The KEK is used to encrypt the session key so that it may be safely exchanged between the two devices. Thus, the KEK never encrypts any data except the session keys and may be used for a much longer time period with a smaller risk of successful attack. Furthermore, if a single key is lost or disclosed, you can quickly and easily reconfigure the system to ignore that key. Replacing the key is relatively easy since it affects only two devices or users.

This technique is best used in the following circumstances:

■ *Simple topology—a central site or a very small number of sites:*
Every pair of communicating devices must have its own key, so it is important to limit the number of pairs of devices. If all communication is between remote sites and a single, central site (Figure 15-6),

Figure 15-6

Connecting to a Central Site with Preshared Secret Keys

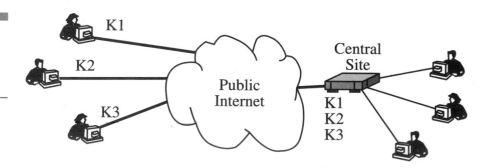

then each remote device can be assigned a unique key with a copy stored on the central site's crypto device. If communications must take place between three or more users or devices, then each communicating pair needs a unique, secret key. This rapidly leads to a combinatorial explosion as the number of separate users increases.

■ *All communicating devices are identified beforehand:* Since all communicating sites must have keys before communications can take place, it's not practical to momentarily decide to communicate to another user or site. The site must share keys first. Furthermore, adding another site or device potentially increases the number of keys by a large number, so it is not feasible to assign and distribute keys except when it's known that they are needed.

■ *Central host's vulnerability to attack presents an acceptable level of risk:* If the connection topology is organized around a central host, then all of the secret keys will reside on this single, central host. This makes the central host's key list a very attractive target to an attacker. Unfortunately, it is very difficult (perhaps impossible) to protect such a database from all attacks. This approach is practical only when the risk of such an attack is acceptable.

■ *Key revocation must be timely and reliable:* If a key has been compromised somehow, then reconfiguring the two devices that use that key can quickly revoke it. This will prevent the pair of users or devices from communicating until a new key can be distributed, but it is easier to distribute a new key to two devices than to several.

■ *Turnkey, off-the-shelf availability:* Numerous working products have been developed that use this technique. The products are relatively mature and easy to use subject to their essential technical limitations. In some cases, vendors provide this as a basic technique to allow interoperability with other vendors' products.

The principal shortcoming of preshared keys is that the number of keys becomes impossible to manage as the number of users that must directly communicate with other users increases.

Key Distribution Centers

Key Distribution Centers (KDCs) were developed to solve the problem of too many keys when connecting numerous sites. This technique is also described in ANSI X9.17 standard. It is also the basis of the Kerberos system, a well-known architecture and toolkit for distributed access control. Each user is assigned a single *KDC key* for communicating with the KDC. Any user can establish an individual session key for communicating with any other user by contacting the KDC. The KDC keys are used to encrypt this session key so that the individual users may decrypt them. Variants of KDC technology appear in a variety of products and systems; some provide it as a "turnkey" part of the package, while others provide a toolbox for building KDC-aware systems and applications.

KDCs are best used under the following situations:

- *Lots of users need to communicate directly to one another:*   Each user only needs a KDC key in order to establish a secure link with any other user. The administrative effort scales in a simple way as the number of users increases.

- *KDC's resistance to attack is comparable to the rest of the system's level of risk:*   The KDC needs to store a plain-text copy of all of the individual KDC keys in order to do its job. This makes the KDC's key list a very attractive target to an attacker. Unfortunately, it is very difficult (perhaps impossible) to protect such a database from all attacks. A KDC should be used only if the enterprise is comfortable with the risk of the KDC itself being attacked.

- *KDC reliability defines acceptable communications reliability:*   The KDC is a bottleneck in the communications system since everyone must contact it in order to establish a communications session. If the KDC goes down, then users will not be able to establish new sessions until it returns to service. Installing backup servers might increase reliability, but this increases the risk of attack on the KDC database by providing additional targets.

- *Key revocation must be timely and reliable:*   If a user's KDC key is compromised, we can quickly revoke it by updating the KDC's key list. This will not interfere with the activities of any other KDC users. The compromised user will not be able to establish encrypted connections until a new KDC key has been delivered.

The major shortcoming of the KDC concept is that it relies on a central database of keys. This database is either a bottleneck that affects performance or reliability. The database is very vulnerable, particularly if it is replicated in order to improve reliability.

Public Key

Public-key techniques use public-key encryption in order to distribute private session keys between pairs of users or crypto devices. This is one of the typical applications of public-key encryption: it is rarely used to encrypt data; instead it is used to encrypt random secret data used to generate keys for use in conventional secret key algorithms. Each user has a personally assigned private key that is never disclosed, and the corresponding public key is distributed to all other users. That user can only decrypt data encrypted by a given user's public key. A user can send a secret session key to another user by encrypting the session key with the recipient's public key (see Figure 15-7). Since the public key cannot be made to disclose the private-key value, users may distribute their public keys freely to anyone who might need to communicate with them.

Figure 15-7
Key Distribution
Using Public-Key
Cryptography

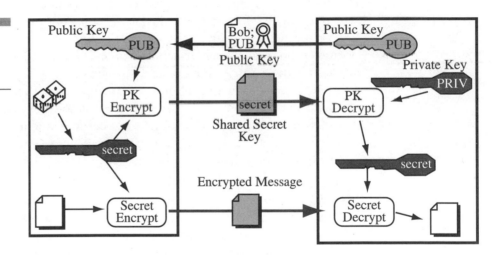

Public keys for key management are best used under the following situations:

- *Lots of users need to communicate directly to one another:* One user can communicate with any other user whose public key is available. Individual users can collect keys and they can be stored in shared directories or they can be distributed when communications takes place. The U.S. government uses public-key techniques in their secure telephone, the STU-III. Any STU-III can call any other, and they negotiate a secret key for the call using public keys.

- *The risk of a central key repository is unacceptable:*   If the enterprise's activities provide a particularly attractive target to attackers, then the central key repository may be too easy to breach. A database of public keys does not pose a security threat to the key's owners or to their traffic, so it is safer from attack than a KDC.

- *Central host must not be a performance or reliability bottleneck:* Some environments must be able to operate reliably even if a few systems fail. Since public keys may be safely stored in a variety of places, there is no central host that must always be online when establishing new communications sessions.

- *The risk of inefficient key revocation is acceptable:*   Since public keys may be easily copied and stored in a variety of locations for efficiency and performance reasons, it is simply impossible to keep track of exactly where every copy of a given public key might be stored. If the corresponding private key is compromised, then there is no way of efficiently getting rid of copies of the compromised public key. Users are faced with the quandary of either ignoring all uses of a possibly compromised public key or of allowing such communication although its security is suspect.

  Current products don't provide much of a solution for this problem. The solution most often suggested is the *revocation list,* which identifies every public key that has been revoked and uses procedures that always check such lists before using a public key. Unfortunately, these lists and procedures are rarely implemented or maintained in current products.

- *The costs of a custom-engineered system solution is acceptable:* The underlying technology of public keys holds great promise for simplifying the operation of cryptographic products and systems. Unfortunately, this simplicity hasn't been achieved very often. Except for a few notable exceptions, like Lotus Notes, public-key facilities are usually provided as a set of components that must be integrated to make them work. This usually requires special training or outside consultants to produce a working system in most enterprises. This may be an appropriate expense in some cases.

Public-key technology currently suffers from two shortcomings. The principal problem is the relative immaturity of public-key products. Few reflect the robustness and ease of use that most organizations require, except when they are tightly integrated into a relatively mature product. The second problem is that there is no simple way to revoke a public key. It is not clear how this will be resolved in practical products.

An important aspect of public-key management is the handling of public-key certificates. A *certificate* is a data item that contains an authenticated public key along with the identity of the key's owner. The certificate is authenticated with the digital signature of some third party that vouches for the fact that the given key, in fact, belongs to the named user. Turnkey software for generating public-key certificates is relatively new and is still evolving.

Automatic Encryption

Automatic encryption products apply their protections to all data passing through a protected connection. Users can't disable the encryption by accident or on purpose, regardless of whether the data really needs protection or not. These products can provide relatively reliable protection in high-security applications. However, the products pay no attention to the data being protected, so they waste resources by protecting unimportant data as well as critical data.

Automatic encryption products are available in two categories: link encryptors and network encryptors. *Link encryptors* are built to provide protection to dedicated, private data links connecting two sites. *Network encryptors* are built to protect data that can pass over public networks like the Internet.

Link Encryption

Link encryptors probably have the longest history of any computer-based encryption product. They are designed to take all data transmitted through a communications link and encrypt it. The receiving end decrypts the data stream as it is received. Typically, a link encryptor product is a hardware device that connects directly to the network's "wire." Instead of connecting directly to the network, the computer plugs into one side of the link encryptor and the other side of the encryptor is connected to the network. Thus, all information passing between the network and the computer must pass through the link encryptor.

This physical arrangement provides the highest possible degree of secrecy. A well-designed link encryptor provides no way for messages to pass between the network and the computer unless crypto processing is performed. Since the encryptor is physically separate from the computer, there is no easy way for the user or applications software to disable or otherwise interfere with the encryption. On the other hand, this effectively prevents communication with computers except for those with compatible encryptors that share the same crypto keys.

Link encryptors are usually designed to work with specific types of communications links. Specific products are built and sold to encrypt serial modem links, frame relay, asynchronous transfer mode, and so on. Computers that need to exchange encrypted data must construct the appropriate link between them or lease the appropriate link from a telecommunications provider.

As shown in Figure 15-8, all data transmitted across the data link is encrypted, except for any data link control information that is needed to operate the data link reliably. Internet packet headers are treated as data at this level of networking, so Internet addresses and control information are all encrypted. Because of this, link-encrypted data must be decrypted before it can be passed through an Internet router.

Figure 15-8

How Data Is Encrypted by a Link Encryptor

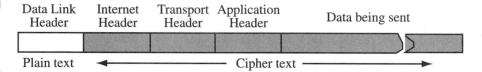

Data Link Header	Internet Header	Transport Header	Application Header	Data being sent

Plain text ⟵ ————————— Cipher text ————————— ⟶

In an Internet environment, link encryptors may be used in one of two ways. First, they may be used to protect a link between a remote client and the site that provides it with Internet service. In such a case, the remote client's unique crypto key can provide strong identification of the client and a large measure of accountability for actions originated by that client.

The second way is to perform link encryption on a dedicated data link between two sites. Typically, the dedicated link enters a router at each site after passing through a link encryptor. The users of Internet protocols at each site may be totally unaware that encryption is being used and prevented from any sort of interference in the encryption process. This provides a very high level of protection for the data traffic. Safety-conscious sites will place the router, data link endpoint, and the link encryptor in a secured machine room to ensure the integrity of the physical arrangement and of the crypto keys being used.

Commercial link encryptor products use the whole variety of key management techniques. Older products use the classic manual keying technique. One commercial device uses preshared keys that are initially established by directly connecting pairs of encryptors before they are deployed at their remote sites. Subsequent connections use the preshared secret information in order to generate new session keys to encrypt communicated data. It is also possible to use some products with a KDC. Another vendor has implemented public key-based key exchange. It is important to identify the type of key exchange supported by a product before choosing it for a particular application.

Network Encryption

Network encryption has evolved over the past several years in conjunction with the growth of Internet technology. Whereas link encryption protects data only while traversing a single kind of networking technology, network encryption is designed to traverse several different networks without requiring decryption. As shown in Figure 15-9, network encryption leaves more data in a packet plain text, which allows additional levels of network software to play a role in delivering the packet. Link-encrypted packets can be carried only across the network on which they originated. Because more network control information is available, network encryption allows the packet to traverse multiple networks on the way to its final destination.

Figure 15-9
Internet Style Network Encryption Leaves IP Addresses in Plain Text

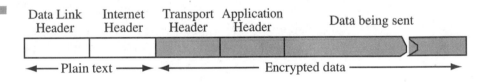

The Internet community has developed the *IP Security Protocol* (IPSec) to provide network level cryptographic protection to Internet traffic. Figure 15-10 illustrates how an IPSec-encrypted message can

Figure 15-10
IPSec-Encrypted Packets Pass Through Standard Internet Routers

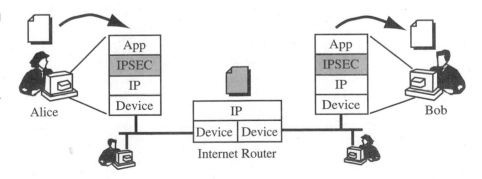

originate on one network and be delivered on another. Note the presence of the "IP layer" in conjunction with the conventional application, network, and device product packages. The IP layer handles the routing of packets between different networks, and it is an important part of the network software on Internet-capable computers.

In Figure 15-10, on the left, the user Alice needs to send an encrypted message to the user Bob, who is on a different network. Alice produces her message using a standard Internet application program that does not necessarily know anything about encryption. The application passes the message to the network software, which performs the encryption before the message reaches the IP layer.

The IP layer is responsible for sending a packet to its destination or as close to its destination as possible, based on the IP address of the recipient's host computer. If the recipient's computer resides on the same network as the sender, then the IP layer will direct the packet to that computer. Otherwise, the IP layer routes the packet to another computer that will take the packet closer to its destination. These routing decisions are based on the IP layer's *routing table,* which associates various IP destination addresses with data link addresses on the local network.

Figure 15-10 also shows how a special device, an *Internet router,* can deliver packets originating on one network to another. Since Alice's computer is not on the same network as Bob's, her computer has determined that the message to Bob must travel via the router. The router has two different network device interfaces that connect to two different networks: Alice's and Bob's. When packets from Alice to Bob arrive at the router, its IP software identifies Bob's network and the link address of Bob's host on that network. Then the router transmits Alice's packets to Bob's computer. If Bob's computer had not been on a network connected to that router, the router would have sent the traffic to another router, and another, until it arrived at a router on Bob's network. Upon arrival at Bob's computer, Alice's packets are processed by its device interface and IP layer. Then the packets are decrypted and passed to the application software running on Bob's computer.

Note the significant difference from link encryption. If the packets were protected with link encryption, they would have to be decrypted before entering a router. Since the IPSec encryption leaves the IP header information in plain text, routers can receive and route IPSec-encrypted packets without decrypting them or otherwise affecting their cryptographic protections. The packets don't have to be decrypted until they arrive at the destination host.

In practice, many sites use IPSec in a proxy mode to implement cryptographically protected VPNs. This allows a site to exchange data safely between sites connected via the Internet. If a site uses the Internet to implement its VPN, then it must decide whether it will restrict all traffic to travel on the VPN or whether it will allow conventional Internet access to public sites as well. Sites that have very strong secrecy requirements will do best by restricting all traffic to the VPN and blocking all access to public sites. This eliminates any possible ambiguity in the processing of data as it enters and leaves the site. If both plain text and crypto-protected data are allowed to pass in and out of the site, then there are opportunities to confuse one for the other or to transmit sensitive information that unintentionally lacks the cryptographic protection it should have. An example is shown in Figure 15-11.

Figure 15-11
Risk of Allowing Public Traffic Combined with Encrypted VPN Traffic

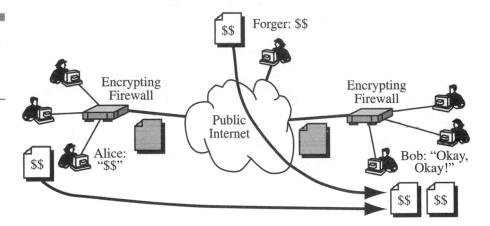

IPSec is not the only network encryption protocol available in products today. There are a few proprietary products based on network security protocols developed for the U.S. government: the *Secure Data Network System* (SDNS). These protocols are similar to IPSec since SDNS was a major source of IPSec design concepts.

Another important network encryption protocol is the *Point-to-Point Tunneling Protocol* (PPTP) that is available in some Microsoft products. PPTP establishes a data stream within an IP transport connection and uses this data stream to encapsulate a variety of network protocols, including IP packets and proprietary protocols like those from Novell. The cryptographic protections are applied using a special subprotocol defined and implemented by Microsoft in several different versions. Analysts have identified a variety of security weaknesses in the different protocol versions. In some cases, the level of protection is significantly less than might otherwise be expected by a protocol that uses 40-bit secret keys. As of this writing, Microsoft is reportedly adding IPSec support to upcoming products, notably Windows NT version 5.

IPSec products use the whole range of key management techniques. Manual keying is a required capability according to IPSec protocol specifications. Automatic rekeying is provided by two separate and incompatible keying protocols called SKIP and IKE. The *Simple Key Interchange Protocol,* or SKIP, was developed by Sun Microsystems and presented as an early proposal for a key interchange protocol. The *Internet Key Exchange* (IKE) protocol was developed in a collaborative process by a working group of the Internet Engineering Task Force and is considered an official part of the IPSec protocol.

IKE-based products support both preshared keys and public keys, with the corresponding features and limitations of each technique. In fact, these keys are used only to authenticate the host computers participating in the key exchange. The actual protocol, called the *Internet Security Association Key Management Protocol* (ISAKMP), uses the Diffie-Hellman public-key algorithm to establish a shared secret that, in turn, generates shared secret keys. The authentication keys (preshared or public) are used to authenticate the Diffie-Hellman public values exchanged by the hosts. When using preshared keys, authentication is based on hashed message authentication codes that incorporate the hosts' preshared key. When using public-key techniques, the authentication is based either on digital signatures or on public-key encryption of secret information.

At present, IPSec products provide the highest degree of interoperability and the lowest level of intrinsic security when using manual keying. Many products can also interoperate by using IKE with preshared keys. Such deployments are, of course, subject to a rapidly increasing and hard-to-manage number of keys if a large number of hosts must intercommunicate. Most products that support IKE also provide public key-based authentication for key exchange. This provides the most flexible support for large numbers of intercommunicating sites. However, public keys present the biggest challenge in IPSec product interoperability, and their utility is subject to the availability of effective products for managing public keys.

Cryptography in Applications

The most common cryptographic software today is arguably provided in Internet applications software, particularly Web browsers. Netscape

Communications claims that over 40 million copies of its crypto-capable browser have been distributed worldwide.

Crypto capabilities are most easily distributed and installed when incorporated into applications. The shortcoming is that the security protections are then applied only to data processed by that particular application.

Cryptography-enabled applications typically appear in two forms, which are reviewed in the following section:

- *Web browsers,* using the *Secure Sockets Layer* (SSL) protocol, which is applied to the data at the socket interface. The Web data are unprotected except when in transit between server and client.

- *Email applications,* which are usually built around one of a handful of similar but incompatible email security protocols. These protocols apply security measures to an email message if the author decides to protect the message. Generally, the protection is applied to the message as a static data file, so the message may be stored in its protected form if desired.

Secure Sockets Layer (SSL)

The SSL protocol protects network data by applying crypto protection to the data stream as it is passed through the socket interface from the application software to the network software. This approach protects the information while it flows between different systems on the network. Although the SSL software is generally packaged with the application software, its design allows it to be integrated into existing, connection-based network applications without requiring extensive changes. Thus, many of the components in an SSL-encrypted data packet remain in plain text after protection is applied. As shown in Figure 15-12, only the application protocol information and the application data are encrypted and all other protocol headers are transmitted in plain text.

Figure 15-12
Encryption of Data at the Socket Level

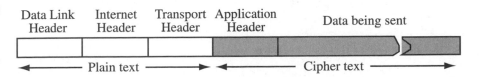

In a typical Web browser application, SSL protection is applied when a Web link contains a distinctive tag. Web links (called *uniform resource locators* or URLs) are generally prefixed with a tag to indicate the transport protocol to be used, which is typically *http:* or perhaps *ftp:* or *file:*, depending on how the information is stored. A tag of *https:* tells the hosts that the URL should be protected with SSL when it is retrieved. When this occurs, the Web server and browser establish an SSL session. First, the browser and server exchange random and secret information that they use to generate shared secret keys. Then they use the keys thus established to protect the integrity and secrecy of data identified with the *https:* protocol tag.

In a typical transaction, the Web server will send a copy of its public-key certificate to the Web browser when they are setting up the session. The browser will use the server's public key to protect random, secret data that the browser has generated for use in shared secret keys. This allows both the server and client to generate a common set of keys from data that have not been seen by outsiders or by potential attackers.

The browser also uses the server's public-key certificate to verify that it is talking to the correct server. First, it checks its digital signature using a copy of the certifier's public key, which is stored in the browser, and validates the server's certificate. Second, the browser compares the Internet host name it uses in URLs to contact that host against the host name appearing in the public-key certificate used to establish the connection.

In basic SSL, the protocol does not verify the client's identity to the server. Usually the server will use its own techniques to identify and authenticate users, depending on what the server is doing. For example, commercial vendors will use credit card numbers in conjunction with verifiable personal identity information. Sites providing proprietary content often require personal user identifiers with secret passwords. Most browsers also support automated user authentication with public-key certificates. Each authorized user must then have a personal set of public-key credentials, including a public-key certificate and a private key that is accessible by the browser software. At present, the major limitation of public-key user authentication is that very few browser users have their own public-key credentials.

SSL provides a very appealing combination of capabilities for many Web-based applications. A server site can choose to require browsers to use SSL, providing a level of safety similar to lower level "automatic" crypto products. The server can even require specific types of SSL protection before it provides data to the browser. This flexibility is supported in the protocol and in many secure Web servers. Accountability can be applied to both the server and the browser. Since the server must provide an authentic public-key certificate, the browser has strong confidence in the server's identity. The server also has a variety of choices for authenticating the browser's user and can trade off between cost, convenience, and authenticity. Since the SSL capability is embedded in a standard browser and invoked according to the URL being accessed, the browser can choose between accessing public, unprotected sites or SSL-protected sites. Since SSL uses public-key cryptography for server authentication and key exchange, it is not restricted to operations in a centralized environment, nor is it limited to communications with browsers carrying predistributed secret keys.

Encrypted Electronic Mail

Email cryptography is purely an application level activity. As shown in Figure 15-13, even if the email is encrypted, most of the protocol headers remain in plain text, including some application-level protocol headers; only the data are encrypted. Unlike other crypto security techniques, email protection can be applied without involving other networking software at all. Typically, the email message is protected just as if it were a data file, regardless of whether it needs to be transmitted across a network or not.

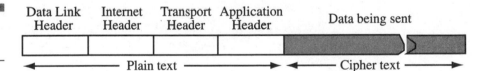

Figure 15-13
Application Level
Data Encryption

| Data Link Header | Internet Header | Transport Header | Application Header | Data being sent |

Plain text ← → Cipher text

Email crypto software is generally packaged in three different forms. One popular approach provides a separate software package that applies crypto protection to data files: encrypting them, integrity-sealing them, or both. Then the encrypted file is imported into a separate email application and either pasted into a message or sent as an attachment. Such packages are not very convenient to use but they are easy to implement and distribute. Another form implements the crypto software as an add-on package for existing email products. The Eudora email package supports a variety of email crypto products that way—most notably, Pretty Good Privacy (PGP). Military messaging software for the Defense Message System (DMS) is implemented as an add-on for Microsoft email applications. The third form tightly integrates the email crypto software into an existing email package—Lotus Notes and Netscape Communicator use this approach.

Email provides full flexibility to communicate with either public or crypto-protected destinations. Although this flexibility is important, it also yields the principal weakness of email cryptography. It is extremely difficult to ensure that users apply crypto protection when it is needed. Even if the crypto protection is very convenient to use, there is the problem that users must choose to apply it correctly. Generally, it is up to the users to choose to apply crypto protection. There is generally no way that the email software can judge whether or not protection is necessary for a given message, nor can it tell for certain what type of protection is necessary. The military has installed *mail guards* to help with this problem: a mail guard checks outgoing email to ensure that it bears a digital signature and/or adequate encryption before allowing the email to leave the local site. However, these devices are costly and tailored to address some specific security requirements—it is not clear that they would serve a comparably useful role in commercial applications.

Since all of the accepted email crypto protocols are based on public-key techniques, email crypto generally provides very strong accountability and convenient distributed message exchange. Some of the important email crypto protocols are:

- *Pretty Good Privacy (PGP):*   PGP is generally implemented in a self-contained software package that can encrypt and/or sign email messages, and reverse the process for incoming messages. PGP includes software to create public/private key pairs, to digitally sign keys, and to keep track of the authenticity of keys. Unlike other products, PGP does not require separate software for generating public-key certificates, since the necessary functions are generally included in PGP.

- *Secure Multipart Internet Message Extensions (S/MIME):* S/MIME is a relatively recent creation that is being used in Netscape Communicator and in other browser-based email packages. It uses public-key certificates that comply with the X.509 standard.

- *Message Security Protocol (MSP):*   MSP was developed to support military messaging and is being used in the Defense Message System (DMS). MSP uses a variant of X.509 certificates.

- *Privacy Enhanced Mail (PEM):*   PEM is mostly of historical interest since few, if any, products remain that implement it. However, it has been immortalized in a series of Internet specifications that have served as the blueprints for most of the subsequent developments in email security. PEM also pioneered many of the secure email usage concepts for X.509 certificates.

One of the principal features of email crypto is its ability to apply digital signatures to email messages. Since digital signatures can represent strong evidence tying the message's contents to the author, signed email has great potential for applications where accountability is essential. In DMS applications, the military uses digital signatures to ensure that orders originated from appropriate command authorities and to verify that messages released by mail guards have not been tampered with in transit. In commercial applications, digital signatures can protect the integrity of data being transferred in electronic document interchange (EDI) applications or even in retail sales applications.

WRAP-UP

This chapter examined the selection of Internet cryptographic products based on reasonable deployment criteria. There are a variety of cryptographic products available to protect Internet users. Any of these products can protect Internet traffic against a variety of threats. The challenge is to pick the right product for a given purpose. Cryptography can provide strong, foolproof protection, but easy protection can interfere with easy communication. A proper choice depends on the practical goals of Internet access and what types of threats might interfere with those goals.

CHAPTER 16

Security: Policy, Privacy, and Protocols

This chapter expands the typical discussion of security protocols beyond considerations of technical scope to include privacy and the legal export environment. Themes pertinent to both the product developer and the product user communities are considered under these banners. This chapter is organized around what might be called the three traditional "Ps" of corporate computer security: policy, privacy, and protocols. Not covered are the important issues of data integrity and authentication, which are examined in Chapters 9 ("Identification, Authentication, and Authorization on the World Wide Web"), Chapter 19 ("Cryptography in Electronic Commerce Systems") and Chapter 14 ("ICSA Product Certification," with reference to Figures 14-1 and 14-3).

At the heart of computer security for a corporate entity is the formation of a viable computer security policy. Security policies must be implemented correctly with computer system users directly in mind. Failure to do so portends trouble. It is not unusual for those who are directed to abide by a security policy to bypass the positive controls that need to be enforced because they are considered burdensome. By developing a policy with system users, compliance is greatly increased.

Implementing any security policy represents a strategic corporate decision. In support of this decision, technical associations and standards committees have developed industry standards and protocols to make computer security technology more understandable to the corporate user. Security standards provide users with both choice and product interoperability.

Managers tend to view security as an economic issue. From a purely economic standpoint, it is difficult for managers to justify implementation of computer security protocols because: (1) other security measures are perceived to add more to corporate production goals; (2) security implementations are considered performance detractors and hence, unnecessary costs; (3) computer security is not accepted but expected by corporate users to be established at a reasonable level; (4) security functions are outsourced in many organizations; (5) additional nonphysical controls are looked upon as unproductive; and (6) they may not be aware of computer security incidents, as they are rarely reported by employees.

It is a sad fact that security standards have not been implemented very widely in the corporate arena. Perhaps they are still too complex, communicated within too narrow a group, and/or simply unbudgeted as unimportant by managers. In addition, legal considerations play a powerful role in the process that is decisively counter to security implementation in the corporate world.

This chapter looks at computer *security policy,* in reference to objectives and goals, and *protocols* in reference to specific rules or agreements to implement those goals, in a more positive light. It addresses the legal and business considerations of security protocols leading to security policy implementation. It surveys selected protocols from a technical perspective. This is not the only perspective one can take. However, this chapter seeks to provide a more positive understanding of the overall process.

Security Policy

Security policy implementation must be based on business strategic goals and objectives that address market needs and respond to customer concerns. Threats to business computer-based applications and data are the driving force to develop and implement an effective computer security policy.

Threats are traditionally characterized as unauthorized release, unauthorized modification of information, or unauthorized denial of information. Any one of these threats may have originated from a malicious or nonmalicious source. It might be more nearly correct to call them *confidentiality threats*.

A *computer security policy* may be defined as a finite set of rules that delimits computer information access. Examples of computer security policy are: no sharing, simultaneous use, localized subsystems, confinement, filtering, data aggregation, data inference, privacy, revocation, file restrictions, and confidentiality.

The two previous definitions focus on the issue of confidentiality. This is certainly only part of a wider definition. Many technical practitioners view security policy and access control policy as congruent. In point of fact, security policy is much broader than access control policy. It must answer the three fundamental questions: (1) what has to be protected, (2) how much protection is needed, and (3) for how long must the protection continue? Since these three fundamental policy questions may, and generally do, differ for each of the basic issues—confidentiality, data integrity, and availability—the problem is at least nine-dimensional. International Computer Security Association (ICSA) has defined its certification process on an even larger matrix than that. (The reader might refer to Figures 14-1 to 14-3 to review the 11 basic threat scenarios, safeguards, and five-tiered policy for testing and validation of products.)

Threats are often external to the system and the environment in which it operates. To be of concern, threats must be characterized by both a willingness to do harm and the capability to do so. There must be a vulnerability for the threat to exploit, or there is no risk. Security breaches that are the result of nonmalicious forces are more a matter of reliability than of security.

In developing a security policy, a manager must conduct a cost-benefit analysis and a risk assessment to evaluate security mechanisms and controls against the potential risks to the organization. The security policy must consider privacy protection, need-to-know privileges, defense against unauthorized access, use, modification, operational disruption, or physical damage of data, files, networks, software and hardware assets. The security policy should address communication links to the Internet and company intranets. The policy should consider protection of information from interception to reception and must also cover not only privacy, but data integrity and authentication goals as well.

Three sources of information for developing a valid security policy are: ICSA; Software Engineering Institute (SEI); and Hutt, Bosworth, and Hoyt. ICSA is the leader in providing computer security certification and evaluation of vendor products. ICSA certifies Web site, IPSec, cryptographic, biometric, antivirus, and firewall vendor products manufactured to provide computer security solutions established within a corporate computer security policy. ICSA offers a complete Web-site vulnerability analysis, known as *TruSecure,* which investigates every facet of security needed to protect a corporation's computer communications and intra/inter networks. TruSecure is timely, comprehensive, and aggressively ahead of the curve in terms of computer security and threat intelligence.

The Software Engineering Institute (SEI) at Carnegie Mellon University in Pittsburgh has developed a Capability Maturity Model (CMM) for Security Engineering that provides help in understanding the required content for an effective security policy. SEI provides information on the security improvement process model. This model incorporates policies, practices, tools, and improvement techniques that have been proven effective in protecting networked systems against historical threats.

Another excellent source of information is *The Computer Security Handbook,* 3d ed., by Hutt, Bosworth, and Hoyt. It includes practical articles on management responsibility, basic safeguards, physical, software, and technical protection, and appendices with sample policies and agreements.

Privacy Concerns

Traditionally, it has been prudent to consider privacy issues when developing a security policy for the corporation. The "right to privacy" by governments, businesses, and citizens is under debate at both the national and international levels. In 1970, a Lou Harris poll (Privacy and American Business, October 1993, p. 3) on Americans' concerns about threats to personal privacy found that 34 percent were concerned and by 1993, 83 percent were concerned. Many nations view security-related subjects as critical to protect vital resources and information but also a critical threat to maintaining law and order. The balancing act between providing a free and global marketplace to an enterprising world and providing crime prevention and control is extremely important. The wisdom of "what is right" versus "what is wrong" will be the dominating argument that drives our future. It is likely that the debate will have philosophical and economical ramifications on the direction of government controls.

Privacy Law

The Privacy Act of 1974 is an important law to consider when developing a security policy. It protects individual rights, U.S. citizen records, and the use of such information by certain branches of the federal government. Other laws like the Freedom of Information Act (FOIA) allow public access to government files. An essential definition in the Privacy Act of 1974 is to understand the term "record" which is defined as:

> Any item, collection, or grouping of information about an individual that is maintained by an agency, including, but not limited to, his education, financial transactions, medical history, and criminal or employment history and that contains his name, or identifying number, symbol, or other identifying particular assigned to the individual, such as a finger or a voice print or a photograph.

Investigative records maintained by the Central Intelligence Agency, the Federal Bureau of Investigation, the Department of Defense and other law enforcement agencies are exempt from the Privacy Act. The Privacy Act of 1974 applies only to government records.

Security disciplines such as cryptography actually permit the private citizen to keep his life private. The national debate over cryptographic policy was captured in a speech delivered almost 20 years before the personal computer was ever invented. In April 1968, Thomas J. Watson, Jr., Chairman of the Board of IBM, was discussing privacy in computer systems in an address to the Commonwealth Club of California. He said:

> ...The problem of privacy in the end is nothing more and nothing less than the root problem of the relation of each one of us to our fellow men. What

belongs to the citizen alone? What belongs to society? Those, at bottom, are the questions we face, timeless questions on the nature and place and destiny of man....

Professor Robert P. Bigelow says:

We have computer security to protect us from people and people to protect us from computers.

Caroline Kennedy points out that the word "privacy" does not appear in the United States Constitution. Yet, many will tell you that they have a fundamental right to privacy. They will also tell you that privacy is under siege. Professor Hoffman explains that the notion of privacy developed by the courts grew as a natural process in support of the Bill of Rights.

The notion that information can be kept secret to any degree vanished with the advent of the worldwide virtual cyberspace. Computers ensure that even the most private information is accessible to the public. No more physical cabinets are required to store files. A child can get on the Internet and access information. What's more, since information exists in cyberspace rather than real space, it can be stolen and "copied" without individuals knowing it. It is conceivable that in the future, the whole universe of information about credit reports, insurance records, medical history, and employment history may be recorded on *smartcards* that will fit in individual wallets. They might even be called *electronic wallets*.

Perhaps the biggest threat to privacy comes in the area known as *information privacy*. Information about individuals and companies are collected not only by the IRS, FBI, and intelligence agencies, but also by the Medical Information Bureau, National Change Of Address database, and the National Crime Information Center, as well as credit bureaus, credit unions, credit card companies, mortgagers, banks, and employers. We now have cellular telephones, (not cordless or real telephones), email, fax, voice mail, talking cars, talking elevators, and even junk mail received via the Internet. Computers have changed the notion of privacy.

Individuals and businesses must realize that this new openness has dire effects on their information privacy. Serious consideration must be given in a security policy to handle this openness and ensure confidentiality of records that may be considered sensitive to the organization.

There are more than 2000 national databases that compromise our privacy. The Internet is a global network of databases. Personal profiles are so complete and available, it is like having another self living in a parallel dimension; it's a virtual self one cannot see, but it affects lives just the same. Even if individuals don't own a computer, they have joined the revolution—individuals are vulnerable!

Consider the unfortunately funny case of the young Gulf War veteran who had some minor surgery at an Eastern VA hospital. The insurance clerk entered a wrong code on the database—a code that showed that his appendicitis had been fatal. The good news was that his insurance company paid the hospital bill. The bad news was that he couldn't prove that he was alive! When he tried to pay his mortgage, when he tried to renew his driver's license, when he tried to cash a check, when he tried to buy a new car, and when he tried to purchase a riding lawn mower at a department store, he found the same strange faces (after the computer check). It took three months to undo the computer error. The patient who has a dosage plan changed in the computer, or a customer whose bank account reflects a different balance than expected, is concerned with both privacy and data integrity.

From the privacy point of view, this is the most unsettling period in the revolution for government, business, and individuals. Technology is far ahead of the laws. Those well-versed in computers already have begun to protect their communications with *encryption*. Many corporations do the same but there is an incredible amount of information that remains unprotected. For every means to secure privacy, people have generated methods to invade it.

The government [especially the Federal Bureau of Investigation (FBI)] is concerned that if criminals begin communicating electronically and scrambling their messages with cryptography, police cannot just tap in (like the wiretaps used against organized crime.) The government's first solution was the *Clipper Chip,* an approved method of encryption that required trusted key escrow and permitted law enforcement to decode with a warrant and then to make the methodology standard in the industry. Privacy advocates were not happy, nor were software companies, civil libertarians, or Internet freedom advocates. Big Brother was definitely "in our faces."

The life-giving principle of cyberspace is the free flow of information. It is the ultimate democracy where principles of open records and unfettered speech prevail. This presents a problem to law enforcement, national security interests, and intelligence operations. It is also a problem for privacy advocates and persons who do not want attention. Within the political atmosphere described, one must take responsibility for the management of individual and business records and develop a security policy that is understood and enforceable.

The Federal Privacy Act of 1974

Opposition to the establishment of a uniform federal data bank, spearheaded by IBM, was responsible for the fact that we do not have such a data bank (per se) today. With the help of undersecretaries Elliot L. Richardson and Casper Weinberger of HEW, sponsored by Senator Ervin, and signed by President Ford on January 1, 1975, the Privacy Act of 1974, PL 93-579, became law. This law is critical to protection of individual rights and should be stated in the security policy.

There is a basic rule that government files are open to the public, unless there is a specific reason, enacted by the legislature, saying that certain files are not available. At the federal level, this principle is demonstrated by the Freedom of Information Act (FOIA), 5 U.S.C. sec. 552, under which a citizen or organization can obtain most governmental records. The Privacy Act, most of which is codified in 5 U.S.C. sec 552a, applies only to records maintained by certain branches of the federal government, specifically executive departments, independent regulatory agencies, government corporations, and government-controlled corporations such as the Federal Reserve Banks. It is not applicable to Congress or to the District of Columbia. When corporations do business under federal agency contracts, their contractor employees are subject to the same rules under the Privacy Act, including criminal penalties for failure to comply with the act.

Agencies can maintain information about individuals only when it is relevant and necessary to accomplish the agency's purpose. The act prohibits the disclosure of any record except within the agency maintaining it unless the individual makes a written request for the data. However, there are exceptions. The agency must give public notice of the existence of each record system. (The 1993 listing of records systems of just the DOD alone consumed 935 pages of the Federal Register.) The agency must also include any proposal to match the record against those of another federal or state agency, keep track of certain disclosures, and establish rules of conduct for those who design and operate the systems. [58 Fed Reg. 10002-10935, 22 February 1993; the Computer Matching and Privacy Act of 1988, PL 100-503, added subsections to 5 U.S.C. sec. 552a.]

The act also established specific rules prohibiting any federal, state, or local governmental agency from denying an individual benefits or privileges because he/she refused to disclose a Social Security Number (SSN). [PL 93-579, sec. 7, requires the governmental agency asking for the SSN to "inform the individual whether that disclosure is mandatory or voluntary, by what statutory or other authority such number is solicited, and what uses will be made of it."] This also shows what significance is put on the SSN as an entry key to most federal databases. It also gives you the prime targets of data or identifies thieves. An effective countermeasure would be to encrypt the information. The notable exception to the rule is the requirement for SSNs on state drivers' licenses. Why is it that most grocery stores want either your driver's license or SSN? Welfare recipients in Texas have been issued a smart "debit" card, which uses the SSN as its key to the database for tracking purchases, both legal and prohibited, by the state.

Out of this act has come a Privacy Protection Commission to make recommendations to Congress (most were not passed) and an outgrowth called privacy implications of the National Information Infrastructure Superhighway system.

In 1996, Vice President Al Gore led the charge in protecting intellectual property and privacy. The Office of Manaagement and Budget published a report on protecting intellectual property and privacy called "National Information Infrastructure: Draft Principles for Providing and Using Personal Information and Commentary" [60 Fed. Reg. 4362, 20 January 1995]. It is still controversial today.

State Laws

Most states have Public Records Acts modeled after the FOIA and whose basic thrust is to make all records available to the citizen, subject to exceptions for law enforcement, trade secrets, and the like. Other states have enacted Fair Information Practices Acts regulating the information that state agencies could maintain about individuals. Several states have enacted Uniform Information Practices Codes and one municipality, Berkeley, California, has enacted a citywide ordinance on privacy. Specific state laws should be addressed in an effective security policy.

International Privacy

A number of other countries also have privacy acts covering both governmental and private corporate records. Most of the laws apply to computerized data banks, which must be licensed by a governmental authority. The rules of disclosure are quite strict, and there are particular prohibitions against the transfer of information in these databanks across national boundaries.

International Commerce Laws

There are various laws that must be understood when developing a security policy and when implementing security protocols for a business. Of first priority are laws that affect international commerce. It is imperative that businesses, which operate both inside and outside the United States, understand the impacts of the U.S. International Trade in Arms Regulation (ITAR) and the Export Administration Regulation, and should ensure that their security policy addresses such issues as cryptography products used for encrypting and decrypting electronic files.

Prior to the end of 1996, Cryptography products were controlled by virtue of being on the ITAR munitions list, which required a special license prior to export. A license was needed regardless of how the technical data was transmitted. In 1996, some encryption products were transferred by Executive Order to Department of Commerce responsibility and were added to the Commerce Control List. In issuing the Memorandum, President Clinton stated:

> Encryption products, when used outside the United States, can jeopardize our foreign policy and national security interests. Moreover, such products, when used by international criminal organizations, can threaten the safety of U.S. citizens here and abroad, as well as the safety of the citizens of other countries. The exportation of encryption products must be controlled to further U.S. foreign policy objectives, and promote our national security, including the protection of the safety of U.S. citizens abroad. This initiative will support the growth of electronic commerce; increase the security of the global information infrastructure; protect privacy, intellectual property and other valuable information; and sustain the economic competitiveness of U.S. encryption product manufacturers during the transition to a key management infrastructure. Under this initiative, non-recoverable encryption items up to 56-bit key length DES or equivalent strength will be permitted for export and re-export. {Such action is subject to} a one-time review of the item and {proof} that the exporter makes satisfactory commitments to build and/or market recoverable encryption items, to support an international key management infrastructure. This policy will apply to hardware and software and will last through December 31, 1998.

No matter what changes are made, it is important that executed corporate security policy conform to current law.

Due to several changes in regulations, it is important to review those rules that may still be in effect. Some modern cryptographic systems are still subject to the well-known ITAR regulations that placed cryptography on the munitions list and require licensing prior to export. A license may still be required regardless of the manner in which the technical data is transmitted, whether the transfer is in person, by telephone, through correspondence, or electronically [22 C.F.R. paragraph 125.2]. The export license may also be required for the export of unclassified technical data. Category XIII(b)1 of the Munitions Control List covers cryptographic equipment.

ITAR governed what products were subjected to export controls. These regulations clearly define a set of conditions in which information considered to be in the "public domain" cannot be subject to these controls. In the ITAR itself, *public domain* is defined as information published and that is generally accessible or available to the public:

- through sales at bookstores
- at libraries
- through patents available at the patent office
- through public release in any form after approval by the cognizant U.S. government department or agency

The Department of Commerce Export Administration Regulation Part 742.15, pages 19 to 22, dated January 1998, covers the Commerce Control List's Encryption license requirements and policy. The Bureau of Export Administration (BXA) Export Services Web site offers counseling, workshops, electronic services, and automated services concerning export issues.

As the world market opens for encryption products, issues arise that may be counterproductive to business. A good security policy, whether the organization is a national business or international business, is important to sustain and compete in the market place. The Internet in many ways has opened a tremendous gateway. Lawmakers no longer have the luxury of imposing national boundaries on a virtual network. They must define laws that meet a balance in protecting their citizens as well as establishing their sovereign needs of national security.

General Nature of Security Protocols

The word *protocol* comes to us from the Greek *prot,* meaning "before," and *kollan,* meaning "to glue together." It has been used to describe an original draft or record of a transaction, or a preliminary agreement.

Through the years it has taken on various similar meanings, usually associated with diplomatic discourse regarding the correct etiquette and precedence to be followed in formal negotiations. In the twentieth-century world of computers, a *protocol* is a complete and unambiguous sequence of well-defined actions designed to achieve an interaction between two or more parties as defined by a *security policy*.

Breaking down this definition:

- *Complete* means that there is an action defined for all possible situations.
- *Unambiguous and well-defined* means that each action has one and only one interpretation.
- *Sequence* means ordered.

Protocols

A protocol enables people that do not know each other to enter into transactions with each other efficiently. Protocols do not guarantee security or mean that the people needing this interaction are necessarily trustworthy. It would be irresponsible to assume that everyone could potentially deal with each other over the Internet as benign participants. However, protocols establish a point of departure from which weaknesses can be studied and protocol improvements can be developed to make transactions as immune from subversion as possible.

Protocol Standards

In June 1992, the Internet Architecture Board (IAB) was chartered to be the component of the Internet society responsible for oversight of the protocols and procedures used by the Internet. The IAB provided oversight of the process used to create Internet Standards. Most of the standards development takes place through the IAB's Internet Engineering Task Force's (IETF's) subsidiary group the Internet Engineering Steering Group (IESG).

The IESG's goal is to coordinate developing standards within the Internet community. It accomplishes this by having proposed standards go through a series of maturity levels: *proposed standard, draft standard,* and *standard.* Each level involves increased testing and investigation. Advancement usually involves a minimum amount of time to allow for comments and gaining some operational experience, including interaction between at least two implementations.

When a proposed protocol standard completes this process and is recommended by the IESG, it is assigned a standard (abbreviated STD) number. The IAB maintains a list of documents that define the standards for the Internet protocol suite. This series of documents is called the *Request For Comment* (RFC) series and is the path used to publish proposed standards and other research for the Internet community. The current Internet Official Protocol Standards list is contained in RFC 2200.

Some of the protocols standardized by the IESG include SMTP (Simple Mail Transport Protocol—RFC 821), FTP (File Transfer Protocol—RFC 959), and PPP (Point-to-Point Protocol—RFC 1661). Some other common protocols have not, at the time of this writing, become an IETF standard and are still "Proposed Standards." These include HTTP (HyperText Transfer Protocol—RFC 2068), which is the underlying protocol of the World Wide Web, along with HTML (HyperText Markup Language—RFC 1866), which is the format of the documents on the World Wide Web.

Protocols developed by other standards organizations, or vendors, may be of interest. Some have attained popular support and become important without IESG recommendation.

Survey of Protocols by OSI Layer

Beginning in 1946, the Organization International de Normalization (International Standards Organization, or ISO) has been the body responsible for developing standards. ISO introduced the *Open Systems Interconnection* (OSI) model, adopted in 1984, to help define interoperability and communications between systems. This model is composed of seven layers as shown in Figure 16-1, and is independent of any specific hardware or software implementation. Each layer performs a transformation of the information given to it by the layer above or below it to accomplish communications between systems.

Most layers of the OSI model can provide or enhance network security in the protocol implementations themselves, or in the ways the network is constructed. In the following we take a brief look at some layers and the dominant protocols currently in use.

Figure 16-1
OSI Model Layers
and Functions

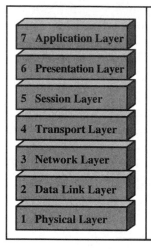

Figure 16-1
OSI Model Layers
and Functions

7 Application Layer	The Application Layer defines how a user accesses the network and provides the end-user services.
6 Presentation Layer	The Presentation Layer formats or otherwise interprets information for applications.
5 Session Layer	The Session Layer establishes and synchronizes communications between the two ends of the communications path via the necessary network services.
4 Transport Layer	The Transport Layer performs network management functions and provides end-to-end transmission control. This includes error detection, correction and restoring service following a network failure.
3 Network Layer	The Network Layer performs network addressing and physical routing of the data including disassembly/reassembly of the message. On the Internet this layer handles the routing through gateways to other networks.
2 Data Link Layer	The Data Link Layer formats the messages for transmission and handles synchronization and error control over the physical link.
1 Physical Layer	The Physical Layer is the actual cable connection over which the information is transmitted.

The Physical Layer

The *Physical Layer* is the medium through which a raw bit stream of signals is transmitted from one point in a network to another. Most people usually think of "cable," or "coax cable" when they think about the physical connectivity of a network. However, there are many media that are in daily use with the Internet, such as coaxial cable, twisted pair, fiber optics, radio signals, microwaves, and infrared light. Many of these media can be intercepted without the knowledge of end users. Thus, there is a security risk at this layer.

For this layer, the physical implementation of the network, the security measures must also be physical, such as encapsulating cables in tamperproof pipes, for example, or otherwise arranging physical security for nodes or portions of the network not under the owners direct physical control are needed.

The Data Link Layer

The protocols of the *Data Link Layer* handle the mundane, but important, activity of ensuring that the data sent by one party is reliably received by the other. These protocols address the problems of handling transmission errors and regulating the flow of the bits of information. Thus, error detection and correction, and making sure that the physical layer is not overwhelmed are performed here.

The two most widely used protocols for this layer are SLIP (Serial

Line Interface Protocol) and PPP (Point-to-Point Protocol). SLIP is the older of the two protocols and as such has some shortcomings for more up-to-date networks. For the security manager, the most serious of these is the fact that SLIP does not provide any form of authentication at either end of the communication path. With dial-up telephone lines, this is a significant risk.

PPP solved many of the problems of SLIP and is the preferred protocol of the two. Most important for security considerations, it permits authentication and the real-time negotiation of link and network control protocols to be used—important features when you don't know what the far end of the connection looks like.

Authentication at this layer consists of each end checking the identity of the far end. If neither party is satisfied at this point, the connection is terminated.

Link encryption or implementing a cryptographic hardware solution between nodes is probably the most common form of securing communications for this layer. Unfortunately, this limits the user to nodes and routers, which are privy to the encryption since the datagrams must be decoded at each point. This leaves the communication subject to possible compromise.

The Network Layer

The Network Layer *is* the Internet!

The skeleton of the Internet is contained in the network layer protocol IP (Internet Protocol). IP was designed to be as flexible as possible and to support the transmission of information without regard to the network being used.

Among the options IPv4 (version 4) provides is a field in the header, called "Security." In theory, this field tells how secret the information contained in the message is. Thus, a military network could use this field to control the flow through specific routers. In practice, however, all routers ignore this field. After all, the Internet is one big happy family, right?

Wrong! Many IP-based security "protocols" have been designed in the past, but none have really become very popular. The latest IP-based security protocol is called *IPSec* (IP Security). Due to its superior functionality, tight security, and the time being right for such security, this security protocol promises to become the de facto IP network-layer security protocol for both IPv4 and its successor, IPv6.

In its current form, IPv4 can no longer support the rapid expansion of the Internet into homes and businesses from its original habitat of universities and government laboratories. This is due in large part to the limited size of the address field and the need to have portable computers tie into the Internet at multiple locations, or even to be mobile while connected. IPv6 solves these and other problems of IPv4. (IPv5 identified an experimental protocol.)

During the process of creating IPv6 the topic of security created much controversy. Although everyone agreed it was needed in an ever expanding and unsure network environment they had trouble agreeing on where, what layer, and how.

Many reasoned that by placing security explicitly in the network layer it would be something that everyone could use without thinking. The purists, however, declared that nothing less than complete source-to-destination encryption, performed by the respective applications, would be satisfactory. Thus data security wasn't needed in this layer and they shouldn't have to suffer any performance degradations because of it. Anything less, they argued, subjected their information to bad or improper implementations and potential compromise.

The "how" side of the question is more problematical. As discussed earlier, cryptographic methods and algorithms are subject to a wide range of rules and regulations, including export controls. Many countries greatly restrict the use of cryptography within their borders as internal security measures. If IPv6 is to have an embedded cryptographic capability, what should it be? Strong cryptographic implementations won't be available in some places and weak ones won't provide the needed protection.

The compromise agreed upon was that IPv6 would use separate authentication and encryption mechanisms. Thus IPSec was broken into two protocols: *AH* (Authentication Header) and *ESP* (Encapsulating Security Payload).

AH carries a state-of-the-art checksum for authentication and integrity of the IP message, whereas ESP encrypts the message as well as authenticates it. Both protocols may use a number of different security algorithms. The algorithm used depends on export restrictions, how secure the message must be, or how fast the message must travel since each security algorithm has different characteristics for the preceding three criteria. DES, 3DES, CAST, RC5, IDEA, and Blowfish are all examples of encryption algorithms used for confidentiality in IPSec. HMAC-MD5, HMAC-SHA and HMAC-RIPEMD160 are algorithms used for authentication and integrity.

Firewalls are usually installed in networks as part of this layer to provide packet filtering. A *firewall* is usually a dedicated piece of hardware with resident applications that can be programmed by the proper network security agent in order to inspect incoming and outgoing packets for validity. Packets that fail inspection are not passed. In this way, attacks from outside the organization may be foiled and internal users can be prevented from inadvertently connecting to a suspect external site.

The Transport Layer

There are two protocols currently in use in the *Transport Layer:* TCP (Transmission Control Protocol) and UDP (User Data Protocol). The principal difference between the two is connectivity between sender and receiver.

TCP is a connection-oriented protocol that provides reliable, port-to-port communication. A *port* is a specific, numbered connection on the sending or receiving machine that operates in full-duplex mode. Many port numbers, those below 1024, are generally reserved and used for standard services, for example, port #21 for FTP, or port #23 for TELNET. (RFC 2200 contains such a list of port numbers.)

TCP operates on a stream of bytes with each entity sending and receiving segments of varying lengths. The specific TCP software implementation determines the proper size of these segments, usually a few thousand bytes. This is subject to the limitations of the actual networks across which the segments travel. Thus, a router may fragment a segment too large for a client network.

What makes this protocol reliable is that the receiver must acknowledge the receipt of a segment within a certain amount of time. The sender, having started a timer upon transmission, will automatically resend a segment if the time-out period is exceeded.

Some interesting situations can arise with TCP, such as segments arriving out of sequence due to different network paths. Alternatively, the segments may be fragmented in transmission and multiple pieces of the same original may appear at the destination. TCP implementations must handle these, and other problems, effectively.

UDP is a connectionless protocol, meaning that the message is not guaranteed to arrive at the destination. A checksum is used to enable the receiver to determine if the datagram was received properly. UDP is widely used in client-server applications where a simple request-response mechanism does not require the overhead processing of TCP's acknowledgment and timer implementation. For most applications, TCP is to be preferred over UDP due to the ability to guarantee delivery.

Although entire process-to-process connections can be encrypted in the transport layer, there and not very many sufficiently good implementations currently.

A security protocol that sometimes is placed in the Transport Layer and sometimes at the Session Layer is SSL/TLS (Secure Sockets Layer/Transport Layer Security). Although originally designed for Web-based transactions, its use can be moved to other applications that lack security such as FTP and Telnet.

Application Layer Protocols

SNMPv2 (Simple Network Management Protocol Version 2) is the protocol used to manage the entities residing on the network. SNMP provides monitoring and administration support for managing nodes, routers, bridges, and other components. This is accomplished by "agents" in each component controlled by a management process on a designated computer. In this way, all the required reasoning capabilities necessary are localized and the distributed components can be relatively simple instruments.

The SNMP protocol has a rigid and exact set of information each agent must provide to the network manager. Defined by ASN.1 (Abstract Syntax Notation One), seven messages are defined—these consist primarily of status or state information, which the manager can query, usually by polling the agent on a regular basis. The manager can also change the state of objects by instructing the agent.

The user most easily controls network security through the application layer. Thus, one is not subject to the vagaries of intervening layer implementations. Traditional cryptographic methods, DES, and RSA algorithms can all be found here as adjunct capabilities.

Perhaps the most widely used application type is electronic mail, or email. RFCs 821- and 822-based email systems are the most prevalent on the Internet. MIME (Multipurpose Internet Mail Extensions), defined in RFC 1521, adds the ability to handle multiple languages, including nonalphabetic ones, and text mixed with audio and video.

On the Internet, email is handled by the Simple Mail Transfer Protocol (SMTP). Using TCP, the local machine establishes a connection with the destination and begins conversing to effect the email transfer. By adding a "gateway," both ends of the conversation do not have to be connected at the same time. The gateway will handle buffering email on both ends.

Other email-related protocols include: DMSP (Distributed Mail System Protocol); IMAP (Interactive Mail Access Protocol); and POP3 (Post Office Protocol). These are described in RFCs 1056, 1064, and 1225, respectively. Within email, PGP (Pretty Good Privacy) and PEM (Privacy Enhanced Mail) offer some protection between distant users.

Another popular feature of the Internet is the USENET, a newsgroup oriented service. The USENET is implemented using NNTP (Network News Transfer Protocol) as defined in RFC 977. NNTP enables news to be rapidly transmitted across the Internet.

Finally, the HyperText Transfer Protocol (HTTP) has driven to the forefront of the Internet. Using HyperText Markup Language (HTML), developers can provide users a myriad of sounds, images, and connections. These permit viewers of one page to jump to a related topic on another page in an almost endless stream of consciousness. Making use of URLs (Uniform Resource Locators), Web pages developed by different people, at different times, who have never met, can be linked together, and those links maintained.

Strategies and Deployment of Products Along Layers

The OSI model layers provide a great abstraction so that many different protocols can exist together without any knowledge of any of the other protocols, which, unfortunately, may lead to some problems.

If, for example, an application layer security protocol is trying to secure a connection at the same time as a network layer security protocol, then not only is time wasted but one of the layers is providing redundant and useless security.

While the preceding example doesn't make anything worse, the example of compression does. When encryption is introduced at the application, transport, or network layer it scrambles the message to random data. This random data no longer compresses very well (or at all) at the data link layer when PPP tries to compress it. To solve this issue, compression must take place before any encryption. *IPComp* (IP Compression) remedies this problem at the network layer so that IPSec can encrypt after IPComp has compressed the data.

Other issues arise with tunneling protocols at different layers such as IPSec, L2F (Layer 2 Forwarding), and SOCKS. While all provide tunneling capabilities, each with its pros and cons, utilizing more than one at the same time would cost bandwidth and might render one protocol useless.

Coordinating which protocols at which layers are active is currently the responsibility of the network administrator, since no coordinating protocol exists today. An organization must be careful to choose the correct protocol combinations.

Discussion of IPv6 and the Future

The choice of 32-bit addresses for IPv4 in the 1970s might have seemed to be a good choice at a time when there were only a handful of networked computers, but today IPv4's theoretical limit ($\approx 4,294,967,296$) seems to be within sight. IPv6's addresses are four times as large, allowing for about 3.4×10^{28} addresses. We hope that this will be enough for the Internet in the future!

IPv6, in the form of IPSec, will also make security mandatory (IPSec is voluntary only for IPv4). Security, along with guaranteed bandwidth, will make the Internet viable for a whole range of applications that have not yet migrated onto the Internet. This will provide even more growth for the Internet, which undoubtedly will produce more protocols dedicated to making the Internet more usable (by everyone). I'm sure someday I'll have my personal wireless Internet connection plugged into my mind, transferring data at speeds that are unthinkable today.

WRAP-UP

We started this chapter discussing security policies and ended up with the future protocols on the Internet. Along the way, we discussed the issue of privacy and its requirement to be included in a corporate computer security policy. There is an ongoing debate between advocates of privacy, the purists who want the absolute free flow of information on the Internet, corporate denizens, and the U.S. government. The latter has the awesome responsibility of protecting the nation's security interests without severing corporate efforts either to provide free-market solutions or to diminish the Constitutional rights of the citizen. The politics are fierce to say the least.

All sides have their valid points. However, of first priority are laws that affect international commerce. It is imperative that businesses, which operate both inside and outside the United States, understand the impacts of the U.S. International Trade in Arms Regulation (ITAR) and the Export Administration Regulation, and should ensure that their security policy addresses issues relating to cryptography products used for encrypting and decrypting electronic files. The laws are changing. Attitudes are changing. Leaders are meeting to negotiate the issues. No matter what changes are made, it is important that executed corporate security policy conform to current law.

This chapter reviewed computer security policy and selected protocols. It addressed the legal and business considerations of security protocols leading to security policy implementation. It surveyed selected protocols from only a technical perspective.

In developing a security policy, a manager must conduct a cost-benefit analysis and a risk assessment to evaluate security mechanisms and controls against the potential risks to the organization. The security policy should address communication links to the Internet and other company intranets. The policy should consider protection of information from its interception to reception. A complete security policy must cover not only privacy, but data integrity and authentication goals as well.

CHAPTER 17

Smartcards

It has been said that smartcards will one day be as important as computers are today. This statement contains a bit of an error because it implies that smartcards are not computers, when in fact, they are. In this chapter, we describe the history of smartcards, some different types, their low-level properties, the standards that affect their adoption in mainstream society, and how they relate to today's computer security systems.

Because smartcards are indeed tiny computers, it's difficult to predict the variety of applications that will be possible with them in the future. It's quite possible that smartcards will follow the same trend of rapid increases in processing power that computers have, following "Moore's Law"* and doubling in performance while halving in cost every 18 months.

Smartcards have proven to be quite useful as a transaction/authorization/identification medium in European countries. As their capabilities grow, they could become the ultimate thin client, eventually replacing all of the things we carry around in our wallets, including credit cards, licenses, cash, and even family photographs. (The photographs could be viewed and/or exchanged by capable terminals or personal computers.) By containing various identification certificates, smartcards could be used to voluntarily identify attributes of ourselves no matter where we are or to which computer network we are attached.

This chapter does not try to predict the future of smartcard application possibilities, nor their impact on society, but instead focuses on the state of the art for smartcards and their use in computer and network security systems. It is not scientifically comprehensive regarding every detail of integrated circuit cards, but instead tries to strike a balance between accuracy and comprehensibility. The standards and references that are mentioned throughout the chapter can be used to find more specific information.

History

The roots of the current-day smartcard can be traced back to the United States in the early 1950s when Diners Club produced the first all-plastic

---

*Moore's Law is attributed to Gordon E. Moore. It states that the performance of silicon doubles every 18 months with proportional decreases in cost. Surprisingly, computer systems have roughly followed this law for about two decades.

card to be used for payment applications. The synthetic material PVC was used, which allowed for longer-lasting cards than previously conventional paper-based cards. In this system, the mere fact that you were issued a Diners Club card allowed you to pay with your "good name" rather than cash. In effect, the card identified you as a member of a select group, and was accepted by certain restaurants and hotels that recognized this group.

VISA and MasterCard then entered the market, but eventually the cost pressures of fraud, tampering, merchant handling, and bank charges made a machine-readable card necessary. The magnetic stripe was introduced, and this allowed further digitized data to be stored on the cards in a machine-readable format. This type of embossed card with a magnetic stripe is still the most commonly used method of payment. Magnetic stripe (mag-stripe) technology suffers from a critical weakness, however, in that anyone with access to the appropriate device can read, rewrite, or delete the data. Thus a mag-stripe card is unsuitable for storing sensitive data and, as such, requires an extensive online, centralized, back-end infrastructure for verification and processing.

As it turns out, this type of a back-end infrastructure became available in the United States but was not as readily available in European countries. As in any client/server architecture, one solution to a lack of back-end processing power is to beef up the back-end server side, but another solution is to make the client piece more powerful, thus relieving some of the duties of the back end. European countries seem to have preferred the client-side approach and made a huge improvement over mag-stripe technology by introducing the integrated circuit card (ICC).

In 1968, German inventors Jürgen Dethloff and Helmut Grötrupp applied for the first ICC-related patents. Similar applications followed in Japan in 1970 and France in 1974. In 1984, the French PTT (Postal and Telecommunications services) successfully carried out a field trial with telephone cards. By 1986, many millions of French telephone smartcards were in circulation. Their number reached nearly 60 million in 1990, and approximately 170 million in 1997.

As cryptography made great progress in the 1960s and security mechanisms could be proved mathematically, smartcards proved to be an ideal medium for safely storing cryptographic keys and algorithms. French banks were the first to field this type of card by introducing a chip-incorporating bank card in 1984. German banks began introducing them around 1997. Another application fielded in Germany included the issue of over 70 million smartcards that carried health insurance information.

Types of Cards

The International Organization for Standardization (ISO) standard 7810 "Identification Cards—Physical Characteristics" defines physical properties such as flexibility, temperature resistance, and dimensions for three different card formats: ID-1, ID-2, and ID-3. The smartcard standard, ISO 7816, is based on the ID-1 format. In order to give perspective, several different types of ID-1 cards are described in this section. One type in particular—namely cryptographic coprocessor cards—is becoming very important to current computer and network security systems.

Embossed Cards

Embossing allows for textual information or designs on the card to be transferred to paper by using a simple and inexpensive device. ISO 7811 specifies the embossed marks, covering their form, size, embossing height, and positioning. Transfer of information via embossing may seem primitive, but the simplicity of the system has made worldwide proliferation possible.

Magnetic Stripe Cards

The primary advantage that magnetic stripe technology offers over embossing is a reduction in the flood of paper documents. Parts 2, 4, and 5 of ISO 7811 specify the properties of the magnetic stripe, coding techniques, and positioning. The stripe's storage capacity is about 1000 bits and anyone with the appropriate read/write device can view or alter the data.

The following integrated circuit cards have conventionally come to be known as *smartcards*. These are the newest and most clever additions to the ID-1 family, and they also follow the details laid down in the ISO 7816 series. These types of cards allow far greater orders of magnitude in terms of data storage—cards with over 20 kbytes of memory are currently available. Also, and perhaps most important, the stored data can be protected against unauthorized access and tampering. Memory functions such as reading, writing, and erasing can be linked to specific conditions, controlled by both hardware and software. Another advantage of smartcards over magnetic stripe cards is that they are more reliable and have longer expected lifetimes.

Memory Cards

Though referred to as smartcards, memory cards are typically much less expensive and much less functional than microprocessor cards. They contain EEPROM and ROM memory, as well as some address and security logic. In the simplest designs, logic exists to prevent writing and erasing of the data. More complex designs allow for memory-read access to be restricted. Typical memory card applications are prepaid telephone cards and health insurance cards.

Microprocessor Cards

Components of this type of architecture include a CPU, RAM, ROM, and EEPROM. The operating system is typically stored in ROM, the CPU uses RAM as its working memory, and most of the data is stored in EEPROM. A rule of thumb for smartcard silicon is that RAM requires four times as much space as EEPROM, which in turn requires four times as much space as ROM. Properties of typical conventional smartcard architectures are detailed in Table 17-1.

TABLE 17-1

Conventional Smartcard Architectures

RAM	256 bytes to 1 kbyte
EEPROM	1 kbyte to 16 kbytes
ROM	6 kbytes to 24 kbytes
Microprocessor	8 bits at approximately 5 MHz
Interface Speed	9600 bps minimum, half-duplex

The serial I/O interface usually consists of a single register, through which the data is transferred in a half-duplex manner, bit by bit. Although the chip can be thought of as a tiny computer, the external terminal must supply the voltage, ground, and clock.

Cryptographic Coprocessor Cards

Although technically these are in the category of microprocessor cards, they are separated here because of differences in cost and functionality. Because the common asymmetric cryptographic algorithms of the day (such as RSA) require very large integer math calculations, an 8-bit microprocessor with very little RAM can take on the order of several minutes to perform a 1024-bit private key operation. However, if a cryptographic coprocessor is added to the architecture, the time required for this same operation is reduced to around a few hundred microseconds. The coprocessors include additional arithmetic units developed specifically for large integer math and fast exponentiation.

There is a drawback, however, and it is the cost. The addition of a cryptographic coprocessor can increase the cost of today's smartcards by 50 to 100 percent. These cost increases will likely diminish, as coprocessors become more widespread. In spite of the increased cost, the benefits to computer and network security of including the cryptographic coprocessor are great, for it allows for the private key never to leave the smartcard. As we see in the following sections, this becomes a critical factor for operations such as digital signatures, authentication, and non-repudiation. Eventually, though, the need for a cryptographic coprocessor and its associated cost will likely go away. The basic processors could become powerful enough to perform the math-intensive operations, or other algorithms, such as those based on elliptic curve technology, could become popular. Elliptic curve algorithms provide strong security without the need for large integer math, but haven't yet found their way into widespread use.

Contactless Smartcards

Although the reliability of smartcard contacts has improved to very acceptable levels over the years, contacts are one of the most frequent failure points of any electromechanical system due to dirt, wear, and so forth. The contactless card solves this problem and also provides the issuer an interesting range of new possibilities during use. Cards need no longer be inserted into a reader, which could improve end-user acceptance. No chip contacts are visible on the surface of the card so that card graphics can express more freedom. Still, despite these benefits, contactless cards have not yet seen wide acceptance. The cost is higher and not enough experience has been gained to make the technology reliable. Nevertheless, this elegant solution will likely have its day in the sun at some time in the future.

Optical Memory Cards

ISO/IEC standards 11693 and 11694 define standards for optical memory cards. These cards can carry many megabytes of data, but the cards can be written only once and never erased with today's technology. Though the read and write devices for optical cards are still very expensive, they may find use in applications such as health care, where large amounts of data must be stored.

Characteristic Features of Smartcards

This section addresses the low-level details of smartcards.

Physical and Electrical Properties

The physical size of a smartcard is designated as ID-1, described in ISO 7810. The dimensions are 85.6×54 mm, with a corner radius of 3.18 mm and a thickness of 0.76 mm. At the time ISO 7810 was created in 1985, it did not address chip placement but instead addressed embossing, magnetic stripes, and so forth. Smartcard chip placement is defined in ISO 7816-2, dated 1988. These physical characteristics are depicted in Figure 17-1.

Figure 17-1
Smartcard Physical Dimensions

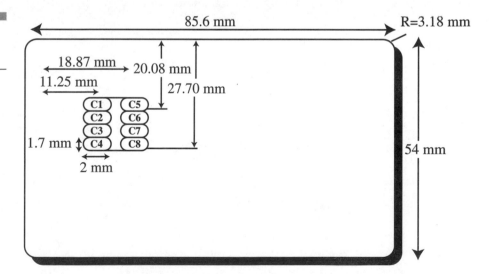

The minimum requirements as far as card robustness are specified in ISO 7810, 7813, and 7816 part 1. These specifications address such things as UV radiation, X-ray radiation, the card's surface profile, mechanical robustness of card and contacts, electromagnetic susceptibility, electromagnetic discharges, and temperature resistance. ISO/IEC 10373 specifies the test methods for many of these requirements.

The electrical specifications for smartcards are defined in ISO/IEC 7816 parts 2 and 3, and GSM 11.11. Most smartcards have eight contact fields on the front face; however, two of these are reserved for future use so some manufacturers produce cards with only six contact fields, which slightly reduces production costs. Electrical contacts are typically numbered C1 through C8 from top left to bottom right. Figure 17-2 shows the layout of these contacts for both the six-field and eight-field configurations. Table 17-2 describes their functions.

Figure 17-2
Smartcard Electrical
Contacts

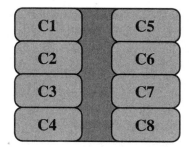 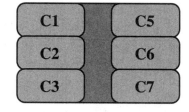

TABLE 17-2

Description of
Contacts

Position	Technical Abbreviation	Function
C1	Vcc	Supply voltage
C2	RST	Reset
C3	CLK	Clock frequency
C4	RFU	Reserved for future use
C5	GND	Ground
C6	Vpp	External programming voltage
C7	I/O	Serial input/output communications
C8	RFU	Reserved for future use

The Vpp contact was used several years ago to supply voltage to EEP-ROMs for programming and erasing. However, with the advent of charge pumps that exist on the chip, the Vpp contact is rarely used today. The Vcc supply voltage is specified at 5 volts ±10%. There is an industry push for smartcard standards to support 3-volt technology because all mobile phone components are available in a 3-volt configuration, and smartcards are the only remaining component requiring a mobile phone to have a charge converter. It is theoretically possible to develop 3-volt smartcards, but interoperability with current 5-volt systems would be a problem. Nonetheless, a wider voltage range handling 3 to 5 volts will probably become mandatory in the near future.

Operating System

Though typically only a few thousand bytes of program code, the operating system for the smartcard microprocessor must handle such tasks as:

- Data transmission over the bidirectional, serial terminal interface
- Loading, operating, and management of applications
- Execution control and instruction processing
- Protected access to data
- Memory management
- File management
- Management and execution of cryptographic algorithms

In contrast to personal computer operating systems such as Unix, DOS, and Windows, smartcard operating systems do not feature user interfaces or the ability to access external peripherals or storage media. The size is typically between 3 and 24 kbytes. The lower limit is that used by specialized applications and the upper limit by multiapplication operating systems.

Because smartcard memory space is so severely limited, not all standardized instructions and file structures can be generally implemented in all smartcard operating systems. For this reason, so-called profiles have been introduced in ISO 7816-4 and EN 726-3. A *profile* defines the minimum requirements for data structures and commands. For example, Profile O in ISO 7816-4 defines the minimums as shown in Table 17-3.

Cryptographic Capabilities

Current state-of-the art smartcards have sufficient cryptographic capabilities to support popular security applications and protocols. This section describes common capabilities found in the crypto-enabled smartcards from leading vendors.

RSA signatures and verifications are supported with a choice of 512-, 768-, or 1024-bit key lengths. The algorithms typically use the Chinese

TABLE 17-3

Profile O

Data Structures:	Transparent Linear fixed Linear variable Cyclic
Commands:	READ BINARY, UPDATE BINARY, no implicit selection and maximum length up to 256 bytes READ RECORD, UPDATE RECORD, without automatic selection APPEND RECORD SELECT FILE VERIFY INTERNAL AUTHENTICATE EXTERNAL AUTHENTICATE GET CHALLENGE

Remainder Theorem (CRT) in order to speed up the processing. Even at the 1024-bit key length, the time needed to perform a signature is typically under 1 second. Usually the EEPROM file that contains the private key is designed such that the sensitive key material never leaves the chip. Even the cardholder can't access the key material in this case. The usage of the private key is protected by the user's PIN, so that possession of the card does not imply the ability to sign with the card. RSA's PKCS#1 padding is implemented by some cards.

Although smartcards have the ability to generate RSA keypairs, this can be very slow. Typical times needed for a 1024-bit RSA keypair range from 8 seconds to 3 minutes. The larger times violate the ISO specifications for a communications time-out so that specialized hardware or software is sometimes necessary. Also, the quality of the keypairs may not be extremely high. The lack of computing power implies a relatively weak random number source as well as relatively weak algorithms for selecting large prime numbers.

The Digital Signature Algorithm (DSA) is less widely implemented than RSA. When it is implemented, it is typically found only at the 512-bit key length. Smartcards support the ability to configure multiple PINs that can have different purposes. Applications can configure one PIN to be a "Security Officer" PIN, which can unblock the user PIN, after a set number of bad PIN attempts, or reinitialize the card. Other PINs can be configured to control access to sensitive files or purse functions.

DES and triple DES are commonly found in the leading smartcards.

They usually have the option to be used in a message authentication code (MAC) function. However, because the serial interface of a smartcard has a low bandwidth, bulk symmetric encryption is very slow.

So that it is difficult to extract information about the chip operating and file systems, various methods of hardware security monitoring are enabled on leading smartcards. A one-time, irreversible fuse typically disables any test code built into the EEPROM. In order to avoid card cloning, an unalterable serial number is often burned into the memory. The cards are designed to reset themselves to a power-on state if they detect fluctuations in voltage, temperature, or clock frequency. Reading or writing of the ROM is usually disabled. Because every vendor has its own, usually proprietary, schemes for these measures, it's always good to inquire and/or request reports from independent testing laboratories.

Electronic purse functionalities are often present, but they are typically based on symmetric-key technologies such as DES and triple DES. Thus, a shared secret key enforces the security of many of these schemes. Hashing algorithms commonly found include SHA-1 and MD-5; but again the low bandwidth serial connection hinders effective use of bulk hashing on the card.

Random number generation (RNG) varies among card vendors. Some implement a pseudo RNG where each card has a unique seed. In this case, random numbers cycle through, dependent on the algorithm and the seed. Some cards have a true, hardware-based RNG using some physical aspect of the silicon. It's best to check with the vendor for details of the RNG if it will be used in a cryptographically sensitive context.

Communications protocols on smartcards at the command level many times will have a security protocol built in. These are typically based on symmetric-key technology and allow the smartcard itself to authenticate the read/write terminal or vice versa. However, the cryptograms and algorithms for these protocols are usually specific to a given application and terminal set.

Data Transmission

All communications to and from the smartcard are carried out over the C7 contact. Thus, only one party can communicate at a time, whether it is the card or the terminal—this is termed *half-duplex*. Communication is always initiated by the terminal, which implies a type of client/server relationship between card and terminal.

After a card is inserted into a terminal, it is powered up by the terminal, executes a power-on-reset, and sends an answer to reset (ATR) to the terminal. The ATR is parsed, various parameters are extracted, and the terminal then submits the initial instruction to the card. The card generates a reply and sends it back to the terminal. The client/server relationship continues in this manner until processing is completed and the card is removed from the terminal.

The physical transmission layer is defined in ISO/IEC 7816-3. It defines the voltage level specifics, which end up translating into the "0" and "1" bits.

Logically, there are several different protocols for exchanging information in the client/server relationship. They are designated "T = " plus a number, and are summarized in Table 17-4. The two protocols most commonly seen are T = 0 and T = 1, T = 0 being the most popular. A brief overview of the T = 0 protocol is given in Figure 17-3. The references contain more detailed information and descriptions of all the protocols.

TABLE 17-4

Protocols for Exchanging Information

Protocol	Description
T = 0	Asynchronous, half-duplex, byte-oriented, see ISO/IEC 7816-3
T = 1	Asynchronous, half-duplex, block-oriented, see ISO/IEC 7816-3, Adm.1
T = 2	Asynchronous, full-duplex, block-oriented, see ISO/IEC 10536-4
T = 3	Full-duplex, not yet covered
T = 4	Asynchronous, half-duplex, byte-oriented (expansion of T = 0)
T = 5 to T = 13	Reserved for future use
T = 14	For national functions, no ISO standard
T = 15	Reserved for future use

Figure 17-3

Typical T = 0 Instruction

In the T = 0 protocol, the terminal initiates communications by sending a 5-byte instruction header, which includes a class byte (CLA), an instruction byte (INS), and three parameter bytes (P1, P2, and P3). This is followed optionally by a data section. Most commands are either incoming or outgoing from the card's perspective and the P3 byte specifies the length of the data that will be incoming or outgoing. Error checking is handled exclusively by a parity bit appended to each transmitted byte. If the card correctly receives the 5 bytes, it will return a 1-byte acknowledgment equivalent to the received INS byte. If the terminal is sending more data (incoming command), it will send the number of bytes it specified in P3. Now the card has received the complete instruction and can process it and generate a response.

All commands have a 2-byte response code, SW1 and SW2, which reports success or an error condition. If a successful command must return additional bytes, the number of bytes is specified in the SW2 byte. In this case, the GET RESPONSE command is used, which is itself a 5-byte instruction conforming to the protocol. In the GET RESPONSE instruction, P3 will be equal to the number of bytes specified in the previous SW2 byte. GET RESPONSE is an outgoing command from the card's point of view. The terminal and card communicate in this manner, using incoming or outgoing commands, until processing is complete.

Instruction Sets

There are four international standards that define typical smartcard instruction sets. More than 50 instructions and their corresponding execution parameters are defined. Although found in four separate standards, the instructions are largely compatible. The specifications are GSM 11.11 (prETS 300608), EN 726-3, ISO/IEC 7816-4, and the preliminary CEN standard prEN 1546. Instructions can be classified by function as shown in Table 17-5. Typically, a smartcard will implement only a subset of the possible instructions, specific to its application. This is due to memory or cost limitations.

Smartcard Readers (Terminals)

Although commonly referred to as *smartcard readers,* by definition, all smartcard-enabled terminals have the ability to read and write as long as the smartcard supports it and the proper access conditions have been fulfilled. In contrast to smartcards, which all have very similar construction, smartcard readers come in a variety of form factors with varying levels of mechanical and logical sophistication. Some examples include: reader integrated into a vending machine, handheld battery-operated reader with a small LCD screen, reader integrated into a GSM mobile

TABLE 17-5

Sample Instruction Types

File selection

File reading and writing

File searching

File operations

Identification

Authentication

Cryptographic functions

File management

Instructions for electronic purses or credit cards

Operating system completion

Hardware testing

Special instructions for specific applications

Transmission protocol support

phone, and a reader attached to a personal computer. Mechanically, readers have various options including: whether the user must insert/remove the card versus automated insertion/ejection mechanism; sliding contacts versus landing contacts; and provisions for displays and keystroke entry. Electrically, the reader must conform to the ISO/IEC 7816-3 standard.

The options for readers are numerous. This section focuses on readers attached to personal computer systems, because those have the largest impact on computer and network security. Many reader types are available off the shelf in today's market, and each has its pros and cons, some of which are listed in Table 17-6.

Computer Security-Related Standards

Many of the standards mentioned thus far focus on the details of the smartcard, read/write terminal, and low-level software layers. Another important class of standards focuses on how smartcards are integrated into applications that provide computer and network security. This sec-

TABLE 17-6

Pros and Cons for
Various Readers

Physical Connection	Pros	Cons
Serial Port	Very common; robust, inexpensive. Cross-platform support for Windows, Mac, and Unix.	Many desktop computers have no free serial ports. Requires external power tap or battery.
PCMCIA	Excellent for users traveling with laptop computers.	Can be slightly more expensive. Many desktop systems don't have PCMCIA slots.
PS/2 Keyboard Port	Easy to install with a wedge adapter. Supports protected PIN path.	Slower communication speeds.
Floppy	Very easy to install.	Requires a battery. Communications speed can be an issue.
USB	Very high data transfer speeds.	Not yet widely available. Shared bus could pose a security issue.
Built-in	No need for hardware or software installation.	Not yet widely available.

tion discusses the principles of these standards, prominent standards, and the players that define and utilize them.

Principles of Smartcard Security Standards

Any standard designed to facilitate the integration of smartcards into computer security systems should follow certain principles in order to be useful and gain acceptance. A few examples of these principles are found in Table 17-7.

Prominent Smartcard Specifications and Standards

The following are emerging as important standards with respect to the integration of smartcards into computer and network security applications.

TABLE 17-7

Principles of Security Standards

Multiplatform

Standard should be applicable to numerous modern-day operating systems and computer architectures such as Windows, Unix, Mac, x86, Sparc, and so forth.

Open Participation

Standard should accept input and peer review from members of industry, academia, and government.

Interoperability

Standard should be interoperable with other leading standards and protocols.

Real, Functional

Standard should apply to real-world problems and markets and adequately address their requirements.

Experience, Products

Standard should be created by a group of people with experience in security-related products and standards.

Extensibility

Standard should facilitate expansion to new applications, protocols, and smartcard capabilities that weren't yet around when the standard was created.

PKCS#11: Cryptographic Token Interface Standard

This standard specifies an Application Programming Interface (API), called *Cryptoki* (pronounced crypto-key and short for *cryptographic token interface*) to devices that hold cryptographic information and perform cryptographic functions. Cryptoki follows a simple object-based approach, addressing the goals of technology independence (any kind of device) and resource sharing (multiple applications accessing multiple devices). PKCS#11 presents to applications a common, logical view of the device called a cryptographic token. The standard was created in 1994 by RSA with input from industry, academia, and government.

PC/SC

The PC/SC Workgroup was formed in May 1997. It was created to address critical technical issues related to the integration of smartcards with the PC. PC/SC Workgroup members include Bull Personal Transaction Systems, Gemplus, Hewlett-Packard, IBM, Microsoft, Schlumberger, Siemens-Nixdorf, Sun Microsystems, Toshiba, and VeriFone. The specification addresses limitations in existing standards that complicate integration of ICC devices with the PC and fail to adequately address interoperability, from a PC application perspective, between products from multiple vendors. It provides standardized interfaces to interface devices (IFDs) and the specification of common PC programming interfaces and control mechanisms. Version 1.0 was released in December of 1997.

OpenCard

OpenCard is a standard framework announced by IBM, Netscape, NCI, and Sun Microsystems that provides for interoperable smartcard solutions across many hardware and software platforms. The OpenCard Framework is an open standard providing architecture and a set of APIs that enable application developers and service providers to build and deploy smartcard-aware solutions in any OpenCard-compliant environment. It was first announced in March 1997.

JavaCard

The JavaCard API is a specification that enables the Write Once, Run Anywhere ™ capabilities of Java on smartcards and other devices with limited memory. The JavaCard API was developed in conjunction with leading members of the smartcard industry and has been adopted by over 95 percent of the manufacturers in that industry, including Bull/CP8, Dallas Semiconductor, De La Rue, Geisecke & Devrient, Gemplus, Inside Technologies, Motorola, Oberthur, Schlumberger, and Toshiba.

Common Data Security Architecture

Developed by Intel, the Common Data Security Architecture (CDSA) provides an open, interoperable, extensible, and cross-platform software framework that makes computer platforms more secure for all applications including electronic commerce, communications, and digital content. The CDSA 2.0 specifications were adopted by The Open Group in December 1997.

Microsoft Cryptographic API

The Microsoft Cryptographic API (CryptoAPI) provides services that enable application developers to add cryptography and certificate management functionality to their Win32 applications. Applications can use the functions in CryptoAPI without knowing anything about the underlying implementation, in much the same way that an application can use a graphics library without knowing anything about the particular graphics hardware configuration.

Importance of Smartcards as a Design Mechanism for Computer Networks

This section highlights the fundamental security challenges that face us in this increasingly computer network-oriented world, and how smartcards can provide key advantages toward security.

Fundamental Security Challenges

Because computers and networks are becoming so central to our lives in this digital age, many new security challenges are arising. This is the era of full connectivity, both electronically and physically. Not only can smartcards facilitate this connectivity and other value-added capabilities, they can provide the necessary security assurances not available through other means.

On the Internet, smartcards increase the security of the building blocks of authentication, authorization, privacy, integrity, and nonrepudiation. Primarily, this is because the private signing key never leaves the smartcard so it's very difficult to gain knowledge of the private key through a compromise of the host computer system.

In a corporate enterprise system, multiple disjointed systems often have their security based on different technologies. Smartcards can bring these together by storing multiple certificates and passwords on the same card. Secure email and intranet access, dial-up network access, encrypted files, digitally signed Web forms, and building access are all improved by the smartcard.

In an extranet situation, where one company would like to administer security to business partners and suppliers, smartcards can be distributed that allow access to certain corporate resources. The smartcard's importance in this situation is evident because of the need for the strongest security possible when permitting anyone through the corporate firewall and proxy defenses. When distributing credentials by smartcard, a company can have a higher assurance that those credentials cannot be shared, copied, or otherwise compromised.

The Smartcard Security Advantage

Some reasons why smartcards can enhance the security of modern-day systems are:

- *PKI is better than passwords — smartcards enhance PKI:*   Public Key Infrastructure systems are more secure than password-based systems because there is no shared knowledge of the secret. The private key need only be known in one place, rather than two or more. If the one place is on a smartcard, and the private key never leaves the smartcard, the crucial secret for the system is never in a situation where it is easily compromised. A smartcard allows for the private key to be usable and yet never appear on a network or in the host computer system.

- *Smartcards increase the security of password-based systems:* Though smartcards have obvious advantages for PKI systems, they can also increase the security of password-based systems. One of the biggest problems in typical password systems is that users write down their password and attach it to their monitor or keyboard. They also tend to choose weak passwords and share their passwords with other people. If a smartcard is used to store a user's multiple passwords, they need only remember the PIN to the smartcard in order to access all of the passwords. Additionally, if a security officer initializes the smartcard, very strong passwords can be chosen and stored on the smartcard. The end user need never even know the passwords, so that they can't be written down or shared with others.

■ *Two-factor authentication, and more:*   Security systems benefit from multiple-factor authentication. Commonly used factors are: something you know, something you have, something you are, and something you do. Password-based systems typically use only the first factor, something you know; smartcards add an additional factor, something you have. Two-factor authentication has proven to be much more effective than single because the "something you know" factor is so easily compromised or shared. Smartcards can also be enhanced to include the remaining two features. Prototype designs are available that accept a thumbprint on the surface of the card in addition to the PIN in order to unlock the services of the card. Alternatively, a thumbprint template, retina template, or other biometric information can be stored on the card, only to be checked against data obtained from a separate biometric input device. Similarly, "something you do" such as typing patterns, handwritten signature characteristics, or voice inflection templates can be stored on the card and be matched against data accepted from external input devices.

■ *Portability of keys and certificates:*   Public-key certificates and private keys can be utilized by Web browsers and other popular software packages but they in some sense identify the workstation rather than the user. The key and certificate data are stored in a proprietary browser storage area and must be export/imported in order to be moved from one workstation to another. With smartcards the certificate and private key are portable, and can be used on multiple workstations, whether they are at work, at home, or on the road. If the lower-level software layers support it, they can be used by different software programs from different vendors, on different platforms, such as Windows, Unix, and Mac.

■ *Autodisabling PINs versus dictionary attacks:*   If a private key is stored in a browser storage file on a hard drive, it is typically protected by a password. This file can be "dictionary attacked" where commonly used passwords are attempted in a brute-force manner until knowledge of the private key is obtained. On the other hand, a smartcard will typically lock itself up after some low number of consecutive bad PIN attempts, for example 10. Thus, the dictionary attack is no longer a feasible way to access the private key if it has been securely stored on a smartcard.

■ *Nonrepudiation:*   The ability to deny, after the fact, that your private key performed a digital signature is called *repudiation.* If, however, your private signing key exists only on a single smartcard and only you know the PIN to that smartcard, it is very difficult for others to impersonate your digital signature by using your private key. Many digital signature systems require *hardware-strength nonrepudiation,* meaning that the private key is always protected within the security perimeter of a hardware token and can't be used without the knowledge of the proper PIN. Smartcards can provide hardware-strength nonrepudiation.

■ *Counting the number of private key usages:*   So many of the important things in our lives are authorized by our handwritten signature. Smartcard-based digital signatures provide benefits over handwritten signatures because they are much more difficult to forge and they can enforce the integrity of the document through technologies such as hashing. Also, because the signature is based in a device that is actually a computer, many new benefits can be conceived. For example, a smartcard could count the number of times that your private key was used, thus giving you an accurate measure of how many times you utilized your digital signature over a given period of time.

Legalities

As with any technology, there are legal issues to keep in mind when dealing with smartcards. Commonly, a smartcard has the ability to perform certain licensed algorithms, such as the RSA asymmetric cipher. Usually any license fees associated with the algorithm are bundled into the cost of the smartcard. If a smartcard can perform restricted technologies such as encryption at large key lengths, it is classified as a *munition* by certain U.S. commerce laws. As such, it can be considered illegal to export or import such an item in certain regions.

New digital signature laws are being written by many states that make it the end user's responsibility to protect his/her private key. If the private key can never leave an automatically PIN-disabling smartcard, then the end user can find it easier to meet these responsibilities. Certificate authorities can help in this area by supporting certificate extensions that specify the private key was generated in a secure environment and has never left the confines of a smartcard. With this mechanism, higher levels of nonrepudiation can be achieved when verifying a smartcard-based signature while using a certificate containing such an extension. In other words, a digital signature carries more weight if its associated certificate validates that the private key resides on a smartcard and can never be extracted.

Smartcard-Enabled Products

This section lists popular security products and explains how smartcards can be used to enhance their security.

Web Browsers (SSL, TLS)

Web browsers use technology such as Secure Sockets Layer (SSL) and Transport Layer Security (TLS) to provide security while browsing the World Wide Web. These technologies can authenticate the client and/or server to each other and also provide an encrypted channel for any message traffic or file transfer. The authentication is enhanced because the private key is stored securely on the smartcard. The encrypted channel typically uses a symmetric cipher where the encryption is performed in the host computer because of the low data transfer speeds to and from the smartcard. Nonetheless, the randomly generated session key that is used for symmetric encryption is wrapped with the partner's public key, meaning that it can be unwrapped only on the smartcard. Thus it is very difficult for an eavesdropper to gain knowledge of the session key and message traffic.

Secure Email (S/MIME, OpenPGP)

S/MIME and OpenPGP allow for email to be encrypted and/or digitally signed. As with SSL, smartcards enhance the security of these operations by protecting the secrecy of the private key and also unwrapping session keys within a security perimeter.

Form Signing

Web-based HTML forms can be digitally signed by your private key. This could prove to be a very important technology for Internet-based business because it allows for digital documents to be hosted by Web servers and accessed by Web browsers in a paperless fashion. Online expense reports, W-4 forms, purchase requests, and group insurance forms are some examples. For form signing, smartcards provide portability of the private key and certificate as well as hardware strength nonrepudiation.

Object Signing

If an organization writes code that can be downloaded over the Web and then executed on client computers, it is best to sign that code so the clients can be sure it indeed came from a reputable source. Smartcards can be used by the signing organization so the private key can't be compromised by a rogue organization in order to impersonate the valid one.

Kiosk/Portable Preferences

Certain applications operate best in a "kiosk mode," where one computer is shared by a number of users but becomes configured to their preferences when they insert their smartcard. The station can then be used for secure email, Web browsing, and so forth, and the private key would never leave the smartcard into the environment of the kiosk computer. The kiosk can even be configured to accept no mouse or keyboard input until an authorized user inserts the proper smartcard and supplies the proper PIN.

File Encryption

Even though the 9600-baud serial interface of the smartcard usually prevents it from being a convenient mechanism for bulk file encryption, it can enhance the security of this function. If a different, random session key is used for each file to be encrypted, the bulk encryption can be performed in the host computer system at fast speeds and the session key can then be wrapped by the smartcard. Then, the only way to easily decrypt the file is by possessing the proper smartcard and submitting the proper PIN so that the session key can be unwrapped.

Workstation Logon

Logon credentials can be securely stored on a smartcard. The normal login mechanism of the workstation, which usually prompts for a username and password, can be replaced with one that communicates to the smartcard.

Dial-up Access (RAS, PPTP, RADIUS, TACACS)

Many of the common remote access dial-up protocols use passwords as their security mechanism. As previously discussed, smartcards enhance the security of passwords. Also, as many of these protocols evolve to support public-key-based systems, smartcards can be used to increase the security and portability of the private key and certificate.

Payment Protocols (SET)

The Secure Electronic Transactions (SET) protocol allows for credit card data to be transferred securely between customer, merchant, and issuer. Because SET relies on public-key technology, smartcards are a good choice for storage of the certificate and private key.

Digital Cash

Smartcards can implement protocols whereby digital cash can be carried around on a smartcard. In these systems, the underlying keys that secure the architecture never leave the security perimeter of hardware devices. Mondex, VisaCash, EMV (Europay-MasterCard-Visa), and Proton are examples of digital cash protocols designed for use with smartcards.

Building Access

Even though the insertion, processing time, and removal of a standard smartcard could be a hassle when entering a building, magnetic stripe or proximity chip technology can be added to smartcards so that a single token provides computer security and physical access.

Problems with Smartcards

Even though smartcards provide many obvious benefits to computer security, they still haven't caught on with great popularity in countries like the United States. This is not only because of the prevalence, infrastructure, and acceptability of magnetic stripe cards, but also because of a few problems associated with smartcards. Lack of a standard infrastructure for smartcard reader/writers is often cited as a complaint. Until very recently, the major computer manufacturers haven't given much thought to offering a smartcard reader as a standard component. Many companies don't want to absorb the cost of outfitting computers with smartcard readers until the economies of scale drive down their cost. In the meantime, many vendors provide bundled solutions to outfit any personal computer with smartcard capabilities.

Lack of widely adopted smartcard standards is often cited as a complaint. The number of smartcard-related standards are high and many of them address only a certain vertical market or only a certain layer of communications. This problem is lessening recently as Web browsers and other mainstream applications are including smartcards as an option. Applications like these are helping to speed up the evolution of standards.

Attacking Smartcards

Attacks on smartcards generally fall into four categories:

1. *Logical attacks:*   Logical attacks occur when a smartcard is operating under normal physical conditions, but sensitive information is gained by examining the bytes going to and from the smartcard.

One example is the so-called timing attack described by Paul Kocher.* In this attack, various byte patterns are sent to the card to be signed by the private key. Information such as the time required to perform the operation and the number of 0s and 1s in the input bytes are used to eventually obtain the private key. There are logical countermeasures to this attack but not all smartcard manufacturers have implemented them. This attack does require that the PIN to the card be known, so that many private-key operations can be performed on chosen input bytes.

2. *Physical attacks:* Physical attacks occur when normal physical conditions, such as temperature, clock frequency, voltage, and so forth, are altered in order to gain access to sensitive information on the smartcard. Most smartcard operating systems write sensitive data to the EEPROM area in a proprietary, encrypted manner so that it is difficult to obtain clear-text keys by directly hacking into the EEPROM. Other physical attacks that have proven to be successful involve an intense physical fluctuation at the precise time and location where the PIN verification takes place. Thus, sensitive card functions can be performed even though the PIN is unknown. This type of attack can be combined with the logical attack mentioned earlier in order to gain knowledge of the private key. Most physical attacks require special equipment.

3. *Trojan horse attacks:* This attack involves a rogue, Trojan horse application that has been planted on an unsuspecting user's workstation. The Trojan horse waits until the user submits a valid PIN from a trusted application, thus enabling usage of the private key, and then asks the smartcard to digitally sign some rogue data. The operation completes but users never know that their private key was just used against their will. The countermeasure to prevent this attack is to use "single-access device driver" architecture. With this type of architecture, the operating system enforces that only one application can have access to the serial device (and thus the smartcard) at any given time. This prevents the attack but also lessens the convenience of the smartcard because multiple applications cannot use the services of the card at the same time. Another way to prevent the attack is by using a smartcard that enforces a "one private key usage per PIN entry" policy model. In this model, users

*http://www.cryptography.com/timingattack/paper.html

must enter their PIN every single time the private key is to be used and therefore the Trojan horse would not have access to the key.

4. *Social engineering attacks:* In computer security systems, this type of attack is usually the most successful, especially when the security technology is properly implemented and configured. Usually, these attacks rely on the faults in human beings. An example of a social engineering attack has a hacker impersonating a network service technician. The service technician approaches a low-level employee and requests his/her password for network servicing purposes. With smartcards, this type of attack is a bit more difficult. Most people would not trust an impersonator wishing to have their smartcard and PIN for service purposes.

Any security system, including smartcards, is breakable. However, there is usually an estimate for the cost required to break the system, which should be much greater than the value of the data being protected by the system. Independent security labs test for common security attacks on leading smartcards, and can usually provide an estimate of the cost in equipment and expertise of breaking the smartcard. When choosing a smartcard for an architecture, one can ask the manufacturer for references to independent labs that have done security testing. Using this information, designers can strive to ensure that the cost of breaking the system would be much greater than the value of any information obtained.

WRAP-UP

We have focused on the state of the art for smartcards and their use in computer and network security systems. Smartcards have proven to be useful for transaction, authorization, and identification media. As their capabilities grow, they could become the ultimate thin client, eventually replacing all of the things we carry around in our wallets, including credit cards, licenses, cash, and even family photographs. By containing various identification certificates, smartcards could be used to voluntarily identify attributes of ourselves no matter where we are or to which computer network we are attached. Current state-of-the-art smartcards have sufficient cryptographic capabilities to support popular security applications and protocols.

CHAPTER 18

IP Security and Secure Virtual Private Networks

In today's distributed computing environment, the virtual private network (VPN) offers an attractive solution to network managers. At each corporate site, workstations, servers, and databases are linked by one or more local area networks (LANs). The LANs are under the control of the network manager and can be configured and tuned for cost-effective performance. The Internet or some other public network can be used to interconnect sites. This would provide a cost saving over the use of a private network and the public network provider would then be responsible for wide-area network management. That same public network provides an access path for telecommuters and other mobile employees to log on to corporate systems from remote sites.

But the manager faces a fundamental requirement: security. Use of a public network exposes corporate traffic to eavesdropping and provides an entry point for unauthorized users. To counter this problem, the manager may choose from a variety of encryption and authentication packages and products. Proprietary solutions raise a number of problems. First, how secure is the solution? If proprietary encryption or authentication schemes are used, there may be little reassurance in the technical literature as to the level of security provided. Second is the question of compatibility. No manager wants to be limited in the choice of workstations, servers, routers, firewalls, and so on, by a need for compatibility with the security facility—enter the Internet Protocol Security (IPSec) set of Internet standards.

The Need for IPSec Standards

In 1994, the Internet Architecture Board (IAB) issued a report on "Security in the Internet Architecture" (RFC 1636). The report stated the general consensus that the Internet needs more and better security, and identified key areas for security mechanisms. Among these were the need to secure the network infrastructure from unauthorized monitoring and control of network traffic and the need to secure end-user-to-end-user traffic using authentication and encryption mechanisms. These concerns are fully justified. As confirmation, the 1996 annual report from the Computer Emergency Response Team (CERT) listed over 2500 reported security incidents affecting nearly 11,000 sites. The most serious types of attacks included IP spoofing, in which intruders created packets with false IP addresses and exploited applications that use authentication based on IP, as well as various forms of eavesdropping and packet sniffing, in which attackers read transmitted information, including logon information and database contents.

In response to these issues, the IAB included authentication and encryption as necessary security features in the next-generation IP, which has been issued as IPv6. Fortunately, these security capabilities were designed to be usable both with the current IPv4 and the future IPv6. This means that vendors can begin offering these features now and many vendors do now have some IPSec capability in their products. Capability does not always translate to interoperability with other products. Only six manufacturers of such equipment are interoperable in a general sense. The IPSec specification was initially issued in 1995 as a set of Proposed Internet Standards. A revision of this specification now exists as a set of Internet Drafts and should move onto the Internet standards track in the latter part of 1998.

Applications of IPSec

IPSec provides the capability to secure communications across a LAN, across private and public WANs, and across the Internet. Examples of its use include:

- *Secure branch office connectivity over the Internet:* A company can build a secure virtual private network over the Internet or over a public WAN. This enables a business to rely heavily on the Internet and reduce its need for private networks, saving costs and network management overhead.

- *Secure remote access over the Internet:* An end user whose system is equipped with IP security protocols can make a local call to an Internet Service Provider (ISP) and gain secure access to a company network. This reduces the cost of toll charges for traveling employees and telecommuters.

- *Establishing extranet and intranet connectivity with partners:* IPSec can be used to secure communication with other organizations, ensuring authentication and confidentiality and providing a key-exchange mechanism.

- *Enhancing electronic commerce security:* Even though some Web and electronic commerce applications have built-in security protocols, the use of IPSec enhances that security. IPSec guarantees that all traffic designated by the network administrator is both encrypted and authenticated, adding an additional layer of security to whatever is provided at the application level.

The principal feature of IPSec that enables it to support these varied applications is that it can encrypt and/or authenticate all traffic at the IP level. Thus, all distributed applications, including remote logon, client/server, email, file transfer, Web access, and so on, can be secured.

Figure 18-1 is a typical scenario of IPSec usage. An organization maintains LANs at dispersed locations. Nonsecure IP traffic is conducted on each LAN. For traffic off-site, through some sort of private or public WAN, IPSec protocols are used. These protocols operate in networking devices, such as a router or firewall that connects each LAN to the outside world. The IPSec networking device will typically encrypt and compress all traffic going into the WAN, and decrypt and decompress traffic coming from the WAN; these operations are transparent to workstations and servers on the LAN. Secure transmission is also possible with individual users who dial into the WAN. Such user workstations must implement the IPSec protocols to provide security.

Figure 18-1
A VPN Scenario

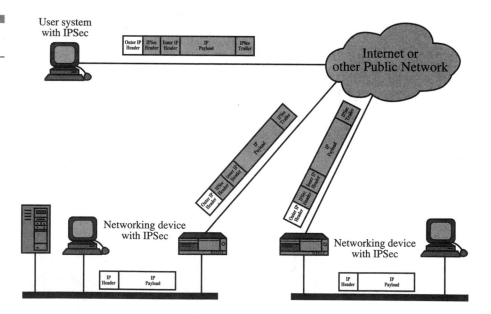

Benefits of IPSec

Some of the major benefits of IPSec:

- When IPSec is implemented in a firewall or router it provides strong security that can be applied to all traffic crossing the perimeter. Traffic within a company or workgroup does not incur the overhead of security-related processing.

■ IPSec is below the transport layer (TCP, UDP), so it is transparent to applications. There is no need to change software on a user or server system when IPSec is implemented in the firewall or router. Even if IPSec is implemented in end systems, upper layer software, including applications, is not affected.

■ IPSec is usually transparent to end users. There is no need to train users on security mechanisms, issue keying material on a per-user basis, or revoke keying material when users leave the organization.

■ IPSec can provide security for individual users if needed. This implementation would be of particular usefulness for off-site employees and for setting up a secure virtual subnetwork within an organization for any sensitive applications.

Is IPSec the Right Choice?

IPSec is on its way to being an Internet standard. There are already a number of products that implement part or all of IPSec that may not necessarily be the security solution of choice for a network administrator. Christian Huitema, who at the time was the head of the Internet Architecture Board (IAB), reported that the debates over how to provide Internet-based security were among the most heated that he ever observed. One issue has to do with whether security is being provided at the right protocol layer. To provide security at the IP level, it is necessary for IPSec to be a part of the network code deployed on all participating platforms, including Windows NT, Unix, and Macintosh systems. Unless a desired feature is available on all of the deployed platforms, a given application may not be able to use that feature. On the other hand, if the application such as a Web browser/server combination incorporates the function, the developer can guarantee that the features are available on all platforms for which the application is available. A related point is that many Internet applications are now being released with embedded security features. For example, Netscape and Internet Explorer support Secure Sockets Layer (SSL), which protects Web traffic. Also, a number of vendors are planning to support Secure Electronic Transaction (SET), which protects credit-card transactions over the Internet. However, for a virtual private network, a network-level facility is needed—and this is what IPSec provides.

IPSec Functions

IPSec provides three main facilities: an authentication-only function referred to as Authentication Header (AH), a combined authentication/ encryption function called Encapsulating Security Payload (ESP), and a key exchange function. For VPNs, both authentication and encryption are generally desired, because it is important both to (1) ensure that unauthorized users do not penetrate the virtual private network and (2) ensure that eavesdroppers on the Internet cannot read messages sent over the virtual private network. Because both features are generally desirable, most implementations are likely to use ESP rather than AH. The key exchange function allows for manual exchange of keys as well as an automated scheme.

The current IPSec specification requires that IPSec support the Data Encryption Standard (DES) for encryption but a variety of other encryption algorithms may also be used. Because of concern about the strength of DES, it is likely that other algorithms, such as triple DES, will be widely used, possibly as early as this year and certainly by some time in 1999. For authentication, a relatively new scheme, known as *HMAC* (H stands for embedded Hash Algorithm and MAC stands for Message Authentication Code), is required.

Transport and Tunnel Modes

ESP supports two modes of use: transport and tunnel mode. *Transport mode* provides protection primarily for upper-layer protocols; that is, transport mode protection extends to the payload of an IP packet. Typically, transport mode is used for end-to-end communication between two hosts (e.g., a client and a server, or two workstations). ESP in transport mode encrypts and optionally authenticates the IP payload but not the IP header (Figure 18-2).

This configuration is useful for relatively small networks in which each host and server is equipped with IPSec; however, for a full-blown VPN, *tunnel mode* is not only far more efficient, but also provides protection to the entire IP packet. To achieve this, after the ESP fields are added to the IP packet, the entire packet plus security fields is treated as the payload of a new "outer" IP packet with a new outer IP header. The entire original or inner packet travels through a "tunnel" from one point of an IP network to another; no routers along the way are able to

Figure 18-2
Scope of ESP Encryption and Authentication

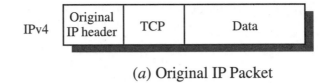

(*a*) Original IP Packet

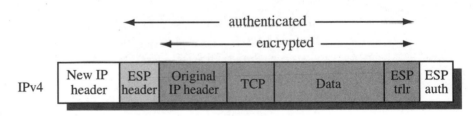

(*b*) Transport Mode

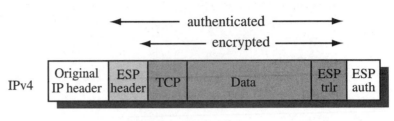

(*c*) Tunnel Mode

examine the inner IP header. Because the original packet is encapsulated, the new, larger packet may have totally different sources and destination addresses, adding to the security. Tunnel mode is used when one (or both) end(s) is a security gateway, such as a firewall or router that implements IPSec. With tunnel mode, a number of hosts on networks behind firewalls may engage in secure communications without implementing IPSec. The unprotected packets generated by such hosts are tunneled through external networks by tunnel-mode SAs (security associations) set up by the IPSec software in the firewall or secure router at the boundary of the local network.

Here is an example of how tunnel-mode IPSec operates. Host A on a network generates an IP packet with the destination address of host B on another network. This packet is routed from the originating host to a firewall or secure router at the boundary of A's network. The firewall filters all outgoing packets to determine the need for IPSec processing. If this packet from A to B requires IPSec, the firewall performs IPSec processing and encapsulates the packet in an outer IP header. The source IP address of this outer IP packet is this firewall and the destination address may be a firewall that forms the boundary to B's local network. This packet is now routed to B's firewall with intermediate routers examining only the outer IP header. At B's firewall, the outer IP header is stripped off and the inner packet is delivered to B.

ESP in tunnel mode encrypts and optionally authenticates the entire inner IP packet, including the inner IP header.

Key Management

The key management portion of IPSec involves the determination and distribution of secret keys. The IPSec Architecture document mandates support for two types of key management:

- *Manual:*   A system administrator manually configures each system with its own keys and with the keys of other communicating systems. This is practical for small, relatively static environments.

- *Automated:*   An automated system enables the on-demand creation of keys for SAs and facilitates the use of keys in a large distributed system with an evolving configuration. An automated system is more flexible but requires more effort to configure and requires more software. So, smaller installations are likely to opt for manual key management.

The default automated key management protocol for IPSec is referred to as *ISAKMP/Oakley,* consisting of the following elements:

- *Oakley Key Determination Protocol:*   Oakley is a key-exchange protocol based on the Diffie-Hellman algorithm but providing added security. In particular, Diffie-Hellman alone does not authenticate the two users that are exchanging keys, making the protocol vulnerable to impersonation. Oakley includes mechanisms to authenticate users.

- *Internet Security Association and Key Management Protocol (ISAKMP):*   ISAKMP provides a framework for Internet key management and provides the specific protocol support, including formats for negotiation of security attributes.

ISAKMP by itself does not dictate a specific key-exchange algorithm; rather, ISAKMP consists of a set of message types that enable the use of a variety of key exchange algorithms. Oakley is the specific key exchange algorithm mandated for use with the initial version of ISAKMP.

Security Associations

A central concept that appears for IPSec is the *security association* (SA), which is a one-way relationship between a sender and a receiver. If a peer relationship is needed for two-way secure exchange, then two security associations are required.

An Internet destination address and a *security parameter index* (SPI) uniquely identify a security association. Hence, in any IP datagram, the Destination Address in the IP header and the SPI in the enclosed ESP header uniquely identify the security association. The SA defines the parameters for IP exchange, including the encryption and authentication algorithms, the encryption and authentication keys, and filters that determine which IP traffic will be subject to IPSec processing. Thus, the SA gives the VPN manager great flexibility in how the VPN is configured.

Authentication

In this section and the next, we look into more detail of the two security mechanisms provided by IPSec: authentication and privacy.

The Authentication Header (AH) provides support for data integrity and authentication of IP packets. The data integrity feature ensures that undetected modification to a packet's content in transit is not possible. The authentication feature enables an end system or network device to authenticate the user or application and filter traffic accordingly; it also prevents the address spoofing attacks observed in today's Internet. Authentication is based on the use of a message authentication code, known as HMAC, which requires that the two parties share a secret key. The AH also guards against the replay attack described in the following section.

The Authentication Header consists of the following fields (Figure 18-3):

■ *Next Header (8 bits):* Identifies the type of header immediately following this header.

Figure 18-3
IPSec Authentication
Header

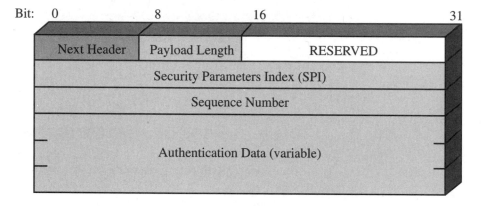

- *Payload Length (8 bits):*   Length of Authentication Header in 32-bit words, minus 2. For example, the default length of the authentication data field is 96 bits, or three 32-bit words. With a three-word fixed header, there are a total of six words in the authentication header, and the Payload Length field has a value of 4.
- *Reserved (16 bits):*   For future use.
- *Security Parameters Index (32 bits):*   Identifies a security association.
- *Sequence Number (32 bits):*   A monotonically increasing counter value, used in replay protection.
- *Authentication Data (variable):*   A variable-length field (must be an integral number of 32-bit words) that contains the MAC for this packet.

Anti-Replay Service

A *replay attack* is one in which an attacker obtains a copy of an authenticated packet and later transmits it to the intended destination. The receipt of duplicate, authenticated IP packets may disrupt service in some way or may have some other undesired consequence. The Sequence Number field is designed to thwart such attacks.

When a new SA is established, the sender initializes a sequence number counter to 0. Each time that a packet is sent on this SA, the sender increments the counter and places the value in the Sequence Number field. Thus the first value to be used is 1. If anti-replay is enabled (the default), the sender must not allow the sequence number to cycle past $2^{32}-1$ back to zero. Otherwise, there would be multiple valid packets with the same sequence number. If the limit of 232−1 is reached, the sender should terminate this SA and negotiate a new SA with a new key.

Because IP is a connectionless, unreliable service, the protocol does not guarantee that packets will be delivered in order and does not guarantee that all packets will be delivered. Therefore, the IPSec authentication document dictates that the receiver should implement a window of size W, with a default of $W = 64$. The right edge of the window represents the highest sequence number N received so far for a valid packet. For any packet with a sequence number in the range from $N-W+1$ to N that has been correctly received (i.e., properly authenticated), the corresponding slot in the window is marked.

Inbound processing proceeds as follows when a packet is received:

1. If the received packet falls within the window and is new, the MAC is checked. If the packet is authenticated, the corresponding slot in the window is marked.

2. If the received packet is to the right of the window and is new, the MAC is checked. If the packet is authenticated, the window is advanced so that this sequence number is the right edge of the window, and the corresponding slot in the window is marked.

3. If the received packet is to the left of the window or if authentication fails, the packet is discarded; this is an easily audited event.

Message Authentication Code

The *message authentication algorithm* is used to calculate a message authentication code known as a MAC, using an algorithm known as HMAC, which takes as input a portion of the message and a secret key and produces a MAC as output. This MAC value is stored in the Authentication Data field of the AH header. The calculation takes place over the entire enclosed TPC segment plus the authentication header. When this IP packet is received at the destination, the same calculation is performed using the same key. If the calculated MAC equals the value of the received MAC, then the packet is assumed to be authentic.

Privacy and Authentication

The Encapsulating Security Payload (ESP) provides confidentiality services, including confidentiality of message contents and limited traffic flow confidentiality. As an optional feature, ESP can also provide the same authentication services as AH.

ESP Format

Figure 18-4 shows the format of an ESP packet. It contains the following fields:

Figure 18-4
IPSec ESP Format

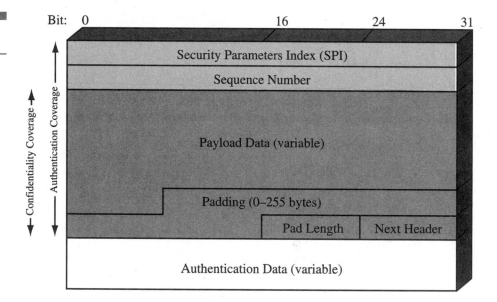

- *Security Parameters Index (32 bits):*   Identifies a security association.
- *Sequence Number (32 bits):*   A monotonically increasing counter value; this provides an anti-replay function, as discussed for AH.
- Payload Data (variable):   This is a transport-level segment (transport mode) or IP packet (tunnel mode) that is protected by encryption.
- *Padding (0-255 bytes)*:   The purpose of this field is discussed later.
- *Pad Length (8 bits):*   Indicates the number of pad bytes immediately preceding this field.
- *Next Header (8 bits):*   Identifies the type of data contained in the payload data field by identifying the first header in that payload

(for example, an extension header in IPv6, or an upper-layer proto-col such as TCP).

- *Authentication Data (variable):* A variable-length field (must be an integral number of 32-bit words) that contains the Integrity Check Value computed over the ESP packet minus the Authentication Data field.

Encryption and Authentication Algorithms

The Payload Data, Padding, Pad Length, and Next Header fields are encrypted by the ESP service. If the algorithm used to encrypt the pay-load requires cryptographic synchronization data, such as an initialization vector (IV), then this data may be carried explicitly at the beginning of the Payload Data field. If included, an IV is usually not encrypted, although it is often referred to as being part of the cipher text.

The current specification dictates that a compliant implementation must support DES. A number of other algorithms, discussed in Chapter 8, have been assigned identifiers and could therefore be used for encryption; these include:

- Three-key triple DES
- RC5
- IDEA
- Three-key triple IDEA
- CAST
- Blowfish

As with AH, ESP supports the use of a MAC, using HMAC.

Padding Field

The Padding field serves several purposes:

1. If an encryption algorithm requires the plain text to be a multiple of some number of bytes (e.g., the multiple of a single block for a block cipher), the Padding field is used to expand the plain text (consisting of the Payload Data, Padding, Pad Length, and Next Header fields) to the required length.

2. The ESP format requires that the Pad Length and Next Header

fields be right aligned within a 32-bit word. Equivalently, the cipher text must be an integer multiple of 32 bits. The Padding field is used to ensure this alignment.

3. Additional padding may be added to provide partial traffic flow confidentiality by concealing the actual length of the payload.

WRAP-UP

The driving force for the acceptance and deployment of secure IP is the need for business and government users to connect their private WAN/LAN infrastructure to the Internet for (1) access to Internet services and (2) use of the Internet as a component of the WAN transport system. Users need to isolate their networks and at the same time send and receive traffic over the Internet. The authentication and privacy mechanisms of secure IP provide the basis for a security strategy.

Because IP security mechanisms have been defined independent of their use with either the current IP or IPv6, deployment of these mechanisms does not depend on deployment of IPv6. Indeed, it is likely that we will see widespread use of secure IP features long before IPv6 becomes popular, because the need for IP-level security is greater than the need for the added functions that IPv6 provides compared to the current IP.

With the arrival of IPSec, managers have a standardized means of implementing security for VPNs. Furthermore, all of the encryption and authentication algorithms, and security protocols, used in IPSec are well studied and have survived years of scrutiny. As a result, the user can be confident that the IPSec facility indeed provides strong security.

IPSec can be implemented in routers or firewalls owned and operated by the organization. This gives the network manager complete control over security aspects of the VPN, which is much to be desired. However, IPSec is a complex set of functions and modules and the management and configuration responsibility is formidable. The alternative is to seek a solution from a service provider. A service provider can simplify the job of planning, implementing and maintaining Internet-based VPNs for secure access to network resources and secure communication between sites.

CHAPTER 19

Cryptography in Electronic Commerce Systems

Importance of Cryptography in Electronic Commerce

Commerce comes down to the one fundamental agreement that legal detriment flows between two parties in an exchange. Furthermore, it is assumed that both parties to a commercial exchange behave in a reasonable and honest manner. In normal commerce, parties are generally able to verify that their exchange was honest and mutual. A contract is judged as honest if legal consideration for the agreement exists for both parties to the exchange and all the essential terms and conditions have been met. Electronic commerce (e-commerce) is a natural extension of commerce. However, the nature of the electronic environment requires different mechanisms to ensure that any exchange is honest. Computers have helped usher in an improved level of global commerce but they have also registered new challenges. Vendors and end users alike have new concerns when entering the electronic commercial theater of operations. Vendors must account for the following three security issues for their products, which although not unique, have been intensified due to the growth of electronic commerce on the Internet:

1. *Leakage:*   Software and hardware complexities secure information leakage to unauthorized parties to a transaction.

2. *Theft:*   Data copying and storage is virtually undetectable.

3. *Open Systems:*   Data can be rapidly transmitted and distributed to all communication nodes—even unauthorized ones.

The real-world analogy of these security concerns would be the ability to locate and steal an item from a company without detection, and within minutes, make millions of copies of it for immediate release around the world. Such unauthorized duplications could have an enormous financial impact on all but many of the largest companies.

It must be assumed that information can be intercepted, copied, and stored without the knowledge of the sending and receiving parties. Given that these three challenges are an integral part of computing and cannot be removed, additional security mechanisms have to be developed to prevent losses resulting from information leakage, theft, and duplication. These mechanisms are based on privacy and access control techniques.

If data are stored and transmitted in such a way that only the intended recipient can access and understand it, the information is useless to an adversary. Unauthorized recipients can access, copy, and distribute the protected data, but they cannot read or use it. When the recipients can read information which is intended only for them, distribution and storage no longer need to be controlled.

The use of cryptography for electronic commerce has two public objectives: (1) to reduce the amount of secure information that needs to be stored or transmitted and (2) to ensure secrecy of commercial transactions. Employing cryptographic systems in e-commerce represents a fundamental solution to the more general problem of computer system *access control management* (ACM)—the granting or withholding of privileges in commercial computer systems.

Cryptography Used in Electronic Commerce

Symmetric Systems

Encryption separates a sensitive commercial file into two components: a secret part and a nonsecret part. The secret component, known as a *key,* is generally a small (usually 56-128 bits) chunk of information that is chosen randomly. The nonsecret part (the encrypted data) is a larger collection of random appearing data, usually the same size as the original file.

The smaller component is the key to restore the larger component via a reverse process called decryption. One of the advantages of encryption is that the amount of sensitive information is dramatically reduced and that confidentiality is ensured.

Elemental discussions of cryptography use an analogy of a safe or lockbox to illustrate cryptographic principles, although the analogy of a safe is not entirely accurate; a better analogy is that encryption allows the size of the safe to be reduced. Instead of having a room full of sensitive documents locked away in a safe, the encrypted documents can be stored anywhere without worry. One sheet of paper, containing the keys can be stored in the safe. The simple act of reducing the amount of information that is both sensitive and needs to be protected has many benefits.

Encryption alone does not make a system secure, because the key is as vulnerable as the original data, if not more so. Encryption reduces but does not eliminate the amount of information that needs to be handled in a secure fashion. All cryptographic systems require due diligence in the management and generation of their keys. Key management in cryptography is a fundamental notion since keys represent the most secret part of a cryptosystem. In electronic commerce applications, key management is the central requirement of access control.

Public-Key (PK) Cryptography

Public-key cryptography employs two different keys, a public and a private key that are linked to each other by some mathematical construct (Chapter 8). Although the process of PK encryption and decryption work in a similar fashion to symmetric encryption, the same key is not used to both encrypt and decrypt the data. When a file is encrypted with the public key, it can be decrypted only with the corresponding private key. When a file is encrypted with the private key, it can be decrypted only with the corresponding public key.

From an electronic commerce standpoint, this is an interesting feature. If users' public keys are openly made available, other users can encrypt data with it and send data to them, knowing that no one else can access it. Users can also encrypt data with their private key, and thus validate that they have received the data.

Despite obvious advantages, public-key cryptography has not been as widely deployed in electronic commerce systems as one might expect; this is true, even though it offers consumers a way to protect their online purchases. Public-key cryptography will become widespread when users recognize the importance of their public key/private key pair and the only way that the system can be compromised is by the deliberate revelation of a user's private key. As public-key infrastructures (PKIs) are deployed, the use of public-key cryptography will increase dramatically.

Hashing

Hashing is a way of compressing data to a practical byte size. The hash value resulting from any e-commerce file might range between 32 to 128 bytes long. Hashing is a unique mathematical operation, and is used to verify file integrity without revealing anything about the file contents. Hashing can be used in authentication systems to permit data to be transferred "in the clear" between systems. For example, if vendors wish to store credit card information for their customers, but do not want to have the database vulnerable to theft, they may use a hash of the credit card information for purchasers. This renders the database useless to an adversary and has the additional benefit that purchasers need no longer send their credit card numbers over an insecure or public network. Customers who send the hash of their credit card number rather than the number itself, authorize the vendor to verify their hash through a lookup procedure on a central database.

Authentication

Authentication is another important component of any access control system. Authentication systems range from a password challenge to token cards to biometrics, depending on the security level required. In electronic commerce, the most important type of authentication system is the *funds transfer mechanism* (FTM), which includes credit card, direct debit, and other emerging electronic transaction and cash systems such as SET and CyberCash.

Access Control Without Cryptography

Many business transactions do not employ cryptography for protection. Transactions that occur over a reasonably secure channel exchange sensitive data in the clear. An example of this situation is a telephone credit card purchase. For many applications, the added overhead of cryptography and the associated protocols are not cost justified. A common economic threshold is $1000. If the communication channels are reasonably trusted, then it is not economical to spend more than the threshold amount for the additional security of encryption.

The nature of electronic commerce emphasizes the need for user access control, as commercial transactions are more prone to abuse than nonelectronic transactions. Many e-commerce sites ask for credit card information on a *nonsecure page*. The credit card information is sent unencrypted and stored unencrypted. This offers the highest potential for fraud, as credit card information can be intercepted or stolen. This potential becomes a major concern when credit card information is stored in a database. A listing of thousands of users' names, credit card numbers, and card expiration dates is a tempting target for the experienced criminal.

Access Control Mechanisms

Access control mechanisms are the backbone of e-commerce. Access control ensures the access rights, describes entity privileges, and states how and under what condition(s) these entities are allowed to access the object. Access control mechanisms mediate and protect all accesses to information from a person's personal information file to an organization's core database. Without access control mechanisms, the electronic commerce marketplace would not exist.

One approach to increasing the security of e-commerce transactions sent over commercial computer networks is to encrypt the sensitive authentication data exchanged between purchaser and vendor. Accomplishing this goal requires addressing two Internet areas: general security and financial-transaction security. Credit card giants like MasterCard and Visa and software giants like Microsoft and Netscape have led the way in both.

SSL

Netscape developed the *Secure Socket Layer* (SSL) cryptosystem. Microsoft and IBM have developed other implementations of SSL. One of the prime goals of these organizations was to incorporate SSL into their client/server applications, which affect millions of consumers.

The SSL protocol is designed primarily to provide privacy between two communicating computer applications (a *client* and a *server*). It is also designed to authenticate the server, and optionally, the client. The SSL protocol deals with a wide range of general Internet security issues. It uses encryption to ensure that all information transmitted between a browser and a server is secure and authentication to ensure that the intended user and server are who they say they are.

As a standard, SSL is based more on market acceptance than certification by a standards organization. Netscape's version of SSL appears to be gaining acceptance and approval from both industry and the standards organizations. SSL and Netscape's efforts are thoroughly discussed at their Web site: *http://www.netscape.com/assist/security/ssl/*.

SET

Financial-transaction security has been addressed through the *SET* standard—*Secure Electronic Transaction* specification—which mimics the current structure of the existing credit card processing system and replaces every telephone call or transaction slip of paper with its electronic counterpart. MasterCard, Visa, AMEX, and other industry leaders such as Microsoft, IBM, SAIC, GTE, RSA, Terisa Systems, and Verisign have endorsed the SET standard. The goal is to develop a single technical standard for safeguarding payment card purchases made over open or unsecured networks like the Internet.

The SET specification uses digital certificates to verify the actual cardholder as the purchaser. This digital certificate provides the nonrepudiation feature that prevents the purchaser from arbitrarily disclaiming his/her purchase. SET provides merchants, vendors, and financial institutions with a secure way to position themselves in the emerging electronic commercial marketplace.

SET was designed to make cyberspace a safe place for conducting business and to promote consumer confidence in the e-commerce marketplace. The focus of SET is to maintain confidentiality of information, ensure message integrity, and to authenticate the parties involved in an e-commerce transaction.

Both the SET and SSL protocols use encryption to protect sensitive data transmitted between the purchaser and vendor. When a user logs onto a secure site, data transferred from vendor to user is encrypted. Similarly, vendor to vendor and vendor to bank or financial institution is usually encrypted. However, data resident on a vendor's system (data which need to be readily accessible from customer service) may not be encrypted. This offers a good compromise of transaction security, as an adversary would have to compromise the security of the vendor's computer system before gaining access to any sensitive data. Passive eavesdropping will not usually be effective. A transmission security system is used when access control verification is required on a server. When software can run on the user's system, many different approaches to authentication and access control can be used.

Cryptography Integrated with Access Control

Public-key cryptography offers many possibilities for direct integration of cryptography into access control mechanisms. For example, if a vendor wants to send a personalized encrypted file to a purchaser, the following protocol might work:

1. The public key and payment information is sent to the user by the vendor.

2. Vendor performs payment transaction and returns data encrypted with the public key.

3. User receives encrypted data and decrypts it with his/her corresponding private key.

Note that no financial institution was involved as a middleman.

Since a user would have to reveal his/her private key to allow decryption by anyone other than him/herself, access to the payment data is naturally restricted to the paying user. If the user's private key is located on a token card or smartcard, this type of a system is more secure because with smartcards, the user is prevented from revealing the private key, even if he/she was inclined to.

An alternate mechanism that would accomplish a similar result would be to encrypt the data with the purchaser's credit card number and expiration date. Most users would hesitate to pass around their key if it contained such information.

Transmission Security for Soft Goods

Electronic commerce for hard goods has been very successful. Bookstores, computer companies, and many others will allow users to browse and purchase items over the Internet and these items are then delivered through traditional channels. Whereas the distributors of physical products were the first to capitalize on the new electronic marketplace, the sale of soft goods or information is increasing dramatically. As network connectivity and computing becomes more widespread, this trend is positive. Examples of soft goods that are already for sale on the Internet include digital photographs, papers and documents, and software components.

Access control and transaction authentication mechanisms are common for e-commerce systems involving both soft and hard goods. These systems are well understood and standardized. However, unlike hard goods, e-commerce transactions are not the only system component that needs to be made secure. Solutions for the secure delivery of soft goods are still largely being developed. Six major e-commerce systems for delivering soft goods via the Internet are:

1. No cryptographic protection

2. Protected while in transit

3. Protected until unlocked with a key

4. Protected with a user-defined key

5. Protected with a user-dependent key

6. Protection using a persistent rights management system

No Protection

With all the concerns about computer security, it may seem surprising that many Internet electronic commerce sites have no security other than transaction processing. While this is unacceptable to many people, for some users, the value of the product and the probability of theft do not justify higher security levels.

No delivery security is equivalent to an unencrypted file sitting on an ordinary Web server; it does not mean, however, that the file is easily accessible. These files usually have a complicated name or path or cannot be accessed unless the user has purchased it. This method is essentially security by obscurity, but when combined with transaction security can be made reasonably adequate (see Table 19-1).

TABLE 19-1

Transaction Processing Without Cryptographic Protection

Advantages	Disadvantages
■ No specialized servers required	■ Server needs to be secure
■ Easy for the user	■ Data can be accessed while in transit
	■ No security if server access control bypassed

Protected While in Transit

Once the purchase has been verified, the data are encrypted while traveling over the network; after arriving at the user's computer, data are automatically decrypted. This is the mechanism used by SSL (Secure Socket Layer) and TLS (Transport Level Security) to protect data while being transmitted over a network (refer to Table 19-2).

Secure Sockets Layer (SSL) is currently the most widely used electronic commerce security technology. Only one security architecture needs to be implemented since SSL protects the transaction and data transferred. Because many secure Web servers and clients are available,

TABLE 19-2

In-Transit Transmission Security

Advantages	Disadvantages
▪ Data are secure while in transit	▪ Server needs to be secure
▪ Easy for the user	▪ Server needs to be able to encrypt the data on the fly (specialized hardware required for high volume)
	▪ No security if server access control bypassed

a secure Web-based e-commerce site can be implemented easily and inexpensively. A typical secure Web-based commerce site will implement several Web pages that permit the user to enter transaction information. If the transaction is approved, then the user is permitted to download data directly off the Web server. Although this system is easy to build, customizable, user-friendly, and cost effective, once the data have been downloaded it has no restrictions. In addition, if the server is ever compromised, the data stored on it can be accessed directly.

The ability to open a secure point-to-point channel is a useful building block for many security protocols. Most transaction systems depend on a secure channel for communicating. This has been one of the main thrusts of public-key cryptography, which is used to create a one-way secure channel between a sender and receiver without having to reveal a sensitive key. Traditional secure channels involved a key exchange process that was usually the weakest part of the system. When a transmission security mechanism like SSL is based on public-key cryptography, then the system is analogous to a file protected by a user-defined key. There are two differences: (1) the encrypted variant is not stored and (2) the user sends his/her public key to the vendor as the primary user identifier.

Protected Until Unlocked with a Key

In this method, the vendor data is preencrypted with a key and then stored on the server. When a user initiates a purchase, he/she is given the key that unlocks the vendor preencrypted datafile. The prime advantage is that this permits the encrypted vendor data to be passed around and stored on unsecured servers and in public spaces with a limited risk. The main disadvantage is that the key is passed around between users. As the encrypted file can be stored in many different

TABLE 19-3

Key-Based Unlocking

Advantages	Disadvantages
■ Data are secure while in transit ■ Server does not need to be secure ■ Data are secure on the client until decrypted ■ Low overhead ■ Data can reside in public areas ■ Data can be passed from user to user in encrypted format	■ If the key becomes available, the data cannot be controlled ■ Data must be preencrypted ■ Key must be communicated to the user

places, access cannot easily be revoked. Once the key becomes publicly known, the item is no longer secure (refer to Table 19-3).

This key-based unlocking system is widely used to protect software. Whereas most implementations do not use encryption, they accomplish a similar result by requiring an activation key or serial number to operate; and whereas some earlier electronic commerce systems used raw encryption to provide security, most have added user-defined or user-dependent key mechanisms.

Protected with a User-Defined Key

With this model, the data are encrypted with a key that is specific to the user who is purchasing the goods. Two different approaches exist depending on whether public or private key cryptography is employed.

1. When public-key cryptography is employed, users can send their public key to the vendor. Because this key is public, no security precautions need to be taken. After the purchase has been verified, the vendor data can be encrypted with the public key. Since the intended recipient's private key can decrypt only the data, the intended user can decrypt only the vendor data.

2. In private-key cryptography, the data are encrypted with a key made up from information that the user will not reveal. An example of this is encrypting the data with a user's credit card number and expiration date. This form of delivery system is becoming more common. By binding a purchase to a user, the user is much less likely to share passwords or keys. It also enables delivery by unsecured channels such as email and anonymous ftp (Table 19-4).

TABLE 19-4

*User-Defined Key-
Based Unlocking*

Advantages	Disadvantages
■ Data are secure while in transit	■ Server needs to be secure
■ Data are secure on the client until decrypted	■ User must communicate key to the vendor
■ Data can reside in public areas ■ Data can be accessed only by the specified user	■ Server needs to be able to encrypt the data on the fly (specialized hardware required for high volume)
	■ Data cannot be passed from user to user in encrypted format

Protected with a User-Dependent Key

Unlike a user-defined key, the user-dependent key is a system based on protection until unlocked, where each user has a different unlocking key, unique to each. When data are protected with a user-defined key, only one encrypted file needs to be prepared that many different people can unlock. There are two important variants of protection using a user-dependent key:

1. Vendor data are preencrypted

2. Encrypted on demand

Both of these implementations require pertinent data to be downloaded before an item is purchased. When vendor data are preencrypted, the system is called a *Static User-Dependent Unlocking* system. When vendor data are encrypted on the fly—for example, the results of a database query—then the system is called a *Dynamic User-Dependent Unlocking* system. This process is shown in Figure 19-1 and summarized in Table 19-5.

Figure 19-1

*User-Dependent Key-
Based Unlocking*

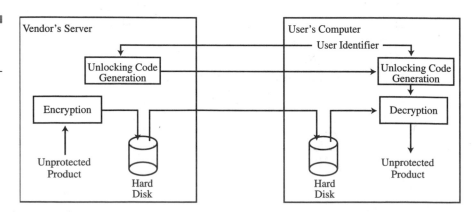

TABLE 19-5

User-Dependant Key-Based Unlocking

Advantages	Disadvantages
■ Data are secure while in transit	■ User must communicate key to the vendor
■ Server does not need to be secure (static only)	■ Server must be secure (dynamic only)
■ Low overhead	
■ Data can reside in public areas	
■ Data can be passed from user to user in encrypted format	
■ Any given key is valid only for a specific user	

The user-dependent key system attempts to blend the advantages of user-defined keys while allowing the encrypted file to be passed on. It is usually based on an encrypted file where the key is not made directly available to the user. The key that the user is given is dependent on computer system hardware or software and, consequently, will work only for that computer. This allows the encrypted file to be passed from user to user, with each user receiving a unique key to unlock the data specific for each user.

Protection Using a Persistent Rights Management System

Continuous data protection and rights enforcement is one of the goals in the data security industry. A system that always maintains and enforces the rights that a user is granted would permit payment mechanisms to be elegantly integrated, while not restricting the use of the information. Additionally, the data can be passed around from user to user, while retaining the protective security wrapping, even if it is embedded within a document. This permits the security policies to be enforced throughout the life of the data, both in the original format and in derivative works.

Such systems are very complex and difficult to implement. They must prevent data from being extracted from the wrapper and ensure that assigned rights are always enforced. Persistent rights management systems (PRMS) must be integrated into applications and the operating system before data secured by them can be compromised.

When a rights management system is fully implemented, it offers end-to-end security and payment options. End-to-end security entails the maintaining of security restrictions throughout the life of the data.

For example, an image could be purchased from a stock photograph supplier and embedded in a document. The image would still be protected. If the document were then sold, the owner of the image would get payment for the additional copies of the image. The ability for users to resell other people's data while ensuring that the original owners receive payment is an exciting possibility. This type of system would protect the rights of both the owners and users of data and would greatly increase the flexibility of digital selling (Table 19-6).

TABLE 19-6

PRMS Comparison

Advantages	Disadvantages
▪ Data are always secure	▪ Difficult to implement
▪ Data remain secure during and after use	▪ High overhead
▪ Data can reside in public areas	▪ Almost impossible to eliminate leakage
▪ Data can be passed from user to user	
▪ Every user pays for access	
▪ Supports payment for use in derivative works	
▪ Eliminates nonpayment and theft	
▪ Guarantees verified access control and rights enforcement	

Several vendor systems using the PRMS approach are currently in development. Complete systems exist but currently require that all applications be modified to support the protected content. Information leakage is still a problem because data can be extracted from its protective wrapper. This, unfortunately, allows the rights management and payment security modules to be bypassed. As with any complex system, security implementation is important.

Comparisons

As expected, all of these delivery systems have advantages and disadvantages. The user must consider costs, maintenance, and security requirements when implementing any one of the six solutions to the challenge of electronic commerce for soft goods. Table 19-7 shows core capabilities/features of the various delivery models for soft goods delivery.

TABLE 19-7

Delivery Systems
Comparison

Browse, Purchase, Download, Use Models	
No security:	Simple and easy to use
SSL:	Simple and no security with secure server

Browse, Purchase, Download, Unlock, Use Models	
Key-based unlocking:	Cannot be accessed without key
User-defined key unlocking:	User has disincentive to reveal key to others

Browse, Download, Purchase, Use Models	
User-dependent key unlocking (static)	Secure server not required for storage
User-dependent key unlocking (dynamic)	Supports custom packaging of multiple items
Enforced Rights Management	End-to-end security; complex implementations

A User's View of the Electronic Commerce Model (Browse, Download, Purchase, and Use Model)

The actions required by the publisher and purchasers of data in a user-defined or user-dependent protection system are quite different from the actions required for an SSL or PK-encrypted system. In most e-commerce systems, users must pay before they are allowed to download the data that they have purchased. With user-defined and user-dependent systems, data are downloaded before the transaction occurs. This has several advantages. For people with slower Internet connections, this permits easy recovery. In a traditional e-commerce system, if a download is not successful, users must reauthenticate to download the file a second time. In some cases, they have to pay a second time and apply for a reimbursement. A second advantage of having users download the file before they purchase it is that additional information can be included with the download. For software, systems have been implemented to allow users to evaluate software for a trial period before they have purchased it. When they decide to purchase the software, additional program features such as file saving and external printing are enabled. Paradata Systems Corporation developed one particularly interesting soft goods delivery system. It is instructive to review the features in their model.

Step 1—Browsing

Once the potential purchaser is at the vendor's site, he/she can browse or search through the database of purchasable items. By navigating through the presentation data that has been prepared, the user is able to decide whether to proceed.

Step 2—Downloading Soft Goods

- *Static User-Dependent Key Unlocking:*   For preencrypted static items, when the user has selected the item he/she intends to purchase, he/she will download the encrypted item. The user then triggers an unlocking application to run, for which the unlocking operation requires transaction information to be entered at that time. When accepted, the item description information is unlocked and transferred to the hard disk. The user can assign the encrypted download to other users, who can then pay for the data themselves.
- *Dynamic User-Dependent Key Unlocking:*   With a dynamic implementation, after the user has selected the items that he/she wants to purchase, the items are packaged up into a single encrypted file to be downloaded. The unlocking application is executed, transaction information is entered and accepted, and then items (indices) are transferred to the hard disk. The user can pass the encrypted download on to other users, who can then pay for the purchase.

Step 3—Purchase

The downloaded file on the user's system contains a protective wrapper and an unlocking application. When the user wishes to access the information contained within the file, he/she runs the unlocking program. Usually, there is just one file that contains the unlocking application and its protected data. When the unlocking application is run, it connects to a server and allows the user to enter transaction information. Once the transaction has been approved, the unlocking application decrypts this data and stores it for transfer.

Step 4—Use

The downloaded file has been unlocked and is free to be used according to the license agreement.

A Publisher's View

When buying into an electronic commerce system the publisher must evaluate its needs and mission. For soft goods, depending on the business model that is to be followed, this business model will depend on the timeliness of the soft goods and the amount of soft goods to be offered— there are many options. For example, a publisher with a large timely database would prefer the Dynamic User-Dependent Key Unlocking (a Dynamic Encrypter), whereas a software publisher with three applications for sale would prefer the Static User-Dependent Key Unlocking (a Static Encrypter). The publisher has the following considerations:

Step 1—Selection

The first step required to sell the soft goods is to decide what is going to be offered for sale. These goods must be put into a saleable format and prices need to be determined.

Step 2—Presentation

Once the soft goods for sale have been selected and prices have been decided, a format needs to be developed for how the soft goods should be presented to prospective customers. This can range from a simple text listing to an elaborate graphical presentation that displays extensive information about the soft good. The presentation information is usually formatted as a series of navigable World Wide Web pages that are linked into the site of the publisher.

Step 3—Payment Mechanism

A payment mechanism now needs to be put in place. This can range from telephone credit-card-based transactions to a SET online transaction system. As almost all Internet electronic commerce transactions occur using credit cards, the corresponding financial authorization bridges and accounts need to be established with the various credit card companies. Many different systems exist to provide Web-based transaction processing that allows users to pay.

Step 4—Content Preparation for Downloading

- *Static User-Dependent Key Unlocking (Static Encrypter):* Items are preencrypted with an evaluation "wrapper." That is, the soft good is secured in a digital container. All the "wrapped" soft goods for sale will reside on the publisher's FTP site ready for download. All of the transactions occur on the user's system and a transaction system does not need to be set up on the Web site of the vendor.

- *Dynamic User-Dependent Key Unlocking (Dynamic Encrypter):* With a dynamic user-dependent key unlocking implementation, the items are encrypted on the fly based on user's request. As with static user-dependent key unlocking, the transaction occurs after the download and on the client's system. This architecture is traditionally for databases, where a custom query can be packaged out and downloaded for purchase. Buyers of digital data want to create their own "digitally secure package" for download. They also want the flexibility of querying a publisher's database for the information needed.

A Walkthrough of a Dynamic User-Dependent Commerce System

The Dynamic User-Dependent Commerce System allows a data publisher to enable a database without significant modification to the existing server infrastructure. The base of this system is solely dependent on a networked dynamic server. The dynamic server robustly encrypts information sourced from a database and embeds within the file a small executable application that controls the access to this information. It enables an end user to easily download this securely "wrapped" data and purchase digital products at their desktop.

When one of these "wrapped" items reaches the end user's desktop computer, a double-click on the "wrapper" generates a purchase window displaying that item's name, description, price, and a machine-dependent "product code." The end user then purchases the corresponding "release code," which decrypts (unlocks) the item.

The dynamic server provides a flexible solution that works in conjunction with WWW, query, view, search, and database servers. Interactive catalogs that intuitively guide the customers to the product offerings can be developed and integrated with the existing Web strategy using templates and tools such as Microsoft's Frontpage, Adobe Pagemill, Java, or any HTML editor.

The Dynamic User-Dependent Commerce System promotes browsing and downloading of information without any financial commitment required. Traditional commerce systems require payment prior to downloading, which is a disincentive to the impulse buyer and can be problematic when there are problems in the download process. Information residing in the desktop enables purchase orders to be created directly by corporate users.

The Dynamic User-Dependent Commerce System is scalable. As the bulk of the transaction processing takes place at the client end, the publisher's server doesn't do all the work.

The dynamic server model allows a buyer to make a data request from the product database through the World Wide Web. Once the data query is found, the data are sent to the dynamic server where the data are "wrapped" in an encrypted data container. This container is then sent to the buyers' desktop where the unlocking operation is performed. A live demonstration of the Dynamic User-Dependent Commerce System described in Figure 19-2 may be found at: *http://www.paradata.com/ demo1.html.*

The buyer browses the Internet as usual with his/her favorite Internet Web browser. No password or subscription needs to be set up for the user to query the data publisher's online product database. In Step 1 of Figure 19-2, the user browses the data publisher's database using a popular Internet Web browser. In Step 2, the buyer selects the desired data for purchase. In Step 3, the buyer downloads the "wrapped" files to the desktop ready for purchase. In Step 4, the buyer unlocks the "wrapped" files by providing financial information and the related product codes and, in return, receives the release codes that will unlock the data on the desktop.

Figure 19-2
The Buying Process

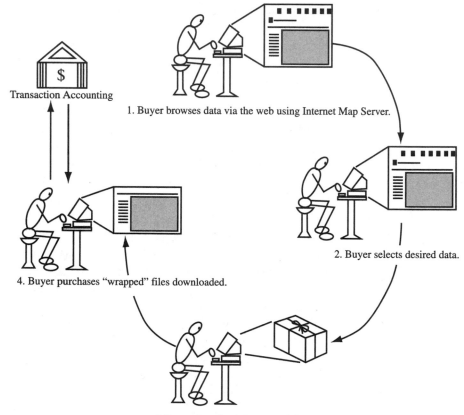

1. Buyer browses data via the web using Internet Map Server.

Transaction Accounting

2. Buyer selects desired data.

4. Buyer purchases "wrapped" files downloaded.

3. Buyer downloads "wrapped" files for purchase.

TABLE 19-8

Secure Commerce
Solution Providers

Broadcast Software	*www.broadcastsoft.com*	Static User-Dependent Locking
Digital Delivery	*www.digitaldelivery.com*	Static User-Dependent Locking
Rainbow Systems	*www.rnbo.com*	Static User-Dependent Locking
Release Software	*www.releasesoftware.com*	Static User-Dependent Locking
TechWave	*www.techwave.com*	Static User-Dependent Locking
Ziplock	*www.ziplock.com*	Static User-Dependent Locking
Paradata Systems	*www.paradata.com*	Dynamic User-Dependent Locking
Tragoes	*www.tragoes.com*	Enforced Rights Management

Table 19-8 gives a listing of secure commerce provider Web sites where more information may be found.

WRAP-UP

Cryptography plays a key role in electronic commerce systems. Cryptography verifies that an electronic exchange between two parties is honest and mutual. Electronic exchanges require different mechanisms than do normal commerce exchanges. Security problems facing the electronic commerce marketplace include: (1) leakage of information to unauthorized parties, (2) undetectable data copying and storage, and (3) unauthorized transfer of information. Access control mechanisms and cryptosystems are installed to combat these problems.

The cryptographic algorithms described previously have specific tasks that are suitable for an electronic commerce system. Cryptography alone does not make an electronic commerce system safe. However, there is a natural synergism between cryptographic and e-commerce management systems that improve the security of the vendor offerings.

CHAPTER 20

Role-Based
Cryptography

Role-based technology will play a key role in the enterprise deployment of robust security. This chapter provides insight into the impact this technology will have on the management of security processes including access and cryptography. First, role-based access control is described, why it is important in the management of systems, and how it is being expanded to support role-based cryptography. Finally, this chapter describes how the combination of role-based and public-key cryptography can be instrumental in reducing key and certificate management and enterprise scalability concerns.

Concept/Purpose of Role-Based Security and Cryptography

In today's dynamic information age, electronic communications are an integral part of everyday life that increasingly uses telephones, fax machines, videoconferencing, computers, corporate networks, intranets, and the Internet to exchange information. Playing a critical role in global business-to-business operations, these information infrastructures are vital to the ongoing success of an organization and its ability to deliver competitive solutions.

If companies today are struggling to adequately secure and manage corporate networks supporting thousands of users, what will the business community have to deal with in the future as it tries to secure and manage "virtual electronic commerce" networks supporting millions of users?

Establishing a comprehensive security policy and implementing an infrastructure is the first step. Unfortunately, it is not as easy as it sounds. According to a 1997 *InformationWeek*/Ernst & Young Security Survey, 60 percent of all respondents cited lack of money and 55 percent cited lack of human resources as obstacles in addressing security concerns. The results: without adequate security many organizations are exposed to malicious activity from internal or outside intruders.

A successful security program must begin with a corporate security policy endorsed by senior management and applicable to all employees. This plan must address multiple levels of risk and support a phased implementation of security solutions. The technical implementation should provide a solid security foundation establishing multiple barriers between unauthorized, malicious intruders and valuable corporate information.

These barriers are required to control access to applications and resources: identify and authenticate users, implement authorization levels, ensure the confidentiality and integrity of information stored or transmitted, and provide proof of participation in an electronic transaction. However, as we add barriers, we also add to the complexity and manageability of the system, resulting in a crucial balancing act. Information technology (IT) professionals are required to balance information accessibility (so employees can do their job) with an acceptable level of security while keeping deployment costs in line to support the security infrastructure. Although the security of information is the primary objective, the implementation and management of these systems must be addressed in parallel. If the implementation and ongoing administrative costs exceed the perceived benefit—a trusted, user-friendly system—corporations will continue to struggle with this balancing act.

A role-based security model provides a valuable level of abstraction that promotes security administration at the business organization level versus administration at the user identity level. The concept is simple: establish access to information based on the functional role in the organization and then assign users to a role. Because employees frequently come and go, an identity-based model is dynamic and difficult to manage, whereas roles are more static and easier to maintain. Companies will add new roles or reorganize, but on a less-frequent basis.

Role-based security administration provides a powerful mechanism that dramatically reduces administrative tasks associated with managing user access and security privileges. Relatively new to the distributed environment, a role-based access model has been used in mainframe security, database architectures, and defense systems for years. The role-based security model was instrumental in bringing manageable access control to the mainframe environment and will be the common denominator in bringing enterprise-wide security administration to the network security model.

Importance of Role-Based Security

Access is the privilege to do something with a computer resource (e.g., view, read, write, update, modify, delete, encrypt, decrypt, etc.). *Access control* is the mechanism used to protect information from unauthorized access; access controls can define not only who or what process may have access to a specific resource, but also the type of access that is permitted.

Current systems, including access control products, firewalls, VPNs, and others, use *access control lists* (ACLs), which are based on a resource or user's identity and are very cumbersome to handle because each resource or user's identity must be present on every server that the user accesses. As changes are made, for example, the addition or deletion of a user, an administrator must make changes on every server affected. As a result, the potential for error and system vulnerability increases exponentially.

And technology continues to change computing boundaries! Eighty-two percent of U.S. IT managers responding to the 1997 *Information-Week*/Ernst & Young Security Survey stated that they will link their corporate networks to the Internet. Companies typically protect their Web servers with SSL/TLS (Secure Sockets Layer/Transport Layer Security), where each user, administered through ACLs and server is associated with a certified name and public key. SSL/TLS protects the communications to and from the Web server, but the administration of ACLs, public keys, and certificates adds to the administrative nightmare.

Role-based access control (RBAC) utilizes a *mandatory access control* (MAC) mechanism associating functional role with each individual who accesses information. Extensive research in role-based access control has been completed by the National Institute of Standards and Technology (NIST) and other organizations. This, and other research, is now being implemented in commercial systems to reduce the administration of network security models. In addition, RBAC is an integral part of the security model for Secure European System for Applications in a Multi-vendor Environment (SESAME) distributed system and the database language SQL3.

The role-based model applies to any entity that utilizes some type of access control mechanism. Role hierarchies are an intuitive way of organizing roles to mirror established authority and responsibility. RBAC is being implemented in Web servers, databases, directory services, query tools, and many security products.

With RBAC, access decisions are based on the role that individual users have as part of an organization. A *role* defines the set of capabilities required to carry out a specific job function with a company and supports a role hierarchy. A *high-level* role would be defined as, for example, operations *employee* or finance *employee*, whereas a *specialized* role would be defined as operations *manager*, finance *manager*, and so forth. Once roles are established, access rights are grouped by role and privileges are restricted to individuals authorized to assume the associated role. For example, in a hospital system, the role of doctor can electronically view and update patient diagnosis information, prescribe medication, and order laboratory tests; whereas the role of the researcher can be limited to viewing anonymous clinical information for studies only.

From an administrative perspective, when Jane Doe joins Company XYZ as a financial analyst, a systems administrator simply has to add Jane as a new member to the analyst role. Because the role has been predefined based on the structure of the organization and access privileges are already associated with the role, an administrator can very quickly add Jane as a user. In addition, as employees leave the company or take on new responsibilities, administrators need only make one change to establish systemwide privileges, which minimizes human error and eliminates many backdoor security holes.

How often is a hostile individual inadvertently provided access to a system simply because someone forgot to remove one of many access privileges somewhere in the network? Very few companies know or can determine the magnitude of loss associated with these errors. Because only one change is required in an RBAC model, RBAC reduces security holes introduced in traditional identity-based systems that only associate an individual's ID with privileges.

Or just as important, what is the administrative impact of RBAC to a company? There is a very simple but powerful, mathematical formula to determine this cost:

Cost to company = (number of administrative changes/year)

$\times$ (average days or hours to implement change)

$\times$ (average cost of employee/hour)

$\times$ (percentage of job function related to system access)

For example, Company ABC adds an average of five new employees per day earning an average of $15/hour and it takes two working days to set them up with the appropriate access privileges. Applying the following formula we can begin to understand the direct and hidden costs associated with the deployment of identity-based systems.

(265 work days) $\times$ (5 new employees per day)   = 1325
(Employee set-ups/year at $15.00/hr per employee)
     $\times$ (16-hr setup lag time)   = $240

(Cost in downtime per employee
waiting for access privileges)

$\times$ (75% of job function
computer-related)   = \$318,000 $\times$ .75

Cost to company   = \$238,000 hidden security cost

Today, it is typical for a large organization to make 100+ administrative changes per day and a 3-5-day turnaround is more common than not. One option is to add more staff, but this is only a temporary solution. We must address the underlying administrative problem.

RBAC simplifies the administration and management of privileges because it is accomplished at a higher level, by role, a one-to-many relationship instead of at an individual user level. In addition, companies can more effectively implement their security policy through rules associated with the various roles in an organization. With RBAC, companies can reduce administrative cost, errors, and vulnerability to malicious intrusion.

Laying the groundwork for an easily managed, common security environment, security solutions including enterprise security administration systems, single sign-on, firewalls, VPNs, and cryptography, based on a role-based model, are being introduced by vendors including CKS, Hewlett-Packard, IBM Tivoli, Siemens Nixdorf, Sterling Commerce and Technologic Software Concepts, and others.

Role-Based Cryptography

The Internet is driving the need to ensure the confidentiality and integrity of information as it is transmitted across unsecured networks. To address this security concern, many organizations are beginning to deploy encryption. The majority of all encryption solutions available today are based on a public-key infrastructure. Public-key systems are *identity-based,* that is, they are based on the identity of each individual involved in the transaction or communication and as such, have the same management issues as identity-based access control systems. For example, an employee, server, or computer resource is assigned multiple key pairs to digitally sign an electronic transaction and/or to encrypt data. *All public-key processes, including keys and certificates, must be managed for every user or resource.*

Public-key systems combine symmetric and asymmetric key encryption. The symmetric or secret key, because of processing speed, is used to encrypt the data, and then the symmetric key is encrypted with the intended recipient's public key and attached to the encrypted file. Upon receipt, the recipient uses his or her private key to decrypt the symmetric key and is then able to use the symmetric key to decrypt the file.

Although incredibly efficient from a performance perspective, symmetric-key encryption had several weaknesses that limited its commercial usefulness. First, the secure establishment and distribution of "shared" secret keys in a complex global society became a challenge. How did you securely exchange keys between people needing access to the information? The answer was a manual exchange process that was both expensive and inefficient to use.

Second, an organization's information flows in many directions and a separate symmetric key was required for each pair of users in a network, creating a key management nightmare. For example, a network with 100 users required almost 5000 symmetric keys to communicate. Doubling the network to 200 users increased the number of keys to almost 20,000, a 400 percent increase in key volume. This implementation was impractical except in limited, controlled environments.

The final inhibitor to traditional symmetric-key systems was the lack of appropriate security safeguards. Since the same key was used to lock and unlock all data between two users, if the key was compromised (lost, hacked, stolen, etc.), all data encrypted with the compromised key was vulnerable to multiple levels of penetration.

Public-key cryptography was not a replacement for symmetric keys (Chapter 7), but complemented symmetric-key encryption by simplifying and securing symmetric session key distribution. The acceptance of public-key cryptography increased the use of encryption throughout diverse organizations worldwide and created the new requirement to associate public keys with legitimate, authenticated owners.

This requirement was addressed through the creation of internally and externally managed certificates. Similar to notary public endorsements, certificates are electronic documents attached to public keys that provide proof that a public key belongs to a legitimate owner and has not been compromised. Generated by an internal or external certificate authority—a reputable, independent third party—certificates are issued, revoked, and managed from a secure, central location (refer to Chapter 12).

Designed to address the key distribution problems inherent in traditional symmetric-key implementations, public-key systems are ideal for one sender to one recipient communication situations where the validation benefits of digital signature authentication and nonrepudiation are required. Much like a human signature uniquely identifies the person signing his/her name to a physical document, a digital signature uniquely authenticates the person "signing" an electronic document. Digital signatures enable one party in an electronic transaction to digitally sign a document with a private signature key and a public verification key (also see Chapter 10).

A certificate authority (CA), a trusted third party, issues a digital certificate that verifies a private signature key holder's right to use a public key, just as the DMV issues drivers' licenses that are honored by the public. Since only the user has access to his or her private key or code, forging a digital signature is very difficult.

Digital signatures are changing the way purchases are made online. Digital signatures, combined with certification services, enable nonrepudiable transactions that cannot be denied after the fact. To date, 39 states have laws recognizing digital signatures and there are currently five bills before Congress that make digital signatures legally enforceable. Internationally, in 1998, Germany passed legislation addressing the validity and generation of digital signatures and other countries are also in the process of adopting similar legislation.

Public-key infrastructures (PKIs) are identity-based systems and have created a nightmarish task of managing multiple sets of keys and certificates for users. Users will have multiple key pairs, typically one pair for a digital signature and another for data encryption, and may have different key pairs for different applications, based on levels of trust and authority. As the number of keys increases, so do the potential management problems. Users will forget passwords that protect private keys or will lose keys. Employees and contractors will leave organizations. Administrators must be able to recover information and revoke keys and certificates to ensure that unauthorized users cannot access critical systems and information.

Over time, certificate revocation lists (CRLs) can become very large, such that performance and storage requirements become an issue. In addition, the frequency of certificate revocation update may impact the integrity of the system. If a CRL has not been updated in hours, days, or weeks, the user or application cannot get absolute verification of the certificate's validity and an illegal or unauthorized transaction may occur. Furthermore, if a CA revokes a certificate before the next scheduled publication of the CRL, there is a vulnerable period in which an application might accept an invalid certificate.

Keys and certificates are *time-sensitive* and must be changed periodically to ensure their integrity. Similar to mandated password changes, companies will also dictate that users must get new key pairs and certificates at regularly scheduled intervals. The issue of key and certificate management also raises further questions about the long-term *scalability* of a PKI primarily due to the performance demands of the certificate generation and revocation mechanism.

Digital signatures are the only legally acceptable proof of participation in an electronic transaction and will continue to become more critical as e-business and electronic commerce solutions become more widely deployed. Organizations, supporting a PKI, will demand scalable solutions that reduce management and system overhead. Whereas digital signatures will require identity-based public keys, the ability to encrypt a document does provide an alternate, more manageable role-based solution.

To gain the full administrative benefit from a role-based security model, other identity-based security solutions must adopt this model. For the same reasons identity-based access control solutions are moving to a role-based model, cryptography solutions are making the transition for the same reason—to address a management nightmare.

After access control, the second most significant impact on implementation is cryptography. By implementing a role's access and *encryption privileges* based on a role model, administration and security vulnerabilities can be dramatically reduced. Roles can be extended to define the set of encryption permissions a user is authorized to perform including decrypt only, encrypt only, or both decrypt/encrypt. These permissions combine to identify overlapping access rights and are a natural means of tying user authority directly to a user's role and access privileges.

Role-Based Cryptography Operations

The primary objective of role-based cryptography (RBC) is to enable organizations to meet specific security and business requirements based on the type of electronic transaction to be protected. Designed to support multiple key management systems, authentication procedures and encryption algorithms, RBC also supports communications between thousands of users generating transactions in the millions. RBC reduces network traffic and minimizes network impact.

RBC dynamically generates a unique symmetric session key "just-in-time" (JIT) to encrypt or decrypt an electronic transaction, that is, file, data stream, or memory-based data, and immediately destroys it after use. The session key is generated from multiple pieces of information referred to as *cryptographic split key*. The split keys are input to a key combiner process and the output of the combiner process is a unique number that is used as the basis for the session key used to encrypt or decrypt data. This process eliminates the need to distribute the session key with a public-key pair because the decryption process works in reverse upon authentication of the recipient.

Combining the proven processing efficiency of symmetric key encryption and role-based cryptography, organizations can reduce the key management burden and increase its scalability, compared with a public-key solution.

The Role-Based Cryptography Process

RBC allows organizations to secure files (such as) word processing documents, data streams (such as) the information contained in buffers as data are uploaded or downloaded between systems, and memory-level data (such as) that used in clipboard cut and paste operations. Role-based encryption and decryption processes are straightforward. The following is an example of a user-driven process.

Role-Based Encryption Process

1. The sender logs on through a multifactor authentication process that validates the sender's identity.
2. The sender establishes the access relationship between the recipient(s) and the sensitive information contained in a file with a point-and-click process.
3. The sender selects the file to be encrypted and initiates the encryption process, another point-and-click maneuver. RBC encrypts the data.

Role-Based Decryption Process

1. The recipient also logs onto RBC through a multifactor authentication process that validates the recipient's identity.
2. The recipient selects the data to be decrypted and initiates the automatic decryption process, another point-and-click maneuver.

3. Transparent to the end user, RBC automatically checks if the recipient has appropriate access authority to the information. If valid access authority is confirmed, decryption takes place and access is granted. If access authority does not exist, decryption is denied.

User Authentication and Security Features

RBC authenticates the user before and during the encryption and decryption processes. To encrypt or decrypt data, senders and recipients must first log on and authenticate themselves to the RBC system. Using a multifactor system of authentication, RBC validates user identity through a combination of (1) "something you have," (2) "something you know," and (3) "something you have access to."

During system setup, user profiles containing data access permissions, the user's name, and other information are encrypted and saved to a *token,* which is a personal, portable authentication device such as a floppy disk, a smartcard, or a biometric device. Giving the user something to keep by way of physical possession, RBC provides "something you have" security.

Associated with each token is a unique passphrase known only to the end user. This passphrase provides "something you know" security and authenticates the end user. The passphrase together with the token permit entrance into the RBC system, providing "something you access" security.

By requiring both sender and recipient multifactor authentication, RBC ensures authorized participation. The automated matching and validation of recipient access authority and encryption privileges are implemented through role-based labels. Labels used in the encryption process must match the label set defined to the user role in the decryption process. Upon completion of authorized decryption, the sender's user name and user ID are available to the recipient, providing an initial means of authenticating the sender's identity. This mathematically complex process provides an audit trail between the sender of an encrypted document and the recipient of the document.

Adding smartcards and biometric devices provides an RBC system with an additional level of user authentication and can provide information for generating a public-key digital signature. A corporation's security policy may dictate the digital signing of certain electronic transactions. These transactions may include purchase orders, contracts, or the electronic exchange of money.

Roles and Labels

Roles uniquely define the relationship and access authority between users and encrypted information. Based on their role within an organization, users are granted various levels of access as well as encryption and decryption privileges. These permissions combine to identify overlapping access rights, and are a natural means of tying user authority and responsibility directly to the information flow of sensitive data.

Planning is the key to success for implementing and managing RBC. It is important to examine how information moves through an organization. By analyzing a typical company, information patterns begin to emerge. Information can be broadcast *vertically,* usually from a high-level manager to everyone that reports to him/her or to everyone affected by his/her responsibility. For example, a company president might distribute quarterly financial results to an executive team, the human resource benefits manager might announce a corporate salary policy to all managers, or a department head might announce a pending special promotion to everyone in his/her department.

Information flows *horizontally,* between members of a team. In many organizations information is exchanged in a matrix approach that may not follow traditional communication paths. An example might be a special project to create a team to develop an Internet strategy for a company. This team would be comprised of members from diverse locations within the company that would communicate in a matrix fashion.

These information flows are well documented and are easily mapped to the cryptography process through role-based labels (RBLs). A derivative of encryption technology from the defense industry, these labels uniquely establish the link between the encrypted information and the recipient, based on the recipient's role within the organization. Labels can be implemented as an end-user selection model or programmatically. Implemented as an end-user selectable pull-down list, the following labels might be included: *Label 1:* (Position) Vice President or Manager or Administrative Assistant; *Label 2:* (Location) Finance or Corporate or Dallas; *Label 3:* (Subject) Project ABC or Top Secret or General Information.

Assume Project ABC requires team-based management that crosses multiple functional areas. If the "Project ABC" label value is a circle containing all users having access permission to Project ABC data, the "Manager" label value is a circle containing all users having access permission to manager-level data, and the "Corporate" label is a circle containing all users having access permission to corporate data, then a file encrypted using "Subject: Project ABC, To: Manager, Location: Corporate" in its label set could be decrypted and read only by the users in the very center who have been assigned "encrypt" or "decrypt/encrypt" permission to all three labels. See Figure 20-1.

Figure 20-1

Role-Based Example

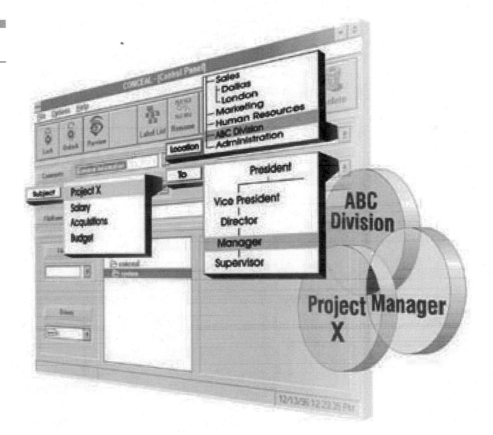

Target recipients would be limited to individuals with manager or higher-level role, such as directors, vice presidents, or the president of the company, who has access authority to any information. These recipients would be further limited to those with access to corporate and Project ABC information. These overlapping access permissions easily support matrix management across separate functional areas that do not normally have established vertical or horizontal lines of communication.

Advantages of RBC

RBC also defines access, key length, encrypting engine, and specific encryption privileges including encrypt only, decrypt only, or both encrypt/decrypt. Once the transactions associated with a role are established, the transactions tend to remain constant. RBC's role-based labels allow administrators to easily define and centrally implement a company's security policy. And, as with RBAC, because the role has been predefined, an administrator can very quickly add new users or change privileges systemwide.

The flexibility of role-based labels means that even large organizations with thousands of users need very few labels to effectively control the secure storage and flow of sensitive information. In addition, RBLs allow parties of separate organizations to securely exchange confidential information using special label access permissions. Typical applications could include exchanging sensitive communications between a company and a legal firm or its trading partners.

RBC enables an end user to selectively encrypt multiple sections or subsets of information within one document by using different label permissions. For example, the vice president of human resources would be able to distribute a single document containing separate, uniquely encrypted sections regarding department-specific salary information.

Each encrypted section would be readable only by the respective department heads with appropriate label permissions. Using the same point-and-click maneuvers with which they have become accustomed, end users have ultimate control over intended audiences, and network traffic is minimized because only one document need be transmitted.

The role-based label function uses a 96-bit seed generated from a seed pool. The unique seed is identified with a label. Once a seed has been created for the label, it is combined with a 512-bit key that creates split keys for each label via a pseudorandom number generator. Critical to the just-in-time key management process, these split keys, combined with other split keys, create the symmetric session key used in the actual encryption or decryption of file, stream, or memory data.

User Profiles

Similar to access control privileges, RBC privileges are assigned and administered based on a *user profile,* which is used at login time to authenticate the user and establish the user's encryption/decryption privileges. Information contained in a user profile includes user name, user ID, role-based labels, and authorized cryptographic algorithms and privileges.

Combining public key with RBC, a user's private keys, and the CA's certificates can also be included in the user profile. Utilizing the label/seed combination to create user profiles, encryption-only, decryption-only, or encrypt and decrypt privileges can be assigned to a specific person or group. User profiles may be stored on smartcards, tokens, as a soft token on a hard drive, or in an LDAP directory.

A directory-enabled infrastructure is important not only to the management of a role-based cryptography system, but also to the administration of an organization's security policy, as well as the consolidation and manageability of multiple security and network technologies in support of this policy. By storing information common to multiple products in a directory, administrators can centralize the administration and management of network resources while reducing administrative cost, human errors, and vulnerability to malicious activity.

In addition to acting as an information repository, the directory can also provide online user revocation of profiles, certificates, and so forth, to help ensure the integrity of systems and users. Similar to a credit-card authorizations system, when a user logs on to a network and attempts to encrypt or decrypt a file, a check is made to see whether his/her access has been revoked. If access has been revoked, the requested operation will not be allowed. This gives the administrator the ability to immediately lock out unauthorized users.

Just-in-Time Key Management

Using a "just-in-time" (JIT) key management process, RBC exploits the performance advantages of symmetric encryption processes and reduces key management by eliminating the public-key pair needed to distribute the session keys used to encrypt the data.

Just as the process implies, the RBC symmetric session key is created in RAM *just in time* for the user to encrypt or decrypt a file. A primary benefit is that the actual unique session key is constructed in the local computer's RAM a mere fraction of a second before the key is loaded into the cryptographic engine and is then immediately destroyed after the encryption/decryption is completed.

In a typical RBC, there are 10 or more split keys used in the encryption and decryption process. These 512-bit split keys are obtained from multiple sources including: a prepositioned set of role-based labels, the workstation's hard disk, the user's token, the application DLL files, the operating system time data, and other sources. The split keys are combined mathematically to construct the unique 512-bit symmetric session key.

The 512-bit split keys are stored in multiple locations. The split keys associated with the labels and other user profile information can be stored encrypted in tables in a directory, database, on a token or smart-card. In addition, the user profiles can be stored in a combination of places to provide multiple security levels, that is, stored on a smartcard to authenticate a user and in a directory to provide online profile validation.

Other split keys are stored encrypted in the software, in the workstation, and in the file header, and are derived from the time structure in the operating system at the time of encryption. More important, the session key created by the key combiner from the split keys is never stored or passed with the encrypted file.

To ensure the confidentiality of information, RBC uses 64-byte (512-bit) symmetric keys, reasonably long enough to withstand most brute-force attacks. Neither the encrypting party nor the decrypting parties have any direct contact with the split keys. Furthermore, since time data, accurate to 1/1000th of a second, is included in the combining of the split keys, the probability of the repeated use of a given session key is zero.

To activate the encryption process, the encryptor selects a set of three or more rational labels. The application automatically locates the split keys for each label and combines them with the other split keys to form the 512-bit symmetric session key. The key management process automatically strips off the number of bits required for the respective encryption engine and passes the appropriate length symmetric session key and data to the encryption engine to complete the encryption process.

RBC supports standard encryption engines, including the four U.S. government-approved Data Encryption Standard (DES) algorithms: Single Codebook, Single Cipher Feedback, Triple Codebook, and Triple Cipher Feedback; and the international standard, IDEA. For users with more advanced encryption algorithm requirements, the RBC framework enables simultaneous management of many different encryption algorithms, combining these and other proprietary encryption algorithms of an organization's selection.

Based on an organization's security and performance requirements, and government regulations on the use of strong encryption, end-user access to specific encryption algorithms is managed by a security administrator. The administrator defines the appropriate encryption algorithms in the user profile, which is created at the time of setup. Depending on which algorithms have been allocated to specific users, RBC then reflects these encryption engines, maximizing flexibility and security at the participant level.

Ideal for applications with complex communication flows involving one sender and many recipients, RBC creates and attaches a static 1024-byte header to the encrypted file during the encryption process. The file header structure is divided into two areas: (1) a *common area,* which is left in plain text, and (2) a *private area,* which includes a subset of the information used in the JIT key management process to construct the file key. Information stored in the common area is generally only nonsensitive information used as meaningful representation of the document contents. See Figure 20-2.

Figure 20-2
Header Information

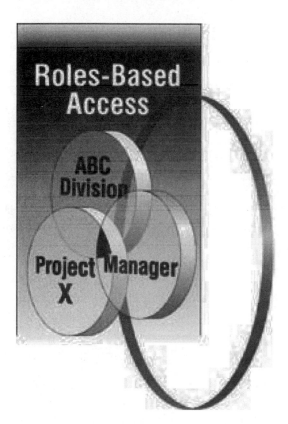

Information in the private area may include the name and path of the original plain-text file; the application and version number used to create the original plain-text file; user name and ID; and the encryption engine used to encrypt the file, key recovery information, signed certificate and digital signature, and so forth.

Five pieces of information in the private area are significant: the time of encryption (composed from the operating system time data), the three label names only (not split keys), and the object (file) name. The information in the private area is encrypted with the output of a nonlinear pseudorandom number generator to ensure the confidentiality of this information while it is attached to a file.

It is important to note that in an RBC system, the header contains only a subset of the ten key splits used to create the symmetric session key. Because the key splits are separately stored in different physical locations, it is virtually impossible for an unauthorized person to accumulate the required information necessary to re-create a session key.

Other Security Issues

No security solution is 100 percent secure. To minimize the impact of a successful attack, RBC creates a unique session key for each transaction, so if an intruder was successful in an attempt to gain unauthorized access to the data, only that file or packet of data is compromised. The information gained from this experience will not help the attacker decrypt any other information.

Email systems are instrumental in the integration of the Internet into corporations. Given this, and the need to ensure the confidentiality of sensitive information transmitted via email, the requirement to encrypt information will continue to increase. It is not uncommon for a large organization to generate hundreds of thousands of emails with an average copy going to three or more recipients.

In a public-key system, the encryption of the symmetric session key with each recipient's public key and the requirement to attach the uniquely encrypted key to the file creates excessive overhead and can negatively impact network performance. In an RBC system, recipient access is controlled through role-based labels, and the multipurpose header does not increase in size if a message is sent to one person or 10,000 people, resulting in a scalable, network-efficient solution.

In order to decrypt a file, an authenticated user selects a decrypt button or option and the application automatically decrypts the header and determines whether the user is authorized to decrypt the information. If all the authorizations are confirmed, the application decrypts the labels and associated split keys in the user's possession. The label split keys and other split keys are automatically combined and used to reconstruct the symmetric session key. This session key is then used to automatically decrypt the information.

RBC administration functions can be administered by one or multiple security persons, depending on the organization's security policy and specific security requirements. Separating the administration of the label creation, modification, and deletion functions from profile administration and token creation enables an organization to assign multiple persons to functional responsibilities. This ensures that no one person would have access to all 10 key splits necessary to re-create a session key. Just as a two-person missile silo system requires collusion between two trusted persons to fire a missile without higher authorization, RBC requires collusion between trusted security administrators to violate security.

Key Recovery

RBC systems support key recovery. Encryption and decryption keys—like passwords and lock combinations—are important assets. Like car keys, written records, and memory, keys can be lost, damaged, or destroyed. In a corporate setting, the risks are increased by the number of keys that may be generated, the number of employees who may have access, and the value of the transactions that may be compromised. Key recovery is an increasingly important aspect of corporate security.

Key management techniques for public-key and role-based systems exist to manage the life cycle of cryptographic keys, including the creation, distribution, validation, update, storage, usage, and expiration of keys. Should keys become forgotten, damaged, or rendered unavailable to authorized parties, then information recovery techniques are necessary to allow recovery of plain text, typically by re-creation or recovering the data encryption key.

Key recovery agents hold a subset of the key splits on deposit and manage the re-creation of session keys required to decrypt data should the need arise. Combining the information held on deposit with information obtained from the encrypted header, key recovery agents could regenerate "session" keys and decrypt data. In addition, because RBC keeps track of all communication paths and all token permissions that were assigned to users, if a token is lost or damaged, the key recovery agent could also generate a new token for the user. An organization can serve as its own internal key recovery agent or, if desired, RBC systems normally support multiple external key recovery agents.

RBC also provides automatic audit trails for all appropriate system functionality. For example, RBC tracks all encryption, decryption, preview, and logon/logoff activity, providing a historic path that can be used to determine "who did what, when, and where". Other audit trails track the creation of user profiles and tokens by capturing unique user IDs, user names, role-based label files, locations where tokens were created, assigned label and encryption engine permissions, and creation date-time stamps, should an organization need to replicate past activity.

Role-Based Cryptography and Smartcards

Smartcards are used to store key components of an RBC system and provide a secure means of storing highly sensitive data such as user signature private keys, user profiles, certificate authority public keys, and the like. Given the smartcard's built-in authentication mechanisms, secure data storage, and secure communication channels between the smartcard and software applications running on the host computer, one can be confident that information stored on the smartcard is secure.

Each user in a corporate enterprise wishing to access the RBC system must possess a user profile. In addition to storing the user profiles on diskette, hard disk, or LDAP directory service, RBC systems also support the storage of user profiles on a smartcard. The security administrator selects the role-based labels and associated split keys, encryption and decryption privileges, encryption engines, and other privileges available to the user. This information is encrypted using attributes of the user's identity plus a key generated from a user's passphrase, and is written to a user's smartcard. Only by providing the smartcard and the correct passphrase can a user access the system.

RBC's JIT key management process enables strong encryption and decryption without passing encryption keys with the cipher text; only the label names are passed. The split keys associated with RBC labels are stored securely in the user profile on the smartcard. Although the RBC user profile is stored encrypted, it must still be protected from unauthorized access on the smartcard. RBC supports multiple security features in a smartcard implementation:

1. User and application authentication
2. Secure messaging
3. Smartcard/application antispoofing

Both user and application authentication are controlled through the use of passphrases. Each smartcard has a single user passphrase that locks all access to the card. Additionally, each application's files are locked by an application-read passphrase and an application-write passphrase. Both user and application authentication are required to gain access to the smartcard and its files. Application-level access authentication to decrypt information does not automatically imply the ability to encrypt. To gain both encrypt and decrypt access privilege an application must authenticate using both the encrypt and decrypt passphrases.

Rather than requiring users to enter passphrases for each authentication level, RBC requires only a single passphrase. When initializing the smartcard and creating the user profile, the RBC/profiler administrator ensures that the RBC passphrase matches the smartcard user authentication passphrase. RBC uses the passphrase entered at login for both smartcard user authentication and user profile decryption.

RBC's smartcard implementation supports secure messaging as defined in the ISO-7816 requirements specification. This protects command and response transmission between the smartcard and the application running on the host computer.

RBC also supports antispoofing techniques to provide a level of trust between the smartcard and application, techniques that ensure the application is talking to the smartcard through the intended smartcard reader and not a Trojan horse program masquerading as the smartcard reader. In addition, the smartcard verifies the application sending data is an application to which it should communicate and not a Trojan horse program taking over communications with the smartcard.

RBC can also utilize the smartcard's onboard random number generator to create seed values for each label. Many smartcards also have an onboard processor that implements various security algorithms for purposes such as creating and verifying digital signatures. RBC's implementation of smartcard technology provides robust user authentication and provides an extremely strong means of securing role-based and public keys.

Role-Based Cryptography and Digital Signatures

Architected to support multiple key management systems, RBC also supports a public-key infrastructure (PKI) for digital signatures. Digital signatures provide an additional level of authentication, data integrity, and nonrepudiation. Trust is based on a certificate authority that signs all user certificates. Checking the signature of the person who signed a file provides authentication. The signed certificate attached with the data includes the name of the user to whom the certificate belongs and the signature of the CA who produced the certificate, validating that the signature has not been forged.

Nonrepudiation guarantees that the person who signed the data cannot later deny having signed it. Each user has his/her own private signing key that only he/she has access to. This key is never backed up. The digital signature key pair is kept only with the client in the user profile. If they are compromised, a new signing key pair must be generated. This helps to ensure nonrepudiation of an electronic transaction between two parties.

The digital signature key pair includes a private signing key and a public verification key: the private signing key is kept in the RBC user profile; the public verification key is in a certificate that has been signed by a CA and also stored in the RBC user profile. It is signed so other users can verify that the public key is authentic and can be trusted.

When a user digitally signs an electronic transaction, a hash value is generated from the data. This hash value is encrypted with the user's private signing key. The encrypted hash is attached to the data along with the user's public verification key. Any user that receives the data will verify this certificate by validating the user name and the signature of the CA. In addition, the certificate revocation list (CRL) in which the certificate belongs will also verify that the certificate has not been revoked. If it has been revoked, the user will be warned.

Digital signatures can also verify the integrity of the data. The user also uses the public verification key to decrypt the hash code included with the data. The automatic calculation of a second hash value from the data and the comparison of the hash values determine whether the data have been altered. If the hash values are not the same, the data have been altered. Data integrity has thus been confirmed.

Balancing Public-Key and Role-Based Encryption

Access control, role-based, symmetric and asymmetric cryptography are a powerful combination enabling an organization to address diverse requirements to authenticate users, ensure the integrity and confidentiality of the data, and validate participants in an electronic transaction. This combination, and the ability to select the appropriate level of authentication and key management process, based on the type of electronic transaction to be secured, will promote the successful deployment of cryptography throughout an organization.

In addition, organizations will be able to more effectively manage the impact to network resources and reduce system administration. Guidelines to consider in determining the use of public-key versus role-based data encryption include, but are not limited to:

1. *Key management:* Public-key systems effectively manage the establishment and distribution of symmetric session keys used to digitally sign a document or encrypt data. Public-key systems increase key management complexity by requiring the secure creation and maintenance of a centralized repository of public keys. Because each repetitive use of a public key allows an attacker to build a store of information that can be used to compromise the key and gain unauthorized access to confidential information, public keys require a limited lifetime to minimize damage from a compromised key.

Public-key systems require secure distribution of both public and private keys with the added obligation of continuously issuing, updating, distributing, and revoking key pairs. This complicates key management but addresses specific authentication needs.

2. *Certificate management:* Certificates enhance public-key cryptography by providing the mechanism to validate public keys used in the data encryption or digital signature process. A certificate functions like the stamp of a notary public, in that public keys are packaged in certificates to aid in ensuring the correct association of a public key with its proper owner or assignee.

As in identity-based access control systems, managing keys or certificates on an *individual* basis perpetuates the security deployment nightmare and affects both the scalability and cost of corporate networks. Public-key pairs and certificates have a limited life, certificates must be revoked, and revocation of certificates must be published. In addition, key pairs require backup, recovery, and other maintenance in an enterprise public-key infrastructure.

In a role-based cryptography model, dynamically (JIT) created symmetric session keys reduce public key management by eliminating the need for one of the public key pairs—the data encryption key pair used to distribute the symmetric key. This eliminates the key and certificate management and administration associated with the public key process for data encryption.

3. *Resource constraints:* A proven solution for situations with one-to-one communication paths, the public-key option is less efficient for complex information flows with large numbers of recipients. For example, in a typical public-key implementation, an encrypted message sent by the vice president of sales to 200 sales representatives would require that the encryption process obtain all 200 public keys from a central repository, validate the certificates on each key, and encrypt the symmetric session key once using each recipient's public key (200 times in total). The 200 newly encrypted symmetric session keys would then be attached to the encrypted data and transmitted. Voluminous inquiries and certificate validation using a centralized public key repository combined with expanded file sizes significantly increases network traffic.

The label process in a role-based cryptography model is ideal for applications with complex communication flows involving one sender and many recipients because RBC creates and attaches a small, static header (typically 1024 bits or smaller) to the encrypted data during the encryption process. The header contains minimal information only, including the sender's identity, label names, file name, and so forth. Because recipient access is controlled through the labels, this multipurpose header does not increase in size if a message is sent to one person or thousands of people, resulting in a scalable, network-efficient solution.

4. *Security:*   Depending on the sensitivity of the data, organizations need the flexibility to pick and choose the level of security to meet specific requirements. For more confidential information, public-key systems may be less secure because they typically attach the encrypted symmetric session key to the sensitive transmitted or stored data. Much like the contents of a safe are compromised by hiding the combination to the safe in an envelope and attaching the envelope to the front of the safe, attaching the encrypted key to the data jeopardizes the security of the data. Depending on the implementation, a successful attack on the encrypted session key may compromise the data.

In an RBC system, the keys are never stored with the encrypted information; therefore, the session key can never be intercepted. RBC's JIT key generation process automatically manages and distributes the multiple key splits used to create session keys, simplifying administration by shifting the security administrator's burden of managing keys to managing access authority. See Figure 20-3.

Figure 20-3
Key Management

WRAP-UP

A role-based model for information security, although embryonic in stage, will be instrumental in centralizing and bringing the administration of diverse security solutions to an acceptable level in the balancing of information access, deployment cost, and security. In addition, this model supports a phased approach to implementing technology, allowing an organization to establish multiple barriers, while building an enterprise infrastructure to support safe and reliable electronic business transactions across the Internet and other global networks.

PART 5

New Dimensions

CHAPTER 21

Cryptanalysis and System Identification

Changer son fusil d'épaule.
Try a new line of attack.

—*Bazeries*

Cryptanalysis is the science of reading someone's secrets without that person's ever knowing it. It is mathematics at its best or its worst. A better part of this book has focused on changing valid messages into cipher text via an encryption algorithm. Now we attempt to remove the message from its secret form without knowledge or use of secret keys.

We need a broad brush to paint pieces of the process at an understandable level. We divide this chapter into increasingly complex cryptanalytical topics: (1) cryptanalytical strategies, (2) vertical classification of systems using classical techniques, (3) password crackers and reverse engineering, (4) system identification using feature vectors, and (5) key-cluster techniques for elemental key separation and identification. We discuss the latter two points based on historical studies initiated by Drs. I. J. Kumar and T. L. Rao and current confirming studies performed by the ICSA and COMSEC Solutions cryptography laboratories.

Cryptanalytic Strategies

There are an infinite number of cryptanalytic methods and they may be roughly classified into these strategies to *compromise* the cryptosystem:

Pure cryptanalysis represents the purest form of unauthorized decryption because no assumptions are made whatsoever. Pure cryptanalysis does not use a linguist, because only mathematics is required. It functions in any language, even one that the unauthorized decryptor does not know. Many like this line of attack because it is so amenable to computer programming and machine solution. Pure cryptanalysis requires long texts to derive the appropriate data. Pure cryptanalysis—such as determination of the period in a polyalphabetic substitution or Kerckhoff's superimposition of several polyalphabetic alphabets—represents a reduction to an intermediate language that is a monoalphabetic, possibly polygraphic, encryption of the plain-text language. The *cipher text-only attack* is a more general form of an attack than pure cryptanalysis, because it allows reflections and assumptions based on the kind of language the plain text is taken from. Typically the frequency distribution of single characters in the cipher text is investigated. The *frequency distribution* may be used to determine the language and exclude encryption methods that level frequencies. Frequency examination is used to break a monoalphabetic substitution system or strip a simple substitution from a transposition.

If a frequency distribution portends a polyalphabetic or polygraphic substitution, pure cryptanalysis can be used to reduce the system to monoalphabetic terms. This type of examination is usually a linguistic one.

Much more linguistic are methods that exploit a *plain text-cipher text compromise*. They use probable words or phrases as starting points for pattern finding. There is the *known-plain text attack* and the *chosen plain text attack,* which differ only in the way the compromise is achieved, passively or actively. The known-plain text attack requires clever guesses at plain-text fragments. It helps to understand your adversary, his language, his background, and his ways of thinking. These often lead to a useful *crib* for entry into a cryptogram. *Known-plain text attacks* may require the unauthorized decryptor to be in possession of all the results of intelligence, reconnaissance, espionage, and decryptions by all other decryptors. This requirement is in conflict with security measures based on the "need to know" doctrine.

The *chosen plain text attack* needs only cunning to produce a compromise—cunning is unlimited. The famous World War II Battle of Midway ruse of reporting the breakdown of the freshwater distillation plant to confirm "AF" as the coordinates of Midway's location on the Japanese CHI-HE system is a good example of the required cunning. A *derived plain text attack* represents a third case. It comes from a cipher text-cipher text compromise if one of the systems is already broken and the plain text can be obtained. The process of deliberate *gardening* was essentially a continuation of the break and led to additional cipher text-cipher text compromises.

The *cipher text-cipher text* compromise is particularly insidious because it originates as a consequence of cryptological thoughtlessness such as repeating indicators with the Enigma or exploitation of a *stagger* (a repeated transmission with the same key after a one- or two-letter error) via superimposition. Cipher text-cipher text compromises allow pure cryptanalysis to be performed on large or networked computers. For public-key systems, the cipher text-cipher text compromise is an inherent feature (and risk) in the system.

For composition of encryption methods, one normally aims at stripping off one encryption after another. This is easier, if a *superencryption* is made over an encryption method that has been used for some time and has been broken, thus making the intermediate cipher text a known language and system.

Four Basic Operations of Cryptanalysis

The American master cryptanalyst, William F. Friedman, taught us that there are four classical operations for the solution of practically every cryptogram:

1. The determination of the language employed in the plain-text version.

2. The determination of the general system of cryptography employed.

3. The reconstruction of the specific key in the case of a cipher system or the reconstruction partial or complete, of the codebook, in the case of a code system or both in the case of an enciphered code system.

4. The reconstruction or establishment of the plain text.

In some cases, Step 2 may proceed Step 1. This is the *classical approach* to cryptanalysis. It may be further reduced to:

1. Arrangement and rearrangement of data to disclose nonrandom characteristics or manifestations (i.e., frequency counts, repetitions, patterns, symmetrical phenomena)

2. Recognition of the nonrandom characteristics or manifestations when disclosed (via statistics or other techniques)

3. Explanation of nonrandom characteristics when recognized (by luck, intelligence, or perseverance)

Much of the work comes from determining the general system. In the final analysis, the solution of every cryptogram involving a form of substitution depends upon its reduction to monoalphabetic terms, if it is not originally in those terms. The preceding procedures may be applied in modified form to modern cryptograms. Because of the computer, we deal with 256 ASCII character substitutions or a similar number of hexadecimal equivalents, rather than just 26 English letters.

Solving recreational substitution and transposition ciphers is the mission of the American Cryptogram Association (ACA), which offers public education courses covering over 75 cipher systems of varying difficulty. Since 1929, the ACA has published *The Cryptogram* magazine devoted to classical cryptography. The author's first two books *Classical Cryptography Course,* volumes I and II are devoted to the cryptanalysis of these simpler cryptographic systems and, of course, are highly recommended.

Classical cryptography presents some interesting theory that permits a vertical classification/differentiation of cryptographic algorithms and suggests their vulnerability to easy to moderate attack. We look at cornerstone tests: Chi, Kappa, Psi, and I.C., and for the most part we use English to illustrate the theory. We then apply these techniques in an automated test suite to vertically classify the difficulty of cryptosystems. Later in this chapter, we build on the classification scheme using pattern recognition for cryptosystem identification and follow that by key clustering to sort out the right key.

Chi Test

William F. Friedman originally developed the theory of *monographic coincidence* in plain text. It was applied in his technical paper written in 1925 dealing with his solution of messages enciphered by a cryptographic machine known as the "Herbern Electric Super-Code." (The paper is among his Riverbank Publications in 1934.)

If two plain-text messages are compared, it is possible that the same letter will occur in both messages at the same point in the message. Similarly, if two messages enciphered in the same system are compared, it is also possible that the same cipher letter (representing the same plain-text letter) will occur at the same point in each message. We need to determine the probability of this type of coincidence occurring. The probability of coincidence of two As in plain text is the square of the probability of occurrence of the single letter A in such text; same thing with Bs through Zs.

The sum of these squares for all letters of the alphabet as shown in Table 21-1, is found to be 0.0667. This is almost double the combined probability of random text for hitting two random text letters coincidentally or:

$$\text{Kr} = 26 \text{ letters} \times 1/26 \times 1/26 = 1/26 = 0.0385$$

The value 0.0667 is denoted Kp and it is the probability that any two letters selected at random in a large volume of normal English plain text will coincide.

Given a 50-letter plain-text distribution:

```
3  1171  23  1256   2562  2
A B C D E F G H I J K L M N O P Q R S T U V W X Y Z
```

The number of pairings that can be made are $n(n-1)/2 = (50 \times 49)/2 = 1225$ comparisons. According to the theory of coincidences, there should

TABLE 21-1

Calculation of Monographic Coincidence Probability

Letter	Frequency in 1000 Letters of Separate Letter	Probability of Occurrence of Each Letter	Square of Probability Occurrence
A	73.66	0.0737	0.0054
B	9.74	.0097	.0001
C	30.68	.0307	.0009
D	42.44	.0424	.0018
E	129.96	.1300	.0169
F	28.32	.0283	.0008
G	16.38	.0164	.0003
H	33.88	.0339	.0012
I	73.52	.0735	.0054
J	1.64	.0016	.0000
K	2.96	.0030	.0000
L	36.42	.0364	.0013
M	24.74	.0247	.0006
N	79.50	.0795	.0063
O	75.28	.0753	.0057
P	26.70	.0267	.0007
Q	3.50	.0035	.0000
R	75.76	.0758	.0057
S	61.16	.0612	.0037
T	91.90	.0919	.0084
U	26.00	.0260	.0007
V	15.32	.0153	.0002
W	15.60	.0156	.0002
X	4.62	.0046	.0000
Y	19.34	.0193	.0004
Z	.98	.0010	.0000
Total	1000.00	1.0000	0.0667

be $1225 \times 0.0667 = 81.7065$, or approximately 82 coincidences of single letters. We look at the distribution and find there are 82 for a very close agreement. The top row is the number of occurrences. The bottom numbers are the value $n(n - 1)/2$.

```
3   1 1 7  1   2 3      1 2 5   6      2 5
A B C D E  F G H I  J K L M N   O  P Q R S
3+0+0+0+21+0+0+1+3+0+0+0+1+10+15+0+0+1+10
  6   2   2
  T   U V W X Y Z
+15+1+0+1+0+0+0=82
```

If N is the total number of letters in the distribution, then the number of comparisons is $N(N-1)/2$ and the expected number of coincidences may be written:

$$.0067N(N-1)/2 \qquad \text{[Eq. 21-1]}$$

or

$$(.0067N^2 - 0.0667N)/2 \qquad \text{[Eq. 21-2]}$$

If we let Fa = number of occurrences of A in the foregoing distribution, the number of coincidences for letter A is $Fa(Fa-1)/2$. Similarly for B, we have $Fb(Fb-1)/2$. The total number of coincidences for the distribution is:

$$Fa(Fa-1)/2 + Fb(Fb-1)/2 + \cdots + Fz(Fz-1)/2 \qquad \text{[Eq. 21-3]}$$

Let $F\beta$ = any letter A...Z and Σ = the sum of all terms that follow it. The distribution $\Sigma(F\beta^2 - F\beta)/2$ represents the actual coincidences.

Although derived from different sources we equate the terms.

$$\Sigma(F\beta^2 - F\beta)/2 = (.0067N^2 - 0.0667N)/2 \qquad \text{[Eq. 21-4]}$$

$$\Sigma F\beta = N \qquad \text{[Eq. 21-5]}$$

$$\Sigma(F\beta^2 - F\beta) = (.0067N^2 - 0.0667N) \qquad \text{[Eq. 21-6]}$$

$$\Sigma F\beta^2 - N = (.0067N^2 - 0.0667N) \qquad \text{[Eq. 21-7]}$$

$$\Sigma F\beta^2 = .0067N^2 + 0.9333N \qquad \text{[Eq. 21-8]}$$

The last equation tells us the sum of the squares of the absolute frequencies of a distribution is equal to 0.0667 times the square of the total number of letters in the distribution, plus 0.933 times the total number of letters in the distribution. Now, we will see if we can replace the $\Sigma F\beta^2$ term with a more practical measure.

Suppose two monoalphabetic distributions pertain to the same cipher alphabet. If they are to be correctly combined into a single distribution, the latter must still be monoalphabetic. We use subscripts 1 and 2 to indicate the distributions in question. So:

$$\Sigma(F\beta_1 + F\beta_2)^2 = .0067(N_1 + N_2)^2 + 0.9333(N_1 + N_2) \qquad \text{[Eq. 21-9]}$$

expanding terms:

$$\Sigma F\beta_1^2 + 2\Sigma F\beta_1 F\beta_2 + \Sigma F\beta_2^2 = 0.0667(N_1^2 + 2N_1N_2 + N_2^2) + .9333N_1 + .9333N_2 \qquad \text{[Eq. 21-10]}$$

$$\Sigma F\beta_1^2 = .0067N_1^2 + 0.9333N_1 \qquad \text{[Eq. 21-11]}$$

$$\Sigma F\beta_2^2 = .0067N_2^2 + 0.9333N_2 \qquad \text{[Eq. 21-12]}$$

and rearranging:

$$.0667N_1^2 + .9333N_1 + 2\,\Sigma\,F\beta_1 F\beta_2 + .0667N_2^2 + .9333N_2$$

$$= .0667(N_1^2 + 2N_1N_2 + N_2^2) + .9333N_1 + .9333N_2 \qquad \text{[Eq. 21-13]}$$

further reducing:

$$2\,\Sigma\,F\beta_1 F\beta_2 = 0.667(2N_1N_2) \qquad \text{[Eq. 21-14]}$$

and finally:

$$\frac{\Sigma\,F\beta_1 F\beta_2}{N_1N_2} = 0.667 \qquad \text{[Eq. 21-15]}$$

This equation permits the establishment of an expectant value for the sum of products of the corresponding frequencies of the two distributions being considered for amalgamation. The Chi test or cross-product test is based on Eq. 21-15.

Given two distributions to be matched:

```
         1 4   3   1       1       1       1     3 2 2 1   1 3   2
 F₁      A B C D E F G H I J K L M N O P Q R S T U V W X Y Z


           2       3       1 1       1 1       3 1 1         1 2
 F₂      A B C D E F G H I J K L M N O P Q R S T U V W X Y Z
```

We juxtapose the frequencies for convenience.

```
                                                  N₁ = 26
 Fβ₁      1 4   3   1       1       1       1     3 2 2 1   1 3   2
          A B C D E F G H I J K L M N O P Q R S T U V W X Y Z
 Fβ₂      2       3       1 1       1 1       3 1 1         1 2
                                                  N₂ = 17
 Fβ₁Fβ₂  0 8 0   0 0 3 0 0 1 0 0 0 0 0 1 0 0 9 2 2 0 0 0 0 0 4
            Σ = 30
```

$$N_1N_2 = 26 \times 17 = 442 \qquad \text{[Eq. 21-16]}$$

$$\Sigma\,\frac{F\beta_1 F\beta_2}{N_1N_2} = \frac{30}{442} = 0.0711 \qquad \text{[Eq. 21-17]}$$

Compared to $442 \times 0.0667 = 28.15$, the *expected* value, versus 30, the *actual* value, the two distributions very probably belong together.

To point out the effectiveness of the correct Chi test placement, we look at the example, but juxtaposed one interval to the left.

$$N_1 = 26$$

	1	4	3	1		1		1		1		3	2	2	1		1	3		2	
F_1	A	B	C	D	E	F	G	H	I	J	K	L	M	N	O	P	Q	R	S	T	U V W X Y Z

F_1 A B C D E F G H I J K L M N O P Q R S T U V W X Y Z
F_2 B C D E F G H I J K L M N O P Q R S T U V W X Y Z A

| 2 | | | 3 | | 1 | 1 | | 1 | 1 | | 3 | 1 | 1 | | | | 1 | 2 |

$$N_2 = 17$$

$F\beta_1 F\beta_2$ 0 0 0 0 0 0 0 0 0 0 0 0 0 0 0 0 3 2 0 0 0 0 3 0 0

$$\Sigma F\beta_1 F\beta_2 = 2 + 3 + 2 + 3 = 10$$

$$\frac{\Sigma \, F\beta_1 F\beta_2}{N_1 N_2} = \frac{10}{442} = 0.226 \qquad \textbf{[Eq. 21-18]}$$

Thus, if the two distributions pertain to the same primary components, then they are not properly superimposed. The Chi test may also be applied to cases where two or more frequency distributions must be shifted relatively in order to find the correct superimposition. The problem determines whether we use *direct* superimposition or *shifted* superimposition of the second distribution in question.

Basic Theory of Coincidences— Kappa Test

We know that the probability of monographic coincidence of random text employing a 26-letter alphabet is 0.0385, and in English telegraphic plain text is 0.0667. We define these values as Kr and Kp, respectively.

One of the most important techniques in classical cryptanalysis is that of applying the *Kappa test* or *test of coincidences,* the most important purpose for which is to ascertain whether two or more sequences are correctly superimposed, where "correct" means the sequences are so arranged to facilitate or make possible a solution. The Kappa test has the following theoretical basis:

1. If any two rather lengthy sequences of characters are superimposed, as successive pairs of letters are brought into vertical juxtaposition, it will be found that in a certain number of cases the two superimposed letters will coincide.

2. If we are dealing with random text (26-letter alphabet), there will be 38 or 39 cases of coincidence per 1000 pairs of letters examined because Kr = 0.0385.

3. If we are dealing with plain text (English), there will be 66 or 67 cases of coincidence per 1000 pairs of letters examined because Kp = 0.0667.

4. If the superimposed sequences are wholly monoalphabetic encipherments of plain text by the same cipher alphabet, there will be 66 or 67 cases of coincidence per 1000 pairs of letters examined because in monoalphabetic substitution there is a fixed or unvarying relation between plain text and cipher text, so that for statistical purposes the cipher text behaves just as if it were normal plain text.

5. Even if the two superimposed sequences are polyalphabetic in character, there will still be 66 or 67 cases of coincidence or identity per 1000 pairs of letters examined provided the two sequences really belong to the same cryptographic system and are superimposed at the proper point with respect to the keying sequence.

This last point may be seen in the following two polyalphabetic messages; they have been enciphered polyalphabetically by the same two primary components sliding against each other. The two messages begin at the same point in the keying sequence. Consequently, they are identically enciphered; letter for letter, the only differences between them are due to differences in plain text.

No. 1

Alphabet:	16	21	13	5	6	4	17	19	21	21	2	6	3	6	13	13	1	7	12	6
Plain:	W	H	E	N	I	N	T	H	E	C	O	U	R	S	E	L	O	N	G	M
Cipher:	E	*Q*	*N*	B	T	F	Y	R	C	X	X	L	Q	J	N	Z	O	Y	A	W

No. 2

Alphabet:	16	21	13	5	6	4	17	19	21	21	2	6	3	6	13	13	1	7	12	6
Plain:	T	H	E	G	E	N	E	R	A	L	A	B	S	O	L	U	T	E	L	Y
Cipher:	P	*Q*	*N*	T	U	F	B	W	D	J	L	Q	H	Y	Z	P	T	M	Q	I

Note, that (1) in every case in which two superimposed cipher letters are the same, the plain-text letters are identical and (2) in every case in which two superimposed cipher letters are the different, the plain-text letters are different. In such a system, even though the cipher alphabet changes from letter to letter, the number of cases of identity or coincidence in the two members of a pair of superimposed cipher letters will still be about 66 or 67 per 1000 cases examined, because the two members of each pair of superimposed letters are in the same alphabet and it has been seen previously (in point 4) that in monoalphabetic cipher text, K is the same as for plain text, namely, 0.0667. The fact that in this case each monoalphabet contains just two letters does not affect the theoretical value of K (Kappa) and whether the actual number of coincidences agrees closely with the expected number based upon Kp = 0.0667 depends upon the lengths of the two superimposed sequences. The No. 1 and No. 2 messages are said to be superimposed correctly, that is, brought into proper juxtaposition with respect to the keying sequences.

Now change the situation by changing the juxtaposition to an incorrect superimposition with respect to the keying sequence.

No. 1

Alphabet:	16	21	13	5	6	4	17	19	21	21	2	6	3	6	13	13	1	7	12	6
Plain:	W	H	E	N	I	N	T	H	E	C	O	U	R	S	E	L	O	N	G	M
Cipher:	E	Q	N	B	T	F	Y	R	C	X	X	L	Q	J	N	Z	O	Y	A	W

No. 2

Alphabet:	16	21	13	5	6	4	17	19	21	21	2	6	3	6	13	13	1	7	12	6
Plain:	T	H	E	G	E	N	E	R	A	L	A	B	S	O	L	U	T	E	L	Y
Cipher:	P	Q	N	T	U	F	B	W	D	J	L	Q	H	Y	Z	P	T	M	Q	I

It is evident that the two members of every pair are not in the same cipher alphabets and any identical letters after superimposition is strictly accidental. Actually, the number of repetitions will approximate Kr = 0.0385.

Note again that, in every case in which two superimposed cipher letters are the same, the plain-text letters are not identical and in every case in which two superimposed cipher letters are different, the plain-text letters are not always different. Look at the superimposed **T** (cipher) representing two different plain-text letters and note that the **S** in "COURSE" gives the value J (cipher) and in the word "ABSOLUTE-LY" gives H (cipher). It should be clear that an incorrect superimposition by two different plain-text letters enciphered by two different alphabets may, by chance, produce identical cipher letters. On superimposition they yield coincidences but have no external indications as to dissimilarity in plain-text equivalents. This incorrect superimposition will coincide by a value of Kr = 0.0385.

Note the **Z**s in each message represent the plain text **L**. This occurred because the same cipher alphabet came into play twice, by chance, to encipher the same plain-text letter both times. This may distort the Kr value for some systems.

In general, in the case of correct superimposition, the probability of identity or coincidence is Kp = 0.0667; in the case of incorrect superimposition, the probability is greater than or equal to Kr = 0.0385. The Kappa test (aka coincidence test) is defined by these values (and is specific in the preceding example to English coding).

Applying the Kappa Test

When we say Kp = 0.0667, this means that in a 1000 cases where two letters are drawn at random from a large volume of plain text, we should expect 66 or 67 cases of two letters to coincide or be identical. Nothing is specified what these letters shall be; they can be two Zs or two E's. Another way is to consider that at random, 6.67 percent of the comparisons made will yield coincidences. So for 2000 examinations, we expect $2000 \times 6.67\% = 133.4$ coincidences, or 20,000 comparisons mean 1334 coincidences.

A more practical approach is to find the ratio of the observed number of coincidences to the total number of cases in question that may occur, that is, the total number of comparisons of superimposed letters. When the ratio is closer to 0.0667 than 0.0385, the correct superimposition has been found. This is true because both members of each pair of superimposed letters belong to the same monoalphabet and therefore the probability of their coinciding is 0.067; whereas, in the case of incorrect superimposition, each pair belongs to different monoalphabets and the probability of their coinciding approaches 0.0385 rather than 0.0667.

To use the Kappa test requires calculating the total number of comparisons in a given case and the actual number of coincidences in the case under consideration. When two messages are superimposed, the total number of comparisons made equals the number of superimposed letters. When more than two messages are superimposed in a superimposition diagram it is necessary to calculate the number of comparisons based on the number of letters in the column.

$$n \text{ letters} = n(n-1)/2 \text{ pairs or comparisons in column} \qquad \textbf{[Eq. 21-19]}$$

For a column of 3 letters, there are $3(2)/2 = 3$ comparisons.

We compare the first with the second, second with the third, and the first with the third columns. The more general probability formula is:

$$nCr = n!/r!(n-r)! \qquad \textbf{[Eq. 21-20]}$$

where we determine the number of combinations of n different things taken r at a time. For two letters, r is always 2, so $n!/r!(n-r)!$ is the same as

$$n(n-1)(n-2)/2(n-2) \qquad \textbf{[Eq. 21-21]}$$

and becomes

$$n(n-1)/2 \qquad \text{[Eq. 21-22]}$$

with the cancellation of terms using $(n - 2)$.

The number of comparisons per column times the number of columns in the superimposition diagram of letters gives the total number of comparisons. The extension to this reasoning is where the superimposition diagram involves columns of various lengths. In this case, we add the number of comparisons for columns of different lengths to obtain a grand total. Table 21-2 shows the number of letters in a column versus the number of comparisons calculated.

In ascertaining the number of coincidences in the case of a column containing several letters, we still use the $n(n - 1)/2$ formula, only in

TABLE 21-2

Number of Letters in a Column vs. Number of Comparisons Calculated

Number of Letters in Column	Number of Comparisons
2	1
3	3
4	6
5	10
6	15
7	21
8	28
9	36
10	45
11	55
12	66
13	78
14	91
15	105
16	120
17	136
18	153
19	171
20	190
21	210
22	231
23	253
24	276
25	300
26	325
27	351
28	378
29	406
30	435

this case, n is the number of identical letters in the column. The reasoning is essentially the same as previously. The total number of coincidences is the sum of the number of coincidences for each case of identity.

Given the column:

C
K
B
K
Z
K
C
B
B
K

There are 10 letters with 3 Bs, 2 Cs, 4 Ks, and 1 Z. The 3 Bs yield 3 coincidences, the 2 Cs yield 1 coincidence, and the 4 Ks yield 6 coincidences. The sum is $3 + 1 + 6 = 10$ coincidences in 45 comparisons = 0.2222.

Derivation of Approach to Randomness—Psi and I.C. Calculations

The property that distinguishes a monoalphabetic distribution from that corresponding to a polyalphabetic message is the former has a greater variation among the frequencies of the individual letters. The greater the number of alphabets employed in the encryption process (or the greater the number of substitution characters available and used—ASCII), the more nearly the cipher distribution will average out and take on a "flattened" appearance. If all 26 letters of English represented an alphabet (A-Z) and were used, we would expect the relative frequencies of all cipher letters to be approximately equal, that is, $1/26 = 0.03846$. If the entire ASCII set is employed and each character represents an expanded alphabet, the frequency of all letters would be $1/256 = 0.003906$. Designers of cryptographic systems try to match this parameter because it is as close to true randomness as possible. The closer the distribution is to random "noise," the more difficult the job for the cryptanalyst.

By the amount of *roughness* of a distribution, qualitatively speaking, we mean the amount by which individual frequencies differ from normal expectations. *A truly flat distribution has zero variation.* In order to use this concept as a tool in our attempt to vertically classify, a more precise definition is required.

The relative frequency of an event x is defined as:

$$\frac{\text{Number of occurrences of } x}{\text{Total number of experiments}} \qquad \textbf{[Eq. 21-23]}$$

If the letter B occurs 48 times in 1000-letter cipher text, the relative frequency of B, denoted $f(b)$, is 0.048.

If we add all the frequencies of English (26) letters in a sample text of 1000 letters, we get:

$$\frac{f(a)}{1000} + \frac{f(b)}{1000} + \cdots + \frac{f(z)}{1000} = 1.000 \qquad \textbf{[Eq. 21-24]}$$

or for ASCII (1-256):

$$\frac{f(01)}{1000} + \frac{f(02)}{1000} + \cdots + \frac{f(256)}{1000} = 1.000 \qquad \textbf{[Eq. 21-25]}$$

where 01 = ASCII element 01, and so forth.

The probability of occurrence of an event x is defined as the limit of relative frequencies of x as the total number n of experiments increases:

$$p(b) = \lim_{n \to \infty} \frac{\text{number of occurrences of B}}{n} \qquad \textbf{[Eq. 21-26]}$$

If all the letters of the alphabet occurred with the same frequency, we would have:

$$f(a) = f(b) = \cdots = f(z) \qquad \textbf{[Eq. 21-27]}$$

or for ASCII

$$f(01) = f(02) = \cdots = f(256) \qquad \textbf{[Eq. 21-28]}$$

now

$$\sum_{i=A}^{i=Z} \frac{f(i)}{n} = 1 \qquad \sum_{i=1}^{i=256} \frac{f(i)}{n} = 1$$
$$\text{English} \qquad\quad \text{ASCII Coding} \qquad \textbf{[Eq. 21-29]}$$

then

$$\frac{f(a)}{n} = \frac{f(b)}{n} = \cdots = \frac{f(z)}{n} = \frac{1}{26} = 0.03846 \qquad \textbf{[Eq. 21-30]}$$

$$p(a) = p(b) = \cdots = p(z) = \frac{1}{26} \qquad \textbf{[Eq. 21-31]}$$

$$\frac{f(01)}{n} = \frac{f(02)}{n} = \cdots = \frac{f(256)}{n} = \frac{1}{256} = 0.003906 \qquad \textbf{[Eq. 21-32]}$$

$$p(01) = p(02) = \cdots = p(256) = \frac{1}{256} = 0.003906 \qquad \textbf{[Eq. 21-33]}$$

We know that the 26 letters of English do not occur with equal frequencies and therefore their probabilities $p(a)$, $p(b)$,..., are not equal. They have positive values between zero and one and add up to one. This same kind of statement can be made for an ASCII distribution.

$$\sum_{\substack{i = A \\ \text{English}}}^{i = Z} p(i) = 1 \qquad \sum_{\substack{I = 1 \\ \text{ASCII Coding}}}^{i = 256} p(i) = 1 \qquad \textbf{[Eq. 21-34]}$$

The amount that $p(a)$ differs from 1/26, that is, its deviation from the average probability, is $p(a) - (1/26)$. For any letter i, a measure of roughness M.R. of the distribution would be a function of these 26 quantities $p(i) - (1/26)$. For an ASCII system, the measure is a function of these 256 quantities $p(i) - (1/256)$.

The desired measure could not be anything so simple as just the sum of the deviations because some are positive and some are negative. They balance out when added and yield 0. To get around this problem, we could sum the magnitudes or the absolute values of the deviations:

$$\sum_{\substack{i = A \\ \text{English}}}^{i = Z} \left| (p(i) - \frac{1}{26} \right| \qquad \sum_{\substack{i = 1 \\ \text{ASCII Coding}}}^{i = 256} \left| p(i) - \frac{1}{256} \right| \qquad \textbf{[Eq. 21-35]}$$

An even better route is to make all the terms positive by squaring each deviation. So:

$$\text{M.R.} = \sum_{\substack{i = A \\ \text{English}}}^{i = Z} [p(i) - 1/26]^2 \qquad \text{M.R.} = \sum_{\substack{i = 1 \\ \text{ASCII Coding}}}^{i = 256} [p(i) - 1/256]^2 \qquad \textbf{[Eq. 21-36]}$$

where M.R. is defined as the measure of roughness.

M.R. can be simplified somewhat. We square the binomial $p(i)-(1/26)$:

$$p(i)^2 - 2p(i)(1/26) + (1/26)^2 \qquad \textbf{[Eq. 21-37]}$$

Summing for all values of i from A to Z we obtain:

$$\text{M.R.} = \sum_{i = A}^{i = Z} p(i)^2 - \sum_{i = A}^{i = Z} 2p(i)(1/26) + \sum_{i = A}^{i = Z} (1/26)^2 \qquad \textbf{[Eq. 21-38]}$$

The last term is the same for all i, so $26(1/26)^2 = 1/26$; the middle term is $2(1/26) \sum_{i=A}^{i=Z} p(i)$. Since

$$\sum_{i=A}^{i=Z} p(i) = 1 \qquad \textbf{[Eq. 21-39]}$$

this term reduces to $2(1/26)$.

$$\text{M.R.} = \sum_{i=A}^{i=Z} p(i)^2 - 2(1/26) + 1/26 = \sum_{i=A}^{i=Z} p(i)^2 - 1/26 \qquad \textbf{[Eq. 21-40]}$$

$$\text{M.R.} \sim \sum_{i=A}^{i=Z} p(i)^2 - 0.03846 \qquad \textbf{[Eq. 21-41]}$$

For ASCII the approach is the same:

$$p(i)^2 - 2p(i)(1/256) + (1/256)^2 \qquad \textbf{[Eq. 21-42]}$$

Summing for all values of i from 01 to 256 we obtain

$$\text{M.R.} = \sum_{i=01}^{i=256} p(i)^2 - \sum_{i=01}^{i=256} 2p(i)(1/256) + \sum_{i=01}^{i=256} (1/256)^2 \qquad \textbf{[Eq. 21-43]}$$

The last term is same for all i, so $256(1/256)^2 = 1/256$. The middle term is $2(1/256) \sum_{i=1}^{i=256} p(i)$. Since

$$\sum_{i=1}^{i=256} p(i) = 1 \qquad \textbf{[Eq. 21-44]}$$

this term reduces to $2(1/256)$.

$$\text{M.R.} = \sum_{i=1}^{i=256} p(i)^2 - 2(1/256) + 1/256 = \sum_{i=1}^{i=256} p(i)^2 - 1/256 \qquad \textbf{[Eq. 21-45]}$$

$$\text{M.R.} \sim \sum_{i=1}^{i=256} p(i)^2 - 0.003906$$

ASCII Coding   **[Eq. 21-46]**

If we are dealing with an English language distribution, we could calculate M.R. by summing the squares of all the characteristic frequencies and subtracting 0.038. We know the characteristic frequencies of the letters of plain text. The sum of their squares is 0.066. Thus M.R. for the plain text is $0.066 - 0.038 = 0.028$. For a flat distribution (in which all the letters have the same probability of occurrence), $p(i) = 1/26$ for all i. For this case the M.R. = 0.

$$\sum_{i=A}^{i=Z} p(i)^2 = \sum_{i=A}^{i=Z} (1/26)^2 = 26(1/26)^2 = 1/26 \qquad \textbf{[Eq. 21-47]}$$

$$\text{M.R.} = 1/26 - 1/26 = 0 \qquad \textbf{[Eq. 21-48]}$$

The ASCII distribution is uncertain; call it Y. So the characteristic frequencies using ASCII sum of their squares $= Y$. The M.R. for plain text in the ASCII field is $Y - 1/256$. For ASCII substitutions:

$$\text{M.R.} = 1/256 - 1/256 = 0 \qquad \text{[Eq. 21-49]}$$

Therefore the measure of roughness varies from 0 to 0.028 for English and from 0 to $(Y - 1/256)$ for an ASCII distribution. An interesting observation is that if at least 100 letters are being used in the ASCII set and that if at least 18 letters are in play, the estimate of this range is close to polyalphabetic for large data sets, or 0.038. So the measure of roughness will vary approximately from 0 to $(0.038 - 1/256) = 0.034$. The variation in either case is enough to permit us to distinguish between monoalphabets and polyalphabets, provided we are able to determine

$$\sum_{i=A}^{i=Z} p(i)^2 \qquad or \qquad \sum_{i=01}^{i=256} p(i)^2$$
$$\text{English} \qquad\qquad\qquad \text{ASCII} \qquad\qquad \text{[Eq. 21-50]}$$

We choose to vertically classify systems based on the most restrictive measure of roughness. The monoalphabeticity-based limit works for both English and ASCII data sets. Dr. J. P. Hoyt gave us a way to approximate the former limit in the general case: $p(a)$ represents the probability that an arbitrary selected letter in a cipher will be an A. Then $p(a)^2$ represents the probability that two letters selected at random will both be A; same thing for $p(b)^2$ representing both to B, and so forth. The probability that two letters picked at random would be the same regardless of their identity is:

$$p(a)^2 + p(b)^2 + \cdots + p(z)^2 = \sum_{i=A}^{i=Z} p(i)^2 \qquad \text{[Eq. 21-51]}$$

and for ASCII coding

$$p(01)^2 + p(02)^2 + \cdots + p(256)^2 = \sum_{i=01}^{i=256} p(i)^2 \qquad \text{[Eq. 21-52]}$$

We now need a means of approximating $\sum_{i=A}^{i=Z} p(i)^2$, without a knowledge of the quantities $p(i)$. We also need a way to estimate the ASCII data set, too.

In both cases, it is the probability that two letters or two symbols chosen at random will be the same. What we need to do is count how many pairs of identical letters or symbols there are in the cipher message and divide that number by the total number of possible pairs. How many pairs of letters can be formed from a given set? Suppose we have x letters in the set. Then the number of pairs we can get is determined as follows. As a first choice we can select any one of the letters, and that makes x possibilities. There then remain $x - 1$ letters for the second choice making a total of $x(x - 1)$ possibilities. But, in this count, each pair has been counted twice since the pair can be obtained in two different orders. Therefore, the number of pairs of letters that can be chosen from a set of x is $\frac{1}{2}[x(x - 1)]$.

If the observed frequency of A in a cipher message is $f(a)$, then the number of pairs of As that can be formed from these $f(A)$ letters is $\frac{1}{2}\{f(a)[f(a) - 1]\}$. The total number of like pairs regardless of identity of the letter is the sum:

$$\text{English Plain:} \quad \sum_{i = A}^{i = Z} \{f(i)[f(i) - 1]\}/2 \qquad \textbf{[Eq. 21-53]}$$

$$\text{ASCII:} \quad \sum_{i = 01}^{i = 256} \{f(i)[f(i) - 1]\}/2 \qquad \textbf{[Eq. 21-54]}$$

If the total number of letters is N, then the total possible number of pairs of letters is $\frac{1}{2}N(N-1)$. Note that this applies to the ASCII data set and doesn't require identity of the character or letter. Since the chance that two letters would be alike is the number of like pairs divided by the total number of pairs, we get one of the most famous equations in cryptography:

$$\textbf{I.C.} \sim \sum_{i = A}^{i = z} \{f(i)[f(i) - 1]\}/N(N - 1) \qquad \textbf{[Eq. 21-55]}$$

I.C., the *Index of Coincidence,* represents the chance that two letters in the distribution are alike, and is a more user-friendly measure than M.R. We found that the M.R. varies from 0 to 0 .028. Therefore,

$$\sum_{i = A}^{i = Z} p(i)^2 = \text{M.R.} + 0.038 \qquad \textbf{[Eq. 21-56]}$$

It varies from 0.038 to 0.066. The I.C. approximates the summation from A to Z (English) $p(i)^2$ and has the same range of variation: 0.038 to 0.066. The lower bound corresponds to a flat distribution and the upper bound corresponds to monoalphabeticity. For the ASCII data sets, the upper bound stays the same for design purposes but the lower bound is based on the 256 characters and symbols in the data set. The I.C. is calculated as:

$$\text{I.C.} \sim \sum_{i = 01}^{i = 256} \{f(i)[f(i) - 1]\}/N(N - 1) \qquad \textbf{[Eq. 21-57]}$$

$$\text{M.R.} \sim \sum_{\substack{i = 01 \\ \text{ASCII}}}^{i = 256} p(i)^2 - 0.003906$$

[Eq. 21-58]

So, the range would be $1/256 = 0.003906$ to 0.066 (approximately).

A measure of how this variation of values is related to the number of alphabets or characters and symbols and, hence, the flatness of the distribution can be calculated. The expected value that would be obtained for the I.C. for m alphabets and N letters enciphered (with each alphabet being applied to the same number of plain-text letters) is:

$$\text{I.C.} = \frac{1}{m} \frac{N - m}{N - 1} (0.066) + \frac{m - 1}{m} \frac{N}{N - 1} (0.038)$$

[Eq. 21-59]

m	I.C.
1	.066
2	.052
3	.044
4	.041
large	.038

for N relatively large and messages that are reasonably long. For ASCII, the equation is changed in the lower limit (we have assumed the upper limit is stable).

$$\text{I.C.} = \frac{1}{m} \frac{N - m}{N - 1} (0.066) + \frac{m - 1}{m} \frac{N}{N - 1} (0.003906)$$

[Eq. 21-60]

m	I.C.
1	.066
2	.034
3	.016
4	.009
large	.00392

Table 21-3 points out the relationship between the I.C. and sigma deviation surrounding a distribution. The sigma in the first column will be equaled or exceeded, by chance, on the average once every x times as shown in Table 21-3. The distribution of the δI.C. is closely approximated by the Chi-square distribution up to 4σ; this latter is a good measure for evaluating the sigma of the δI.C. For example, a distribution of 60 random letters or symbols in ASCII has a standard deviation δ of 0.12. Now, if a 60-letter sample under study has an observed δI.C. of 1.36

TABLE 21-3

Relationship Between I.C. and Sigma Deviation in a Distribution

Sigma S Calculated by δI.C.−1.00	Values of x Chi-Square Distribution Categories	
σ	10	26
1	6.6	6.4
$1\frac{1}{2}$	12	13
2	24	28
$2\frac{1}{2}$	49	64
3	100	160
$3\frac{1}{2}$	220	430
4	480	1200

then the sigma S = 1.36−1.00/.12 = 3, which found in the table shows one chance in 160 of equaling or exceeding this deviation if the sample were drawn from a random population.

Friedman defined:

Psi(p) = kp[$N(N-1)$], where kp = the repeat rate for a particular language; for English, the monoalphabetic kp = 0.0667.

Psi(r) = 1/c[$N(N-1)$], where N is the number of tallies in the distribution and c is the number of categories (symbols) in the alphabet or symbol group. For ASCII, $c = 256$.

Psi(o) = Σ[$f(i)$][$f(i) - 1$]], where $f(i)$ is the frequency of each element in the distribution.

$\sigma = \sqrt{2(c-1)}/\sqrt{[N(N-1)]}$ = standard deviation of the σI.C. of samples drawn from a flat population.

Vertical Differentiation of Cryptographic Systems Using Classical Parameters

COMSEC Solutions developed a cryptographic classification test suite for ICSA. ICSA is continuing to improve this suite to classify the strength of cryptographic products and evaluate the potential that a particular product, via its basis algorithm, might be vulnerable to easy-to-moderate attack. The tests are performed using known plain texts.

The suite has had some surprising success turning up potential implementation errors. COMSEC Solutions Suite consists of several classification tests: (1) Repetitions, (2) Entropy (both Shannon form and Pincus approximation), (3) Degree of Randomness or Approach to Mono/Poly Alphabeticity, (4) Graphical, and (5) Random number generator attacks. The suite can also be used to determine the approximate amount of cryptographic traffic carried along a VPN, or computer network backbone, for example, the auto industry's AIAX. Each test measures a different dimension of the tested cryptographic algorithm. Although the basis plain-text/cipher-text messages are in English, this is not a restriction. Supporting data have been included for other languages.

Test sets ranged from 400 characters to 30,000 characters. Cipher text was prepared using both selected keys and random chosen keys from a wide range of known key sets. A separate set of test sets was generated incrementing key length and salt values (random data added to the key to deter the cryptanalytical attack). Data sets were developed from a variety of data representations: binary, ASCII, BMP, TIF, GIF, JPG, WAV, MPEG, and plain text—military, standard, and nonstandard English.

The test suite program permits lab personnel to investigate test ciphers over the complete ASCII range of 0-256. It calculates file maximum, minimum, mode, standard deviation, character occurrences frequency distribution, weights, character entropies, cipher entropy, randomness, measures of letter affiliation and bonding Psi(random), Psi(plain-English), Psi(observed), I.C. (Incidence of Coincidence), and graphical measures of roughness and flatness. Viewed as a group, the preceding attributes can be used to effectively differentiate a cryptosystem and suggest its potential vulnerability to cryptanalytic attack of moderate form.

Evaluation Criteria

COMSEC Solutions and ICSA have performed repeatable evaluations on nearly 1800 cases on 40 different cryptosystems and vendor products. These evaluations have been performed on specific cryptosystems, and combinations of cryptosystems applied to known plain text or cipher text. Among the product offerings are: file encryptors, VPNs, tool kits, which have been tested extensively; and smartcards and accelerators, which still require significant research work. Three attack criteria—repetitions, entropy, and degree of randomness—have given clear and definitive system classification results. For technical sufficiency and credibility for certification, the ICSA automated test suite was designed to be repeatable, open, and use known algorithms. The entropy calculations were normalized to binary and ASCII basis.

The measures of degree of randomness, Psi calculations for the underlying language of the cipher text, the Incidence of Coincidence (I.C.), and the random number generator tests jointly yield selection criteria. The I.C. criteria are a measure of the natural bonding and affinity of the letters of a language (e.g., for English: TH, QU, ER). Every language exhibits letter affinities—especially for group frequencies and low-frequency consonants. Superencipherment does not guarantee that these natural bondings will be split. The Psi calculations are a measure of the roughness of the cipher-text distribution. They show the approach to random text or to monoalphabeticity or polyalphabeticity for an observed cipher text.

The test program shows the complete graphical distribution of ASCII characters for any file and calculates per-character values. It also segregates the alphanumerics on the graph. Plain text/cipher text enciphered by weak (vulnerable) cryptographic algorithms also showed marked peaks and troughs. Plain text/cipher text enciphered by strong cryptographic algorithms showed marked peaks and troughs. Although not a criterion per se, graphical analysis can be very dramatic and clear. The IRIS implementation of the Bazeries classical cipher is a good example. The Bazeries has known weaknesses and can be broken by hand. The IRIS implementation adds a masking effect as well as the ASCII diffusion. The graphical view shows the marked peaks and troughs in the cipher-text tests, and hence suggests potential cryptanalytic weakness.

Discussion

Refer to Figure 21-1 for the following discussion. The ICSA test suite established clear cutoff points, with respect to the cryptanalytical work required, to identify the four *arbitrary* classes of cryptosystems: Easy (trivial), Moderate (nontrivial), Strong, and Very Difficult (Figure 21-1).

Tests by COMSEC Solutions demonstrated that as a group, the classical systems placed in the Class I (Easy) classification and that the World War II rotor machines could be classified as Class II (Moderate). Tests further showed that the entire class of rotor machines clustered very well as a group. This is an advantage in the classification process

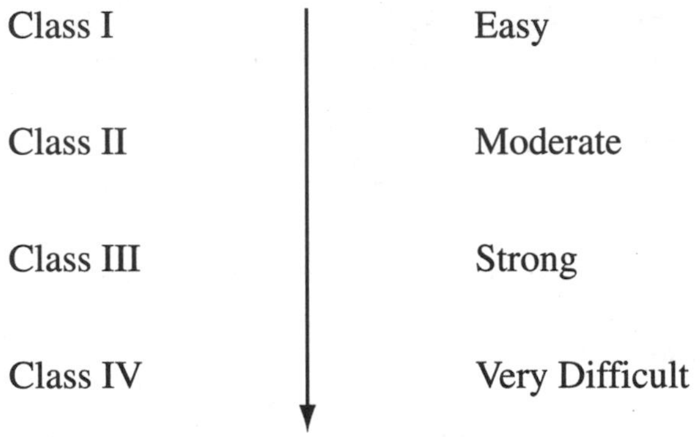

Figure 21-1
Vertical Differentia-
tion of Cryptosystems

Class I	Easy
Class II	Moderate
Class III	Strong
Class IV	Very Difficult

because it gives a clear demarcation of "moderate difficulty" systems to cryptanalyze. No assumptions about the calculations of system entropy or expected approach to randomness were made. Some algorithms required additional data for seed purposes. Consistent values were chosen between tests. Padding of test passwords was run in parametric form up to 128 bits.

Tables 21-4 to 21-6 show a small portion of the ongoing classification work. Table 21-4 gives the PKZIP 2.40g compression (Criterion = repetitions) values for 20 well-known cryptosystems. Note the clear distinction between the difficulty of cryptanalytic attack. In general, the lower the compression factor, the better the scrambling of data and fewer repetitions are available to feed the cryptanalyst for a wedge. The compression scale is 0% best-100% worst.

Table 21-5 shows the Shannon entropy (amount of information and degree of organization) that exists in the data. Note again that we have a clear definition of cryptosystems. The *entropy calculation* is a measure of predictability and organization of data. It originally came from the measurement of thermodynamic systems, where it represented the loss of energy (decay) in a thermodynamic process. The higher the entropy, the more chaotic and disorganized the information is, hence the more unpredictable the cryptographic shifts and more difficult the system is to break. The table also presents the calculated entropy from the weighted contributions of the cipher text. Entropy calculations have been standardized to the binary form.

Table 21-6 classifies the subject ciphers on the basis of approach to randomness of the cipher text. Calculations of the Psi(r), Psi(p), Psi(o), and I.C. (Index of Coincidence of two letters) help to classify the subject cryptosystem on the basis of probability and language bonds. The separation establishes a limit at complete random text and shows the

TABLE 21-4

Compression
(Repetitions)

Difficulty Class, %	Cryptosystem			
Easy 100 → 56	Test 100	Playfair 100	Viggy 99	
	Quadmire Isologs 69	Quadmire Periodic 69	ADFGVX (IRIS) 58	
	Homophonic Polyalphabetic 56			
Moderate (nontrivial) 40 → 35	4-Rotor Enigma 37 (cutoff)	Hebern 39	Autoclave 39	CSP1500 39
Strong 27 → 10	ZIP/PGP 27	PGP2.62 21	Blowfish 17	
Very Strong 10 → 0	RDES-Iris 0	3DES 0	RC4 6	RC5 6
	RDESCBC 0	RDESOFB 0	VPGP4.0 0	
	RPGP 0			

observed cipher text in relation to known values of monoalphabeticity or polyalphabeticity for a cryptosystem.

The attack criterion has been successful for the cipher tests.

Table 21-6 details results on some additional cryptosystems. These systems were excluded because not enough information was available or the cryptographic algorithm is proprietary.

Compression

Cipher-text repetitions provide a distinctive wedge into a cryptogram. One way to measure the number of repetitions is to use PKZIP V2.40g and to calculate the compression factor for the cipher text. PKZIP V2.40g is a well-known compression algorithm. It analyzes the subject file, searches for repeated bytes in succession or sequences, and replaces them with tokens to reduce the overall size of the file. Compression represents an inherent weakness in the basis encryption algorithm. In the-

TABLE 21-5

Entropy and Normalized Entropy

Difficulty Class, %	Cryptosystem			
Easy 0 → 4.4 (normalized basis)	Test 1.388 2.002	Playfair 1.474 2.127	ADFGVX 1.763 2.544	
	Homophonic Polyalphabetic 2.249 3.245	Quagmire Isologs 2.590 3.730	Viggy 2.899 4.183	
	Quadmire Periodic 3.058 4.412			
Moderate (nontrivial) 4.45 → 5	4-Rotor Enigma 3.322 4.794	Autoclave 3.090 4.459	CSP1500 3.297 4.757	Hebern 3.312 4.779
Strong >5 → 7	RDES-Iris 3.435 4.956	VPGP 4.180 6.031	VPGP4.0 4.776 6.892	
	Blowfish 3.573 5.155			
Very Strong >7	ZIP/PGP 5.281 7.620	RPGP 5.366 7.743		

DES		
DESOFB 5.352 7.722	DESCBC 5.368 7.746	EID95 5.368 7.746
3DES 5.433 7.839	RC4 5.432 7.839	RC5 5.433 7.839

The top number indicates entropy for each file and the bottom number is the normalized [$E/\ln(2)$] entropy. The higher the value of entropy, the stronger the disorganization effect of the basis cryptographic algorithm.

TABLE 21-6

Approach to
Random Text PSI
Values and I.C.

Difficulty Class, %	Cryptosystem	

Easy
I.C. ~ > 0.1

Test	Playfair	ADFGVX
Psi(r) 2.198e6	Psi(r) 6.94e6	Psi(r) 3.763e3
Psi(o) 3.450e8	Psi(o) 6.82e8	Psi(o) 1.698e5
Psi(p) 3.753e7	Psi(p) 1.19e8	Psi(p) 6.425e4
I.C. 0.613	I.C. 0.383	I.C. 0.176

Homophonic Polyalphabetic	Quagmire Isologs	Quagmire Periodic
Psi(r) 2.367e3	Psi(r) 6.526e3	Psi(r) 2.826e3
Psi(o) 9.140e4	Psi(o) 3.144e5	Psi(o) 5.814e4
Psi(p) 4.042e4	Psi(p) 1.11e5	Psi(p) 4.825e4
I.C. 0.151	I.C. 0.188	I.C. 0.080

Viggy		
Psi(r) 2.198e6		
Psi(o) 5.577e7		
Psi(p) 3.753e7		
I.C. 0.099		

Moderate (nontrivial)
I.C. ~ 0.075-0.038

Autoclave	Enigma	CSP1500
Psi(r) 1.714e3	Psi(r) 5.800e3	Psi(r) 3.049e3
Psi(o) 3.302e4	Psi(o) 5.302e4	Psi(o) 2.956e4
Psi(p) 2.928e4	Psi(p) 9.903e4	Psi(p) 5.206e4
I.C. 0.075	I.C. 0.036	I.C. 0.038

Hebern		
Psi(r) 8.807e3		
Psi(o) 8.271e4		
Psi(p) 1.504e5		
I.C. 0.037		

Strong
I.C. ~ 0. 015-0.005

VPGP	VPGP4.0	
Psi(r) 2.806e3	Psi(r) 1.951e2	
Psi(o) 1.073e4	Psi(o) 2.620e2	
Psi(p) 4.791e04	Psi(p) 3.332e3	
I.C. 0.015	I.C. 0.005	

Blowfish		
Psi(r) 2.595e6		
Psi(o) 3.893e7		
Psi(p) 4.431e7		
I.C. 0.0059		

TABLE 21-6

Approach to
Random Text PSI
Values and I.C.
(*Continued*)

Difficulty Class, %		Cryptosystem			
Very Strong					
I.C. ~ 0.004					
ZIP/PGP		RPGP			
Psi(r)	1.249e3	Psi(r)	3.063E3		
Psi(o)	1.286e3	Psi(o)	3.184E3		
Psi(p)	2.133e4	Psi(p)	5.230E4		
I.C.	0.004	I.C.	0.004		
DESOFB		DESCBC			
Psi(r)	2.301e3	Psi(r)	2.301e3		
Psi(o)	2.396e3	Psi(o)	2.284e3		
Psi(p)	3.929e4	Psi(p)	3.929e4		
I.C.	0.004	I.C.	0.004		
3DES		RC4		RC5	
Psi(r)	2.595e6	Psi(r)	2.594e6	Psi(r)	2.595e6
Psi(o)	4.630e6	Psi(o)	4.635e6	Psi(o)	4.639e6
Psi(p)	4.431e7	Psi(p)	4.429e7	Psi(p)	4.431e7
I.C.	0.007	I.C.	0.007	I.C.	0.007
DES					
EID95					
Psi(r)	3.147e3				
Psi(o)	3.300e3				
Psi(p)	5.373e4				
I.C.	0.004				

ory, a perfect algorithm produces no "fingerprints" or repetitions. Table 21-4 gives the PKZIP 2.40g compression values for 22 well-known cryptosystems. Note the clear distinction between the levels of difficulty of cryptanalytic attack. To repeat, in general, the lower the compression factor, the better the scrambling of data and less available repetitions to feed to the cryptanalyst for a wedge.

An expected result was observed when Class I or II cipher systems were compressed using ZIP before transformation by algorithm. The strength of the cipher and resulting entropy was increased. Using ZIP on Class IV ciphers had an adverse effect, actually dropping the entropy of the system.

Entropy

The entropy calculation is a measure of predictability and organization of data. The higher the entropy, the more chaotic and disorganized the information, hence the more unpredictable the cryptographic shifts and more difficult the cipher is to break without significant work factor. If entropy is low, the data is well organized and orderly; a higher entropy indicates a stronger level of obfuscation of data. A form of Shannon entropy is calculated as:

$$E(s) = \Sigma \left[X_i/X_t \log(X_t/X_i) \right] \qquad \textbf{[Eq. 21-61]}$$

$$E(\text{S-Bin}) = E(s)/\ln(2) \qquad \textbf{[Eq. 21-62]}$$

where: X_i/X_t = fraction of ith ASCII character
X_t/X_i = inverted fraction of ith ASCII character
$E(s)$ = file entropy
$E(\text{S-Bin})$ = normalized entropy (per-bit basis)

Randomness and Approach to Mono/Poly Alphabeticity

The simplest way to think of these calculations is to view cipher text as two cases of a continuum:

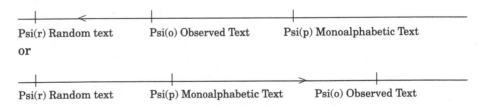

Psi(r) Random text   Psi(o) Observed Text   Psi(p) Monoalphabetic Text

or

Psi(r) Random text   Psi(p) Monoalphabetic Text   Psi(o) Observed Text

The goal of cryptography is to hide the meaning of the text. The closer the observed cipher text is to random text, the more difficult it will be to recover the original meaningful plain text. A second good reference point is monoalphabetic text and derives from the basis language and letter-group frequency distribution associated with it. *The principle of crypto-graphic universality applies—the monoalphabetic text reference point can be calculated for every known language based on phonemes.* Here is the xenocryptic data for some common languages:

	Monoalphabetic Text	Digraphic Text
English	$0.0661N(N-1)$	$0.0069N(N-1)$
French	$0.0778N(N-1)$	$0.0093N(N-1)$
German	$0.0762N(N-1)$	$0.0112N(N-1)$
Italian	$0.0738N(N-1)$	$0.0081N(N-1)$
Japanese	$0.0819N(N-1)$	$0.0116N(N-1)$
Portuguese	$0.0791N(N-1)$	
Russian	$0.0529N(N-1)$	$0.0058N(N-1)$
Spanish	$0.0775N(N-1)$	$0.0093N(N-1)$

Random Text

Monographic	Digraphic	Trigraphic
$.038N(N-1)$	$.0015N(N-1)$	$.000057N(N-1)$

The goal was to identify the level of randomness for category separation. Even with 256 ASCII characters being substituted, shifted, and so forth, the underlying language will leave a small trace of the natural language bonds. This assumes enough cipher text to adequately categorize the system.

There appears to be an upper limit on the number of substitutions available as we increase either the number of alphabets or characters available.

```
             20                x x xxx
No.          18            x
of           16          x
letters      14         x              Sharp break after
in           12        x               100 alphabets or
active       10       x                substitutive
play         08     x                  ASCII
             06    x
             04    x
             02  x
             00  02    10    50   100
```

No. of alphabets or characters used for
substitution (approximately)

However, our interest need not be at upper limits of alphabets or character substitutions but at the lower limit and, specifically, relationships to measure monoalphabetic text and random text. It takes a lot of "work" to disrupt the bonds and tenacity of the phonemic structure of a language. Matyas and Meyer showed that even DES required five rounds to realize intersymbol dependence. That is each cipher-text bit depends on all plain-text bits via message as well as the autoclave dependence. It takes five rounds to eliminate the universal language principles in DES-based systems:

	Output/Input Relation		
Round	$L(j)$ vs U	$R(j)$ vs U	$X(j)$ vs U
1	0.00	10.71	5.36
2	10.71	79.02	44.87
3	79.02	96.43	87.72
4	96.43	100.00	98.21
5	100.00	100.00	100.00

Of prime importance is the relationship of the observed Psi to the number of characters $\times$ number of characters -1, also known as the I.C. for two letters. The I.C. for the cipher text is a very good measure of the strength of the cryptographic system. It shows the tendency for polyalphabetic cipher text to approximate the limits of random text or of monoalphabetic coincidence of cipher-text columns. The lower the I.C., the closer to random text. An I.C. of 0 is impractical because, to calculate an I.C. of 0, N would have to be 1, which means that only one symbol is used for the encryption. This would make it not only extremely difficult for the system attacker to break, but it would also be impossible for the intended recipient to determine what each use of the same symbol represented. Some variation in the symbols is necessary, but the practical question is: how low can the I.C. be and still be decipherable by the intended recipient? Or put another way, how close to perfectly random cipher text can we design the I.C.? Class IV ciphers demonstrated I.C.s approximating 0.004.

For an ASCII system with 256 characters for substitution, a perfectly random or equally likely event is $(1/256) = 0.003906$. The strongest cryptosystems like RC5 or 3DES exhibited an I.C. of slightly over 0.004. The work factor to break this kind of system is extremely high. Table 21-7 notes the attack parameters in relation to classes of difficulty.

Sometimes it is easier to see things graphically. We inspect the I.C. and the Psi(observed) relationship to the Psi(plain) or Psi(random). We also look at the compression to see if there are repeated sequences. Figures 21-2 to 21-10 show examples of each class of difficulty and demon-

TABLE 21-7

Attack Parameters
in Relation to Class
of Difficulty

Compression Limits

Difficulty		Factors
Class I	Easy	$100 \rightarrow 56$
Class II	Moderate (nontrivial)	$40 \rightarrow 35$
Class III	Strong	$27 \rightarrow 10$
Class IV	Very Strong	$10 \rightarrow 0$

Entropy Limits (Normalized)

Difficulty		Factors
Class I	Easy	$0 \rightarrow 4$
Class II	Moderate (nontrivial)	$4.5 \rightarrow 5$
Class III	Strong	$5 \rightarrow 7$
Class IV	Very Strong	$>7+$

I.C. Limits

Difficulty		Factors
Class I	Easy	$\sim 0.1+$
Class II	Moderate (nontrivial)	$\sim 0.075 \rightarrow 0.037$
Class III	Strong	$\sim 0.015 \rightarrow 0.005$
Class IV	Very Strong	$\sim 0.007 \rightarrow 0.004$

Graphical

Difficulty		Factors
Class I	Easy	Many Peaks/Troughs
Class II	Moderate (nontrivial)	Reduced Spikes/Not Flat
Class III	Strong	Near Flat Profile—Small Spikes
Class IV	Very Strong	Flat Profile = "White Noise"

strate the process more dramatically. Figure 21-2 is plain text, testified to by the I.C. of 0.067 and uniform frequency distribution for English. Figure 21-3 is a homophonic classical cipher system with four alphabets employed. It is classified as easy (by hand) to cryptanalyze. An example of the classical Vigenere family is shown in Figure 21-4. The IRIS implementation of this cipher system is clearly weak and can be broken by hand. Figure 21-5 is the Navy CSP1500 rotor cipher machine and represents Class II moderate cryptanalytic difficulty. It has a clear demarcation with an I.C. of approximately 0.36. The test cutoff was actually designed for the famous Enigma machine shown in Figure 21-6. Figure 21-7 shows a Class II strong cipher, the PC1 cipher by McAfee. Notice the flattening out of the cipher text. We now enter Class IV of very difficult ciphers of DES CBC, 3DES, and RC5, shown in Figures 21-8, 21-9, and 21-10, respectively. Cracking these ciphers will require significant work factors. Note the close relationship of the Psi(observed) to Psi(ran-

Figure 21-2
Plain Text

Setpoint Analysis Results   Sunday, July 05, 1998

Directory Name: C:\Black Box test data
File Name: OZY1.TXT

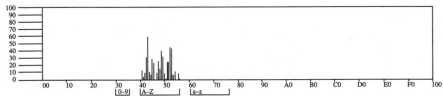

Display Scale: x1
File Entropy: 2.852
Chars: 491
Mean: 75.629
Std dev: 6.875
Min: 0
Psi(r): 9.398e+002
Psi(o): 1.602e+004
Psi(p): 1.605e+004
Mode: 69
Median: 0
Range: 60
Max: 59
I.C.: 0.06660
Compression: 44.00000
Fail

dom) values. Note the dramatic flat "white noise" profiles. These are the dream profiles of cryptographers. The author looks forward to profiling Dr. Rivest's newest RC6 and NSA's Skipjack when available in pristine version.

Whereas vertical differentiation is certain at above 95 percent, horizontal separation of ciphers such as RC5 and 3DES is *very* difficult even with plenty of computer horsepower, but not impossible. A different set of tools is required and many additional data sets must be employed to make the comparisons. Feature vectors can be used to characterize the system and set up a known learning profile for comparison to an unknown sample. It appears that metrics for distinguishing strong ciphers are more observable when the intermediate step of comparison to easier systems is made and that combined data is then used to delineate the stronger systems. The problem is analogous to the chemical engineering design of complex chemical towers separating isotopes by distillation. The temperatures of distillation are very close, the chemical properties are very close and intermediate product streams need to be calculated. The solution involves a tie-component, which is used to

Figure 21-3
Homophonic Class I

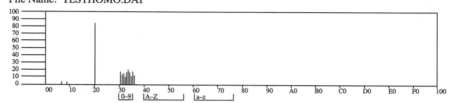

Setpoint Analysis Results   Sunday, July 05, 1998

Directory Name: C:\Black Box test data
File Name: TESTHOMO.DAT

Display Scale: x3
File Entropy: 2.249
Chars: 779
Mean: 44.286
Std dev: 11.571
Min: 0
Psi(r): 2.367e+003
Psi(o): 9.140e+004
Psi(p): 4.042e+004
Mode: 32
Median: 0
Range: 259
Max: 258
I.C.: 0.15080
Compression: 55.00000
Fail

delineate the isotopes and solve the overall material and energy balance. When ciphers produce parametric results so close that system recognition is difficult, then the addition of a known and simpler system as a "tie-line" assists the calculations.

Another important factor is the level of salt, or random data, which when added to the key can influence the results. Therefore, data sets drawn from a great number of random plain-text/cipher-text data sets and enciphered with a wide range of randomly keyed material are required to establish the profiles that Class III and Class IV ciphers need to be compared to. *Research is progressing positively but no claims are intended.* It can be said that no vendor product examined was without *fingerprints*. Research on actual product offerings—to improve success in horizontal separation—is continuing with measurable and gradual success.

We now shift to another form of cryptanalytic attack—the attack not on the system but the password or cryptographic keys to the system.

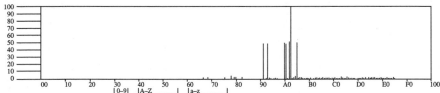

Figure 21-4
Viggy Class I

Setpoint Analysis Results   Sunday, July 05, 1998

Directory Name: C:\torture test 5
File Name: TEST.VIG

Display Scale: x47
File Entropy: 2.899
Chars: 23720
Mean: 164.304
Std dev: 19.742
Min: 0
Psi(r): 2.198e+006
Psi(o): 5.577e+007
Psi(p): 3.753e+007
Mode: 164
Median: 0
Range: 4671
Max: 4670
I.C.: 0.09914
Compression: 99.00000
Fail

Password Vulnerability

Daniel V. Klein of LoneWolf Systems, Pittsburgh, Pennsylvania, performed a study in 1989 using data from clients in both the United States and Great Britain that would imply that the key (password) and its management is the weak link. He outlined some of the problems of current password security and demonstrated the ease with which individual accounts may be broken. His study centered on the Unix system and his results and conclusions were most general in nature and cannot be ignored by users and system administrators of every type of computer system in the country. Although the study is seriously dated, the Klein study is still instructive. It shows that it is not necessary to use brute force to attack a cryptosystem; it is necessary to steal just the passwords, which users will hand to you on a plate more than 25 percent of the time.

The main observation from Klein's work was that a study of cracked

Figure 21-5
CSP1500 Rotor
Machine Class II

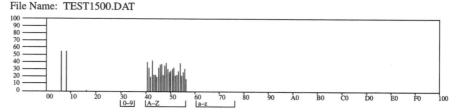

Setpoint Analysis Results   Sunday, July 05, 1998

Directory Name: C:\Black Box test data
File Name: TEST1500.DAT

Display Scale: x1
File Entropy: 3.297
Chars: 884
Mean: 68.619
Std dev: 22.942
Min: 0
Psi(r): 3.049e+003
Psi(o): 2.956e+004
Psi(p): 5.206e+004
Mode: 10
Median: 0
Range: 57
Max: 56
I.C.: 0.03786
Compression: 37.00000
Fail

passwords showed that the user did not readily choose tough passwords but ones that he/she could remember.

Klein built up a database of approximately 15,000 entries from the United States and Great Britain of /etc/passwd files in order to try to crack the passwords. Each of the account entries was tested by a number of intrusion strategies. The possible passwords that were tried were based on the user's name or account number, taken from numerous dictionaries (including some containing foreign words, phrases, patterns of keys on the keyboard, and enumerations), and from permutations and combinations of words in those dictionaries. After nearly 12 CPU-months of rather exhaustive testing, approximately 25 percent of the passwords had been guessed—21 percent of the passwords (nearly 3000 passwords) were guessed in the first week and in the first 15 minutes of testing, 368 passwords (or 2.7 percent) had been cracked using what experience had shown would be the most fruitful line of attack (using the user or account names as passwords).

The results did not indicate what all the uncracked passwords were. Rather it showed that users are likely to use words that are familiar to

Figure 21-6
Enigma Class II Cutoff

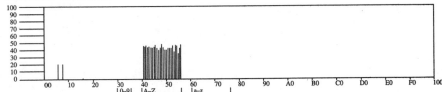

Setpoint Analysis Results   Sunday, July 05, 1998

Directory Name: C:\Black Box test data
File Name: TESTA.E95

Display Scale: x1
File Entropy: 3.322
Chars: 1219
Mean: 74.980
Std dev: 14.405
Min: 0
Psi(r): 5.008e+003
Psi(o): 5.302e+004
Psi(p): 9.903e+004
Mode: 76
Median: 0
Range: 51
Max: 50
I.C.: 0.03571
Compression: 37.00000
Fail

them as their passwords. What new information it did provide, however, was the degree of vulnerability of the systems in question, as well as developing a basis for a proactive password checker. Passwords that can be derived from a dictionary are clearly a bad idea. There are hackers and companies in the business of developing this line of attack on computer systems.

Table 21-8 shows elements of Klein's password attack dictionary. Consider the following when using Table 21-8:

1. The number of matches is the total number of matches given for the particular dictionary, irrespective of the number of permutations that the user applied to it.

2. Duplicate names were eliminated.

3. In all cases, the cost/benefit ratio is the number of matches divided by the search size. The more words that needed to be tested for a match, the lower the cost/benefit ratio.

4. The dictionary used for user/account names checks naturally

Figure 21-7
PC1 Class III

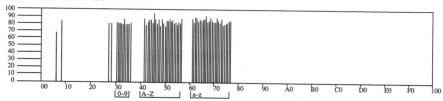

Setpoint Analysis Results   Sunday, July 05, 1998

Directory Name: C:\Black Box test data
File Name: TEST.PC1

Display Scale: x6
File Entropy: 4.189
Chars: 32825
Mean: 83.533
Std dev: 25.944
Min: 0
Psi(r): 4.209e+006
Psi(o): 1.632e+007
Psi(p): 7.187e+007
Mode: 72
Median: 0
Range: 560
Max: 559
I.C.: 0.01515
Compression: 24.00000
Fail

changed for each user. Up to 130 different permutations were tried for each.

5. Although monosyllabic Chinese passwords were tried for all users (with 12 matches), polysyllabic Chinese passwords were tried only for users with Chinese names. The percentage of matches was 8.0 percent—a greater hit ratio than any other method; but the dictionary size is 16×10^6, though, and the cost/benefit ratio is infinitesimal.

6. The results of the word-pair tests are not included in either of the two tables. They represent another 0.4 percent of the passwords cracked in the sample.

Figure 21-8
DESCBC Class IV

Setpoint Analysis Results   Sunday, July 05, 1998

Directory Name: C:\Black Box test data
File Name: DESCBC.TXT

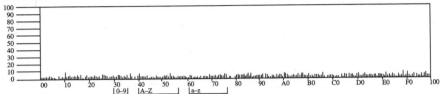

Display Scale: x1
File Entropy: 5.368
Chars: 768
Mean: 129.992
Std dev: 74.595
Min: 0
Psi(r): 2.301e+003
Psi(o): 2.284e+003
Psl(p): 3.929e+004
Mode: 16
Median: 3
Range: 10
Max: 9
I.C.: 0.00388
Compression: 0.00000
Pass

Reverse Engineering to Snag the Password

A much more interesting attack and far more difficult to execute on the password (key) is to reverse engineer the computer program supporting the cryptosystem. It is possible to use a (Windows) debugger combined with a plain-text compromise (false password) to "walk back the cat" to find the location of the password compare statements. The MaeDae/EIW proprietary algorithm was cracked this way in 1998, causing their design team to change the coding so that the comparison point was dynamic rather than statically housed. Table 21-9 gives the salient parts of the published crack by a Frenchman aliased as Casimir. Only the proprietary algorithms were broken—not DES. The developers of this soft-

Figure 21-9
3DES Class IV

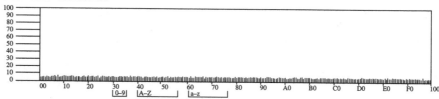

Setpoint Analysis Results   Sunday, July 05, 1998

Directory Name: C:\Black Box test data
File Name: TEST.3DES

Display Scale: x16
File Entropy: 5.433
Chars: 25776
Mean: 120.835
Std dev: 77.587
Min: 62
Psi(r): 2.595e+006
Psi(o): 4.630e+007
Psi(p): 4.431e+007
Mode: 0
Median: 95
Range: 1464
Max: 1525
I.C.: 0.00697
Compression: 5.00000
Pass

ware have fixed the crack, and improved the data structure so that this approach is invalid.

System Identification—New Tools for Vertical Classification of Cryptosystems

We now consider the problem a cryptanalyst encounters when he/she has only cipher text and needs to identify the cryptosystem. Using Kerckhoff's maxim, the cryptanalyst has full knowledge of the cryptosystems in play. He or she may use a set of encryptions on each of these systems as learning sets to discriminate between them through standard pattern recognition techniques. Once the cryptanalyst knows what he/she is dealing with, the next problem is to find the key. In view of the

Figure 21-10
RC5 Class IV

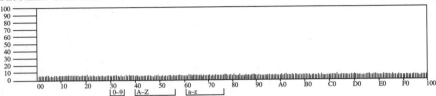

Setpoint Analysis Results   Sunday, July 05, 1998

Directory Name: C:\Black Box test data
File Name: TEST.RC5

Display Scale: x16
File Entropy: 5.433
Chars: 25776
Mean: 120.104
Std dev: 77.546
Min: 72
Psi(r): 2.595e+006
Psi(o): 4.639e+007
Psi(p): 4.431e+007
Mode: 0
Median: 94
Range: 1458
Max: 1529
I.C.: 0.00698
Compression: 5.00000
Pass

impossible task of trying all the keys, the cryptanalyst should have a guess about the subset of the total key space to which the key belongs. Ideally this subset of keys is searchable within a reasonable time and work factor.

We have two distinct problems. First, the system identification problem may be approached using a *feature vector* for any chosen system using known minimum distance classifiers. This leads to separation and classification of a number of systems based only on the available cipher texts. One of the tricks of horizontal separation is to include, in the mix of ciphers, Class I or II systems with the Class IV systems, to act as tie-lines between the Class IV ciphers. This improves the differentiation for the vector mix. Cipher texts are prepared on a range of keys of the system being studied. It turns out that for known systems, based on cipher text, this process will distinguish systems in different classes of difficulty and cipher systems based on the same structure with different degrees of nonlinearity.

The second aspect of the application of *pattern recognition* is the possibility of clustering a set of keys, which are close to each other in

TABLE 21-8

Passwords Cracked for Sample Set of 13,797 Accounts

Type of Password	Dictionary Size	Duplicates Eliminated	Search Size	Number of Matches	Percent of Total	Cost Benefit Ratio
User/Account Name	130+	—	130	368	2.7	2.830
Character Sequences	866	0	866	22	0.2	0.025
Numbers	450	23	427	9	0.1	0.021
Chinese	398	6	392	56	0.4	0.143
Place Names	665	37	628	82	0.6	0.131
Common Names	2,268	29	2,239	548	4.0	0.245
Female Names	4,955	675	4,280	161	1.2	0.038
Male Names	3,901	1,035	2,866	140	1.0	0.049
Uncommon Names	5,559	604	4,955	130	0.0	0.026
Myths and Legends	1,357	111	1,246	66	0.5	0.053
Shakespearean	650	177	473	11	0.1	0.023
Sports Terms	247	9	238	32	0.2	0.134
Science Fiction	772	81	691	59	0.4	0.085
Movies and Actors	118	19	99	12	0.1	0.121
Cartoons	133	41	92	9	0.1	0.098
Famous People	509	219	290	55	0.4	0.190
Phrases and Patterns	998	65	933	253	1.8	0.271
Surnames	160	127	33	9	0.1	0.273
Biology	59	1	58	1	0.0	0.017
usr/dict/words	24,474	4,791	19,683	1,027	7.4	0.052
Machine Names	12,983	3,965	9,018	132	1.0	0.015
Mnemonics	14	0	14	2	0.0	0.143
King James Bible	13,062	5,537	7,525	83	0.6	0.011
Misc Words	8,146	4,934	3,212	54	0.4	0.017
Yiddish Words	69	13	56	0	0.0	0.000
Asteroids	3,459	1,052	2,407	19	0.1	0.007
Totals	86,280	23,553	62,727	3,340	24.2	0.053

respect to some feature vector resulting from the cipher text. It is possible to subdivide the total key structure into various classes, each class containing a subset much smaller than a total set of keys under consideration. There are two steps involved:

1. Classification of a set of keys, or subset of keys, further into classes through clustering techniques based on a feature vector with some standard distance measure.

TABLE 21-9

Sample Cracking
Dialog

CRACKING OF *ENCRYPT-IT* FOR WINDOWS
By CASIMIRPart B

>>>>

This file presents [*a small portion of the published verbatim dialog and code by Casimir on*] cracking procedures for both proprietary algorithms found in the *Encrypt-It* software:

Questions/Answers

Q: OK, so what if we just try any possible input until we find the good one?
A: Well…We don't know password'length (i.e. how many characters it contains). With only 5 characters, we would have 2565 = 1,099,511,627,776 combinations to try, which is a lot even for a fast PC. So just forget it.
Q: Maybe we can just patch EIW so it would let us in even if input is wrong.
A: Right, this method is also used to "register" stolen software. Go on, try it! To disable final CMP, we can modify following instructions:

CS:40EBA7	change	cmp dl,bl	to	cmp dl,dl
CS:40EBB7	change	cmp dl,bl	to	cmp dl,dl

>>>

Conclusion: we must find out what original pwd was to decrypt. So we'll try to build an input that pass final CMP, using same routines as EIW.
Our strategy will depend on password'length (small, medium, or large).

2. Mimic of EIW
Let's sum up actions performed by EIW (chronological order):1- compute Block_size = function of (password)2- build permuted text = function of (original encrypted text , Block_size)
3- build Sum_vector=function of (password)
4- build Xor_vector=function of (Sum_vector , permuted text)
5- build Cmp_vector=function of (Xor_vector , password)
6- check passwork=function of (Cmp_vector , password)

We're going to mimic EIW. We don't know pwd'length, so we try out every possible length (from 5 to 40 (Int.) or 123 (U.S.) characters). Then we must build permuted text. As we don't know password (!), we can't compute Block_size…Never mind, there are only 16 possible values for Block_size (see PART A, Chapter 2), we're going to try each of them. Once permuted text is built, we choose a solving method in function of pwd'length.

Pseudo-code:
For each pwd'length
    {
   For each Block_size
      {
Build permuted text;
Switch(pwd'length)
      {
        case(5=pwd'length=20 chars) : use high speed solving method; break;
        case(21=pwd'length=29 chars) : use medium speed solving method; break;
        case(30=pwd'length=40 chars) : use low speed solving method; break;

TABLE 21-9
Sample Cracking
Dialog (*Continued*)

```
        }
     }
  }
```

We'll use International version of EIW, but it works the same with U.S. Version.

3. The 3 Solving Methods

Every method takes advantage of the "static" data structure used by EIW to store original file name and password. If the pwd is good, we're sure that Cmp_vector must look like this:

Cmp_vector:
| FILENAME.TXT | 0 | PASSWORD0000000000000000000000000000000000 | 0 |
       | <——— Tail (40+1=41 characters) ———-> |
The more 0s we have in Tail (i.e. the smaller pwd is), the easier pwd can be found.

We suppose our permuted text is:

```
        11111111112222222222233333333333344444444444455555
    0123456789012345678901234567890123456789012345 67890123
```
Permuted_txt:
| ABCDEFGHIJKLMNOPQRSTUVWXYZabcdefghijklmnopqrstuvwxyz01 |
      | <——————— 12+1+40+1=54 characters ———————-> |

3.1. High speed solving method [This is the only method shown.]

We search a small pwd (length$<=$20), for instance length = 10. So we must find:
                Pwd[0],Pwd[1],…,Pwd[i],…,Pwd[9].

(Remember Pwd[i] is a character, so: $0x00 <= Pwd[i] <= 0xFF$)
Password: 0123456789 0123456789 0123456789 0123456789 0123456789 0123
Cmp_vector'sstruct: FILENAME.T XT0??????? ???0000000 0000000000 0000000000
0000

```
        0123456789 1111111111 2222222222 3333333333 4444444444 5555
        0123456789 0123456789 0123456789 0123456789 0123
```

If pwd is good, we should have:
Cmp_vector[12] = 0
And
Cmp_vector[23]=Cmp_vector[24]=…=Cmp_vector[52]=Cmp_vector[53]=0 Step_1 We
know that: Cmp_vector[i] = Xor_vector[i]^Pwd[i modulo Pwd'length], so:
$0=$Xor_vector[23]^Pwd[3] $<=>$ Xor_vector[23]=Pwd[3] (remember: $x^y=0 <=> x=y$)
   0 = Xor_vector[24]^Pwd[4] $<=>$ Xor_vector[24]=Pwd[4]
   0 = Xor_vector[25]^Pwd[5] $<=>$ Xor_vector[25]=Pwd[5]
   0 = Xor_vector[26]^Pwd[6] $<=>$ Xor_vector[26]=Pwd[6]
   0 = Xor_vector[27]^Pwd[7] $<=>$ Xor_vector[27]=Pwd[7]

TABLE 21-9
Sample Cracking
Dialog (*Continued*)

$0 = \text{Xor\_vector}[28]^\wedge\text{Pwd}[8] <=> \text{Xor\_vector}[28]=\text{Pwd}[8]$
$0=\text{Xor\_vector}[29]^\wedge\text{Pwd}[9] <=> \text{Xor\_vector}[29]=\text{Pwd}[9]$
$0=\text{Xor\_vector}[30]^\wedge\text{Pwd}[0] <=> \text{Xor\_vector}[30]=\text{Pwd}[0]$
$0=\text{Xor\_vector}[31]^\wedge\text{Pwd}[1] <=> \text{Xor\_vector}[31]=\text{Pwd}[1]$
$0=\text{Xor\_vector}[32]^\wedge\text{Pwd}[2] <=> \text{Xor\_vector}[32]=\text{Pwd}[2]$

Step_2 We know that: $\text{Xor\_vector}[i]=\text{Sum\_vector}[i]^\wedge\text{Permuted\_txt}[i]$, so we have:
$\text{Pwd}[3]=\text{Sum\_vector}[23]^\wedge\text{Permuted\_txt}[23]=\text{Sum\_vector}[23]^\wedge X$ $\text{Pwd}[4] =$
$\text{Sum\_vector}[24]^\wedge\text{Permuted\_txt}[24]=\text{Sum\_vector}[24]^\wedge Y$
$\text{Pwd}[5] = \text{Sum\_vector}[25]^\wedge\text{Permuted\_txt}[25] = \text{Sum\_vector}[25]^\wedge Z$
$\text{Pwd}[6] = \text{Sum\_vector}[26]^\wedge\text{Permuted\_txt}[26] = \text{Sum\_vector}[26]^\wedge a$
$\text{Pwd}[7] = \text{Sum\_vector}[27]^\wedge\text{Permuted\_txt}[27] = \text{Sum\_vector}[27]^\wedge b$
$\text{Pwd}[8] = \text{Sum\_vector}[28]^\wedge\text{Permuted\_txt}[28] = \text{Sum\_vector}[28]^\wedge c$
$\text{Pwd}[9] = \text{Sum\_vector}[29]^\wedge\text{Permuted\_txt}[29] = \text{Sum\_vector}[29]^\wedge d$
$\text{Pwd}[0] = \text{Sum\_vector}[30]^\wedge\text{Permuted\_txt}[30] = \text{Sum\_vector}[30]^\wedge e$
$\text{Pwd}[1] = \text{Sum\_vector}[31]^\wedge\text{Permuted\_txt}[31] = \text{Sum\_vector}[31]^\wedge f$
$\text{Pwd}[2] = \text{Sum\_vector}[32]^\wedge\text{Permuted\_txt}[32] = \text{Sum\_vector}[32]^\wedge g$

Step_3 We know that:
$\text{Sum\_vector}[i]=\{(\text{Pwd'sum}+\text{Pwd}[0]+...+\text{Pwd}[i \bmod \text{Pwd'len}])^\wedge\text{Pwd}[i \bmod \text{Pwd'len}]\}\&\text{FF}$
with: $\text{Pwd'sum}=\text{Pwd}[0]+\text{Pwd}[1]+...+\text{Pwd}[i]+...+\text{Pwd}[9]$Instead of masking result of
xorization, we can mask sum:
$\text{Sum\_vector}[i]=\{(\text{Pwd'sum} + \text{Pwd}[0]+...+\text{Pwd}[i \bmod \text{Pwd'len}])\&\text{FF}\}^\wedge\text{Pwd}[1 \bmod \text{Pwd'len}]$

We formulate:
$\text{Init\_12\_pwd}=\{\text{Pwd'sum}+\text{Pwd}[0]+...+\text{Pwd}[22\bmod 10]\}\&\text{FF} = \{\text{Pwd'sum} +$
$\text{Pwd}[0]+...+\text{Pwd}[2]\}\&\text{FF}$
So: $\text{Sum\_vector}[23] = \{(\text{Init\_12\_pwd}+\text{Pwd}[3])\&\text{FF}\}^\wedge\text{Pwd}[3]$

Problem: we still don't know password (!), so we can't compute Init_12_pwd...

Never mind, because of masking there are only 256 possible values for Init_12_pwd
(0x00,...,0xFF), we'll try them out.
Step_4 We saw in Step_2 that:
$\text{Pwd}[3] = \text{Sum\_vector}[23]^\wedge\text{Permuted\_txt}[23]$,
so:$\text{Pwd}[3] = \{(\text{Init\_12\_pwd}+\text{Pwd}[3])\&\text{FF}\}^\wedge\text{Pwd}[3]^\wedge\text{Permuted\_txt}[23]$; which becomes:
$(\text{Init\_12\_pwd}+\text{Pwd}[3])\&\text{FF} = \text{Permuted\_txt}[23]$
2 cases:
-if $\text{Init\_12\_pwd}<=\text{Permuted\_txt}[23]$: $\text{Pwd}[3]=\text{Permuted\_txt}[23]-\text{Init\_12\_pwd}$
-if $\text{Init\_12\_pwd}> \text{Permuted\_txt}[23]$: $\text{Pwd}[3] =\text{ermuted\_txt}[23]-\text{Init\_12\_pwd}+0x100$

2. Isolation of the useful keys. When an unknown encrypted message
   is received, one first locates the cluster to which the key belongs
   and then uses this cluster to isolate the keys present in the cluster, and not all the keys in the set.

Drs. I. J. Kumar and T. L. Rao pioneered the use of k-clustering to locate
and stabilize a unique clustering for a given set of keys. The second step
can be achieved using the mean vector of a cluster or the maximum/min-
imum techniques.

TABLE 21-9
Sample Cracking
Dialog (*Continued*)

!!!!WE FOUND Pwd[3]!!!!

Step_5 We repeat Step_4 with Pwd[4],Pwd[5],...,Pwd[2]:

$(Init\_12\_pwd+Pwd[3]+Pwd[4])\&FF=Permuted\_txt[24]$ —>Pwd[4] found

$(Init\_12\_pwd+Pwd[3]+Pwd[4]+Pwd[5])\&FF = Permuted\_txt[25]$ —>Pwd[5] found$(Init\_12\_pwd+Pwd[3]+Pwd[4]+...+Pwd[2])\&FF=Permuted\_txt[32]$ —>Pwd[2] found

The whole password is recovered...But is it the GOOD password?

Step_6 Checks

Remember we made assumptions on:
  -password'length
  -Block"size
  -Init_12_pwd

So pwd found must be checked. There are various tests performed:
-we compute Block'size using pwd found, then we check if:
     Block'size computed = Block'size estimated?

-we compute Init_12_pwd using pwd found, then we check if:
     Init_12_pwd computed = Init_12_pwd estimated?

-if pwd passed tests above, then we perform the same test as EIW: we build Cmp_vector using pwd found and we check if:

     Cmp_vector[13]=Pwd[0]?
     Cmp_vector[14]=Pwd[1]?
     Cmp_vector[15]=Pwd[2]?
     Cmp_vector[16]=Pwd[3]?
     Cmp_vector[17]=Pwd[4]?
     Cmp_vector[18]=Pwd[5]?
     Cmp_vector[19]=Pwd[6]?
     Cmp_vector[20]=Pwd[7]?
     Cmp_vector[21]=Pwd[8]?
     Cmp_vector[22]=Pwd[9]?

-to be sure, we can also check that:
     —Cmp_vector[12] = 0?
     and
     —Cmp_vector[23]=Cmp_vector[24]=...=Cmp_vector[52]=Cmp_vector[53]=0?
If a password pass every test, well, this IS the pwd we're looking for! So stop searching and have a beer!

Conclusion

This is a fast method: only 256 possibilities to try, not a big deal! But it requires pwd'length 0s in the Tail to work (for instance, in our example above we needed 10 0s). That's why we can't use it to find passwords with pwd'length>20.

Published with direct permission of CASIMIR. Copyright June 1998 by Casimir. Converted to hypertext June 21, 1998 by Joe Peschel.

Authors note: Published also with specific permission of MaeDae Company, who developed *Encrypt-It* and *EIW* software. Management has assured me that the aforementioned breaks have been fixed!

Pattern Recognition

System identification and key clustering are twin problems. Suppose we know that our adversary uses three cryptosystems A, B, and C. How do we locate the system used to encrypt message *M,* intercepted and received by the cryptanalyst. We probably know:

1. The language employed.

2. The philosophy and details of all three systems. It is possible to obtain larger number of cipher texts corresponding to the given language for a random selection of keys.

3. The amount of cipher text available.

4. The three systems A, B, and C are linearly separable through the cipher texts prepared on them.

Based on the cipher texts prepared in point 2, we attempt to develop a classifier, to sort the various categories of cipher texts made on the different systems. This is performed irrespective of the plain-text messages involved and the keys used on each system. The method of linear discriminant functions is suitable. To achieve classification, we use known classical measures such as percentage frequencies of letters, digraphs, trigraphs, intervals between occurrences of the same letters; Chi, I.C., and Psi relationships; independent binary n-grams, if transformable to binary form; and compression. The separation process works very well on a large number of systems.

Having identified a system to which a large amount of intercepted traffic belongs, the second challenge is to determine the key for the identified system and messages. Modern (Class IV) systems are so highly complex and provide such a large number of independent keys that, in spite of the complete knowledge of the system, the cryptanalyst cannot afford to use a brute-force attack (search) of the entire key space for solution. Ignoring the shortcuts caused by implementation errors, the biggest concern is how to reduce the key-space search to reasonable work factor (the amount of computer work required to search the key space).

Since it is not theoretically possible that all the keys on a system would lead to the same statistical characteristics of the cipher text, nor have the same weighted impact on the feature vector, it is feasible to cluster together keys related by some nearness measure based on the feature vector.

Given a very large N, total key space, ideally the number of clustered M keys, in N would be $\sqrt{M}$ clusters. To obtain a plain-text message:

1. The cryptanalyst studies same-day or same-hour cryptograms, likely to have been encrypted with the same key, and studies these message with respect to the feature vector and feature intervals to locate the cluster to which the feature vector of the cipher text belongs. He/she now tries all of the keys in the smaller cluster, and the search is reduced to $2\sqrt{M}$ instead of M. Out of these $2\sqrt{M}$ trials, $\sqrt{M}$ trials are made to locate the correct cluster and the rest of the trials are used to locate the correct key out of the cluster of $\sqrt{M}$ keys.

2. The cryptanalyst does fix the number of classes in which he/she wants to distribute the total key space. However, as he/she notes the feature vector for each of the keys, the newer classes automatically appear. It is a requirement that the cryptanalyst be able to locate these features in the cipher text.

System identification requires discrimination among encryption systems irrespective of the keys on which the learning cryptograms are prepared. They are system-dependent but not key-independent.

Clustering of keys requires that the cipher texts be totally dependent on the key and not the encrypted plain text. Usually a number of messages are encrypted using each key and the mean feature vector is extracted to represent the key. A mean frequency vector shows good experimental results for system identification. The mean distance vector has been found to be a fair key discriminant feature. Both of the two methods use patterns, or a distinguishable interrelation of data (analog/digital) and concepts. Of first interest is the concept of *proximity*.

Proximity Measurements

Proximity measurements help us differentiate data patterns. They come in two forms: similarity measures and dissimilarity measures. Similarity measures S_{ij} always have values between 0 and 1; dissimilarity measures D_{ij} assume real values. There are several published measures to measure proximity. Two measures of interest and used by the author are the Minkowski Metric and the Mahalanobis D^2 distance.

We define two vectors representing two different data patterns:

$$X_j = [x_{1j}, x_{2j}, x_{nj}] \qquad \text{[Eq. 21-63]}$$

$$X_k = [x_{1k}, x_{2k}, ..., x_{nk}] \qquad \text{[Eq. 21-64]}$$

The Minkowski Metric between the jth and kth data unit is defined:

$$D_{j,k}^p = D_p(X_j, X_k) = \left[\sum_{i=1}^n |x_{ij} - x_{ik}|^p \right]^{1/p} \qquad \text{[Eq. 21-65]}$$

where $p > 1$. For $p = 1$

$$d_{j,k}^1 = \sum_{i=1}^n |x_{ij} - x_{ik}| \qquad \text{[Eq. 21-66]}$$

This term has been nicknamed *city-block distance*. For $p = 2$

$$d_{j,k}^2 = \sum_{i=1}^n \left[|x_{ij} - x_{ik}|^2 \right]^{1/2} \qquad \text{[Eq. 21-67]}$$

This is known as the L_2 metric or *Euclidean distance*. We may weight this Euclidean distance by assigning a weight to each component so that the sum of the weights = 1, or:

$$\Sigma w_i = 1 \qquad \text{[Eq. 21-68]}$$

This means that for $p = 2$

$$d_{j,k}^2 = \left[\sum_{i=1}^n w_i |x_{ij} - x_{ik}|^2 \right]^{1/2} \qquad \text{[Eq. 21-69]}$$

Weights usually take a form similar to:

$$w_i \sim \left(1/\sigma_i^2 \Big/ \sum_{i=1}^n 1/\sigma_i^2 \right) \qquad \text{[Eq. 21-70]}$$

where w_i is proportional to the preceding ratio.

A second measure, the Mahalanobis D^2 distance, is a metric that takes into account the covariance between data groups:

$$D_{ij} = (X_i - X_j)^T \Sigma^{-1} (X_i - X_j) \qquad \text{[Eq. 21-71]}$$

where T is the transpose of the vector.

The symbol Σ is the pooled (within groups) variance covariance matrix. The Mahalanobis D^2 distance has the advantage over either the city-block or Euclidean measures in that we can review covariance or correlations between variables. If these corelations reduce to zero, it is the Euclidean metric with standard variables. Now that we have our measuring stick, we need a framework: we will approach the two-category problem, then the multicategory one, and will stay with recognizable systems, Class I and II, to illustrate the approach. However, the approach can be extended without difficulty to Class III and IV ciphers.

Developing a Multicategory Approach

There are two cryptosystem identification requirements:

1. Cipher texts need to be of reasonable length and available in sufficient number.

2. Cipher texts must represent a large number of randomly selected keys. *This is a critical point.* When ICSA COMSEC Solutions first tried this procedure on Class IV ciphers, they used chosen nonrandom keys to intentionally constrain the process and the results were poor. When they increased the number of random keys in the selection of cipher texts, the results improved dramatically.

Starting with a two-category problem, we have two sets of long cipher texts, from known encryption systems E_1 and E_2 on various keys of these systems, respectively. We label these:

$$E_1^1, E_1^2, ..., E_1^{N1} \quad \text{and} \quad E_2^1, E_2^2, ..., E_2^{N2} \qquad \textbf{[Eq. 21-72]}$$

We start with a 26-dimensional vector $X_k = (x_k^1, x_k^2, ..., x_k^{26})$, where its elements, $x_k^1, x_k^2, ..., x_k^{26}$, represent features, for example the frequencies of letters A, B, ..., Z and so on, in the cipher text of category J, where $J = 1, 2$ and N_j is the number of cipher text in the jth category or system.

It is possible to construct a feature frequency vector:

$$X_j = (x_j^1, x_j^2, ..., x_j^{26}) \qquad \textbf{[Eq. 21-73]}$$

for each ciphertext.

For $J = 2$, with two encryption systems E_1 and E_2 on a number of keys in these systems, we construct the pattern functions $G_1(X)$ and $G_2(X)$ such for each frequency vector X belonging to encryption system E_1

$$G_1(X) > G_2(X) \qquad \textbf{[Eq. 21-74]}$$

and for each cipher text from E_2

$$G_1(X) < G_2(X) \qquad \textbf{[Eq. 21-75]}$$

The multicategory problem, consisting of encryption systems E_1 to E_m, with chosen cipher texts e_k^j, $k = 1$, m; $J = 1$, N_m requires that we construct a new pattern function $G_k(X)$.

This new function has the property that within the space of all cryptograms on E_k, the kth discriminant function $G_k(X)$ will have the maximum value. So:

$$G_k(X) > G_1(X) \; \forall \, X \in E_k \qquad k \neq 1 \qquad \text{[Eq. 21-76]}$$

where $\forall$ means "for all or for any" and $\in$ means "is an element of the set."

The preceding function represents an *ultrametric,* which has the following five properties, where E is the measurement space and X, Y, and Z are any three points in E. The distance function D is an ultrametric if (and note that iff means "if and only if"):

$$D(X, Y) = 0 \quad \text{iff} \quad X = Y \qquad\qquad \text{[Eq. 21-77]}$$

$$D(X, Y) \geq 0 \; \forall \, X \quad \text{and} \quad Y \in E \qquad \text{[Eq. 21-78]}$$

$$D(X, Y) = D(Y, X) \; \forall \, X \quad \text{and} \quad Y \in E \qquad \text{[Eq. 21-79]}$$

$$D(X, Y) < D(X, Z) + D(Y, Z) \qquad X, Y, Z \in E \qquad \text{[Eq. 21-80]}$$

$$D(X, Y) \leq \max\{D(X, Z), D(Y, Z)\} \qquad \text{[Eq. 21-81]}$$

The pattern classification algorithm used to identify the encryption function is the Friedman distributions of letters expanded to include additional parameters. It is applied in a pattern space so that we can track the patterns of occurrence of letters in the cipher text. Mathematically, we consider the space finite, yielding sufficient information to correctly identify the cryptosystem. These distributions include:

1. The uniform distribution of English letters prepared on a system of randomly selected keys selected from a large number of samples.

2. Frequency of blanks.

3. Frequency of digrams, trigrams, tetragrams, and pentagrams.

4. Average distance between the same letters As, Bs giving a distance vector $D(d_a, d_b, ..., d_z)$, where d_a is the average positional distance between the letter A in a given cipher text and similarly for B to Z. The difference between two letters occurring at position m and n is $n-m$.

5. The *jump vector*, defined as the jump distance between any two consecutive letters of the cipher text measured moving from left to right. This measure has mixed blessings. The author attacked its use in ELS (equidistant letter sequences) calculations in *The Bible Code,* Cryptologia, volume XXII, number 2, April 1998.

6. The I.C. and Psi(observed) and its relationship with the Psi(random).

7. Other determinants are the entropy or approximate entropy.

8. The compression of the cipher text (weighted).

The final step in the process is to transform the measurement vectors into points in the feature space. We then develop a decision rule on our known ("labeled") samples, and use it to classify given unlabeled points. There are two effective procedures to accomplish this transformation: (1) linear discriminant functions and (2) piecewise linear discriminant functions. The former is used for Class I and II ciphers and the latter works with Class III and IV ciphers.

Nonparametric Linear Discriminant Functions (LDFs)

From optimization theory we recall the general form of an LDF:

$$G_k(X) = w_{k1}x_1 + w_{k2}x_2 + \cdots + w_{kn}x_n + w_{kn+1}x_{n+1} = W_k^T X \qquad \textbf{[Eq. 21-82]}$$

where W_k and X are column vectors. Moreover, W_k is the augmented weight vector and X is the augmented pattern vector. Since decision surfaces are hypersurfaces in n-dimensions, they may be used to separate known patterns into their classes/categories and also to classify unknown patterns. In a pattern space, each pattern is projected as a point; they occupy different regions because of their different class and discriminating surfaces or decision surfaces can separate them.

The boundary of the two-category problem discussed earlier is:

$$d(X) = W_1^T X_1 - W_2^T X_2 = (W_1 - W_2)^T X = 0 \qquad \textbf{[Eq. 21-83]}$$

This is the hyperplane passing through the origin, in augmented feature space.

We return to the cryptosystem E_k, and we represent the mean vector as:

$$<Y_k> = \frac{1}{N_k} \sum_{j=1}^{N_k} X_j^k \qquad \textbf{[Eq. 21-84]}$$

and represents the mean feature vector of the labeled samples of the kth class.

What the discriminant factor does is to assign the unknown point X to the system that has the average value $<Y_k>$ closest to X. So:

$$X \in E_j \quad \text{if} \quad d(X, <Y_j>) = \min d(X, <Y_k>) \qquad \text{[Eq. 21-85]}$$

$$d^2(X, <Y_k>) = (X - <Y_k>)^T(X - <Y_k>) = X^TX$$
$$- 2X^T<Y_k> + <Y_k>^T<Y_k> \qquad \text{[Eq. 21-86]}$$

X^TX is a constant and can be discarded from the discriminating function. Rearrange and multiply by $\frac{1}{2}$:

$$G_k(X) = X^T<Y_k> - \frac{1}{2}<Y_k>^T<Y_k> \qquad \text{[Eq. 21-87]}$$

This becomes our prototype discriminant function. We replace the weights W_s by

$$<Y_k> \quad \text{and} \quad -\frac{1}{2}<Y_k>^T<Y_k> \qquad \text{[Eq. 21-88]}$$

becomes the linear threshold and is a constant.

The known set of cipher texts e_j^k is assigned to E_k. We assign linear discriminant functions $G_1, G_2,..., G_k$ to k classes such that for class k, $G_k(X) > G_j(X)$ for all $j = 1,..., N$ and for all $k \neq j$, we say that the systems $E_1, E_2,..., E_k$ are *linearly separable*.

Class I and Class II Differentiation

In 1983, I. J. Kumar and T. L. Rao researched three classical systems: Vigenere, Playfair, and Hill algebraic ciphers, using linear discriminant functions. They used two vectors as feature vectors and carried out the discrimination of the systems using the Euclidean distance as a measure of separation. The two vectors were:

1. 26-dimensional frequency vector for English.

2. Mean distance vector corresponding to the mean of distance between the sequential occurrence of each character within the message.

Kumar defined three discriminant functions:

$$G_1(X) = X^T<Y_1> - \frac{1}{2}<Y_1>^T<Y_1> \qquad \text{[Eq. 21-89]}$$

$$G_2(X) = X^T<Y_2> - \frac{1}{2}<Y_2>^T<Y_2> \qquad \text{[Eq. 21-90]}$$

$$G_3(X) = X^T\langle Y_3\rangle - \tfrac{1}{2}\langle Y_3\rangle^T\langle Y_3\rangle \qquad \text{[Eq. 21-91]}$$

where X is the feature vector and X^T is its transpose and $\langle Y_i\rangle$ and $\langle Y_i\rangle^T$ are the mean feature vectors and its transpose for the ith system.

The Kumar study used 50 plain-text/cipher-text learning sets of 400 characters in length. They used a scoring function (the value of the discriminant function for a particular sample) so that each sample was identified to the class for which its "Score" was maximum. So:

$$\text{Score } G_j(X)\Big|X = X_j \qquad i = 1, 2, 3 \cdots ; j = 1, 2, ..., s \qquad \text{[Eq. 21-92]}$$

where score is the value of the ith discriminant function for the jth cipher text and s is the total number of cryptograms to be classified. A sample of 75 samples of unknown origin from the three systems was randomly presented for classification. The learning sets are presented in Figure 21-11. The results of the classification cycle are presented in Figure 21-12.

Kumar found that the performance of the classifier for the design sets (set of labeled samples) was better than that for the test sets. This is a characteristic of all linear classifiers; the performance of the frequency vector-based discriminant was superior to the one based on the mean-distance vector.

Rao extended Kumar's research by testing the discriminating effectiveness of the linear discriminant function with frequency and mean distance vector as feature vectors. Using 100 plain English messages of length 400 characters encrypted with randomly chosen 64-bit keys of

Figure 21-11

Results of Learning Sets Class I and II: Three Classical Cipher Systems

Learning Set of 50 Samples for Systems Classified as	Number of Samples Classified as Vigenere Square	Number of Samples Classified as Playfair	Number of Samples Classified as Hill Cipher
1. Vigenere Square			
(a) Percentage frequency vector	49	0	1
(b) Mean distance vector	36	3	11
2. Playfair			
(a) Percentage frequency vector	1	48	
(b) Mean distance vector	8	35	7
3. Hill Cipher			
(a) Percentage frequency vector	0	0	50
(b) Mean distance vector	6	4	40

Figure 21-12
Classification Results
of Samples—Three
Classical Cipher Sys-
tems

Test Set of 25 Samples of the System	Vigenere Square	Playfair	Hill Cipher
1. Vigenere Square			
(a) Percentage frequency vector	18	2	5
(b) Mean distance vector	19	0	6
2. Playfair			
(a) Percentage frequency vector	5	20	0
(b) Mean distance vector	8	17	6
3. Hill Cipher			
(a) Percentage frequency vector	0	0	25
(b) Mean distance vector	3	7	15

the DES and Geffe generator and cipher texts recorded in hexadecimal, he researched these Class IV level difficulty ciphers using the nonparametric model previously discussed. Figure 21-13 shows the vector classification process and results on DES and the Geffe Generator. The results with DES would indicate that the performance of the classifier deteriorated with reduction of feature vector dimensionality, pointing out the complexity of the system.

Figure 21-13
Results of Classifica-
tion of DES and Geffe
Generator (G.G.)

System	100 Samples of Learning Set		50 Samples of Test Set		Feature Vector Used
	DES	G.G.	DES	G.G.	
DES	64	36	34	16	Percentage frequency vector
G.G.	33	67	19	31	
DES	62	38	30	20	Mean distance vector
G.G.	35	65	21	29	

It turns out that Geffe generators, nonlinear combiners, and shift registers, and all the Class III and IV ciphers require additional subclassification in the test set to prevent misclassification. Because of their wide discriminating strength and wide application, *piecewise linear discriminant functions* were chosen to characterize Class III and Class IV ciphers.

Piecewise Linear Discriminant Functions and Closed System Mechanisms

Piecewise linear discriminant functions can be used for separating subclasses from a particular class. They are very specific and generally cannot be extrapolated out of the region of interest. We use a decision rule known as the *nearest neighbor rule* (NNR) to take into account subclass definitions. A discriminant function developed to discriminate one subclass from another class may perform well only in one region and it may be possible to properly classify the entire class through piecewise linear discriminant functions, each part being valid in a particular region.

Consider:

$$G_j(X) = \max_{J=1,L} G_i^j(X) \qquad \textbf{[Eq. 21-93]}$$

where L is the number of subclasses in class i.

Each $G_i^j(X)$ is called a *subsidiary discriminant function* and

$$G_i^j(X) = W_i^T X \qquad \textbf{[Eq. 21-94]}$$

The regions of validity of the preceding discriminant functions are given as:

$$R_k(i) = \{X \mid W_k^T X \geq W_j^T X \ \forall j \neq k\} \qquad \textbf{[Eq. 21-95]}$$

which translated means that the value of the function corresponding to a given subregion must be larger than the value of the other discriminant functions evaluated in the same region. The patterns are classified by this equation. Subclasses may be determined using minimum distance classifiers. We form the subsidiary discriminant functions:

$$G_i^j(X) = m_{ij}X - \tfrac{1}{2}||m_{ij}||^2 \qquad \textbf{[Eq. 21-96]}$$

where $||m_{ij}||$ means the length of m_{ij}.

The determination of subclasses is not a simple matter and is based on heuristics. One rule that seems to work well is the NNR (nearest neighbor rule). The nearest neighbor is located using the minimum distance criterion, and is used to classify an unknown sample into the appropriate class. This process is followed sequentially:

1. The first sample is stored as a member of a consistent subset, called "store."

2. The second sample is classified as store if the first sample is not the nearest neighbor of the second sample; otherwise it is called "reject."

3. Any later sample is classified if the nearest neighbor does not or does lie in the samples stored thus far.

4. After one complete pass, we have another pass through the rejects to classify them correctly.

5. If the rejected samples get exhausted, we are left with the entire set as the consistent subset. Otherwise we have the consistent subset number and reject is ignored. The consistent subclass so obtained can be used as the representative class for the application of the NNR.

The question is, can this system be used to discriminate between members of the same family but with subtle differences? The answer is yes and very well. Figure 21-14 shows the result of linear discrimination classification of the Hebern, Enigma, and Typex Class II rotor machines made famous in World War II. It can be seen that classification perfor-

Figure 21-14
Three Rotor Machines

Classification of Three Test Sets of 50 Samples Each of Hebern, Enigma, and Typex Based on Subclass Structure

System	Hebern	Enigma	Typex
1. Hebern	19 + 11 = 30	7 + 5 = 12	3 + 5 = 8
2. Enigma	6 + 5 = 11	22 + 8 = 30	4 + 5 = 9
3. Typex	6 + 3 = 9	3 + 4 = 7	23 + 11 = 34

	Class II Store	Class II Reject
Hebern	56	44
Enigma	60	40
Typex	58	42

Results of Linear Discriminant Classification of Three Rotor-Based Systems

System	100 Samples of Learning Set Classified as			50 Samples of Test Set Classified as		
	Hebern	Enigma	Typex	Hebern	Enigma	Typex
1. Hebern	68	20	12	20	25	5
2. Enigma	24	32	44	18	12	20
3. Typex	18	24	58	16	8	26

mance is dramatically improved when a set of six piecewise linear discriminant functions is introduced. The results demonstrate that proper classification of the systems can be achieved by using piecewise linear discrimination, even when the systems mechanisms differ only slightly.

Parametric Classifiers— Probabilistic Issues

The multicategory classification problem is better approached using parametric methods. We attempt to define a model for system identification requiring determination of decision boundaries to separate out sets of messages encrypted on different systems from each other.

Many patterns are not so well defined. As previously mentioned, they are probabilistic in nature, that is, the feature vector is based on a probability distribution of the features. Our test sets become problems in statistical decision theory based on the well-known Bayes theorem. To derive discriminant functions, we need to define a loss function $\lambda(i\,|\,j)$ defined for $i,j = 1, 2,..., R$. This loss function gives the loss incurred when the learning process misclassifies a sample belonging to class i or class j. The classification process based on decision theory minimizes the average loss to optimize the classification. The symbol $i\,|\,j$ means the probability of i given j. The loss function comes from optimization theory and is defined:

$$L_x(i) = \sum_{J=1}^{R} \lambda(i\,|\,j)p(i\,|\,j) \qquad \textbf{[Eq. 21-97]}$$

where $p(i\,|\,j)$ is the probability of X belonging to J; $L_x(i)$ is minimum for $i = i_0$. This classification is the one that results in minimum loss if X is categorized in category i_0. The process, which classifies X with a minimum loss, is therefore the one that classifies X into a particular category for

$$L_x(i_0) \leq L_x(i) \quad \text{for all} \quad i = 1, 2,..., R \qquad \textbf{[Eq. 21-98]}$$

By Bayes theorem:

$$L_x(i) = \frac{1}{P(x)} \sum_{J=1}^{R} \lambda(i\,|\,J)p(X\,|\,J)p(J) \qquad \textbf{[Eq. 21-99]}$$

where $p(x)$ occurs in the calculation of loss $L_x(i)$; X occurs given that it belongs to category J as a probability of occurrence of p. We define a *minimized loss function* $i_x(i)$, which is also minimized by loss of the classifier.

$$i_x(i) = \sum_{J=1}^{R} \lambda(i \mid j) p(X \mid j) p(j) \qquad \textbf{[Eq. 21-100]}$$

We define the *special loss function* of the type

$$\lambda(i \mid j) = 1 - \delta_{ij} \qquad \textbf{[Eq. 21-101]}$$

where δ_{ij} is the Kronecker delta, which has value of 1 for $i = J$ and zero otherwise. This changes the loss function to:

$$i_x(i) = p(x) - p(x \mid i) p(i) \qquad \textbf{[Eq. 21-102]}$$

and defining $g_i(x) = p(x \mid i) p(i)$, which maximizes $p(i)$ and thus minimizes $i_x(i)$. We come to the first milestone:

$$G_j(X) = \log p(x \mid i) + \log p(i) \qquad \textbf{[Eq. 21-103]}$$

This is the *modified discriminant function* $G_j(X)$, and can be used in the multicategory parametric classification model. W. F. Friedman and his student Frank Rowlett proposed a log function used to weight the frequency distribution for solving multialphabetic cryptograms. Kumar, Rao, and Hart rediscovered this process separately many years later. The assumption of normal distribution of frequency of letters not only holds for a multicategory problem, but in some cases the parametric classification scheme is the more effective tool in classification of complex cryptosystems than its nonparametric sister. The problem actually reduces to a standard format involving discrimination of various multivariate populations through decision hypersurfaces.

We return to the calculation/use of Mahalanobis distance and assume Gaussian distribution of feature vectors in each of the systems to be classified. We also assume that all the systems come from one single Gaussian population with the same variance-covariance (dispersion) matrix. We treat the encryption systems E_i, $I = 1, 2,..., R$ as known labeled systems.

The Mahalanobis distance is given by:

$$D^2 = E(X - <Y_k>)^T \sum^{-1} (X - <Y_k>) \qquad \textbf{[Eq. 21-104]}$$

and the normal v-variate probability distribution is

$$p(x) = \frac{1}{(2\pi)^{v/2}|\Sigma|^{1/2}} exp\{-\tfrac{1}{2}(X - <Y_i>)^T \overset{-1}{\sum}(X - <Y_i>)\} \qquad \textbf{[Eq. 21-105]}$$

where X is a dX_1 column vector representing the pattern, and Y_k is the vX_1 column pattern vector. This vector is equal to X_k^T, the mean vector of the design prototypes of kth class and the dispersion matrix:

$$\Sigma = \begin{vmatrix} \sigma_{11} & \sigma_{12} & \cdots & \sigma_{1v} \\ \sigma_{21} & & & \\ \vdots & & & \vdots \\ \sigma_{v1} & & & \sigma_{vv} \end{vmatrix} \qquad \textbf{[Eq. 21-106]}$$

where Σ is the Symmetric Positive Definite Dispersion Matrix or the Covariance Matrix. Each element in it, σ_{ij}, is the variance of x_j:

$$\sigma_{ij} = E[(X_i - X_i)(X_j - X_j)] \qquad i \ne j = 1, 2, ..., v \qquad \textbf{[Eq. 21-107]}$$

The variance-covariance Matrix based on the design set of labeled samples is

$$\Sigma = E[(X - \overline{X})(X - \overline{X})^T] \qquad \textbf{[Eq. 21-108]}$$

The preceding is a quadratic form that implies that a set of normal patterns would be grouped in an ellipsoidal cluster about the design average $\overline{X}$. Defining the mean vectors $<Y_j>$

$$p(x\,|\,i) = \frac{1}{(2\pi)^{v/2}|\Sigma|^{1/2}} exp\{-\tfrac{1}{2}(X - <Y_i>)^T \sum{}^{-1}(X - <Y_i>)\} \qquad i = 1, 2, ..., R \qquad \textbf{[Eq. 21-109]}$$

using $G_i(X) = \log p(x\,|\,i) + \log p(i)$ we get a more interesting equation:

$$G_i(x) = \log p_i - (v/2)\log 2\pi - \tfrac{1}{2}\log |\overset{-1}{\sum}| - \tfrac{1}{2}[(X - <Y_i>)^T\Sigma(X - <Y_i>)\} \qquad \textbf{[Eq. 21-110]}$$

We can reduce this equation by considering the probability of each class as the same and hold the first three terms as a constant. The discriminant function then becomes

$$G_i(x) = C_i - \tfrac{1}{2}[(X - <Y_i>)^T \overset{-1}{\sum}(X - <Y_i>)\} \qquad \textbf{[Eq. 21-111]}$$

We are not done yet. The transpose term is not dependent on i. So,

$$G_i(x) = X^T \sum^{-1} <Y_i> - \tfrac{1}{2}<Y_i>^T \sum^{-1} <Y_i> \qquad \text{[Eq. 21-112]}$$

This is a linear discriminant function with first v weights being as transformed mean vector $\sum^{-1} <Y_i>$ and the $(v + 1)$th in weight is given by the value

$$-\tfrac{1}{2}<Y_i>^T \sum^{-1} <Y_i> \qquad \text{[Eq. 21-113]}$$

which is a constant.

The balance of cipher text is classified on the basis of R scores:

$$\text{Score for the } E_1 = \sum_{J=1}^{v} C_1^J X_j - C_1^{v+1} \qquad \text{[Eq. 21-114]}$$

$$\text{Score for the } E_2 = \sum_{J=1}^{v} C_2^J X_j - C_2^{v+1} \qquad \text{[Eq. 21-115]}$$

$$\text{Score for the } E_R = \sum_{J=1}^{v} C_R^J X_j - C_R^{v+1} \qquad \text{[Eq. 21-116]}$$

The cipher text is assigned to the E_k if its score for the kth class is maximum.

ICSA ran the parametric classification model on the three classical systems that were considered previously. Viewing the Vigenere, Playfair, Hill cipher, and an Aristocrat simple substitution as a multicategory classification problem, ICSA resolved and improved the results to 98 percent correct classification in the design set (Figure 21-15).

Figure 21-15

Discrimination Using Parametric Model on Four Classical Cryptosystems (Design Sets)

Design Set of 50 Samples	Classified as			
	Simple Substitution	Vigenere Square	Playfair	Hill Cipher
1. Simple Substitution	50	0	0	0
2. Vigenere Square	0	47	0	3
3. Playfair	0	0	49	1
4. Hill Cipher	0	0	0	50

Figure 21-16 shows the results of discrimination between four classical systems for test sets of 25 samples for each system. The stars represent the nonparametric discriminant function comparisons. Figure 21-

Figure 21-16
Discrimination Using
Parametric Model on
Four Classical Cryp-
tosystems (Test Sets
and Comparison to
Nonparametric
Model)

Figure 21-16
Discrimination Using
Parametric Model on
Four Classical Cryp-
tosystems (Test Sets
and Comparison to
Nonparametric
Model)

Test Set of 25 Samples	Simple Substitution	Vigenere Square	Playfair	Hill Cipher
1. Simple Substitution	20 / 19*	5 / 6*	0 / 0*	0 / 0*
2. Vigenere	3 / 3*	18 / 15*	2 / 2*	2 / 5*
3. Playfair	0 / 0*	5 / 8*	18 / 16*	2 / 1*
4. Hill Cipher	0 / 3*	2 / 0*	0 / 2*	23 / 20*

Figure 21-17
Parametric Model on
Class I, II, and III Cryp-
tosystems (Design
Sets)

	System 1	System 2	System 3	Set Classified as
Set 1	45	1	4	1
Set 2	8	39	3	2
Set 3	2	0	48	3

17 extends the use of the multicategory model to three unknown systems taken randomly from Class I, II, and III cipher systems. The cipher texts were drawn from a set of 50 of length 200 characters. Figure 21-17 shows that the design sets were classified properly with a very high accuracy of 90 percent. Figure 21-18 shows the results of classification of five random test sets with no information as to source. It turns out that classification was without error.

Figure 21-18
Parametric Model on
Class I, II, and III Cryp-
tosystems (Test Sets)

	System 1	System 2	System 3	Classification of System
Set 1	9	5	1	1
Set 2	3	2	10	3
Set 3	11	2	2	1
Set 4	3	1	11	3
Set 5	15	0	0	1

We have spent significant time on the seminal Kumar and Rao studies. They portend an approach that works in practice. ICSA and COMSEC Solutions have made confirming studies using real products and real algorithms representing all four classes of ciphers. They have found that the techniques of linear discrimination and piecewise linear discrimination are viable system identification tools for a whole range of cryptosystems. The whole range of private-key systems starting with the simple Aristocrat and classical systems, rotor-based systems, stream ciphers, Geffe generator, and DES have been found to be amenable to identification through cipher texts only. The identification of systems is not uniform and is not perfect. Although the design sets may be classified more accurately than the test sets, researchers seem to feel that limitations are due to the number of test sets and dimensionality of the feature vector. They have found that improving the number and types of classifiers used in the feature vector significantly improves the performance of the test set identification against practical systems.

ICSA and COMSEC Solutions have also been able to confirm that parametric classification is more accurate than nonparametric for most of the multicategory cipher-mix identifications. The assumption of a normal distribution of feature vectors based on letter frequencies, and other classical measures is good even in cipher texts that are generated by Class III or IV cipher systems. One final point, the performance of a classifier may be biased by key size and amount of salt in the key. The performance of the classifier is based on the accuracy and amount of information about the system in the design (labeled set). It is recommended that the performance of the classifier be tested independently of the design set.

The results of cryptosystem identification show that the method of piecewise linear discrimination functions after determination of subclasses in the cipher-text sets is quite successful in classifying patterns. This is true when sufficient number of cipher texts on a set of randomly chosen keys are available. If the keys representing the system are adequately chosen, the discriminants can with a high degree of accuracy determine the origin of a set of messages. The problem of tracing the origin of an individual encrypted message, out of a number of known systems, can also be solved with a high probability. COMSEC Solutions is experimenting on the use of quadratic degree discriminant functions to separate elliptical curve cryptosystems.

It must be stressed, however, to the reader, that ICSA and COMSEC Solutions research results discussed in this section are far from complete. Cryptosystem identification research is continuing with measured and gradual successes and with as many false trails to be eliminated.

Key Clustering Through Cipher Texts

Our last topic is key clustering. *Clusters* are defined as a collection of patterns/objects or small groups of patterns or objects, which are similar in some respect or close to each other per some distance criterion. *Clustering* is the process of generating such classes without prior knowledge of the prototype classification. It is a separate and different problem from the system classification problem just discussed.

Cluster analysis is an umbrella term for many different heuristic techniques and applied statistics to discover structure within the complex bodies of data. We generate classes without a previous knowledge of the system classification. For M patterns, $X_1, X_2,..., X_m \in S$, the process of clustering is defined as: to search and seek regions $S_1, S_2,..., S_k$ such that every X_i falls into a region and no X_k falls into two regions. So,

$$S_1 \cup S_2 \cdots \cup S_k = S \qquad \text{[Eq. 21-117]}$$

and

$$S_i \cap S_j = \phi \; \forall \; i \neq j \qquad \text{[Eq. 21-118]}$$

where $\cup$ and $\cap$ mean union and intersection, respectively. Cluster analysis is the final analysis performed after system identification has been achieved. It does not matter whether parametric or nonparametric techniques have been employed. The objective is to recognize a new observation as a member of an existing category.

Researchers have studied many algorithms for clustering. The K-means algorithm seems to have gained some popularity again. The K-means algorithm for clustering the patterns in K number of classes is to randomly allocate each pattern to one of the K-classes, find the center of each class by averaging the feature vectors of members of that class, partition all the patterns again around these centers using the appropriate proximity measure, calculate the centers of this new partition, and repeat the process until the classes are stabilized.

The procedure is:

1. Decide the number of clusters to be created.

2. Extract relevant features of dissimilarity from the data. These are the features of the encryption and cipher-text message and should be key-dependent so that the data can be classified according to key classes.

3. Randomly allocate each encrypted message to one of the clusters.

4. Calculate the centroid of the feature vector for each class; the mean vector represents the corresponding class.

5. Calculate, using the Euclidean metric, the reallocation of messages to the nearest classes meeting the distance from the centroid.

6. Repeat Steps 4 and 5 until all partitions are stabilized. These are the required clusters.

7. If system convergence is not reached, change the random IV allocation and restart the procedure. On more difficult systems, the restart procedure may require eight to nine iterations before system convergence is reached.

The final classification depends on the IV or the initial random vector allocation of the patterns to classes. It may be required to start at a different point until convergence is reached.

Cipher-Text Interactions

Whereas system identification and pattern analysis have been successfully used to separate cryptosystems vertically, and to some degree horizontally, cluster analysis has not yielded as much fruit in terms of key identification. It does work but ineffectively.

The cryptanalyst tries to reduce his/her investment and work factor to reduce the trial set of keys for solving a message to the minimum possible. Cluster analysis tools are useful in this endeavor because they remove those keys that are not close to each other by some similarity measure. The cipher texts that are available provide a suitable vehicle to carry out a classification with respect to keys. The cryptanalyst carries out a design set test prior to investigation of an unknown source of keys. On receiving the new cipher text for analysis, the cryptanalyst will try to locate the cluster that contains this key and try all keys in the known cluster first to decrypt the message.

The *key space* consists of discrete entities whose distance (dissimilarity) from each other is not an index of closeness (or otherwise) of cipher texts. Look at the DES Avalanche effect to see that small changes in a key may result in complete change of the cipher text. Keys that can be said to be close to each other based on system configuration of key-space division may lead to cipher texts of quite different statistical characteristics.

The clustering for key-space division based on the characteristics of cipher texts generated by the keys does provide a *marker* in the key space. It can be an effective marker of keys that lead to cipher texts with the same or nearly the same characteristics. Two keys found in the same cluster may not belong to the same key subspace as per the system configuration. For example, two RC4 keys may have different initialization vector IVs and different key characteristics but still be close enough for a cluster variable. Clustering is an augmentation tool to bring out structure within a large dataset so that each cluster so determined may be analyzed later with factor analysis or additional discriminant analysis. When successful, clustering to classify keys based on corresponding cipher texts permits the placing of cipher text into a proper cluster, either using the mean vectors of clusters or through the use of the K-nearest neighborhood rule.

To succeed in clustering keys via cryptograms only, it is essential to remove the effect of plain-text message variation on the cipher-text characteristic. If the message variation dominates the cipher-text statistics, erroneous classification occurs on the basis of cipher-text characteristics. The key clustering should be based on entities that are free from the effect of message variation. Herein lies the difference from the system identification problem. The search for such entities is basic to the formulation of a feature vector for key classification. To reduce plain-text variations on the cipher text for the same key, we use the mean characteristics of the cipher texts resulting from a number of messages. This leads to the mean or the average representation of the key, which is useful for cluster analysis. This is different from system identification, because we want variation with respect to different keys to be small in comparison to the effect of the transformations on the plain text due to the system.

Having clustered the keys based on average features, we use these clusters for locating the key used on a known system in the NNR cluster and then try the key set in this cluster to see if any meaningful plain text emerges. We have a two-step process:

1. Clustering of the total key space into smaller subspaces

2. Arriving at the key cluster containing the encryption key used for the encryption.

The success in the last step is critical to reduction of the number of trials for arriving at plain text and depends on the degree of certainty with which the unknown cipher-text key is classified in the correct cluster. The correct cluster has the key on which the clustering process prepared the cipher text assigned to it.

We are interested in the performance of a mean feature vector based on messages chosen for clustering. Stream ciphers, which have a very large period of generated key sequences in comparison to the normal message length, provide good fodder for the analysis. We use a number of messages encrypted on the same settings, but encrypted on different parts of the generated sequence. Chances of finding the correct key cluster are usually better than 50 percent. Figure 21-19 shows the clustering of 100 keys of a Geffe Generator. Only one crypto-product in the CPC uses this process and it is a Class IV cipher. A Geffe Generator is a nonlinear shift register-based system. It employs three linear feedback shift registers and a two-to-one multiplexer generating nonlinearity into the system. The key system is composed of IV raw bits and feedback polynomials for each register. Ten messages of 200 characters in length were encrypted on each one of the 100 different settings chosen from five different stage shift registers with different initial register contents. Four different measures of closeness were tested. The results of two classification runs on the data show that 55 percent of the keys could be correctly classified.

Figure 21-19

Results of Key Clustering for Nonlinear Geffe Generator (Using a Mean Vector of 10 Messages and Four Indices of Closeness)

Index of Closeness	No. of Keys Correctly Classified
1. Euclidean distance from the mean	45
2. NN-rule	52
3. K-nearest neighbor, $k = 5$	47
4. Step 1 and a second run for next nearest mean	55

Key clustering works on DES and other Class IV systems. Kumar reported 55 percent success rates in his experiments to cluster DES keys based on cipher texts and NNR techniques. ICSA's confirming studies have indicated that the key-clustering process works, but the success rates on Class IV ciphers is only in the high 40 percent range. Research continues to be fruitful and improvements in performance are likely.

WRAP-UP

Cryptanalysis is a powerful tool that helps us unlock the secrets that others have spent so much time to architect. Vertical differentiation of cryptosystems is clearly possible based on classical principles. The process is easily automated and can be incorporated into a certification program. Research on both vertical and horizontal separation of cryptosystems based on expanded classical attacks is promising but certainly not complete.

Cryptanalysis is not limited to mathematical analysis. Rogue attacks on cryptographic keys can be successful because either our choice of passwords (which act as IVs for keys or are the keys) are not well thought out or randomized. Cryptosystem computer programming structure must be carefully designed or a reengineering effort by an attacker will meet with recognizable plain text. Pattern analysis is an elegant approach to unlocking the mathematical structures in chosen cipher texts. It is possible to carry out cryptosystem identification by application of piecewise minimum distance classifiers on the basis of cipher texts from these systems on randomly selected keys. Cryptosystems based on different philosophies of encryption can be discriminated from each other; also, similar encryption systems may be discriminated with respect to "shades" of variation within those systems. Classification does not fail because of similar designs in cryptosystems. A parametric classification model may be used to identify and classify multicategory cryptosystems.

The approach of clustering of keys is a powerful tool that seems to work on every private-key system and some public-key systems. An important concern in the clustering process is to eliminate the error caused by plain-text variations on the key. Clusters need to be distinctly separate (by a distance many times the deviation due to the plain text) for the clustering process to work effectively.

One last thought about the use of feature vectors. The percentage frequency vector for single, digram, or trigram letters can be used successfully as a feature vector. Cipher texts derived from Class III or IV cryptosystems tend to even out (flatten) the peaks in the frequencies of the letters. Why then is it possible to distinguish cipher texts prepared on different systems through this feature vector? If we look at the enciphering of a very long message with a single key, we see that the frequency graph is quite flat and there is very little to distinguish or discriminate between two cipher texts prepared on two different systems. The fact is that the frequencies are not flattened within the usual message lengths between 200 to 1500 letters and the effect of enciphering by different systems on the frequency distribution in plain message is significantly different on messages of such lengths. The system identification process works best when the number of messages of not too large a length is encrypted on many different systems for samples of cipher text. ICSA and COMSEC Solutions laboratories have improved the feature vector approach introduced by Dr. I. J. Kumar and associates by adding measures of compression, entropy, and letter coincidences to the characterization.

CHAPTER 22

Biometric
Encryption*

---

*Biometric Encryption is a registered trademark of Mytec Technologies, Inc.

Biometrics

A *biometric* is defined as a unique, measurable, biological characteristic or trait for automatically recognizing or verifying the identity of a human being. Statistically analyzing these biological characteristics has become known as the science of *biometrics*. These days, biometric technologies are typically used to analyze human characteristics for security purposes. Five of the most common physical biometric patterns analyzed for security purposes are the fingerprint, hand, eye, face, and voice.

The use of biometric characteristics as a means of identification is not a new concept. By 1926, law enforcement officials in several U.S. cities had begun submitting fingerprint cards to the FBI in an effort to create a database of fingerprints from known criminals. Human experts in the law enforcement field were subsequently able to manually match fingerprint samples collected at a crime scene against the prints in this criminal database. Years of research in developing accurate and distinctive fingerprint classification schemes made these manual matching processes feasible by drastically reducing the required database search space. Various fingerprint classification schemes are discussed in Lee and Gaensslen. In the early 1960s, the FBI invested a large amount of time and effort into the development of automated fingerprint identification systems. This automation of biometric identification for law enforcement purposes coincided with the development of automated systems for nonforensic applications, such as high-security access control. Fingerprint identification systems have been deployed in access control systems since the late 1960s. During the 1970s a biometric product based on measuring the geometry of the hand was introduced in a number of access control applications. Interest in biometric identification eventually moved from measuring characteristics of the hand to include characteristics of the eye. In the mid-1980s the first system that analyzed the unique patterns of the retina was introduced while, concurrently, work was being performed to analyze iris patterns.

In the 1990s, research continues on developing identification systems based on a wide variety of biometric patterns, such as the traditional biometrics mentioned earlier (i.e., fingerprint, hand geometry, iris, and retina), along with the development of voice, signature, palm print, and face recognition systems. A few new, innovative approaches are also being examined for biometric analysis, such as ear shape, DNA, key stroke (typing rhythm), and body odor.

Biometric identification consists of two stages: enrollment and verification. During the *enrollment* stage, a sample of the designated biometric is acquired. Some unique characteristics or features of this sample are then extracted to form a biometric *template* for subsequent comparison purposes. During the *verification* stage, an updated biometric sample is acquired. As in enrollment, features of this biometric sample are extracted. These features are then compared with the previously generated biometric template.

It is convenient to distinguish between the two main objectives of biometric systems: identification and authentication. *Biometric identification* is the process of matching an individual to one of a large set of system users, whereas *biometric authentication* simply verifies that the individual is who he or she claims to be. Law enforcement applications typically require the process of biometric identification; for example, a typical law enforcement application would seek to determine the identity of an individual who has left a latent fingerprint at the scene of a crime. The law enforcement official would enter the collected fingerprint and match its template against all the stored templates in the criminal record fingerprint database. This process may also be termed a *one-to-many search*. Alternatively, in the process of biometric authentication the user submits an identity claim to the system. Thus, only one biometric template is retrieved from the database of users and compared with the verification sample. Authentication is typically used in circumstances where access is being controlled, whether physical access to a room or building, or access to an electronic system such as the logon to a computer system. Biometric authentication thus processes a *one-to-one match* rather than a *one-to-many search*. For both the identification and the authentication systems, a threshold will generally be used to determine the match between templates. The setting of this threshold determines the discrimination sensitivity of the system.

Many systems have been developed for implementing biometric identification and authentication. Even for a single biometric, such as the fingerprint, there are many different methods used to create the biometric template. For example, law enforcement has traditionally used a method of extracting and comparing minutiae points from the fingerprint. *Minutiae points* are locations where a fingerprint ridge ends or splits in two. Other fingerprint characteristics are sweat pore location, ridge density, and distance between ridges. In other systems, the entire fingerprint image may be processed to implement a pattern recognition process, such as correlation.

Merger of Biometrics with Cryptography

With the proliferation of information exchange across the Internet, and the storage of sensitive data on open networks, cryptography is becoming an increasingly important feature of computer security. Many cryptographic algorithms are available for securing information, and several have been discussed previously in this book. In general, data will be secured using a symmetric cipher system, whereas public-key systems will be used for digital signatures and for secure key exchange between users. However, regardless of whether a user deploys a symmetric or a public-key system, the security is dependent on the secrecy of the secret or private key, respectively. Because of the large size of a cryptographically strong key, it would clearly not be feasible to require the user to remember and enter the key each time it is required. Instead, the user is typically required to choose an easily remembered passcode that is used to encrypt the cryptographic key; this encrypted key can then be stored on a computer's hard drive. To retrieve the cryptographic key, the user is prompted to enter the passcode, which will then be used to decrypt the key.

There are two main problems with the method of passcode security. First, the security of the cryptographic key, and hence the cipher system, is now only as good as the passcode. Due to practical problems of remembering various passcodes, some users tend to choose simple words, phrases, or easily remembered personal data, while others resort to writing the passcode down on an accessible document to avoid data loss. Obviously these methods pose potential security risks. The second problem concerns the lack of direct connection between the passcode and the user. Because a passcode is not tied to a user, the system running the cryptographic algorithm is unable to differentiate between the legitimate user and an attacker who fraudulently acquires the passcode of a legitimate user.

As an alternative to passcode protection, biometric authentication offers a new mechanism for key security by using a biometric to secure the cryptographic key. Instead of entering a passcode to access the cryptographic key, the use of this key is guarded by biometric authentication. When a user wishes to access a secured key, he or she will be prompted to allow for the capture of a biometric sample. If this verification sample matches the enrollment template, then the key is released and can be used to encrypt or decrypt the desired data. Thus, biometric authentication can replace the use of passcodes to secure a key. This offers both convenience, as the user no longer has to remember a passcode and secure identity confirmation, since only the valid user can release the key.

There are various methods that can be deployed to secure a key with a biometric. One method involves remote template matching and key storage. The biometric image is captured and the corresponding template is sent to a secure location for template comparison. If the user is verified, then the key is released from the secure location, which provides a convenient mechanism for the user, as he or she no longer needs to remember a passcode. This method would work well in a physical access application where the templates and keys may be stored in a secure location physically separated from the image capture device. In this scenario, the communication line must also be secured to avoid eavesdropper attacks. However, for personal computer use, the keys would likely be stored in the clear on a user's hard drive, which is not secure.

A second method involves hiding the cryptographic key within the enrollment template itself via a trusted (secret) bit-replacement algorithm. Upon successful authentication by the user, this trusted algorithm would simply extract the key bits from the appropriate locations and release the key into the system. Unfortunately, this implies that the cryptographic key will be retrieved from the same location in a template each time a different user is authenticated by the system. Thus, if an attacker could determine the bit locations that specify the key, then the attacker could reconstruct the embedded key from any of the other users' templates. If an attacker had access to the enrollment program then he or she could determine the locations of the key by, for example, enrolling several people in the system using identical keys for each enrollment. The attacker then needs only to locate those bit locations with common information across the templates.

A third method is to use data derived directly from a biometric image. Bodo proposed such a method in a German patent; this patent proposed that data derived from the biometric (in essence, the biometric template) are used directly as a cryptographic key. However, there are two main problems with this method. First, as a result of changes in the biometric image due to environmental and physiological factors, the biometric template is generally not consistent enough to use as a cryptographic key. Second, if the cryptographic key is ever compromised, then the use of that particular biometric is irrevocably lost. In a system where periodic updating of the cryptographic key is required, this is catastrophic.

An innovative technique for securing a key using a biometric has been developed by Mytec Technologies, Inc., based in Toronto, Canada. The solution developed by Mytec does not use an independent, two-stage process to first authenticate the user and then release the key. Instead, the key is linked with the biometric at a more fundamental level during enrollment, and is later retrieved using the biometric during verification. Furthermore, the key is completely independent of the biometric data, which means that, first, the use of the biometric is not forfeited if the key is ever compromised, and second, the key can be easily modified or updated at a later date. The process developed by Mytec Technologies is called *Biometric Encryption*. During enrollment, the Biometric Encryption process combines the biometric image with a digital key to create a secure block of data, known as a *Bioscrypt*.* The digital key can be used as a cryptographic key. The Bioscrypt is secure in that neither the fingerprint nor the key can be independently obtained from it. During verification, the Biometric Encryption algorithm retrieves the cryptographic key by combining the biometric image with the Bioscrypt. Thus, Biometric Encryption does not simply provide a yes/no response in user authentication to facilitate release of a key, but instead retrieves a key that can be recreated only by combining the biometric image with the Bioscrypt.

Note that Biometric Encryption refers to a process of secure key management. Biometric Encryption does not directly provide a mechanism for the encryption/decryption of data, but rather provides a replacement to typical passcode key-protection protocols. Specifically, Biometric Encryption provides a secure method for key management to complement existing cipher systems.

Although the process of Biometric Encryption can be applied to any biometric image, the initial implementation was achieved using fingerprint images. The majority of this chapter, therefore, deals only with fingerprint images. The application of the Biometric Encryption algorithm to other biometrics is briefly discussed in the section entitled "Biometric Encryption Using Other Biometric Templates."

Image Processing

In contrast to feature-based biometric systems, the Biometric Encryption algorithm processes the entire fingerprint image. The mechanism of *correlation* is used as the basis for the algorithm. A general overview of

---

*Bioscrypt is a registered trademark of Mytec Techologies, Inc.

correlation, as it relates to Biometric Encryption, is given in the following section. More detailed discussions of correlation and its applications are given in the references by Goodman, Steward, and VanderLugt.

Correlation

A two-dimensional input image array is denoted by $f(x)$ and its corresponding Fourier transform (FT) mate by $F(u)$. Here x denotes the space domain and u denotes the spatial frequency domain. The capitalization of F denotes an array in the Fourier transform domain. Note that although the arrays defined here are two-dimensional, only a single parameter, namely, x, is used as the array variable to simplify description of the process. A filter function $H(u)$ is derived from an image $f_0(x)$, where the subscript 0 denotes an image obtained during an enrollment session. The correlation function $c(x)$, between a subsequent version of the input $f_1(x)$, obtained during verification, and $f_0(x)$ is formally defined as

$$c(x) = \int_{-\infty}^{\infty} f_1(v) f_0^*(x + v)\, dv$$

where * denotes the complex conjugate. In a practical correlation system, the system output is computed as the inverse Fourier transform (FT^{-1}) of the product of $F_1(u)$ and $F_0^*(u)$, that is

$$c(x) = \text{FT}^{-1}[F_1(u) F_0^*(u)]$$

where $F_0^*(u)$ is typically represented by the filter function $H(u)$, derived from $f_0(x)$. For correlation-based biometric systems, the biometric template used for identification/authentication is the filter function $H(u)$.

Normally in the correlation process the filter function $H(u)$ is designed to produce a distinctive *correlation peak* (which approximates a delta function) at the output of the system. Such a correlation peak can easily be identified in a correlator system, and its position can be used to track an object of interest (see Hahn and Bauchert). Furthermore, a scalar value can be derived from the correlation plane (see Kumar and Hassebrook), and used as a measure of the similarity between $f_1(x)$ and $f_0(x)$. The process of correlation provides an effective mechanism for determining the similarity of objects, and has been successfully used for fingerprint authentication (see Stoianov et al.). In the next section, it is demonstrated that the process of correlation can also be used as the basis for the Biometric Encryption algorithm.

System Requirements

The objective of the Biometric Encryption algorithm is to provide a mechanism for the linking and subsequent retrieval of a digital key using a biometric such as a fingerprint. This digital key can then be used as a cryptographic key. The important system requirements that apply to a key retrieval system using a fingerprint are distortion tolerance, discrimination, and security.

- *Distortion tolerance* is the ability of the system to accommodate the day-to-day distortions of the fingerprint image. These distortions are due to behavioral changes (positioning, rotation, and deformation), as well as environmental (ambient temperature and humidity) and physiological (moisture content) conditions. A key retrieval system must be able to consistently produce the correct key for the different expected versions of a legitimate user's fingerprint.

- *Discrimination* is the ability of a system to distinguish between all of the system users' fingerprints. An attacker should produce an incorrect key when the attacker's fingerprint is combined with a legitimate user's filter.

- *Security* of the system means that neither the digital key nor the legitimate user's fingerprint can be independently extracted from any stored information.

To satisfy these three constraints simultaneously, the process of correlation was used as a mechanism for linking and retrieving the digital key. As discussed earlier, correlation is normally used to provide a single scalar value that indicates the degree of similarity between one input image $f_1(x)$, and another $f_0(x)$, represented by the filter function $H(u)$. The process of Biometric Encryption, on the other hand, needs to extract more information than a simple yes/no response from the system. In fact, Biometric Encryption is designed typically to output 128 bits of information to be used as a cryptographic key. Thus, it is not immediately evident how the process of correlation can be applied to this procedure. However, it is known that the process of correlation can be used to design filter functions that are tolerant to distortions in the input images (see Kumar or Roberge et al.). This distortion tolerance property of the correlation filter is critical to the implementation of Biometric

Encryption. Instead of designing a filter function $H(u)$, which produces a simple output pattern $c(x)$, which approximates a delta function, the process of Biometric Encryption produces a more sophisticated output pattern. This output pattern is linked during enrollment with a particular digital key, and subsequently regenerated during verification to retrieve the same digital key.

Design of the Filter Function

The filter function will be optimized for the following two requirements: (1) that it consistently produces the same output pattern for a legitimate user, and (2) that it is tolerant to distortions present in the input images. To provide a degree of distortion tolerance, the filter function is calculated during an enrollment session using a set of T training images, where $T \geq 1$. Denote the T images of the fingerprint by $\{f_0^1(x), f_0^2(x),\ldots, f_0^T(x)\}$, where the subscript 0 denotes a training image. The filter function that will be constructed using these images is denoted by $H(u)$. Note that we may refer to complex-valued functions such as $H(u)$ independently by their magnitude and phase components, denoted by $|H(u)|$ and $e^{i\phi H(u)}$, respectively. The output pattern produced in response to $f_0^t(x)$ is given by $c_0^t(x)$ and the Fourier transform of $c_0^t(x)$ is given by $C_0^t(u) \equiv F_0^t(u) \cdot H(u)$, where $F_0^t(u)$ is the Fourier transform of the training image $f_0^t(x)$. The desired output pattern from the system is denoted by $r(x)$. Note that the filter will be defined for an arbitrary form of $r(x)$, rather than a delta function, as is normally the case in correlator systems (see Mahalanobis et al.). The output pattern $c(x)$ will be used both to link with the digital key during enrollment and to retrieve the digital key during verification.

For $1 \leq t \leq T$, we require that $c_0^t(x) \approx r(x)$, that is, the output pattern should be as close as possible to the desired output function $r(x)$, for each image $f_0^t(x)$ in the training set. An error term $E_{\text{similarity}}$ can be defined, such that:

$$E_{\text{similarity}} = \frac{1}{T}\sum_{t=1}^{T}\int \left|c_0^t(x) - r(x)\right|^2 dx \qquad \textbf{[Eq. 22-1]}$$

$E_{\text{similarity}}$ is thus defined as a measure of the similarity of the output correlation patterns such that $E_{\text{similarity}} = 0$ implies that the output correlation patterns are identical for all of the training set images. Thus, we seek to minimize $E_{\text{similarity}}$. Also, we wish to minimize the error due to distortion in the input images, that is:

If $\quad f_0{}^t(x) = f_0{}^s(x) + \varepsilon_{\text{input}}{}^{t,s}(x)$

then $\quad c_0{}^t(x) = c_0{}^s(x) + \varepsilon_{\text{output}}{}^{t,s}(x)$

For $\quad s, t \in \{1, \ldots, T\} \quad \text{and} \quad t \neq s$ **[Eq. 22-2]**

Assuming that the distortion terms $\varepsilon_{\text{input}}{}^{t,s}(x)$ are uncorrelated, then it can be shown that the variance of the error term due to either the additive distortion or to changes in $f_0{}^t(x)$ is given by:

$$E_{\text{noise}} = \int \left| H(u) \right|^2 P(u) \, du \qquad \text{[Eq. 22-3]}$$

where

$$P(u) = \frac{2}{T(T-1)} \sum_{t=1}^{T-1} \sum_{s=t+1}^{T} \left| \text{FT} \left\{ \varepsilon_{\text{input}}{}^{t,s}(x) \right\} \right|^2 \qquad \text{[Eq. 22-4]}$$

that is, $P(u)$ represents the power spectrum of the change between the fingerprints in the training set. In general, $P(u)$ is readily approximated by a function that characterizes the type of object for which the filter is designed. For fingerprint images, each element of $P(u)$ can be uniformly set to a value of 1 (see Soutar et al. "Biometric Encryption™—using image processing").

Thus, the term $E_{\text{similarity}}$ characterizes the similarity of system output in response to each of the training set images, and the term E_{noise} characterizes the effect of image-to-image variation. $E_{\text{similarity}}$ determines how selective (or discriminating) the filter function is, and E_{noise} determines how tolerant it is to the expected distortions in the fingerprint images.

We wish to derive a filter that minimizes the total error E_{total}.

$$E_{\text{total}} = \alpha E_{\text{noise}} + \sqrt{1 - \alpha^2} E_{\text{similarity}}, \qquad 0 \leq \alpha \leq 1 \qquad \text{[Eq. 22-5]}$$

By allowing α to vary between 0 and 1, we can optimize the performance of the filter to produce a compromise between discrimination capability and distortion tolerance, following the optimal trade-off procedure developed by Réfrégier. Substituting the filter constraints defined previously into Eq. 22-5 and minimizing E_{total} with respect to $H(u)$, yields the following expression for $H(u)$.

$$H(u) = \sqrt{1 - \alpha^2} \left[\frac{1}{T} \sum_{t=1}^{T} F_0^{*t}(u) \right] R(u) /$$

$$\left\{ \alpha P(u) + \sqrt{1 - \alpha^2} \frac{1}{T} \sum_{t=1}^{T} \left| F_0{}^t(u) \right|^2 \right\} \qquad \text{[Eq. 22-6]}$$

where * denotes complex conjugate. It is convenient to define the following terms:

$$A_0(u) = \frac{1}{T} \sum_{t=1}^{T} F_0^t(u) \qquad \textbf{[Eq. 22-7]}$$

$$D_0(u) = \frac{1}{T} \sum_{t=1}^{T} \left| F_0^t(u) \right|^2 \qquad \textbf{[Eq. 22-8]}$$

Thus,

$$H(u) = \frac{A_0^*(u)R(u)}{\alpha P(u) + \sqrt{1 - \alpha^2} \, D_0(u)} \qquad \textbf{[Eq. 22-9]}$$

where the constant scalar $(1 - \alpha^2)^{1/2}$ has been ignored. Note that the phase component of $H(u)$ is determined by $A_0(u)$ and $R(u)$, as both $P(u)$ and $D_0(u)$ are real positive functions. $P(u)$ and $D_0(u)$ are both normalized according to their respective mean values. The term $R(u)$ is the Fourier transform of $r(x)$, and all other terms are related to the training set of fingerprint images. Although Eq. 22-9 defines a filter $H(u)$ that is optimized for any function $R(u)$, the form of $R(u)$ should be chosen to obtain maximum security of $H(u)$. This concept is further developed in the next section. Note that the term α in $H(u)$ provides a trade-off between the discrimination capability and distortion tolerance of the filter. For $\alpha = 0$, the filter will produce output $c_0^t(x)$ that is very close to $r(x)$ for each corresponding member of the training set; however, it will be very sensitive to distortions presented in nontraining images; that is, the filter is very discriminating, but distortion intolerant. Conversely, for $\alpha = 1$, the system will be extremely tolerant to distortions in the input, but may struggle to discriminate between different users of the system; α can, therefore, be used to produce a tighter or more forgiving system, depending on the system requirements. For the normalized versions of $P(u)$ and $D_0(u)$, the optimal value of α for fingerprint images was determined to be approximately 0.3.

Security of the Filter Function

Equation 22-9 defines a filter function that provides a trade-off between discrimination capability and distortion tolerance. However, the third requirement of the system is that the filter function stored as part of the Bioscrypt must be immune to attack, that is, neither the biometric image $f(x)$ nor the output function $r(x)$ should be independently recoverable from the Bioscrypt. Normally, in a correlation system, the filter function $H(u)$, as defined earlier, would be stored as the Bioscrypt. However, to maximize security, it is appropriate that a modified version of $H(u)$ is stored. This modified $H(u)$ is termed the stored filter function $H_{stored}(u)$. Specifically, the security of $H_{stored}(u)$ is found to be maximized if only the phase component $e^{i\phi_{H(u)}}$ of $H(u)$ is stored and $R(u)$ is a random, uniformly distributed phase function. $H_{stored}(u)$ thus comprises the product of $e^{-i\phi_{A0}(u)}$ and a random phase-only function. It is seen in the section entitled "Secure Filter Design" that the product of an arbitrary phase function $e^{-i\phi_{A0}(u)}$ with a random, uniformly distributed phase function $R(u)$, has perfect secrecy (see Stinson for a definition of perfect secrecy). Therefore, neither $e^{-i\phi_{A0}(u)}$ nor $R(u)$ can be retrieved from $H_{stored}(u)$.

Thus, storing only the phase of $H(u)$ satisfies the security requirement for Biometric Encryption. However, it is obvious from Eq. 22-9 that the optimized filter function $H(u)$ contains magnitude as well as phase information. The ideal form for the stored filter function for security thus differs from the ideal form of the filter function that was optimized for discrimination and distortion tolerance. To simply ignore the magnitude information disregards the optimization procedure.

A solution to this problem is that the magnitude information required for the optimal filter function $H(u)$ is not part of the stored filter function $H_{stored}(u)$, but is instead regenerated during each verification procedure. To accomplish this, the concept of a *transitory filter* is introduced.

Transitory Filter

In this section, the mechanism for calculating an optimal $H(u)$, for consistency, and storing a modified version $H_{stored}(u)$, for security, is described.

Consider generating an array $R(u)$, whose elements have unity magnitude. Thus, $R(u)$ is a phase-only function whose phase values j are random and uniformly distributed, such that $0 \leq j < 2\pi$, that is:

$$R(u) = e^{i\phi_{R(u)}} = e^{i2\pi U(0,1)} \qquad \textbf{[Eq. 22-10]}$$

where $U(0, 1)$ represents an array of elements in which each element m is randomly and uniformly distributed, such that $0 \leq m < 1$. In the discussion that follows, $e^{i\phi_{R(u)}}$ is used to represent the random phase-only function defined earlier. Thus, using the set of training images $\{f_0^1(x), f_0^2(x),..., f_0^T(x)\}$, $H(u)$ can be calculated using Eq. 22-9, that is:

$$H(u) = \frac{A_0^*(u)}{\alpha P(u) + \sqrt{1 - \alpha^2 D_0(u)}} \, e^{i\phi R(u)} \qquad \textbf{[Eq. 22-11]}$$

$H(u)$ was optimized to produce a consistent $c_0(x)$—and as close to $r(x)$ as is possible—whenever a member of the training image $f_0^t(x)$ is presented to the system. Consider the output function $c_0^t(x)$, produced with $f_0^t(x)$ at the input:

$$c_0^t(x) = FT^{-1}\left\{ F_0^t(u) \, \frac{|A_0(u)| \, e^{-i\phi A_0(u)}}{\alpha P(u) + \sqrt{1 - \alpha^2 D_0(u)}} \, e^{i\phi R(u)} \right\} \qquad \textbf{[Eq. 22-12]}$$

Similarly, consider the output function $c_1^t(x)$, produced with a non-training image $f_1^t(x)$ at the input (i.e., during verification):

$$c_1^t(x) = FT^{-1}\left\{ F_1^t(u) \, \frac{|A_0(u)| \, e^{-i\phi A_0(u)}}{\alpha P(u) + \sqrt{1 - \alpha 2 D_0(u)}} \, e^{i\phi R(u)} \right\} \qquad \textbf{[Eq. 22-13]}$$

where the subscript 1 represents an image used in verification. The output pattern $c_1^t(x)$ will be used to retrieve the digital key during verification. Clearly, it is desired that $c_1^t(x)$ is as close to $c_0^t(x)$ as possible, for the legitimate user. Of course, $c_1^t(x) \rightarrow c_0^t(x)$ if the testing image $f_1^t(x)$ is identical to the training image $f_0^t(x)$. It is known, however, that effects due to behavioral, environmental, and physiological changes will determine that $f_1^t(x)$ will not be identical to $f_0^t(x)$. On the other hand, for either enrollment or verification, it is found in Roberge et al. that as the number of fingerprints T in the set increases, the average of the FTs of the images $A_0(u)$ converges to a fixed function (at approximately $T = 6$. Thus, because the set of enrollment images is captured in the same way as the subsequent verification images, at $T = 6$, $A_1(u) \cong A_0(u)$ and $D_1(u) \cong D_0(u)$. Therefore, in Eqs. 22-12 and 22-13, we use $A_0(u)$ to represent $F_0^t(u)$, and $A_1(u)$ to represent $F_1^t(u)$; that is, we use the average of the fingerprint transforms to represent the individual fingerprints. To ensure that we never have to store any magnitude information in the stored filter function (recall that for optimal security, we wish to store only phase terms), we also approximate $|A_0(u)|$ by $|A_1(u)|$ and $D_0(u)$ by $D_1(u)$ in Eq. 22-13. These approximations can be substituted into Eqs. 22-12 and 22-13 to yield:

$$c_0(x) = FT^{-1}\left\{ A_0(u) \, \frac{|A_0(u)| \, e^{-i\phi A_0(u)}}{\alpha P(u) + \sqrt{1 - \alpha^2 D_0(u)}} \, e^{i\phi R(u)} \right\} \qquad \textbf{[Eq. 22-14]}$$

$$= FT^{-1}\left\{ A_0(u) \, \frac{|A_0(u)|}{\alpha P(u) + \sqrt{1 - \alpha^2 D_0(u)}} \, e^{-i\phi A_0(u)} \, e^{i\phi R(u)} \right\} \qquad \textbf{[Eq. 22.15]}$$

$$= \text{FT}^{-1}\left\{A_0(u) \cdot \left| H_0(u) \right| \cdot H_{\text{stored}}(u)\right\} \qquad \textbf{[Eq. 22-16]}$$

and

$$c_1(x) = \text{FT}^{-1}\left\{A_1(u) \frac{\left| A_1(u) \right| e^{-i\phi_{A_0}(u)}}{\alpha P(u) + \sqrt{1 - \alpha^2} D_1(u)} e^{i\phi_R(u)}\right\} \qquad \textbf{[Eq. 22-17]}$$

$$= \text{FT}^{-1}\left\{A_1(u) \frac{\left| A_1(u) \right|}{\alpha P(u) + \sqrt{1 - \alpha^2} D_1(u)} e^{-i\phi_{A_0}(u)} e^{i\phi_R(u)}\right\} \qquad \textbf{[Eq. 22.18]}$$

$$= \text{FT}^{-1}\left\{A_1(u) \cdot \left| H_1(u) \right| \cdot H_{\text{stored}}(u)\right\} \qquad \textbf{[Eq. 22-19]}$$

Thus, as stated in the previous section, of the complex conjugate of the training set images $e^{i\phi_{A_0}(u)}$ and the phase-only function $e^{i\phi_R(u)}$, only the product of the phase is stored as the stored filter function, that is,

$$H_{\text{stored}}(u) = e^{-i\phi_{A_0}(u)} e^{i\phi_R(u)} \qquad \textbf{[Eq. 22-20]}$$

The magnitude terms of the optimal filter are calculated on-the-fly during either enrollment or verification. Therefore, the transitory filter is defined as the product of the stored phase-only term $H_{\text{stored}}(u)$, and the magnitude terms $|H_0(u)|$ and $|H_1(v)|$, for enrollment and verification, respectively. Thus, only phase information is stored (security is obtained) and the magnitude information that is required for the verification procedure is derived from the fingerprint images acquired during the verification session (consistency is preserved).

In the next section, the security aspects of $H_{\text{stored}}(u)$ are further examined. In the section "Implementing the Biometric Encryption Algorithm: Enrollment and Verification," it is demonstrated how the digital key is linked with $c_0(x)$ during enrollment, and retrieved from $c_1(x)$ during verification.

Secure Filter Design

Previously it was stated that the stored filter function $H_{\text{stored}}(u)$ is required to be secure against attack in that neither the user's fingerprint nor $r(x)$ can be independently obtained from it. The concept of the product of two phase-only arrays, which is denoted here as the *phase-phase product,* was used to provide security for $H_{\text{stored}}(u)$. In this section, the security of the phase-phase product is illustrated by using the analogy of the classic cryptographic one-time pad and the concept of perfect secrecy.

The Vernam one-time pad, first described in 1917 by Gilbert Vernam, is a well-known realization of a cryptosystem with perfect secrecy. The one-time pad is defined such that $P = C = K = \{0, 1\}^n$, where $n \geq 1$, and the encryption process comprises the addition modulo 2 of two binary n-bit strings known as the plain text and the key, to create the encrypted data known as the cipher text. Similarly, the decryption process comprises the addition modulo 2 of the cipher-text string with the key. P, C, and K represent the cryptosystem's plain text, cipher text, and key spaces, respectively. Provided that the encryption keys used in a one-time pad cryptosystem are *random* and *used only once*, then the one-time pad provides perfect secrecy.

Now consider a binary phase-phase product cryptosystem with two phase levels, 0 and π. Let $P = K = C = \{0, \pi\}^n$ where $n \geq 1$. Encryption is defined as the product of two phase-only arrays, that is, $e^{i\phi_p} \cdot e^{i\phi_k} = e^{i\phi_c}$, where $\phi_p \in P$, $\phi_k \in K$, and $\phi_c = \phi_p + \phi_k \pmod{2\pi}$. Decryption is thus defined as $e^{i\phi_c} \cdot e^{-i\phi_k} = e^{i\phi_p}$ where $\phi_p = \phi_c - \phi_k \pmod{2\pi}$. However, since $(-\phi_k) \equiv \phi_k \pmod{2\pi}$ for $\phi_k \in \{0, \pi\}$, decryption becomes: $e^{i\phi_c} \cdot e^{i\phi_k} = e^{i\phi_p}$.

The elements of the binary phase-phase product e^{i0} and $e^{i\pi}$ can be combined in the following permutations:

$$e^{i0} \cdot e^{i\pi} = e^{i\pi} \cdot e^{i0} = e^{i\pi}$$

$$e^{i0} \cdot e^{i0} = e^{i\pi} \cdot e^{i\pi} = e^{i0}$$

Let Γ be the transformation: $\Gamma = \{e^{i0} \rightarrow 0, e^{i\pi} \rightarrow 1$, and $\cdot \rightarrow \oplus \}$, where $\cdot$ implies multiplication and $\oplus$ is the exclusive-or operation, that is, addition mod 2. The preceding combinations can thus be transformed as:

$$0 \oplus 1 = 1 \oplus 0 = 1$$

$$0 \oplus 0 = 1 \oplus 1 = 0$$

These are exactly the elements and possible combinations of the one-time pad cryptosystem. Thus, the encryption and decryption procedures of the binary phase-phase product are equivalent to the encryption and decryption procedures of the one-time pad, given the transformation Γ. The binary phase-phase product cryptosystem therefore provides perfect secrecy if the encryption keys chosen are random and used in a single enrollment procedure. It can be shown that this secrecy is also present when the phase arrays possess an arbitrary number of phase levels. Recall now that $H_{\text{stored}}(u)$ is calculated as the product of two phase-only arrays, one of which, $e^{i\phi_R(u)}$, was randomly generated. Also, $e^{i\phi_R(u)}$ is used for a single enrollment and then discarded. Therefore, $H_{\text{stored}}(u)$ is considered to have perfect secrecy; that is, given $H_{\text{stored}}(u)$, neither of the two constituent arrays $e^{-i\phi_{A_0}(u)}$ or $e^{i\phi_R(u)}$ can be reconstructed.

Implementing the Biometric Encryption Algorithm: Enrollment and Verification

This section provides details of the implementation of the Biometric Encryption algorithm. The following lists provide an overview of the processes of enrollment and verification, with reference to Figures 22-1 and 22-2, respectively.

Figure 22-1

Overview of the Enrollment Process for Biometric Encryption

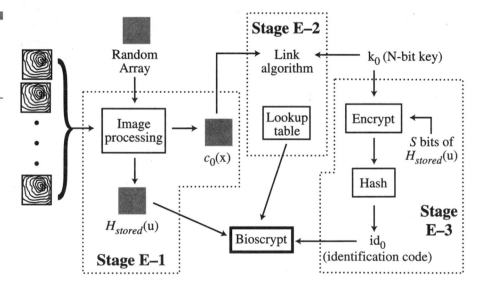

Enrollment:

E-1: Image Processing
Combine a series of input fingerprint images with a random (phase) array to create two output arrays: $H_{\text{stored}}(u)$ and $c_0(x)$.

Figure 22-2
Overview of the Verification Process for Biometric Encryption

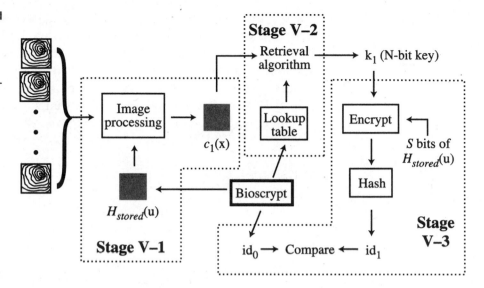

E-2:	Key Linking
	Link a cryptographic key k_0 to the pattern $c_0(x)$ via the link algorithm.
E-3:	Identification Code Creation
	Create an identification code id_0, derived from the key k_0.

Verification:

V-1:	Image Processing
	Combine $H_{stored}(u)$, from the Bioscrypt, with a new series of input fingerprint images to create an output pattern $c_1(x)$.
V-2:	Key Retrieval
	Extract a key k_1, from $c_1(x)$ using the retrieval algorithm.
V-3:	Key Validation
	Validate k_1 by creating a new identification code id_1, and comparing it with id_0.

The processes of enrollment and verification are generally symmetric with respect to the linking and retrieving of the digital key. Previously in this chapter, details were provided on the creation of $c(x)$, that is, stages E-1 and V-1. This section now completes the description of the Biometric Encryption algorithm by discussing the link and retrieval algorithms (stages E-2 and V-2) as well as the identification code creation and key validation processes (stages E-3 and V-3).

For the purposes of explanation, consider that all output arrays $c(x)$, are 128×128 complex-valued arrays, and that the cryptographic key k_0 is 128 bits in length, that is, N = 128 in Figures 22-1 and 22-2.

Enrollment

The objective of the enrollment procedure is to link an arbitrary N-bit key to the user's fingerprint and create the user's Bioscrypt.

With reference to Figure 22-1, the three inputs required for the enrollment procedure are: (1) a set of the legitimate user's fingerprint images; (2) a randomly generated phase-only array $R(u)$; and (3) an N-bit cryptographic key k_0. $R(u)$ is generated using a random number generator (RNG). The key k_0 may be an existing key that is input to the Biometric Encryption algorithm, or it may be generated by the RNG. Note that both the key k_0 and the random phase array $R(u)$ are completely independent from the biometric images.

E-1: Image Processing

With reference to Figure 22-3, the objective of this stage of enrollment is to generate an output pattern $c_0(x)$, to be passed to stage E-2, as well as to generate the stored filter function $H_{stored}(u)$. As discussed previously in this chapter, T fingerprint images are acquired from the system user (typically, four to six images are used). Fourier transforms are then performed on the images and the terms $A_0(u)$ and $D_0(u)$ are calculated using Eqs. 22-7 and 22-8, respectively. The phase term $e^{i\phi_{A_0}(u)}$ is extracted from $^A_0(u)$, and its complex conjugate $e^{-i\phi_{A_0}(u)}$ is used in conjunction with $R(u)$ to calculate $H_{stored}(u)$ according to Eq. 22-20. The output pattern $c_0(x)$ is then calculated via Eq. 22-16. Note that $c_0(x)$ is a 128×128 complex-valued array, whereas $H_{stored}(u)$ is a 128×128 phase-only array. $H_{stored}(u)$ is then stored as part of the Bioscrypt, and $c_0(x)$ is passed to stage E-2 of enrollment.

E-2: Key Link Algorithm

The link algorithm is responsible for linking the output pattern $c_0(x)$ with an N-bit key k_0. Through this linking process a lookup table is cre-

Figure 22-3
Image Processing
Used in Enrollment

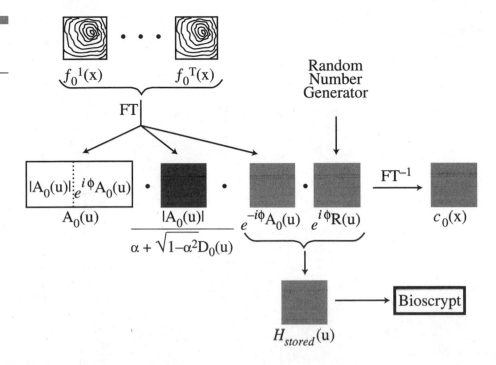

ated and stored in the Bioscrypt for use in key retrieval during verification.

An important consideration for this process is that the output pattern $c_0(x)$, obtained during enrollment, and the pattern $c_1(x)$, obtained during verification, will differ to a certain extent. These differences are due to changes in moisture content of the user's finger, positioning of the finger on the image capture device, and so forth. To accommodate these differences, some redundancy must be incorporated into the enrollment process.

There are various methods for linking k_0 with $c_0(x)$, some of which may incorporate the use of error correcting codes. One particular method using a simple repetitive code is outlined next. With reference to Figure 22-4, the link algorithm comprises the selection of a portion of $c_0(x)$, a binarization process, and the selection of L values to represent each key bit. The central 64×64 portion of $c_0(x)$ is extracted. This extraction is to provide translation invariance during subsequent verification attempts. Next, the real and imaginary components of the extracted portion are concatenated to form an *enrollment template* of dimension 128×64, that is, an array with 128 columns and 64 rows. For example, if the element $a+bi$ appears at position (x, y) of the 64×64

Figure 22-4
Key Link Algorithm

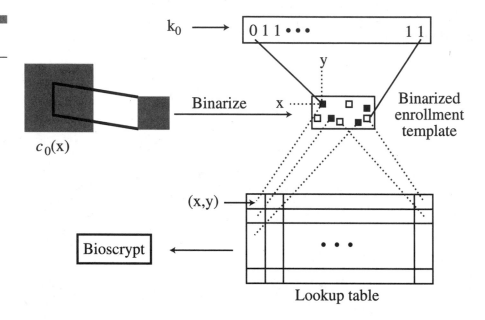

portion of $c_0(x)$, then, in the enrollment template, element a will appear at position (x, y) and element b will appear at position $(x + 64, y)$. This concatenation process converts a 64×64 complex-valued array into a 128×64 real-valued array. The enrollment template now contains 8192 real values d, derived from either the real or imaginary components a or b, respectively. Each value of the enrollment template is then binarized with respect to 0.0, that is,

$$d \rightarrow 1 \quad \text{if} \quad d \geq 0.0$$
$$d \rightarrow 0 \quad \text{if} \quad d < 0.0$$

This forms a 128×64 *binarized enrollment template,* which will be used to link with k_0.

Suppose that the first bit of k_0 is 0. Choose L locations from the binarized enrollment template whose element values are all 0. These locations are then stored as the first column of the lookup table. This process is continued for all other bits of the key. Each location in the binarized enrollment template can be used to represent only one key bit. The lookup table now consists of 128 columns with each column containing L locations in the binarized enrollment template.

Certain constraints on the L values chosen must be observed to create a satisfactory lookup table (see Soutar et al., "Biometric Encryption™—Enrollment and Verification Procedures"). These are summarized here:

- L should be greater than 1, to provide redundancy in the subsequent retrieval of the key.

- The value of L should be limited to ensure a sufficient number of values exist in the binarized enrollment template to link with extreme key permutations (i.e., a key containing significantly more 1s than 0s, or 0s than 1s.).

- The selection of the L constituent bits for each key bit should be chosen to minimize the resulting probability of error in each key bit.

- L should be an odd number so that a majority rule decision process can be used during verification.

E-3: Identification Code Creation

A requirement of the Biometric Encryption algorithm is that an incorrect key should be produced when an attacker uses the system with another user's Bioscrypt. In fact, it is convenient to further constrain the system such that an incorrect key is never released from the algorithm, but instead a *verification failed* message is passed to the cryptographic system. This will avoid the cryptographic system making wasteful attempts at decryption using an incorrect key. Therefore, a key validation scheme is required for the process. Obviously the key k_0 itself cannot be stored in the Bioscrypt for comparison with the key generated at verification. Instead, a combination of standard encryption and hashing algorithms is used to produce a derived identification code id_0. During verification, a corresponding identification code will be similarly derived from the retrieved key k_1. Comparing the identification code created during verification with that created during enrollment allows the system to determine if the key retrieved during verification is correct.

The method used for key validation is as follows. Using the input N-bit key k_0 as an encryption key, encrypt S bits of data. Next, hash the encrypted text using a one-way hash function to create an identification code id_0. Store this identification code in the Bioscrypt.

The S bits, to be encrypted, can be any S bits that will be available at both enrollment and verification. Also, these S bits should be different for each user in order to provide the key validation procedure with maximal security (see Schneier). Given these constraints, we use S bits from the stored filter function $H_{stored}(u)$, as it is available during both the enrollment and verification procedures. Also, because $H_{stored}(u)$ is the product of fingerprint information and a random array, it will be distinct for each user. Therefore, we use the first S bits of $H_{stored}(u)$ as input data to the encryption algorithm.

The choice of encryption algorithm and hash function is independent of the Biometric Encryption process. These algorithms are required simply for creation of the identification code, and the main concern in the choice of these algorithms is that they are secure. Good examples to use are Triple-DES as the encryption engine and SHA-1 as the hash function.

The lookup table and id_0 are now appended to $H_{stored}(u)$ to complete construction of the Bioscrypt, which can be stored on any conventional storage medium.

Verification

The objective of the verification procedure is the successful retrieval of the N-bit key for a legitimate user.

With reference to Figure 22-2, a set of biometric images is acquired from the system user and combined with $H_{stored}(u)$, the lookup table, and id_0, from the Bioscrypt, to retrieve and check the validity of an N-bit key. If this key is found to be correct, it will be passed on to the cryptographic system.

V-1: Image Processing

With reference to Figure 22-5, it is observed that the image processing stage of verification is very similar to the corresponding stage of enrollment. As in enrollment, T fingerprint images are acquired from the system user. Fourier transforms are performed on the images and the terms $A_1(u)$ and $D_1(u)$ are calculated. Using $H_{stored}(u)$ retrieved from the Bioscrypt, the output pattern $c_1(x)$ is calculated according to Eq. 22-19, and is then passed to stage V-2 of the verification procedure to retrieve the N-bit cryptographic key.

The verification pattern $c_1(x)$, will be used to retrieve the cryptographic key. Clearly, the similarity of the output patterns $c_1(x)$ and $c_0(x)$ significantly affects the discrimination capabilities of the system. It is therefore interesting to compare the generation of $c_1(x)$ and $c_0(x)$ for legitimate users and attackers, and to understand how this affects the discrimination of the system.

Consider Eqs. 22-15 and 22-18, which define the enrollment and veri-

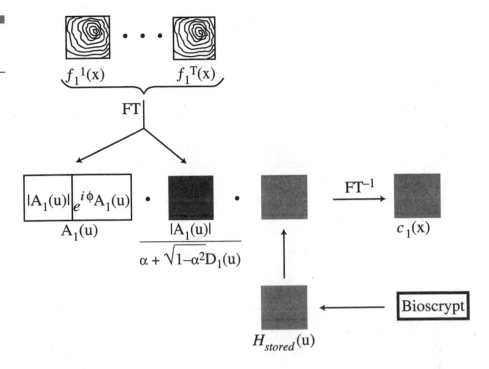

Figure 22-5
Image Processing
Used in Verification

fication output patterns, respectively:

$$c_0(x) = \mathrm{FT}^{-1}\left\{ |A_0(u)|\, e^{i\phi_{A_0}(u)} \cdot \frac{|A_0(u)|}{\alpha P(u) + \sqrt{1-\alpha^2} D_0(u)} \cdot \left[e^{-i\phi_{A0}(u)}\, e^{i\phi_R(u)} \right] \right\}$$

$$c_1(x) = \mathrm{FT}^{-1}\left\{ |A_1(u)|\, e^{i\phi_{A_1}(u)} \cdot \frac{|A_1(u)|}{\alpha P(u) + \sqrt{1-\alpha^2} D_1(u)} \cdot \left[e^{-i\phi_{A0}(u)}\, e^{i\phi_R(u)} \right] \right\}$$

where $[e^{-i\phi_{A0}(u)}\, e^{i\phi_R}(u)$ defines the stored filter function H stored(u), according to Eq. 22-20. Recall that the terms $A_0(u)$, $D_0(u)$ and $A_1(u)$, $D_1(u)$ are calculated using the input fingerprint images acquired during enrollment and verification, respectively.

The magnitude terms in Eq. 22-15, $|A_0(u)|$ and $D_0(u)$ are derived from the user's fingerprint. The phase arrays from the user's fingerprints cancel, leaving $e^{i\phi_R(u)}$, the random phase array, as the sole phase contribution to the output $c_0(x)$. The magnitude terms *moderate* the contribution of the various phase values to produce $c_0(x)$ so that areas in the FT that were more consistent across the enrollment training set are given more weight.

Now consider a $c_1(x)$ pattern generated during verification by a legitimate user and an attacker.

Legitimate user:

$$A_1(x) \approx A_0(x), \quad D_1(x) \approx D_0(x), \quad \text{and} \quad e^{i\phi_{A1}(u)} \cdot e^{-i\phi_{A0}(u)} \approx 1$$

The magnitude information is thus similar to that used during enrollment to generate $c_0(x)$; and the phase information $e^{i\phi_{A1}(u)}$ from the user's fingerprints during verification, essentially cancels out the phase information $e^{-i\phi_{A0}(u)}$ from the user's fingerprints during enrollment. This leaves $e^{i\phi_R(u)}$, the random phase array, as the only phase contribution to $c_1(x)$, as required.

Attacker:

$$A_1(x) \neq A_0(x), \quad D_1(x) \neq D_0(x), \quad \text{and} \quad e^{i\phi_{A1}(u)} \cdot e^{-i\phi_{A0}(u)} \neq 1$$

The magnitude information from the attacker's fingerprints is not equivalent to that derived from the legitimate user. Therefore, the weighting of the contribution of the phase values is not properly moderated. Furthermore, the phase information derived from the attacker's fingerprints does not cancel the enrollment phase information that was implicitly stored in $H_{stored}(u)$. Thus, both the magnitude and phase terms derived from the attacker's fingerprint affect the generation of $c_1(x)$, producing a pattern that is significantly different from the legitimate user's $c_0(x)$ pattern. Thus, the key retrieved from this pattern will not match the key linked to $c_0(x)$ during legitimate user enrollment.

V-2: Key Retrieval Algorithm

The retrieval algorithm is responsible for retrieving a key from the verification output pattern $c_1(x)$. The following section describes the steps required to retrieve an N-bit key that was linked with $c_0(x)$ using the link algorithm described earlier.

Retrieval algorithm (with reference to Figure 22-6):

1. Extract the central 64×64 portion of $c_1(x)$.

2. Concatenate the real and imaginary parts, as in the enrollment stage E-2, to create a verification template of dimension 128×64. Binarize each value, as in E-2, to create a binarized verification template (the equivalent of the binarized enrollment template).

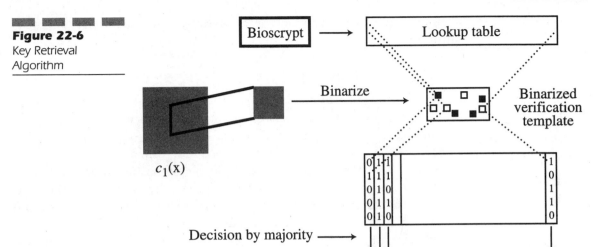

Figure 22-6
Key Retrieval
Algorithm

3. Use the lookup table to extract the constituent bits of the binarized verification template that are required for the key. Define k_1 as an N-element vector. For the nth element of k_1, sum the L bits of the binarized verification template whose indices are specified by the nth column of the lookup table. The nth element of k_1 is set to 1, if the sum of these bits is greater than $L/2$; otherwise, it is set to 0. In other words, a *decision by majority* is used to assign the parity of the nth bit of k_1.

4. Determine the validity of the retrieved key. This process is described in the following section on verification stage V-3.

5. If k_1 is found to be the correct key, release it into the system. If k_1 is found to be incorrect, return to $c_1(x)$ and extract a 64×64 portion of $c_1(x)$ that is offset from the center by one pixel. Continue to repeat Steps 2 to 5 of the retrieval algorithm with all portions of $c_1(x)$ that are one pixel offset from the center, then continue with all portions that are two pixels offset from the center, and so on, up to approximately 16 pixel offsets. If at any point the key retrieved is found to be correct, cease the algorithm and release k_1. If the key is found to be incorrect for all pixel offsets, release a *verification failed* message.

Note that Step 5 of the key retrieval algorithm is required to accommodate relative translations of the input fingerprints between enrollment and verification. We find that, in general, a search of one quarter of the input aperture, or ± 16 pixels in an array of dimension 128×128, is sufficient.

V-3: Key Validation

Step 4 of the retrieval algorithm requires that a key k_1 be checked for validity. This key should be released only if it precisely matches k_0, the key linked to the output pattern during enrollment. To check the validity of k_1, we calculate an identification code id_1, and compare it with the stored id_0. The identification code id_1 is calculated the same way as id_0 was during enrollment stage E-3; that is, using k_1 as an encryption key, encrypt the same S bits of the stored filter function, then hash the encrypted text to produce id_1. The identification code, id_1 is then compared with id_0. If $id_1 = id_0$, then $k_1 = k_0$, with high probability (see Schneier), and k_1 can be released to the cryptographic system. If $id_1 \neq id_0$, then $k_1 \neq k_0$ and either a *verification failed* message is released, or the retrieval algorithm continues with the next pixel offset of $c_1(x)$.

Biometric Encryption Using Other Biometric Templates

Although the Biometric Encryption algorithm was developed primarily for use with image-based biometric templates, the process can also be applied to other biometric templates. This can be achieved simply by representing the non-image-based biometric template as an image array. For example, a minutiae-based fingerprint template can be represented as an image array by embedding a code referring to each minutiae type at the appropriate location in a two-dimensional array, thereby creating a map of the minutiae points. This array can then be input to the Biometric Encryption algorithm, as described previously for fingerprint images. Using a minutiae-based rather than an image-based template may have the added advantage of producing a rotation invariant system, assuming the original minutiae template contained information about the relative orientation of the minutiae.

For some other biometric types, different considerations may modify the algorithm. For example, images of the iris or retina can easily be aligned using the center of the eye's pupil as a reference point. Thus, for these types of images, the Biometric Encryption process is not required to be translation invariant. Therefore, transforms other than the Fourier transform may be appropriate, such as the Gabor transform, which was originally used in the algorithm for iris identification developed by Daugman. Also, the distortion-tolerance requirements of the filter function may be relaxed for biometrics other than fingerprints. The majority of the distortions present in fingerprint images is due to the skin deforming on contact with a glass or metal surface. For other biometrics, such as the iris or retina, there typically is no direct contact between the biometric and the system. Therefore, less distortion will be present in these biometric images, and the distortion tolerance of the filter can be decreased either by adjusting α in Eq. 22-11, or by completely removing the magnitude terms in Eq. 22-15 and 22-18. This will typically make the system more secure by improving the discrimination capabilities of the system.

WRAP-UP

Biometric Encryption is an algorithm for the linking and retrieval of digital keys, which can be used as a method for the secure management of cryptographic keys. The cryptographic key is generated independently from the Biometric Encryption algorithm and can be updated periodically via a reenrollment procedure. The convenience and security provided by Biometric Encryption will undoubtedly help to promote more widespread use of cryptographic systems.

APPENDIX A

STANDARDS

Appendix A gives a sample of the standards that apply to cryptographic systems. The reader is cautioned to obtain the most up-to-date releases as changes to cryptographic standards should be expected.

TABLE A-1

ISO Standards for Generic Cryptographic Techniques

ISO Number	Subject
8372	Modes of operation for a 64-bit cipher
9796	Signatures with message recovery (RSA)
9797	Data integrity mechanism (MAC)
9798-1	Entity authentication—introduction
9798-2	Using symmetric encipherment
9798-3	Using public-key techniques
9798-4	Using keyed-one-way functions
9798-5	Using zero-knowledge techniques
9979	Register of cryptographic algorithms
10116	Modes of operation for n-bit cipher
10118-1	Hash functions—introduction
10118-2	Using block ciphers
10118-3	Customized algorithms
10118-4	Using modular arithmetic
11770-1	Key management—introduction
11770-2	Symmetric techniques
11770-3	Asymmetric techniques
13888-1	Nonrepudiation—introduction
13888-2	Symmetric techniques
13888-3	Asymmetric techniques
14888-1	Signatures with appendix—introduction
14888-2	Identity-based mechanisms
14888-3	Certificate-based mechanisms

TABLE A-2

ANSI Encryption
Standards and
Banking Security
Standards

ANSI Number	Subject
X3.92	Data encryption standard (DEA)
X3.106	Data encryption algorithm (DEA) modes
X9.8	PIN management and security
X9.9	Message authentication (wholesale)
X9.17	Key management (wholesale, symmetric)
X9.19	Message authentication (retail)
X9.23	Encryption of messages (wholesale)
X9.24	Key management (retail)
X9.26	Sign-on authentication (wholesale)
X9.28	Multicenter key management (wholesale)
X9.30-1	Digital signature algorithm (DSA)
X9.30-2	Secure hash algorithm (SHA) for DSA
X9.31-1	RSA signature algorithm (RSA)
X9.31-2	Hashing algorithm for RSA
X9.42	Key management using Diffie-Hellman
X9.45	Attribute certificates and other controls
X9.52	Triple DES modes of operation
X9.55	Certificate extensions (v3) and CRLs
X9.57	Certificate management
X9.62	Elliptic curve digital signature algorithm
X9.63	Elliptic curve key agreement and transport protocols

TABLE A-3

ISO Banking Securi-
ty Standards

ISO Number	Subject
8730	Message authentication—requirements
8731-1	Message authentication—CBC-MAC
8731-2	Message authentication—MAA
8732	Key management/symmetric
9564	PIN management and security
9807	Message authentication
10126	Message encipherment
10202-7	Key management for smartcards
11131	Sign-on authentication
11166-1	Key management/asymmetric—overview
11166-2	Key management using RSA
11568	Key management in six parts
14888-1	Signatures with appendix—introduction
14888-2	Identity-based mechanisms
14888-3	Certificate-based mechanisms

TABLE A-4

ISO Security Architectures and Frameworks

ISO Number	Subject
7498-2	OSI security architecture
9594-8	Authentication framework (X.509)
10181	OSI security frameworks

TABLE A-5

U.S. Government Standards

FIPS Number	Subject
46-2	DES
74	Guidelines for using DES
81	DES modes of operation
112	Password usage
113	Data authentication (CBC-MAC)
140-1	Cryptomodule security requirements
171	Key management using X9.17
180-1	Secure hash standard (SHA-1)
185	Key escrow (Clipper and SKIPJACK)
186	Digital signature standard (DSA)—JJJ entity authentication (asymmetric)

TABLE A-6

Selected Internet RFCs

RFC Number	Subject
1319	MD2 hash function
1320	MD4 hash function
1321	MD5 hash function
1421	PEM—encryption, authentication
1422	PEM—certificates, key management
1423	PEM—algorithms, modes, identifiers
1424	PEM—key certification services
1508	Generic security service API
1510	Kerberos V5 network authentication
1828	Keyed MD5 (as MAC)
1847	Security multiparts for MIME
1848	MIME object security services (MOSS)
1938	One-time password system

TABLE A-7

PKCS Specifications

Number	Subject
1	RSA encryption standard
3	Diffie-Hellman key-agreement standard
5	Password-based encryption standard
6	Extended-certificate syntax standard
7	Cryptographic message syntax standard
8	Private-key information syntax standard
9	Selected attribute types
10	Certification request syntax standard
11	Cryptographic token interface standard

APPENDIX B

XENOCRYPTIC DATA

Cryptography acts as a cultural universal. Although letter frequencies (and their order) are not constant in every language, *group frequencies* are fairly constant. This common thread (the principal of cultural universality) permits cryptanalysis of essentially all phoneme-based languages. Here are some diverse examples of this interesting phenomenon.

German

Absolute Frequencies (Based on 60,046 German plain text letters)

A 3,601	G 1,921	L 1,988	Q 6	V 523
B 1,023	H 2,477	M 1,360	R 4,339	W 899
C 1,620	I 4,879	N 6,336	S 4,127	X 12
D 3,248	J 192	O 1,635	T 3,447	Y 24
E 10,778	K 747	P 499	U 2,753	Z 654
F 958				
				60,046

Monographic Kappa Plain, German Language = 0.0787
I.C. = 2.05

Relative Frequencies reduced to 1000 letters

E 180	T 57	G 32	F 16	P 8
N 106	D 54	O 27	W 15	J 3
I 81	U 46	C 27	K 13	Y —
R 72	H 41	M 23	Z 11	X —
S 69	L 33	B 17	V 9	Q —
A 60				
				1,000

Group Percentage

Vowels: A E I O U Y	=	39.4%
High-frequency consonants: D N R S T	=	35.8%

Medium-frequency consonants: B C F G H L M W = 20.4%
Low-frequency consonants: J K P Q V X Z = 4.4%
8 most frequent letters (E N I R S A T D) = 67.9%
(descending order)

Latin

I	10.1	M	3.4	V	0.7
E	9.2	C	3.3	X	0.6
U	7.4	P	3.0	H	0.5
T	7.2	L	2.1	J	0
A	7.2	D	1.7	K	0
S	6.8	G	1.4	Y	0
R	6.8	Q	1.3	Z	0
N	6.0	B	1.2		
O	4.4	F	0.9		

100.0

Group Percentage

Vowels: I E U A O
Consonants: T S R N M C P L D Q B F V X H
Vowel percentage: 44%
Vowel/consonant ratio: 8/10
Average word length: 7 letters

Norwegian

Norwegian is a beautiful language, which consists of two forms, Bokmal (Book Language) and Nynorsk. Book language is the generally read form. Norwegian is similar to English with the addition of three vowels AE, O, A′. Foreign consonant letters are C, Q, W, X, and Z. Based on 5153 text letters, a frequency analysis reduced to 100 letters is:

16	8	7	6	5	4	2	1	—	0
E	RNS	T	AI	LDO	GKM	UVFHPA′	JB0	Y AE C	WXZQ

Group Percentage

Average word length: 4.77 letters
IC = .0647
Vowels: A E I O   33%
Consonants: D L N R S T   41%

Hungarian

Hungarian (aka Magyar) is related to Finnish and Estonian. Hungarian has 38 sounds based on a Latin alphabet. Hungarian has four special characteristics:

1. It agglutinates—adjectives, possessives are expressed by suffixes.

2. It has vowel harmony—they fall into high and low vowel categories. High: E, I, OE, UE and Low: A O U. In a word they are all either high or low.

3. It assimilates consonants—usually the third or fourth letter from the end. Many doubles.

4. It has no gender differentiation.

Percent letter frequencies based on 10,001 plain text letters:

E	16.04	K	4.47	D	1.93
A	12.55	I	4.29	B	1.78
T	8.35	M	4.11	H	1.42
O	6.56	R	3.48	J	0.99
S	6.56	G	3.16	F	0.94
L	5.66	U	2.33	C	0.52
N	5.49	Y	2.03	P	0.52
Z	4.79	V	1.94		

100.0

Group Percentage

Vowels: A E I O U   41.77%
LNRST: 29.54%
JKQYZ: 9.93%
EATOS: 50.06%
EATOSLNZK: 70.47%
HJFCP: 4.39%

French

Absolute Frequencies (Based on 55,758 French plain text letters)

A 4,480	G 624	L 2,737	Q 616	V 801
B 406	H 276	M 1,617	R 4,117	W 6
C 1,944	I 4,230	N 4,406	S 4,564	X 317
D 2,198	J 184	O 3,255	T 4,057	Y 100
E 9,334	K 25	P 1,689	U 3,054	Z 84
F 646				

55,758

Monographic Kappa Plain, French Language = 0.0777
I.C. = 2.02

Group Percentage

Vowels: A E I O U Y	= 43.8%
High-frequency consonants: N R S T = 30.7%; with L	= 34.0%
Medium-frequency consonants: C D L M P	= 18.3%
Low-frequency consonants: B F G H J K Q V W X Z	= 7.2%
8 most frequent letters (E S A N I R T O)	= 68.9%

Note that the group frequencies between German and French are statistically similar.

Italian

Absolute Frequencies (Based on 57,906 Italian plain text letters)

A 6,771	G 1,168	L 3,592	Q 227	V 1,024
B 527	H 493	M 1,441	R 4,037	W 13
C 2,367	I 6,568	N 4,094	S 2,967	X 9
D 2,258	J 18	O 5,022	T 4,139	Y 14
E 6,784	K 28	P 1,616	U 1,547	Z 527
F 655				

57,906

Monographic Kappa Plain, Italian Language = 0.0745
I.C. = 1.94

Group Percentage

Vowels: A E I O U Y	= 46.1%
High-frequency consonants: L N R T	= 27.4%
Medium-frequency consonants: C D G M P S	= 22.2%
Low-frequency consonants:B F H J K Q W X Z	= 4.3%
8 most frequent letters (E A I O T N R L)	= 70.8%

Spanish

Absolute Frequencies (Based on 60,115 Spanish plain text letters)

A 6,681	G 823	L 2,174	Q 346	V 602
B 799	H 367	M 1,740	R 4,628	W 36
C 3,137	I 4,920	N 4,823	S 4,140	X 127
D 2,687	J 190	O 5,859	T 3,180	Y 413
E 7,801	K 22	P 1,785	U 2,172	Z 182
F 481				

60,115

Monographic Kappa Plain, Spanish Language = 0.0747
I.C. = 1.94

Group Percentage

Vowels: A E I O U Y	= 46.3%
High-frequency consonants: N R S	= 22.6%
Medium-frequency consonants: C D L M P T	= 24.5%
Low-frequency consonants:B F G H J K Q V W X Z	= 6.6%
7 most frequent letters (E A O I N R S)	= 64.6%

Note the similarity of group frequencies between German and Spanish.

Portuguese

Absolute Frequencies (Based on 45,106 Portugese plain text letters)

A 5,362	G 724	L 1,245	Q 34	V 737
B 470	H 304	M 1,699	R 3,292	W 24
C 2,285	I 3,314	N 2,912	S 3,409	X 166
D 1,900	J 160	O 5,001	T 2,679	Y 22
E 5,441	K 17	P 1,377	U 1,491	Z 207
F 520				
				45,106

Monographic Kappa Plain, Portuguese Language = 0.0746
I.C. = 1.940

Group Percentage

Vowels: A E I O U Y	= 45.8%
High-frequency consonants: N R S	= 21.3%
Medium-frequency consonants: C D L M P T	= 24.8%
Low-frequency consonants:B F G H J K Q V W X Y Z	= 8.1%
8 most frequent letters (E A O S I R N T)	= 69.7%

Note that the group frequencies between French, Spanish, Italian, and Portuguese are statistically significant.

APPENDIX C

A SHORT TUTORIAL IN COMPLEXITY THEORY

Appendix C is a short tutorial on complexity theory patterned à la Arto Salomaa and William Stallings. The central issue in determining the resistance of an encryption algorithm to cryptanalysis is the amount of time required for a particular attack to be effective. We can think of the level of effort needed for a cryptanalytical attack as measurable over a particular order of magnitude. We try to compare orders of magnitude to the speed of current or future processing units to determine the level of security of a particular algorithm.

Classical mathematical problems in cryptography can be solved by finitely many trials. However, reduction to finitely many cases does not make sense if the number of cases is unmanageable. If we are not able to decrypt a message within a certain time limit, we might as well forget the whole thing because, as time passes by, the subject matter of the message will eventually become general knowledge.

The *time complexity* of an algorithm is a function of the length of the input n. An algorithm is of time complexity $f(n)$ if for all n and all inputs of length n, the execution of the algorithm takes at most $f(n)$ steps. If n is an integer, its length is the number of digits or bits in n. Definition of steps may involve ambiguities. There might be slow and fast algorithms for the same problem. In some cases, unlimited speed-up may be possible. It is difficult to establish lower bounds for complexity; that is to show, for instance, that every algorithm for a certain problem is of at least *quadratic time complexity*.

The rate for which relative execution time is growing is important. If we want to use a 50-digit ($n = 10^{50}$) or 100-digit key ($n = 10^{100}$) for RSA, it is not necessary to know how long it would take to break each size of key. It is sufficient to have ballpark figures for level of effort and know how much extra relative effort is required to break the larger key sizes.

The exact formula for $f(n)$ may be a difficult definition because *time complexity* depends on the model for algorithms under consideration. The number of steps becomes smaller if more work can be included in one step. Fundamental notions such as polynomial time complexity are largely independent of the model.

As our fundamental model for algorithms, we can choose a classical *Turing machine,* which operates in discrete time. At each moment of time, it is in a specific internal (memory) state, the number of all possible states being finite. A read-write head scans letters written on a tape one at a time. Every pair (q, a) determines a triple (q_1, a_1, m), where the qs are states, as are letters, and m ("move") assumes one of the three values "left," "right," or "no move." This means that, after scanning the letter a in state q, the machine goes to the state q_1, writes a_1, in place of a and moves the read-write head according to m.

If the read-write head is about to "fall off" the tape, that is, a left move is instructed when the machine is scanning the leftmost square of the tape, then a new blank square is added to the tape. The same holds true with respect to the right end of the tape. This capability of indefinitely extending the external memory can be viewed as a built-in hardware feature of every Turing machine.

The tape can be viewed both as a potentially infinite memory and an input and output channel. The machine begins its computation by scanning the leftmost letter of a given input word in a specific initial state. The computation ends if and when the machine reaches a specific final state. Then the machine halts and the word appearing on the tape constitutes the output. When reading the output some auxiliary letters can be ignored.

Now it is clear what a step means. We can define the *time complexity function* associated with a Turing machine A by:

$$f_A(n) = \max\{m \mid A \text{ halts after } m \text{ steps for an input } w \text{ with } \mid w \mid = n\}$$

We assume that A halts and reaches the final state for all inputs. Of course, this is not the case with respect to an arbitrary Turing machine. A Turing machine A is polynomially bounded if there is a polynomial $p(n)$ such that $f_A(n) \le p(n)$ holds for all n. The notation P is used for all problems that can be solved using a polynomially bounded Turing machine.

A problem is referred to as computationally *intractable* (sometimes also impossible) if it is not in P. *Tractable* problems (that is, problems in P) have several subclasses whose definition should be obvious: problems with linear, quadratic, cubic, and so forth, time complexity. The informal reference to a problem as *easy* means that the *values* of the polynomial are *small*, at least within the range considered.

The Turing machine considered previously is *deterministic:* the scanned letter and the internal state determine the behavior *uniquely*. To emphasize that a deterministic Turing machine is involved, we speak of *deterministic time complexity*.

A *nondeterministic* Turing machine may have several possibilities for its behavior when scanning a specific letter in a specific state. Consequently, specific inputs give rise to several computations. This can be visualized as the machine making guesses or using an arbitrary number of parallel processors. For each input w, the shortest successful computation $s(w)$ (that is, a computation leading to the final state) is considered. The time complexity function of a nondeterministic Turing machine A is now defined by:

$$f_A(n) = \max\{1, m \mid s(w) \text{ has } m \text{ steps for } w \text{ with } \mid w \mid = n\}$$

The pair $(1, m)$ is considered because, for some n, possibly no inputs of length n lead to successful computations. The notions of a *polynomially bounded nondeterministic* Turing machine and the corresponding class of problems *NP* are now defined exactly as in the deterministic case.

Problems in P are tractable, whereas the problems in *NP* have the property that it is tractable to check whether or not a good guess for the solution of the problem is correct. A *time bound* for a nondeterministic Turing machine can be visualized as a time bound for checking whether a good guess for the solution is correct. It is not known whether the factorization of an integer is in P but it certainly is in *NP*: one guesses the decomposition and verifies the guess by computing the product.

By definition, P is included in *NP* but it is a celebrated open problem whether or not $P = NP$. However, there are many *NP*-complete problems. A specific problem is *NP*-complete if it is in *NP* and, in addition, it is *NP*-hard. Every problem in *NP* can be reduced in polynomial time to this specific problem. It follows that $P = NP$ if an *NP*-complete problem is in P. In such a case, an arbitrary problem in *NP* can be settled in deterministic polynomial time because it can be reduced in polynomial time to the specific *NP*-complete problem and can be settled in polynomial time. The composition of two polynomials is again a polynomial.

It is generally believed that $P \neq NP$. Therefore, *NP*-complete problems are considered intractable. Besides *NP*, the terms "hard" and "complete" are used in a similar manner about other classes of problems as well.

A specific problem is shown to be *NP*-hard by proving that some problem previously known to be *NP*-hard can be reduced in polynomial time to the specific problem in question. If we want to show that the specific problem is *NP*-complete, we have to show also that it is in *NP*.

However, we need something to start with: a problem whose *NP*-completeness can be established by a direct argument, without any reductions. A problem very suitable for this purpose is the satisfiability problem for well-formed formulas of the propositional calculus "abbreviated *wffpc*s." Such a formula is obtained from variables by using the operations conjunction $\vee$, disjunction $\wedge$, and negation $\sim$ in a well-formed manner. A *truth-value* assignment for a *wffpc* α is a mapping of the set of variables occurring in α into the set {true,false}. The truth-value assignment of α can be computed for any truth-value assignment using the truth tables of conjunction, disjunction, and negation. Two *wffpc*s are equivalent if they assume the same truth-value for all truth-value assignments. A *wffpc* α is satisfiable if it assumes the value "true" for some truth-value assignment. For instance, the *wffpc*

$$(X_1 \vee \sim X_2 \vee X_3) \wedge (X_2 \vee X_3) \wedge (\sim X_1 \vee X_3) \wedge \sim X_3$$

is not satisfiable. The last clause forces the assignment X_3 = false, and by the third clause X_1 = false, and by the second clause X_2 = true. However, this assignment contradicts the first clause. The *wffpc* considered is in conjuctive normal form: a conjunction of disjunctions, where the terms of each disjunction are literals, that is, variables or negated variables. Moreover, it is in 3-conjunctive normal form: each conjunctive clause contains at most three literals.

The satisfiability problem for *wffpc*s can be shown to be *NP*-complete by a direct argument. The computation of a given Turing machine with a given input being successful is equivalent to a certain *wffpc* being satisfiable. The result remains valid if attention is restricted to *wffpc*s in 3-conjunctive normal form. Satisfiability can be found out by checking through all possible truth-value assignments. This however, leads to *exponential time complexity.*

Space complexity is defined analogously. If a Turing machine receives an input of length n, then originally n tape squares are occupied. New squares may be needed during the computation; their number indicates the space complexity. Polynomial bounds can be considered. This gives rise to the classes *P*-SPACE and *NP*-SPACE. A time class is included in the corresponding space class because one time unit is needed to extend the tape by one square. For *space* classes one can actually prove that

$$P\text{-SPACE} = NP\text{-SPACE}$$

Consequently, we have the following chain of inclusions

$$P \subseteq NP \subseteq P\text{-SPACE} = NP\text{-SPACE}$$

Whether or not the two inclusions are proper is also a celebrated open problem.

The *class Co-NP* consists of problems whose "complement" is in *NP.*

For instance, the complement of the problem "Is a given integer prime?" is "Is a given integer composite?" A formal definition can be given by considering problems as languages. It is clear that if a problem is in P, then its complement is also in P; the same algorithm works for the complement as well. This does not hold true in the nondeterministic case. In fact, the interrelation between NP and Co-NP is unknown but it is generally believed that $NP \neq$ Co-NP. If the complement of some NP-complete problem is in NP, then $NP =$ Co-NP.

There are some caveats to be kept in mind when complexity theory is applied to cryptography. When considering polynomial time complexity, the degree of the polynomial is significant. For instance, n^{1000} grows ultimately slower than $n^{\log\log n}$ but is still likely to be a poor upper bound for the values under consideration. *In cryptography, average complexity is more important than worst-case complexity.* Suppose a user chooses at random the encryption key in a public-key cryptosystem. It is then insignificant if computing the corresponding decryption key is intractable in some rarely occurring cases but easy in most cases.

Probabilistic or *stochastic* algorithms are often used in cryptography. Intuitively this means that random choices are made (that is, a random number generator can be called) at certain stages during the execution of the algorithm. The terminology introduced earlier is extended to concern the stochastic case. We may speak of algorithms running in *random polynomial time*. The corresponding class of problems is often denoted by *BPP*.

It is generally believed that $BPP \neq NP$. Stochastic algorithms may fail but the probability of failure can be made arbitrarily small. Usually, the time complexity increases when the probability of failure becomes smaller. The failure is due to the stochastic element. The following terminology is used to indicate different types of failure. A *Monte Carlo algorithm* might give a wrong answer in some cases; a *Las Vegas algorithm* always gives a correct answer but it might end up with the answer "I don't know" in some cases.

When talking about time complexity, we usually do not consider the computation steps of a Turing machine but rather some other elementary operation such as *bit multiplication*. The classes P and NP are invariant under such changes but, for instance, the degree and/or coefficients of the polynomial involved may change.

Table C-1 shows the level of effort for various levels of complexity. Please note how the number of inputs for factorial or exponential time are limited in its per hour handling for various algorithm complexities.

TABLE C-1

Complexity Effort
vs. Complexity

Complexity	Size	Operations
$\text{Log}_2 N$	$(2)^{10^{12}} = 10^{(3 \times 10^{11})}$	10^{12}
$(e)^{\sqrt{\ln n \times \ln(\ln n)}}$	$e^{150} = 10^{65}$	10^{12}
n	10^{12}	10^{12}
n^2	10^6	10^{12}
n^6	10^2	10^{12}
2^n	28	10^{12}
$n!$	15	10^{12}

APPENDIX D

A SHORT TUTORIAL IN NUMBER THEORY

Appendix D presents a basic tutorial on number theory. Number theory is essential to understanding and design of public-key cryptosystems. (See Stallings, Schneier, or Salomaa references for more detailed explanations.)

Prime

An integer a divides another integer b. If $b = da$ holds for some integer d, then a is called a *divisor* or *factor* of b. Let a be an integer greater than 1. Now, a is *prime* if its only positive divisors are 1 and a, otherwise a is called a *composite*. Every integer $n > 1$ can be represented uniquely, disregarding the order of factors, as a product of primes. The essential facts from the point of view of cryptography are that no *tractable factorization algorithms* are known and no nontrivial lower bounds for the time complexity of factorization have been established. No tractable methods are known even for the simple case where two primes p and q have to be recovered from their product $n = p \times q$.

G.C.D.

The *greatest common divisor* of a and b, in symbols g.c.d. (a, b) or briefly (a, b), is the largest integer dividing both a and b. Equivalently, (a, b) is the only positive integer that divides a and b and is divisible by any integer dividing both a and b. Similarly, the *least common multiple* l.c.m. (a, b) is the smallest positive integer divisible by both a and b.

The greatest common divisor can be computed by Euclid's algorithm. It consists of the following chain of equations:

$$a = bq_1 + r_1 \qquad 0 < r_1 < b$$
$$b = r_1q_1 + r_2 \qquad 0 < r_2 < r_1$$
$$r_1 = r_2q_3 + r_3 \qquad 0 < r_3 < r_2$$

$$r_{k-2} = r_{k-1}q_k + r_k \qquad 0 < f_k < f_{k-1}$$

$$r_{k-1} = r_k q_{k+1}$$

Termination is guaranteed because the remainders r_i form a strictly decreasing sequence. It is evident from the chain that r_k is a common divisor of a and b and that any common divisor of a and b divides r_k. Hence, $r_k = (a, b)$.

We can estimate the time complexity of the algorithm and find that the ordinary division algorithm runs in quadratic time. We would still have exponential time complexity if we could have only $r_{i+1} < r_i$. Fortunately, $r_{i+2} < r_i\sqrt{2}$ holds for all i. This yields an upper bound of $2log_2a$ for the total number of equations. Thus, the time complexity is at most *cubic*. Reading the chain of equations bottom up we find, in *cubic* time, integers x and y such that

$$(a, b) = xa + yb$$

Relatively Prime

Two integers a and b are *relatively prime* if $(a, b) = 1$. The Euler phi-function $\phi(n)$, $n > 1$, is defined to be the number of nonnegative integers $a < n$ such that a and n are relatively prime. It follows that $\phi(1) = 1$ and $\phi(p^b) = p^b - p^{b-1}$, where p is prime and $b > 1$. It is also useful that $\phi(mn) = \phi(m)\phi(n)$ if m and n are relatively prime. By these facts $\phi(n)$ can be computed for any n. The computation will be relatively easy if the factorization of n is known.

Congruent

We say that a is congruent to b modulo m, written

$$a \equiv b(\text{mod } m)$$

if m divides the difference $a - b$. The number m is called the *modulus*. We assume that $m > 2$. For every integer x, *exactly one* of the integers 0,

1,..., $m - 1$ is congruent to x modulo m. This particular integer is called the *least nonnegative remainder* of x modulo m and denoted by

$$(x, \bmod m)$$

Denote further by $[x]$ the integer part of x, that is, the greatest integer $<x$. It follows that

$$(x, \bmod m) = x - [x/m] * m$$

Inverse

If a and m are relatively prime, then there are integers x and y such that $1 = xa + ym$. Hence, $xa \equiv 1 (\bmod m)$. The integer x is referred to as the *inverse* of a modulo m and denoted by $a^{-1}(\bmod m)$. The inverse is *unique* when congruent integers are considered to be equal. The time complexity of finding the inverse is roughly the same as that of Euclid's algorithm. This implies that the congruence:

$$az \equiv b(\bmod m), (a,m) = 1$$

can be solved in cubic time. To find z, one first computes $a^{-1}(\bmod m)$ and multiplies it by b.

If $(a, m) = 1$ then, according to Euler's Theorem,

$$a^{\phi(m)} \equiv 1 \ (\bmod m)$$

If m is a prime not dividing a, this result takes the form

$$a^{m-1} \equiv 1 \ (\bmod m)$$

and is referred to as *Fermat's Little Theorem*.

If the moduli m_i is relatively prime then the system of congruences

$$x \equiv a_i(\bmod m_i), i = 1,..., k$$

possesses a solution x, which is unique up to congruence modulo $M = m_1 \cdots m_k$. This result is known as the *Chinese Remainder Theorem*.

Fields

A *field* F is a set together with the operations of addition and multiplication that satisfy the familiar requirements: associativity, commutativity, distributive law, existence of an additive identity 0 and a multiplicative identity 1, additive inverses and multiplicative inverses for all elements except 0. Both the rational numbers and the real numbers constitute a field.

Finite fields $F(q)$ with q elements are important in cryptography— especially elliptic curve cryptography as discussed in Appendix F. For a prime p and $h > 1$ then, $q = p^h$.

Denote by $F^*(q)$ the set of nonzero elements of $F(q)$. An element g of $F^*(q)$ is termed a *generator* of $F^*(q)$, if there is an integer x such that $g^x = a$ holds in $F^*(q)$. There are $\phi(q - 1)$ generators g. The integer x is referred to as the *discrete logarithm* of a to the base g. It is known that the computing of discrete logarithms (when g, a, and q are known) is roughly as hard as *factorization*.

Consider a prime $p > 2$. If an element a of $F^*(p)$ is a square, that is $a = x^2$ for some x, a is called a *quadratic residue* modulo p. Otherwise, a is called a quadratic nonresidue modulo p. Clearly, a with $1 < a < p - 1$ is a quadratic residue modulo p if the congruence

$$x^2 \equiv a(\mathrm{mod}\ p)$$

has a solution x. Then necessarily also $-x$ is a solution, that is, a has two square roots modulo p. All quadratic residues are found by computing the squares of the elements $1,\ldots, (p - 1)/2$. Thus, there are $(p - 1)/2$ quadratic residues and nonresidues.

The *Legendre symbol* for an integer a and prime $p > 2$ is defined by:

$$(a/p) = \begin{cases} 0 \text{ if } p \text{ divides } a \\ 1 \text{ if } a \text{ is a } quadratic\ residue \text{ modulo } p \\ -1 \text{ if } a \text{ is a } quadratic\ nonresidue \text{ modulo } p \end{cases}$$

Clearly, a can be replaced by any integer congruent to $a(\mathrm{mod}\ p)$ without changing the value of the Legendre symbol. The basic result concerning the Legendre symbol is $(*)$

$$(a/p) \equiv a^{(p - 1)/2}(\mathrm{mod}\ p)$$

Finding x, that is, extracting square roots modulo n is a very important task in cryptography.

$$x \equiv a (\mathrm{mod}\ n)$$

Let us consider the case $n = pq$. By assumption, a is a quadratic residue both modulo p and modulo q. This implies the existence of numbers y and z such that

$$(\pm y)^2 \equiv a(\mathrm{mod}\ p) \quad \text{and} \quad (\pm z)^2 \equiv a(\mathrm{mod}\ q)$$

Moreover, y and z can be found in polynomial time (where the degree of the polynomial is at most 4), provided that p and q are known.

From the congruences

$$x \equiv \pm y(\mathrm{mod}\ p) \quad \text{and} \quad x \equiv \pm z(\mathrm{mod}\ q)$$

we get, by the Chinese Remainder Theorem, four square roots x of a modulo n. The square roots can be expressed as $\pm u$ and $\pm w$, where $u \neq \pm w(\mathrm{mod}\ n)$. Such u and w are referred to as different square roots. The following two facts are important in cryptography. The knowledge of two different square roots enables one to factor n.

In fact

$$u^2 - w^2 = (u + w)(u - w) \equiv 0(\mathrm{mod}\ n)$$

This means that n divides $(u + w)(u - w)$. However, by the choice of u and w, n divides neither $u + w$ nor $u - w$. This implies that the greatest common divisor of $u + w$ and n (obtained quickly by Euclid's algorithm) is either p or q.

The second important fact is that, whenever $p \equiv q \equiv 3(\mathrm{mod}\ 4)$, then two different square roots u and w of the same number a modulo n possess different Jacobi symbols:

$$(u/n) = -(w/n)$$

The *Jacobi symbol* in a generalization of the Legendre symbol:

$$(a/n) = (a/p_1)^{i_1} \cdots (a/p^k)^{i_k}$$

where a is an integer, and n is odd > 2. Also, $n = p_1^{i_1} \cdots p_k^{i_k}$ is a prime factorization of n.

This follows because, as seen above, either

$$u \equiv w(\mathrm{mod}\ p) \quad \text{and} \quad u \equiv -w(\mathrm{mod}\ q)$$

or else

$$u \equiv - w(\bmod p) \quad \text{and} \quad u \equiv w(\bmod q)$$

and concerning p and q:

$$(-1/p) = (-1/q) = -1$$

APPENDIX E

ICSA LIST OF ADOPTED ALGORITHMS

The ICSA List of Adopted Algorithms is a continually evolving list of algorithms "accepted" by the cryptographic community. ICSA queries numerous people and organizations potentially including affected vendors, independent consultants, the ICSA Cryptography Products Certification Advisory Board (CPCAB), academia, and other consumer and industry groups. The evolving list is posted on ICSA's public Web conferencing page making it constantly open for public comment and critique. Input from all sources impact on the evolving ICSA List of Adopted Algorithms. Finally, the ICSA Certification Oversight Board (COB) reviews the list. The CPCAB consists of internationally recognized leaders in the field of cryptography while the COB members have broad representation in the general field of computer and information security.

For the most part, algorithms appearing on the ICSA List of Adopted Algorithms are published, publicly tested, and accepted "industrywide." The security of products using algorithms on the ICSA list generally depends on the secrecy of the key rather than the secrecy of the algorithm. Some secret algorithms are widely used in Europe and elsewhere and generally accepted by the user community. Because of their wide acceptance, such algorithms can be on the list until proven unsuitable for the intended applications or until they are no longer generally accepted.

Symmetric Cryptography

Blowfish	Symmetric block cipher developed by Bruce Schneier. Can be used as a replacement for DES or IDEA.
CAST	Developed by Carlisle Adams and Stafford Tavares. A 64-bit block cipher using a 64-bit key.
DES	Data Encryption Standard algorithm. Most commonly used symmetric key

algorithm. Described in ANSI X3.92 and FIPS 46-2.

DESX

Data Encryption Standard extension. Provides a low-complexity extension to DES strength through plain-text modification before and after encryption.

Triple DES

Triple Data Encryption Standard algorithm. DES-based symmetric algorithm, which uses three DES keys by encrypting a block of plain text with the first key, passing the result through the decryption algorithm with the second key, and encrypting the result with the third key. Significantly extends the strength of DES and is highly recommended.

Two-Key Triple DES

An encryption configuration in which the DES algorithm is used three times with only two keys; one key is used twice.

IDEA

International Data Encryption Algorithm. A block cipher operating on 64-bit plain-text blocks. The scheme was developed in Switzerland.

RC4

A variable key-length stream cipher designed by Ron Rivest of MIT. Once a proprietary algorithm of RSA Data Security, Inc.

RC5

Block cipher of several word length options, suitable for hardware or software applications.

SAFER-SK

An iterated block cipher with 64- or 128-bit plain-text and cipher-text blocks.

SEA

Sapher Encryption Algorithm. Approved in 70 countries, rated as strong crypto by U.S. and U.K.

SEAL

Software-optimized encryption Algorithm. A fast stream cipher for 32-bit machines designed by Rogaway and Coppersmith.

Asymmetric Cryptography

Diffie-Hellman

The first public-key algorithm, uses exponential key exchange.

ECKAS-DH

Elliptic Curve Key Agreement Scheme-Diffie-Hellman version. The input to the scheme is elliptic curve parameters (aka ECDH).

RPK

Raike Public Key. A public-key encryption algorithm based on the same math as Diffie-Hellman Key Exchange in $GF(2^n)$ using maximal length LFSRs. Can also be implemented based on Multiplicative Congruential Generators in $GF(p)$ or Elliptic Curve Groups.

RSA

Algorithm invented by Ron Rivest, Adi Shamir, and Len Adelman.

ECES

Elliptic Curve Encryption Scheme. A public-key encryption scheme for encrypting and decrypting

Message Digest/Hash

ARDFP

Algorithm developed by Algorithmic Research Ltd. Certified in Germany, the standard in German banking.

MD5

Developed by Ronald Rivest, distributed by RSA Data Security, it may be used freely without license. It produces a 128-bit hash from a block of text of any length.

| SHA-1 | Secure Hash Algorithm revision one. Maps messages of length less than two-to-the-64th bits to a hash of length exactly 160 bits. Ref: ANSI X9.30 part 2. |
| RIPEM-D 128 (160) | Alternative algorithms designed to produce 128- or 160-bit hash functions. Currently being standardized in Europe. |

Random Number Generation

Blum-Blum-Shub	A pseudorandom generator, which is the simplest and most efficient of a class called complexity-theoretic generators. Because it is comparatively slow, its best use is for key generation in high-security applications.
FIPS 186	A pseudorandom number generator scheme built around SHA-1 and which has been standardized by NIST.
RPK	Raike Public Key. A public-key encryption algorithm based on the same math as Diffie-Hellman Key Exchange in $GF(2^n)$ using maximal length LFSRs. Can also be implemented based on Multiplicative Congruential Generators in $GF(p)$ or Elliptic Curve Groups.

Key Exchange

| Diffie-Hellman | The first public-key algorithm, uses exponential key exchange. |
| Modified Diffie-Hellman | Session key exchange. |

ECKAS-DH — Elliptic Curve Key Agreement Scheme-Diffie-Hellman version. The input to the scheme is elliptic curve parameters (aka ECDH).

ECKAS-MQV — Elliptic Curve Key Agreement Scheme—MQV version. Establishes one or more shared secrets between two parties for subsequent use. Involves the public and private keys of the users.

KEA — Key Exchange Algorithm (Government).

RPK — Raike Public Key. A public-key encryption algorithm based on the same math as Diffie-Hellman Key Exchange in $GF(2^n)$ using maximal length LFSRs. Can also be implemented based on Multiplicative Congruential Generators in $GF(p)$ or Elliptic Curve Groups.

RSA — Algorithm invented by Ron Rivest, Adi Shamir, and Len Adelman.

Digital Signature (Data Authentication and Nonrepudiation)

DES — Data Encryption Standard algorithm. Message authentication via ANSI X9.9. Mutual challenge via ANSI X9.17.

DSA — Digital Signature Algorithm. A public-key digital signature algorithm proposed by NIST for use in the digital signature standard (DSS).

ECAES — Elliptic Curve Authentication Encryption Scheme. Analogous to ECES plus it provides verification of the integrity of the original message.

ECDSA

Elliptic Curve analog of DSA. Uses a signature and verification operation for data integrity and entity authentication. Currently being standardized in ANSI and IEEE.

ECNR

Elliptic Curve Nyberg-Reuppel. Scheme with message appendix. Consists of a signature operation and a verification operation.

RPK

Raike Public Key. A public-key encryption algorithm based on the same math as Diffie-Hellman Key Exchange in $GF(2^n)$ using maximal length LFSRs. Can also be implemented based on Multiplicative Congruential Generators in $GF(p)$ or Elliptic Curve Groups.

RSA

Algorithm invented by Ron Rivest, Adi Shamir, and Len Adelman.

Proprietary Algorithms Used in Telephony in Europe

A3, A3, A8, CAVE

APPENDIX F

ELLIPTIC CURVES AND CRYPTOGRAPHY (ECC)

Appendix F provides background material for the understanding of elliptic curves. One of the foremost leaders in ECC cryptography is Certicom Corporation. Their Web site *http://www.certicom.com* provides white papers and tutorials on both ECC and its basis mathematics. Appendix F draws from those resources and barely scratches the surface of the material available professionally through the aforementioned Web site. ECC represents some of the most advanced concepts in cryptography. The reader is encouraged to improve his/her understanding of this interesting technology. The world-class authorities in ECC are Scott Vanstone, Alfred Menezes, and Paul C. van Oorschot. The author has had the pleasure of attending seminars presented by the former two professors, and can tell you that this technology is here to stay.

Since the introduction of the concept of public-key cryptography by Whitfield Diffie and Martin Hellman in 1976, the cryptographic importance of the well-studied discrete logarithm problem's apparent intractability has been recognized. A *group* is an abstract mathematical object consisting of a set G together with an operation $*$ defined on pairs of elements of G. The operation must have certain properties, similar to those with which we are familiar from ordinary arithmetic. More precisely:

1. (*closure*) $a*b \in G$ for all $a, b \in G$.

2. (*associativity*) $a*(b*c) = (a*b)*c$ for all $a, b, c \in G$.

3. (*existence of identity*) There exists an element $e \in G$, called the *identity*, such that $e*a = a*e = a$ for all $a \in G$.

4. (*existence of inverses*) For each $a \in G$ there is an element $b \in G$ such that $A*b = b*a = e$. The element b is called the *inverse* of a, and is denoted by a^{-1}.

A group G is said to be *abelian* if $a*b = b*a$ for all $a, b \in G$. The *order* of a group is the number of elements in G.

For example, the integers modulo n, namely $Z_n = \{0, 1, 2,..., n - 1\}$, forms a group of order n under the operation of addition modulo n. The (additive) identity of this group is 0. If p is a prime number, then the nonzero elements of Z_p, namely $Z_p* = \{1, 2,..., p - 1\}$, forms a group of order $p - 1$ under the operation of multiplication modulo p. The (multiplicative) identity of this group is 1.

The order of a group element $g \in G$ is the least positive integer n such that $g^n = 1$. For example, in the group $Z_{11}{}^*$, the element $g = 3$ has order 5, since

$$3^1 \equiv 3 \; (\text{mod } 11)$$

$$3^2 \equiv 9 \; (\text{mod } 11)$$

$$3^3 \equiv 5 \; (\text{mod } 11)$$

$$3^4 \equiv 4 \; (\text{mod } 11)$$

$$3^5 \equiv 1 \; (\text{mod } 11)$$

The discrete logarithm problem, as first employed by Diffie and Hellman in their key agreement protocol, was defined explicitly as the problem of finding logarithms in the group $Z_p{}^*$: given $g \in Z_p{}^*$ of order n, and given $h \in Z_p{}^*$, find an integer x, $0 \le x \le n - 1$, such that $g^x \equiv h \; (\text{mod } p)$, provided that such an integer exists. The integer x is called the *discrete logarithm* of h to the base g. For example, consider $p = 17$. Then $g = 10$ is an element of order $n = 16$ in $Z_{17}{}^*$. If $h = 11$, then the discrete logarithm of h to the base g is 13 because $10^{13} \equiv 11 \; (\text{mod } 17)$.

These concepts can be extended to arbitrary groups. Let G be a group of order n, and let α be an element of G. The *discrete logarithm problem* for G is the following: given elements α and $\beta \in G$, find an integer x, $0 \le x \le n - 1$, such that $\alpha^x = \beta$, provided that such an integer exists.

A variety of groups has been proposed for cryptographic use. There are two primary reasons for this. First, the operation in some groups may be easier to implement in software or in hardware. Second, the discrete logarithm problem in the group may be harder than the discrete logarithm problem in $Z_p{}^*$. Consequently, one could use a group G that is smaller than $Z_p{}^*$ while maintaining the same level of security. Such is the case with elliptic curve groups, which were first proposed for cryptographic use independently by Neal Koblitz and Victor Miller in 1985. The result is smaller key sizes, bandwidth savings, and faster implementations.

Both Koblitz and Menezes provide introductions to elliptic curves and elliptic curve systems. For simplicity, we restrict this discussion to elliptic curves over Z_p, where p is a prime greater than 3. We mention though that elliptic curves can more generally be defined over any finite field. In particular, the *characteristic two finite fields* $F_2{}^m$ are of special interest since they lead to the most efficient implementations of the elliptic curve arithmetic.

An *elliptic curve* E over Z_p is defined by an equation of the form

$$y^2 = x^3 + ax + b$$

where a, $b \in Z_p$, and $4a^3 + 27b^2 \neq 0 \pmod{p}$, together with a special point Θ, called the *point at infinity*. The set $E(Z_p)$ consists of all points (x, y), $x \in Z_p$, $y \in Z_p$, together with Θ.

Example 1 (*elliptic curve over Z_{23}*): Let $p = 23$ and consider the elliptic curve E: $y^2 = x^3 + x + 1$ defined over Z_{23}. (Let $a = 1$ and $b = 1$.) Note that $4a^3 + 27b^2 = 4 + 4 = 8 \neq 0$, so E is indeed an elliptic curve. The points in $E(Z_{23})$ are Θ and the following:

(0, 1)	(0, 22)	(1, 7)	(1, 16)	(3, 10)	(3, 13)	(4, 0)	(5, 4)	(5, 19)
(6, 4)	(6, 19)	(7, 11)	(7, 12)	(9, 7)	(9, 16)	(11, 3)	(11, 20)	(12, 4)
(12, 19)	(13, 7)	(13, 16)	(17, 3)	(17, 20)	(18, 3)	(18, 20)	(19, 5)	(19, 18)

Addition Formula

There is a rule for adding two points on an elliptic curve $E(Z_p)$ to give a third elliptic curve point. Together with this addition operation, the set of points $E(Z_p)$ forms a group with Θ serving as its identity. *It is this group that is used in the construction of elliptic curve cryptosystems.*

The addition rule is best explained geometrically. Let $P = (x_1, y_1)$ and $Q = (x_2, y_2)$ be two distinct points on an elliptic curve E. Then the *sum* of P and Q, denoted $R = (x_3, y_3)$, is defined as follows. First draw the line through P and Q; this line intersects the elliptic curve in a third point. Then R is the reflection of this point in the x-axis. This is depicted in Figure F-1. The elliptic curve in the figure consists of two parts, the ellipse and the infinite curve.

If $P = (x_1, y_1)$, then the *double* of P, denoted $R = (x_3, y_3)$ is defined as follows. First, draw the tangent line to the elliptic curve at P. This line intersects the elliptic curve in a second point. Then R is the reflection of this point in the x-axis. This is depicted in Figure F-2.

The following algebraic formulae for the sum of two distinct points and the double of a point can now be derived from the geometric description.

1. $P + \Theta = \Theta + P = P$ for all $P \in E(Z_p)$.

2. If $P = (x, y) \in E(Z_p)$, then $(x, y) + (x, -y) = \Theta$. (The point $(x, -y)$ is denoted by $-P$, and is called the *negative* of P; observe that $-P$ is indeed a point on the curve.)

Figure F-1
Geometric Description of the Addition of Two Distinct Elliptic Curve Points: $P+Q = R$

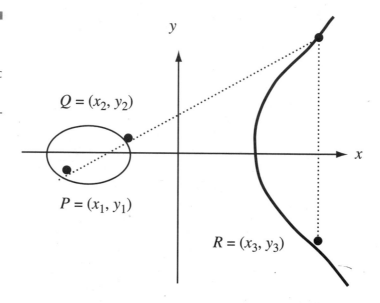

$Q = (x_2, y_2)$

$P = (x_1, y_1)$

$R = (x_3, y_3)$

Figure F-2
Geometric Description of the Doubling of an Elliptic Curve Points: $P+P = R$

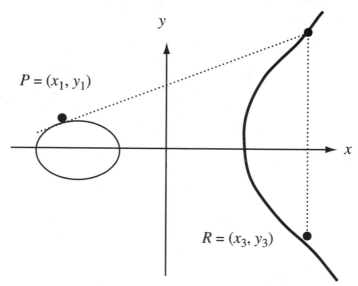

$P = (x_1, y_1)$

$R = (x_3, y_3)$

3. Let $P = (x_1, y_1) \in E(Z_p)$ and $Q = (x_2, y_2) \in E(Z_p)$, where $P \neq -Q$. Then $P + Q = (x_3, y_3)$, where

$$x_3 = \lambda^2 - x_1 - x_2$$
$$y_3 = \lambda(x_1 - x_3) - y_1$$

and

$$\lambda = \begin{cases} \dfrac{y_2 - y_1}{x_2 - x_1} & \text{if } P \neq Q \\[2em] \dfrac{3x_1^2 + a}{2y_1} & \text{if } P = Q \end{cases}$$

Observe that the addition of two elliptic curve points $E(Z_p)$ requires a few arithmetic operations (addition, subtraction, multiplication, and inversion) in the underlying finite field Z_p.

Example 2 (elliptic curve addition): Consider the elliptic curve defined in Example 1.

1. Let $P = (3, 10)$ and $Q = (9, 7)$. Then $P + Q = (x_3, y_3)$ is computed as follows:

$$\lambda = \frac{7 - 10}{9 - 3} = \frac{-3}{6} = \frac{-1}{2} = -2^{-1} = 11 \in Z_{23}$$

Note that $2^{-1} = 12$ since $2 \cdot 12 \equiv 1 \pmod{23}$. Finally,

$$x_3 = 11^2 - 3 - 9 = 6 - 3 - 9 = -6 \equiv 17 \pmod{23}$$

$$y_3 = 11(3 - (-6)) - 10 = 11(9) - 10 = 89 \equiv 20 \pmod{23}$$

Hence, $P + Q = (17, 20)$.

2. Let $P = (3, 10)$. Then $2P = P + P = (x_3, y_3)$ is computed as follows:

$$\lambda = \frac{3(3^2) + 1}{20} = \frac{5}{20} = \frac{1}{4} = 4^{-1} = 6 \in Z_{23}$$

Note that $4^{-1} = 6$ since $4 \cdot 6 \equiv 1 \pmod{23}$. Finally,

$$x_3 = 6^2 - 6 = 30 \equiv 7 \pmod{23}$$

$$y_3 = 6(3-7)-10 = -24 - 10 = -34 \equiv 12 \pmod{23}$$

Hence $2P = (7, 12)$.

Hasse's theorem states that the number of points on an elliptic curve is $\#E(Z_p) = p + 1 - t$ where $|t| \leq \sqrt{2p}$; $\#E(Z_p)$ is called the *order* of the elliptic curve. In other words, the order of an elliptic curve $E(Z_p)$ is roughly equal to the size p of the underlying field. There is a polynomial-time algorithm, due to Schoof, for counting the number of points on an elliptic curve. Although this algorithm is quite cumbersome in practice, several improvements have been proposed in recent years, which make the algorithm practical. For some recent work in this area, see Lercier and Morain.

For historical reasons, the group operation for an elliptic curve $E(Z_p)$ has been called *addition*. By contrast, the group operation in Z_p^* is multiplication. The differences in the resulting additive notation and multiplicative notation can sometimes be confusing. Table F-1 shows the correspondence between notation used for the two groups Z_p^* and $E(Z_p)$.

TABLE F-1

Correspondence Between Z_p^* and $E(Z_p)$ Notation

Group	Z_p^*	$E(Z_p)$
Group elements	Integers $\{1, 2, ..., p - 1\}$	Points (x, y) on E plus Θ
Group operation	Multiplication modulo p	Addition of points
Notation	Elements: g, h Multiplication: $g \cdot h$ Inverse: g^{-1} Division: g/h Exponentiation: g^a	Elements: P, Q Addition: $P + Q$ Negative: $-P$ Subtraction: $P - Q$ Multiple: aP
Discrete Logarithm Problem	Given $g \in Z_p^*$ and $h = g^a \bmod p$ find a	Given $P \in E(Z_p)$ and $Q = aP$, find a

APPENDIX G

PROGRESSION OF CRYPTOGRAPHIC MACHINES

Lauer presented an outline of ten cryptographic systems and representative cipher machines in increasing order of difficulty. The author rearranged his classification methodology to show how the Enigma machine fits into the progression of classical cryptographic/mechanical systems.

1. *Simple Substitution — Cipher Disk*
   Principles: monosubstitution, plain-text and cipher-text sequence keying, transposition keys
   Examples: aristocrats, patristocrats, xenocrypts Caesar substitutions, sliding strips, rotating disks
   Attacks: frequency analysis, word pattern, bigram, trigram analysis, vowel spotting, letter distribution and blanks in message

2. *Periodic Polyalphabetic Substitution — Vigenere Devices*
   Principles: polyalpha-substitution, repeated key sequences
   Examples: Vigenere, Variant, Beaufort, Porta, Gronsfeld
   Attacks: periodicity, Kasiski, trigraphic, traffic analysis, Kerckhoff's method

3. *Running Key and Autokey — Kammel and Weller Devices*
   Principles: polyalpha-substitution, nonrepeated key sequence, plain-text autokey, cipher-text autokey, and running key
   Examples: Running key and autokey ciphers
   Attack: Friedman attack — "Solution of Running Key Ciphers," probable word, known plain text

4. *Simple Progressive*
   Principles: constant shift interval to employ all secondary alphabets (period = 26)
   Examples: Progressive Cipher
   Attacks: Friedman attacks, periodicity at 26, 13, 2, 1, Chi test, matching frequency distributions, decimation intervals, coherent key

5. *Irregular — KRYHA*
   Principles: irregular shifting of primary components noncoherent key, nonrecognizable key, long key derived from two or more

short keys, pseudorandom keys, different interval shifts on pro-
gressive; sum of shifts relatively prime to N in alphabet
Examples: One-time pad, Vernam Key Tape
Attacks: Sacco's solution, Isomorphism, Friedman's techniques

6. *Wheatstone Cryptograph*
   Principles: aperiodic cipher, extra sequence shift, error control
   Examples: Jefferson Device, Hebern machine, Vernam Cipher
   Attack: Friedman's techniques, probable word or phrase, known
   plain text-cipher text

7. *Multiplex Systems*
   Principles: Wheel ciphers
   Examples: Jefferson, M-138, M-94 machines
   Attack: Friedman techniques, De Viaris examination, synoptic
   tables, Mellen attack, Rohrbach method coincidences, genera-
   trices grouping

8. *Hagelin M-209*
   Principles: pin lug mechanism, cylindrical cage, guide arm—
   print wheel rotates number of positions = sum of the lugs on
   those key wheels that were affected by active pins. $\Rightarrow$ key value
   with period of 3,120,180 letters
   Examples: C-36, M-209 machines
   Attack: Barker analysis one wheel to six wheels, statistical
   analysis on settings, probable word

9. *Enigma*
   Principles: electrical rotor or transfer wheel, stepping gears,
   maze between keyboard and indicating device producing 26^N
   different enciphering alphabets, reentrance phenomenon,
   excess contacts, superencipherment
   Examples: Enigma A-E
   Attacks: Polish, BP, Turing, Deavours, Friedman IC, Chi test on
   diagonals, isomorphs, Pohlig with plain text, Konheim analysis,
   Lisicki Grille 1000 $\times$ 1000 rearrangements
   ACA and University of Hamburg: Modern Experiments: remove
   reflecting rotor and replace with reentrance type rotor; install
   bidirectional rotors; increase entropy

10. *Hill System*
    Principles: polygraphic encipherment, nonlinear encipherment
    functions (early forerunner of "S" boxes in DES)

Examples: Hill Device

Attacks: Konheim technique, Rhee analysis, mapping, known plain text, plain text-cipher text compromise

APPENDIX H

U.S. LEGAL AND GOVERNMENT POLICY CONTROLLING CRYPTOGRAPHY

Introduction

Cryptographic tools, like other forms of technology, can be used by criminals and spies to cause harm. The U.S. government has classified cryptographic tools as restricted items for international commerce. In addition, the Clinton administration (1992-2000) proposed a novel system for mandatory key escrow of some cryptographic keys. Throughout the 1990s, debate has been vigorous over the advisability and feasibility of these government policies. This appendix presents a summary of the key issues, pointers to the current literature, and addresses of some Web sites dealing with these topics.

Export Controls

Before the widespread availability of desktop computing, the only sources of strong encryption were expensive hardware-based systems, many of them used by the military. The United States classified cryptographic systems as munitions and they were explicitly controlled in the International Traffic in Arms Regulations (ITAR). Although these regulations allowed unrestricted export from the United States and Canada of encryption used only for financial transaction authentication, all other cryptographic modules were subject to the strict scrutiny of bureaucrats in the State Department. Throughout the Cold War and until 1996, exporting cryptographic tools, although not forbidden in theory, was in practice difficult to get approved by the government. Some manufacturers experienced delays of months to years before their export licenses were granted—if they ever got permission at all. A major complaint from manufacturers and users was that the specific policies used to determine exemptions from the ITAR were not public. Some critics

715

called this FUD—fear, uncertainty, and doubt—and argued that the policy was unpublished precisely in order to discourage organizations from trying to export strong cryptographic modules.

In 1996, the U.S. government announced a shift of responsibility for cryptographic export controls from the State Department to the Commerce Department. Starting in December 1996, export restrictions were significantly eased and were summarized in the Export Administration Regulations (EAR). The allowable key space for unrestricted export of cryptography rose from what was by then an easily cracked 40 bits to the marginally better 56 bits. Several organizations obtained permission to export commercial cryptographic products for use by multinational corporations. However, opposition continued to grow to any restrictions at all on the export of commercial cryptographic products.

In January 1998, the Commerce Department published new regulations affecting cryptographic exports based on the Wassenaar Arrangement, a 1996 agreement among 33 nations to limit export of armaments and technologies with potential applications in warfare (e.g., computers and cryptography). Although some restrictions on applications of cryptography to financial systems (e.g., automated teller machines) were marginally relaxed, most commercial cryptography continued to be tightly controlled (in theory).

The arguments over export controls included the following:

1. *Existence of foreign cryptographic programs:*
   Pro: Export controls did not harm U.S. commercial interests because there were no foreign sources for equivalent cryptographic products.
   Con: Studies by the Software Publishers Association (SPA) and others clearly showed a wealth of suppliers of commercial cryptography outside the United States.

2. *Availability:*
   Pro: What few cryptographic products there were internationally were not easily available, and therefore, export controls did not harm U.S. cryptographic interests.
   Con: Studies by the SPA proved that cryptography was in fact easily available through normal commercial channels anywhere in the world.

3. *Quality:*
   Pro: Cryptographic products sold outside the United States were supposedly weak.
   Con: Studies of foreign cryptographic products showed them to be at least as good as those manufactured in the United States.

4. *Foreign laws:*

> *Pro:* Foreign governments restrict the import of American cryptographic products into their markets.
>
> *Con:* Government spokesmen were unable to provide any examples of significant markets impeded by foreign cryptographic import regulations. Studies showed that many international cryptographic manufacturers used international distributors for wide dissemination of their products.

5. *Conflict of interest:* A more fundamental problem was that the interests of the National Security Agency, the body entrusted with developing cryptographic export policies, were not necessarily in accordance with the best interests of American business practices (including more than manufacturers of cryptographic products). The NSA had a distinct interest in monitoring communications from foreign companies as a matter of national security.

   However, American companies with correspondents overseas were increasingly in need of strong encryption to protect their transmissions from eavesdropping by foreign governments and foreign competitors. Preventing Americans from using strong cryptography in an attempt to deny the same tools to foreigners was viewed as counterproductive by critics of the export controls.

6. *First amendment issues:* Another source of contention was/is the irrationality of export restrictions that forbade export of cryptographic source code on disks or electronically but allowed the same source code to be freely exported in textbooks or journal articles. Opponents sneered that the U.S. government must be of the opinion that foreigners could not type. More serious objections centered on the constitutionality of such restrictions.

   Even as far back as 1978, the constitutionality of export controls on cryptographic algorithms was questioned by no less than an assistant attorney general in the Office of Legal Counsel in a memorandum to the Science Advisor for the President. John M. Harmon reviewed the existing jurisprudence and concluded that the ITAR's prior restraint on publication of cryptographic algorithms was likely to be judged unconstitutional by the Supreme Court. Nonetheless, the control juggernaut lumbered on, and in 1993, a federal grand jury was convened to see if Phil Zimmermann's domestic posting of his freeware PGP (Pretty Good Privacy) encryption program on his Internet site constituted a violation of the ITAR. The case dragged on for three years before being dismissed in 1996.

   In January 1997, Professor Daniel Bernstein's lawyers demanded that the U.S. government not enforce its new export restrictions until they had been examined in a court of law to establish their constitutionality. In August 1997, Judge Marilyn Patel of the U.S. District Court in San Francisco ruled in favor of plaintiff Bernstein, a professor at the University of Illinois in Chicago. Prof. Bernstein was furious that the current cryptography export regulations interfered with his ability to publish encryption algorithms in international journals and to teach classes in cryptography to foreign students at his university. Judge Patel, ruling against the Export Administration Regulations, wrote that the U.S. government's rules lacked all logic in allowing printed source code to be exported but interfering with electronic versions. The government appealed and their arguments were heard in December 1997. A similar case was launched by Peter Junger, a law professor at Case Western Reserve University in Cleveland. He protested the imposition of restrictions on posting his class notes for Computers and the Law on a Web site for his students (but accessible to everyone in the world with a Web browser). This extension of the definitions of export to posting on the Net, reminiscent of the aborted case against Phil Zimmermann, moved him to start a lawsuit against the government in 1996. Results of these attacks on the constitutionality of cryptography-export restrictions were not yet available at time of this writing (June 1998), but it seemed likely that regardless of the outcome, the decisions would be appealed to the Supreme Court of the United States.

Key Escrow

In April 1993, the Clinton administration announced what became known as the *Clipper Initiative.* The government proposed to impose mandatory key escrow on the telephone systems used by a government employees for sensitive but not classified communications. The technology proposed was based on a tamper-resistant hardware chip (the Clipper Chip) that would implement the SKIPJACK algorithm, developed in secret by the NSA. The Clipper Chip would automatically encrypt all communications using a special key called the law enforcement access field (LEAF) that would accompany all encrypted communications. The LEAF would be stored, or escrowed, in two parts; each part was to be held by a different agency of the U.S. government. When law enforcement officials required access to encrypted communications, they could apply for reconstitution of the LEAF under normal judicial procedures for obtaining a warrant. The government expressed the hope that inexpensive encryption integrated into commercially available phone systems would voluntarily be adopted by ordinary users and would thus improve law enforcement's ability to tap conversations in the face of anticipated widespread use of encryption.

Reaction to the Clipper initiative was immediate and hostile. Cryptographers objected to the use of a secret (classified) algorithm, because of the widely accepted view that effectiveness of the cryptographic algorithm should not reside in the secrecy of that algorithm. Within a few months, a panel of distinguished cryptographers was convened to examine the SKIPJACK algorithm under nondisclosure agreements. The scientists subjected the algorithm to extensive examination and formal testing. Their results deemed SKIPJACK cryptographically acceptable. However, a year later, cryptographer Matt Blaze delivered a paper at the Second ACM Conference on Computer and Communications Security (November 1994) in which he describes two approaches for bypassing transmission of the LEAF. Other objections centered on the practical difficulties of securing the escrowed key components. In a particularly embarrassing incident, the manufacturers of the key escrow chip admitted that confidential information had been obtained from their site through dumpster diving. Much of the furor centered on assumptions that the government would attempt to force the use of its encryption technology by eventually banning all other forms of encryption for voice communications.

The debate has continued for several years and has not yet been resolved at the time of this writing (June 1998). Law enforcement officials, including FBI Director Louis J. Freeh in particular, have repeatedly sounded the alarm over the widespread use of strong encryption for communications among criminals. Civil libertarians have been adamant in opposing what they view as the intrusion of government and law into technical developments in cryptography.

In May 1997, a committee of 11 respected cryptographers and computer security experts released a report condemning the proposed U.S. regulations tying permission for export of strong cryptography to implementation of key-recovery technology. William Reinsch, director of the Bureau of Export Administration in the Department of Commerce, retorted that the computer scientists were demolishing a straw man and that the administration has no intention of mandating a centralized key-recovery system. Instead, said Reinsch, the intention is to require individual organizations to maintain their own key-recovery systems; these could then be used under court order to satisfy the requirements of law enforcement agencies.

In June 1997, the Clinton administration began ten pilot projects to create key-recovery systems for its own use. As predicted by critics of key escrow policies, the tests quickly forced the abandonment of a centralized escrow agency because the different parts of government wanted no one else to have access to their particular encryption keys. Furthermore, none of the internal key-recovery systems under development would store the private keys used to authenticate documents with digital signatures; they would store only the temporary "session keys" used to encrypt specific documents in transit.

In September 1997, the Clinton administration proposed a new law that would mandate a back door for decryption of all domestic encryption. In addition, the proposal would have forced telephone companies and ISPs to implement a bypass for decryption of all traffic encrypted by their chosen protocols (e.g., Secure Sockets Layer). Matters became even more problematic for mandatory *key escrow* (now referred to as *key recovery*) when the European Commission rejected the Clinton administration's proposals for key recovery/escrow in encryption systems, dismissing them as not only objectionable because of threats to privacy and commerce but also as ineffective.

In March 1998, the FBI backpedaled from its stance that law enforcement agencies should be given keys to encrypted data, saying it supported voluntary industry controls rather than new laws concerning encryption. In the House of Representatives, the Security and Freedom through Encryption Act, H.R. 695 ("SAFE") would prohibit the use of key escrow to decrypt private data communications but would also penalize using encryption to hide evidence from law enforcement organizations. In April, U.S. Secretary of Commerce William Daley spoke on "The Emerging Digital Economy." He emphasized the importance of cryptography for electronic commerce and described the current policy on key escrow/recovery as a *failure*.

FURTHER READING ▬▬   ▬▬   ▬▬   ▬▬   ▬▬

Foundation papers in the debates over cryptographic policy:

Hoffman, L. J., ed. *Building in Big Brother: The Cryptographic Policy Debate*. New York, Springer-Verlag, 1995. ISBN 0-387-94441-9. 560 pp. Index.

Schneier, B. and D. Banisar, eds. *The Electronic Privacy Papers: Documents on the Battle for Privacy in the Age of Surveillance.* New York, John Wiley & Sons, 1997. ISBN 0-471-12297-1. 747 pp. Index.

Recent papers on cryptographic policy:

Computing Canada, April 20, 1998, **24**(15), p. 11(1), "Cryptography vendors protest export controls"

Newsbytes, April 1, 1998, p. NEW04010039, "Crypto Policy Proposals Worry Canadian Industry"

Computerworld, March 30, 1998, **32**(13), p. 3(1), "Signs point to looser encryption rules" by Machlis, Sharon

Computing Canada, March 23, 1998, **24**(11), p. 1(2), "Proposed policy changes causing angst; Analysts and businesses issue challenge to suggested cryptography policy reform" by Enright, Greg

InfoWorld, March 23, 1998, **20**(12), p. 66(2), "Data encryption gets tangled with U.S. law enforcement" by Nelson, Matthew

Newsbytes, March 20, 1998, p. NEW03200037, "Network Associates Ships 128-Bit Encryption Without License"

Computerworld, March 2, 1998, **32**(9), p. 8(1), "HP wins export license"

PC Week, March 2, 1998, **15**(9), p. 1(18), "Say uncle; industry grapples with government over high-tech jurisdiction" by Moeller, Michael; Jim Kerstetter; John Rendleman; Scott Berinato

Newsbytes, Feb. 27, 1998, **42,** p. NEW02270047, "HP Gets OK On Strong Encryption, Teams With IBM, Microsoft"

Newsbytes, Feb. 26, 1998, **41,** p. NEW02260039, "DES 56-Bit Encryption Cracked In Record Time"

LAN Times, Feb. 16, 1998, **15**(4), p. 54(1), "Easing export" by Paone, Joe

PC Week, Jan. 26, 1998, **15**(4), p. 35(1), "Crypto crew, feds at odds" by Kerstetter, Jim

PC Week, Jan. 26, 1998, **15**(4), p. 38(1), "Here we go again on encryption" by Sullivan, Eamonn

Computerworld, Jan. 19, 1998, **32**(3), p. 10(1) "Crypto bill could see spring passage" by DiDio, Laura

Newsbytes, Dec. 9, 1997, p. NEW12090050, "Judges To Decide If Encryption Is Protected By 1st Amendment"

Newsbytes, Dec. 5, 1997, p. NEW12050023, "Govt Wants Reversal In Bernstein Encryption Appeal"

Web Week, Dec. 1, 1997, **3**(40), p. 44(2), "It's Big Brother vs. business in stubborn encryption debate" by Gardner, Elizabeth

InfoWorld, Nov. 17, 1997, **19**(46), p. 106(1), "Commerce Department OKs 128-bit export for PGP" by Nelson, Matthew

Network, Nov. 1997, **12**(12), p. 16(2), "The latest on crypto regulation" by Steinke, Steve

Newsbytes, Oct. 23, 1997, p. NEW10230051, "4th Cracking Of 56-Bit Code Shows Need For Longer Keys"

InfoWorld, Oct. 20, 1997, **19**(42), p. 86(1), "128-bit encryption offered abroad" by McKay, Niall

PC Week, Oct. 20, 1997, **14**(44), p. 80(2). "Separating crypto and state" (Letters to the Editor)

Computerworld, Oct. 13, 1997, **31**(41), p. 8(1), "EC opposes crypto restrictions"

Newsbytes, Oct. 10, 1997, p. NEW10100058, "US Encryption Policy Stagnating Says Pioneer Diffie"

InternetWeek, Oct. 6, 1997, 684, p. 96(1), "If you water down encryption you'll kill the golden goose" by Kaas, Elliot

Computerworld, Sept. 29, 1997, **31**(39), p. 16(1), "House committee kills crypto controls amendment" by Machlis, Sharon

Computerworld, Sept. 29, 1997, **31**(39), p. 112(1), "The Feds' ludicrous encryption plan" by Gillmor, Dan

InternetWeek, Sept. 29, 1997, 683, p. 12(1), "Backdoor closes, for now, on crypto plan" by Rendleman, John

Newsbytes, Sept. 25, 1997, p. NEW09250044, UK Company Blows Hole In Encryption Export Laws"

Computer Reseller News, Sept. 22, 1997, 755, p. 77(2), "Encryption key to security, revenue" by Dunlap, Charlotte

InternetWeek Sept. 22, 1997, 682, p. 45(1), "How the Internet will change the rule of law" by Frezza, Bill

Newsbytes, Sept. 16, 1997, p. NEW09160048, "EPIC & Privacy Int'l Trash US Govt Crypto Policy"

Forbes, Sept. 8, 1997, **160**(5), p. 172(8), "Politics for the really cool" by McHugh, Josh

Computerworld, Sept. 1, 1997, **31**(35), p. 32(1), "Judge strikes down encryption restriction" by Machlis, Sharon

Government Computer News, Sep, 1, 1997, **16**(26), p. 3(1), "Judge blasts crypto policy"

CommunicationsWeek, August 18, 1997, 677, p. 1(2), "Sun crypto in limbo" by Fontana, John

Databased Web Advisor, August 1997, **15**(8), p. 70(4), "Key recovery spawns debate" by Toigo, Jon William

Network, August 1997, **12**(8), p. 18(1), "Encryption export: the debate continues" by Tribble, Erin

Federal Computer Week, July 14, 1997, **11**(20), p. 10(2), "Battle lines drawn over fed role in key-recovery debate" by Harreld, Heather

Computerworld, July 7, 1997, **31**(27), p. 45(1), "Cryptoware gets nod"

Newsbytes July 2, 1997, p. NEW07020004, "Clinton Sticks To His Encryption Guns In Internet Policy"

CommunicationsWeek, June 30, 1997, 670, p. 1(2), "128-bit barrier falls" by Yasin, Rutrell

InfoWorld, June 30, 1997, **18**(26), p. 77(2), "Hackers prove 56-bit DES is not enough" by Radosevich, Lynda

PC Week, June 30, 1997, **14**(28), p. 30(1), "Vendors get encryption export ok" by Moeller, Michael

Newsbytes, June 25, 1997, p. NEW06250033, "Goodlatte Encryption Bill Moves Through Subcommittee"

Newsbytes, June 20, 1997, p. NEW06200065, "Senate Committee Approves Compromise Encryption Bill"

Newsbytes, June 19, 1997, p. NEW06190018, "EPIC Seeks Disclosure Of Clinton's Crypto Czar's Files"

Newsbytes, June 19, 1997, p. NEW06190049, "Hackers Smash 56-Bit DES Encryption"

Newsbytes, June 18, 1997, p. NEW06180062, "Kerrey Compromise Encryption Bill Hits Roadblocks"

InfoWorld, June 2, 1997, **19**(22), p. 15(1), "Commerce Department eases cryptographic export rules" by Balderston, Jim

PC Week, June 2, 1997, **14**(22), p. 135(2), "The cryptic U.S. policies of encryption" by Paul, Lauren Gibbons

Computing Canada, March 23, 1998, **24**(11), p. 7(1), "Big changes and big worries"

Federal Computer Week, Jan. 19, 1998, **12**(2), p. 40(1), "Former NSA exec Crowell joins Cylink, battles on for public, private encryption"

PC Week, Dec. 1, 1997, **14**(50), p. 27(1), "What does encryption mean to you? Plenty" by Frentzen, Jeff

Communications of the ACM, Aug. 1997, **40**(8), p. 136(1), "Crypto key management" by Neumann, Peter G.

Resources on the World Wide Web:
Electronic Frontier Foundation *http://www.eff.org*

Electronic Privacy Information Center *http://www.epic.org*

Encryption Privacy and Security Resource Page *http://www.crypto.com*

http://www.crypto.com/key_study/
"The risks of key recovery, key escrow, and trusted third-party encryption" by Hal Abelson, Ross Anderson, Steven M. Bellovin, Josh Benaloh, Matt Blaze, Whitfield Diffie, John Gilmore, Peter G. Neumann, Ronald L. Rivest, Jeffrey I. Schiller, and Bruce Schneier. This paper is often known as the "Eleven Cryptographers' Report."

http://www.offshore.com.ai/security/
Vince Cate's Cryptorebel/Cypherpunk Page

ftp://ftp.csua.berkeley.edu/pub/cypherpunks/Home.html
The Cypherpunks Home Page

http://strategis.ic.gc.ca/SSG/cy00001e.html
Industry Canada Cryptography Page

http://www.cl.cam.ac.uk/users/rja14/
British cryptographer Ross Anderson's home page

CRYPTOTERMS AND INTEROPERABILITY GLOSSARY

This glossary includes a sample of the most frequently used acronyms, abbreviations, terms, phrases, buzzwords, and the like, that one may hear in any conversation among cryptography professionals. Cryptography researchers, developers, vendors, and other professionals probably can explain about 85 to 90 percent of the terms listed. But the beginner in cryptography who may be considering the acquisition of a cryptography product or technique to enhance the security of a communications/network/computer system has a pretty good chance of being thoroughly confused by the use of these terms and others when they are not explained in context. This confusion, in part, is responsible for the fact that many potential users are hesitant to acquire and use cryptography products.

A5 The secret algorithm used in European cellular telephones.

ACA The American Cryptogram Association has been the leader in the field of recreational and classical cryptography since 1929.

Access control The control of who or what applications have access to a network, server, PC.

ACL (Access Control List) A listing of users and their associated access rights.

Accidental Repetition A repetition caused by chance, and not by the encipherment of identical plain-text characters by identical keying elements.

Active attack An attack in which the attacker must create or modify information. This includes attacks by Henry the Forger, Play-It-Again Sam, and Bailey the Switcher.

Additional Servers Name servers, other than the primary and secondary name servers, that are available to identify a particular domain name with its corresponding Internet Protocol (IP) address(es).

Additive A single digit or numerical group, or series of digits which, for the purpose of encipherment, is added to a numerical cipher unit, code group, or plain text, usually by cryptographic arithmetic.

Additive method The method of encipherment wherein the cryptographic equations are $P + K = C$, and $P + K - C$.

Additive system A cryptosystem in which encipherment is accomplished through the application of additives.

ADFGVX system A German high-command cipher system used in World War I. Essentially, a bilateral substitution system employing a 6×6 or 5×5 square to which columnar transposition was subsequently applied.

Advanced Research Projects Agency (ARPA) An agency of the U.S. Department of Defense that promotes exploratory research in areas that carry long-term promise for military applications. ARPA funded the major packet switching experiments in the United States that led to the Internet.

AES (advanced encryption standard) To be approved by NIST for next 20-30 years' use.

Agent In network management: that component of a system that responds to management requests and/or preprogrammed traps. In the client/server model: the system component that prepares information and exchanges it for a client or server application.

AH (the IP Authentication Header) Provides authentication services at the IP layer on a packet-by-packet basis.

AKEP (Authentication Key Exchange Protocol) Key transport based on symmetric encryption allowing two parties to end up with a shared secret key, secure against passive adversaries.

Algorithm (encryption algorithm, encryption engine) A set of mathematical rules (logic) used in the processes of encryption and decryption.

Alias An assumed name (dummy) mail address that routes the message to all real addresses associated with the assumed name.

American National Standards Institute (ANSI) An organization that endorses and publishes standards for various industries.

American Registry for Internet Numbers (ARIN) Nonprofit organization that manages the allocation of Internet Protocol (IP) addresses in the Americas, the Caribbean, and sub-Saharan Africa. The National Science Foundation (NSF) approved the establishment of ARIN on June 24, 1997.

Anagram Plain language reconstructed from a transposition cipher by restoring the letters of the cipher text to their original order.

Annual Solar Limit The total amount of energy produced by the sun in a year. It is possible to calculate a worst case upper limit for the number of keys that can be tested with that amount of energy: 2^{192} keys. This suggests that a secret key containing 192 bits is impractical to crack using brute-force methods.

Anonymity Of unknown or undeclared origin or authorship, concealing an entity's identification.

ANSI (American National Standards Institute) Represents the United States in the ISO. A private standards body that develops industry standards through various Accredited Standards Committees (ASC). The X9 committee focuses on security standards for the financial services industry.

Anti-replay integrity (protection) Detects arrival of duplicate IP datagrams within a constrained window.

Aperiodic Characterized by absence of cyclic attributes or usage.

Aperiodic system A system in which the method of keying does not bring about cyclic phenomena in the cryptographic text.

API (application programming interface) Provides means to take advantage of software features.

Application Information processing according to a set of instructions to accomplish a given end. Application examples: electronic mail, credit card verification, electronic data interchange, database search, LAN/WAN connections, remote computing services, distributed data processing, information gateways, international access services, frame-relay services, ATM networks, electronic publishing, electronic trading, authentication, database SQL, and so forth.

Archie A search utility program used to find files on the Internet.

Arcnet A 2.5-Mbps network (twisted-pair or coaxial cable) most often implemented in a physical star configuration using token-passing to control access.

ARP Address Resolution Protocol

ARPANET A pioneering wide area, packet-switched computer network developed by ARPA. The ARPANET was the original backbone for the modern Internet, and many of its protocols were adapted to work on the Internet, including those for email, FTP, and remote terminal connections.

ASC Accredited Standards Committee

ASCII (American Standard Code for Information Interchange)

The standard code, using a coded character set consisting of 7-bit coded characters (8 bits including parity check), used for information.

Asian-Pacific Network Information Center (APNIC) A collaborative effort of national Network Information Centers (NICs) and Internet Service Providers within the Asian-Pacific region. The APNIC manages the allocation of Internet Protocol (IP) addresses in the Asian-Pacific region.

ASN.1 (Abstract Syntax Notation One) ISO/IEC standard for encoding rules, DER (Distinguished Encoding Rules), BER (Basic Encoding Rules).

Asymmetric Does not need the same key on each end of a communication link.

Asymmetric key encryption A separate but integrated user key pair comprised of one public key and one private key. Each key is one way, meaning that key used to encrypt information cannot be used to decrypt information.

Asynchronous Character-by-character or cell-by-cell or data unit-by-data unit transfer. Data units from any one source need not be periodically spaced within the overall data unit stream.

ATM Asynchronous transfer mode

Audit The process of examining the history of a transaction to find out what happened. An operational audit can be an examination of ongoing activities to determine what is happening.

Authentication The process of ensuring the identity of the connecting user or participants exchanging electronic data. Makes sure the person or server at either end of a connection is who they/it claims to be and not an impostor.

Authorization To convey official sanction, access, or legal power to an entity.

Autoenchipherment Encipherment by means of an autokey system.

Autokey The block cipher mode in which the cipher is used to generate the key stream. Also called *output feedback (OFB) mode*.

Autokey system An aperiodic substitution system in which the key, following the application of a previously arranged initial key, is generated from elements of the plain or cipher text of the message.

Availability Requires that computer-system assets be available to authorized parties.

Backbone   A high-performance network of thick wire or fiber optic cables that enables data transmission among networks that are connected to it.

BATAP   Type B Application to Application Protocol, secures TYPE B traffic. It was specified by SITA and is published by IATA.

BER   Basic Encoding Rules

Binary digit   One of the two symbols (0 and 1) commonly used to represent numerical entries in the binary number system.

B-ISDN   A high-speed communications standard for wide area networks that supports wide-bandwidth applications including voice, data, and graphics.

Bit   A single digit in a binary numbering system (e.g., 1 or 0). A contraction of the term "binary digit."

Blind signature   The ability to sign documents without the knowledge of content; notary public.

Block   A string or group of bits that a block algorithm operates on; typical values are 40, 50, 64, 128, 512, 1024, and so forth.

Block cipher (block algorithms)   Algorithms that operate on plain text in blocks (strings or groups) of bits.

Blowfish   A symmetric block cipher system that can be used as a replacement for the DES or IDEA encryption algorithms. It takes a variable-length key, from 32 to 512 bits, making it ideal for both domestic and exportable use. It was designed in 1993 by Bruce Schneier as a fast alternative to the existing encryption algorithms.

Bridge   An internetworking switch usually operating at OSI Level 2, the Data Link Layer. A bridge expands a LAN or connects two LANs.

Browser   Client application software for accessing data on the World Wide Web.

Brute-Force Cracking   The process of trying to recover a crypto key by trying all reasonable possibilities.

Bucket Brigade   An attack against a public key exchange in which attackers substitute their own public key for their requested public key; also called a *Man-in-the-Middle attack*.

Bus   A single data path to which all workstations directly attach, and on which all transmissions are available to every workstation. However, only the workstation to which a transmission is addressed can actually read it.

Bypass A flaw in a security device that allows messages to go around the security mechanisms. Crypto bypass refers to flaws that allow plain text to leak out.

Byte A string of binary digits (usually 8, 16, 32, or 64 bits long) operated on as a basic unit by a digital computer.

CA (Certification Authority, certificate authority) A trusted third party that creates certificates that consist of assertion on various attributes.

CAC (connection admission control) Actions performed by a network to enforce network admissions policies.

CAP Competitive access providers

CAPI Microsoft's crypto API for Windows-based operating systems and applications.

Capstone The U.S. government's long-term project to develop a set of standards for publicly available cryptography. NIST and NSA are the responsible agencies. Capstone specifies Skipjack as the encryption algorithm that is implemented on the Clipper chip. It uses the DSA digital signature algorithm and the SHA hash function.

Cascading Connecting in series

CAST Northern Telcom algorithm developed by Carlisle Adams and Stafford Tavares. A 64-bit block cipher with 8-bit input and 32-bit output.

Causal repetition A repetition produced by encipherment of identical plain-text characters by identical keying elements.

CBC (Cipher Block Chaining) The plain text is XORed with the previous cipher-text block, then encrypted.

CBR Constant bit rate

CCITT Consultative Committee for International Telegraphy and Telephony

CDK (Crypto Developer Kit) A documented environment, including an API for third parties to write secure applications using a specific vendors cryptographic library.

CDMF IBM's 40-bit DES. A mandatory part of the SET protocol.

CDSA (Common Data Security Architecture) Intel Architecture Labs (IAL) use this to address the data security problems inherent to Internet and intranet and for potential use in Intel Internet products.

Cell Fixed-sized packets (the ATM standard is 53 octets, but proprietary lengths, for example, of 16 and 24 octets have been used). Cells are identified and switched by means of a 5-byte header.

Cell relay (cell switching)   Used for high-speed transmission of multiple types of traffic, including voice, data, and video.

CERT (Computer Emergency Response Team)   Security clearinghouse that promotes security awareness. CERT provides 24-hour technical assistance for computer and network security incidents, and is located at the Software Engineering Institute at Carnegie Mellon University in Pittsburgh, PA.

Certificate (digital certificate)   An electronic document attached to a public key by a trusted third party, which provides proof that the public key belongs to a legitimate owner and has not been compromised.

Certificate authority   A trusted third party who issues, revokes, and manages certificates, validating that public keys are not compromised and that they belong to the correct owners.

Certificate Revocation List (CRL)   A list of certificates that have been revoked before their scheduled expiration date.

Certification   The administrative act of approving a computer system, component, product, and the like, for use in a particular application; endorsement of information by a trusted entity.

CFM (Cipher Feedback Mode)   A block cipher that has been implemented as a self-synchronizing stream cipher.

Chain   A series of letters or other textual symbols following one another according to some rule or law.

Chaining   Adds feedback to a cipher block. The results of the encryption of a previous block(s) are fed back into the encryption of the current block.

CHAP (Challenge Authentication Protocol)   Session-based, two-way password authentication scheme.

Checksum   A numeric value used to verify the integrity of a block of data. The value is computed using a checksum procedure. A crypto checksum incorporates secret information in the checksum procedure so that it can't be reproduced by third parties that don't know the secret information.

Chi-square test   A statistical test used for determining the likelihood that two distributions derive from the same source.

Chi-test   A test applied to the distributions of the elements of two cipher texts either to determine whether the distribution results form the encipherment by identical cipher alphabets, or to determine whether there is a relationship between the underlying cipher alphabets.

Cipher (cipher text)   Encrypted plain text.

Cipher alphabet   An ordered arrangement of the letters of a written language and the characters to replace them in a cryptographic process of substitution.

Cipher Block Chaining (CBC)   A block cipher mode that combines the previous block of cipher text with the current block of plain text before encrypting it; very widely used.

Cipher feedback   A block cipher mode that feeds previously encrypted cipher text through the block cipher to generate the key that encrypts the next block of cipher text; also called *CTAK*.

Cipher system (cryptosystem)   The hardware and/or software making up the means to encrypt and decrypt plain text. Encryption and decryption can be implemented in software on the host computer or in hardware devices placed on the links between computers.

Cipher text   Data that have been encrypted with a cipher, as opposed to plain text.

Circuit switching   A method of handling traffic through a switching center, either from local users or from other switching centers, whereby a connection is established between the calling and called parties.

Cleartext   Characters in a human-readable form or bits in a machine-readable form.

Client   A device or application that makes use of the services provided by a server in a client/server architecture.

Clipper   An encryption chip developed and sponsored by the U.S. government that contains the Skipjack encryption algorithm.

CMIP (Common Management Information Protocol)   The OSI Layer 7 protocol for network management covering manager-to-agent and manager-to-manager communication.

Code   A system of instructions making up software. A system of symbols making up cipher text.

Code group   A group of symbols assigned to represent a plain-text element.

Coincidence   A recurrence of textual elements occurring within a message or between messages.

Coincidence test   The Kappa test, applied to two cipher-text messages to determine whether or not they both involve cipherment by the same sequence or cipher alphabets.

Compatibility   Capable of working together harmoniously.

COMSEC (Communications Security)   Protection of all measures designed to deny to unauthorized persons information of value that might be derived from a study of communications.

Confidentiality   Assurance that data is not read or accessed by unauthorized persons.

Connection integrity   Assurance that the connection is not modified by unauthorized entities.

Connection mode   A logical connection is set up between end systems prior to the data exchange. After data transfer the connection is terminated.

Connectionless integrity   Detecting modification to an individual IP datagram regardless of the sequence or order of the datagram in a stream of traffic.

Connectionless mode   Each data unit (packet) is independently routed to the destination; no connection establishment activities are required.

Control vector   A string of bits of arbitrary length attached to a key, which specifies the uses and restrictions for that key in the IBM Secret Key Management Protocol.

Cookie (Persistent Client State HTTP Cookie)   A file or token of sorts, that is passed from the Web server to the Web client (your browser) that is used to identify you and could record personal information such as ID and password, mailing address, credit card number, and so forth.

COS   Corporation for Open Systems

CPC   Cryptography Products Consortium

CRAB   A 1024-byte block cipher similar to MD5, using techniques from a one-way hash function, developed by Burt Kaliski and Matt Robshaw at RSA Laboratories.

Cracking   The process of overcoming a security measure. Cracking a key means an attempt to recover the key's value; cracking some cipher text means an attempt to recover the corresponding plain text.

Credentials   Something that provides a basis for credit or confidence.

Critical application   A computing application in which an attacker could cause incredibly serious damage, including loss of life.

CRL (Certificate Revocation List)   A list of certificates that have been revoked before their scheduled expiration date.

Cross-certification   Two or more organizations or Certificate Authorities that share some level of trust.

Crypt, crypto   Means secret; pertaining to secret.

Cryptanalysis   The art or science of transferring cipher text into plain text without initial knowledge of the key used to encrypt the plain text.

Cryptogram   An encrypted message, file, etc.; a simple word/character substitution cipher.

Cryptography   The branch of cryptographic science that deals with the means, methods, and apparatus of converting plain-text messages into secret messages and vice versa.

CRYPTOKI   Also known as PKCS #11.

Cryptolinguistics   Study of characteristics of languages that have some application in cryptology, that is, frequency data, letter combinations, universal patterns, and so forth.

Cryptologic   Pertaining to cryptology.

Cryptology   Cryptography and cryptanalysis.

Cryptoperiod   The amount of time a particular key has been used; sometimes refers to the amount of data encrypted with it.

Cryptosystem (cipher system)   The hardware and software making up the means to encrypt and decrypt plain text. Encryption and decryption can be implemented in software on computers or in hardware devices placed on the links between computers.

Cyclic phenomena   Periodic cipher-text repetitions in a cryptogram enciphered with a repeating key.

Data   Digital information or just information depending on the context.

Datagram   Packets individually routed through a network and reassembled at the receiving end.

Data Integrity   Ensuring information has not been altered by unauthorized or unknown means.

Data key   A crypto key that encrypts data as opposed to a key that encrypts other keys.

Data link The portion of a system of computers that transfers data between them, including wiring, hardware, interfaces, and device driver software.

DBS Direct broadcast satellite

Deactivation The process of removing a domain name from the zone files for the top-level domains. When a domain name is deactivated, the Domain Name System (DNS) no longer has the information needed to match the domain name with its corresponding Internet Protocol (IP) address(es).

Decimation The process of selecting members of a series by counting off at an arbitrary interval; the original series being treated as cyclic.

Decode That section of a codebook in which the code groups are in alphabetical order or other systematic order. To convert by codebook, not cryptanalysis.

Decrypt To convert cipher text into the original plain text using a cryptosystem. Decryption (and encryption) can be implemented in software on computers or in hardware devices placed on the links between computers.

Deletion The process of removing a domain name and its corresponding record from the Domain Name System (DNS). A deleted domain name cannot be used to locate computers on the Internet and is available for other parties.

DER Distinguished Encoding Rules

DES (Data Encryption Standard) U.S. data encryption standard adopted in 1976 as FIPS 46.

Device driver A software component that controls a peripheral device. For data link devices, it manages the process of sending and receiving data across the data link.

DHCP (dynamic host configuration protocol) ISPs use the DHCP to assign mobile clients an IP address that is good only for the duration of a dial-in phone call.

Dictionary attack A calculated, brute-force attack to reveal a password by trying obvious combinations.

Diffie-Hellman The first public-key algorithm, using discrete logarithms in a finite field, invented in 1976.

Digital Cash Electronic money that is stored and transferred through a variety of complex protocols.

Digital certificate   A signed electronic document (digital ID) that notarizes and binds the connection between a public key and its legitimate owner. Similar to how a driver's license or passport proves the owner's identity. Its purpose is to prevent unauthorized impersonation and provide confidence in public keys.

Digital signature   An electronic identification of a person or thing created by using a public-key algorithm, intended to verify to a recipient the integrity of the data and the identity of the sender of the data.

Direct trust   An establishment of peer-to-peer confidence.

Discrete logarithm   The underlying mathematical problem used in asymmetric algorithms like Diffie-Hellman and Elliptic Curve, the inverse problem of modular exponentiation, which is a one-way function.

DMS (Defense Messaging System)   Standards designed by the U.S. Department of Defense to provide a secure and reliable enterprise-wide messaging infrastructure for government and military agencies.

DN   (1) Domain Name indicates the general domain of the activity or user and could represent many IP addresses, whereas the FQDN corresponds to one IP address; (2) Distinguished Name.

DNS   Domain Name Server, Domain Name Space, Domain Name System

DNSSEC (Domain Name System Security)   An IETF Working Group proposed draft that will specify enhancements to the DNS protocol to protect the DNS against unauthorized modification of data and against masquerading of data origin; adds data integrity and authentication capabilities to the DNS via digital signatures.

Domain   A domain represents a level of the hierarchy in the Domain Name Space and is represented by a domain name. For example, the domain name "icsa.net" represents the second level domain "icsa," which is a subset, or subdomain, of the top-level domain "net," which is in turn a larger subset of the total Domain Name Space.

Domain Name   The textual name assigned to a host on the Internet. The Domain Name Service (DNS) protocol translates between domain names and numerical IP addresses.

Domain Name Server   See *Name Server*.

Domain Name Space   All the domain names that currently represent the networks, computers, and other network devices that can be described and represented by the Domain Name System (DNS).

Domain Name System (DNS) A distributed database of information used to translate domain names into Internet Protocol (IP) addresses.

DSA (Digital Signature Algorithm) A public-key digital signature algorithm proposed by NIST for use in DSS.

DSS (Digital Signature Standard) A NIST-proposed standard (FIPS) for digital standards using DSA.

Due Diligence Such a measure of prudence, activity, or assiduity, as is properly to be expected from, and ordinarily exercised by, a reasonable and prudent person under the particular circumstances; not measured by any absolute standard, but depending on the relative facts of the special case.

EBCDIC Extended Binary Coded Decimal Interchange Code

eCash Electronically transferred money.

EC Electronic commerce; elliptic curve

ECC (Elliptic Curve Cryptography; elliptic curve cryptosystem) Uses the algebraic system defined by the points of an elliptic curve to provide public-key cryptographic algorithms.

ECMA European Computer Manufacturers Association

EDI (Electronic Data Interchange) The direct, standardized computer-to-computer exchange of business documents (purchase orders, invoices, payments, inventory analyses, and others) between your organization and your suppliers and customers.

EEMA European Electronic Messaging Association

EES (Escrowed Encryption Standard) A U.S. government proposed standard for escrowing private keys.

EIA Electronic Industries Association

Electronic Codebook (ECB) A block cipher mode that consists of simply applying the cipher to blocks of data in sequence.

El Gamal Scheme Used for both digital signatures and encryption based on discrete logarithms in a finite field; can be used with the DSA function.

EMA (Electronic Messaging Association) An interindustry forum dedicated to the promotion, development, and use of email, voice mail, fax, EDI, and other messaging technologies for secure global electronic commerce.

email Electronic mail

Encipher To convert a plain text into unintelligible language or signals by means of cipher system.

Encrypt (encode, encipher) To convert plain text into unintelligible forms by means of a cipher system (crypto system). Encryption (and decryption) can be implemented in software on computers or in hardware, the set of mathematical logic that actually converts (encrypts/decrypts) data.

Encryption algorithm Used for both digital signatures and encryption based on discrete logarithms in a finite field; can be used with the DSA function.

End-to-end (hardware) encryption The data is disguised throughout its path, the encoding and decoding devices are synchronized; the data is encrypted at its source and decrypted at its destination; the data link header is in clear text; the source and destination need not be kept secret; not transparent to the hardware, which must detect start/stop instructions and/or be sensitive to data communications procedures.

Entering wedge A weakness in crypto system or other security system that gives an attacker a way to break down some of the system's protections.

Enterprise The collection of systems, computers, networks, and so forth, that society depends upon for information transfer, processing, and management.

Entropy A mathematical measurement of the amount of uncertainty or randomness.

ESP Encapsulating security payload

Ethernet An approach for local area networks using basic copper wire or cable connections. Ethernets have been developed for 10 Mbytes/sec, 100 Mbytes/sec, and higher-speed applications. Ethernets use a protocol called CSMACD which stands for "Carrier Sense, Multiple Access, Collision Detect." "Multiple Access" means that every station is connected to a single copper wire (or a set of wires that are connected together to form a single data path). "Carrier Sense" means that before transmitting data, a station checks the wire to see if any other station is already sending something. If the LAN appears to be idle, then the station can begin to send data. For the "Collision Detect" part, two stations can begin to send data at the same time, and their signals will "collide" nanoseconds later. When such a collision occurs, the two stations stop transmitting, "back off," and try again later after a randomly chosen delay period.

EWOS An open European organization working to provide high-quality contributions to the worldwide efforts to build an effective Global Information Infrastructure, while ensuring proactive support of solutions meeting specific European needs, in areas such as electronic commerce.

Executable contents Data with contents that represent an executable computer program that is capable of modifying persistent data on a host computer.

Export The U.S. government regulates the strength of cryptography products exported outside of the United States and Canada.

FDDI (fiber distributed data interface) An ANSI standard specifying a packet-switched LAN-to-LAN backbone for transporting data at high throughput rates over a variety of multimode fibers. FDDI addresses the bottom two layers of the OSI model.

FEAL A block cipher using a 64-bit block and 64-bit key, designed by A. Shimizu and S. Miyaguchi at NTT Japan.

File A collection of data stored and dealt with as a single, named unit.

File transfer The electrical transfer of a file from one storage or processing unit to another.

FIPS (Federal Information Processing Standards) U.S. government standards published by NIST.

Firewall A device, installed at the point where network connections enter a site, which applies rules to control the type of networking traffic that flows in and out. Most commercial firewalls are built to handle Internet protocols.

Flow ID Traffic Flow identifier used in host-to-host traffic to differentiate traffic flow types.

Forgery A data item with contents that mislead the recipient to believe the item and its contents were produced by someone other than the actual author.

Fortezza Formerly known as Tessera. A PCMCIA card used by the Capstone project (U.S. government).

FPGA Field programmable gate arrays

FQDN (fully qualified domain name) Corresponds or maps to one IP address. A FQDN is registered with one of the international NICs or the InterNIC—a registered, identified user site.

FR (Frame Relay) Packet-mode switching interface for handling high-speed data and interconnecting LANs and WANs in low-error-rate environments. A streamlined version of X.25, uses variable packets (frames) as the transfer format with less overhead and sequence checking. Error checks occur only at the destination point.

Frequency   The number of actual occurrences of a textual element within a given text.

Frequency distribution   A tabulation of the frequency of occurrence of plain or cipher text; a frequency count.

FTP   File transfer protocol

GAK (Government Access to Keys)   A method by which the government escrows an individual's private keys.

Gateway   A major relay station that receives, switches, relays, and transmits ILC traffic. A gateway converts one protocol suite to another when necessary, to allow different computer systems to communicate. A gateway can operate at any OSI layer above OSI Level 3, the Network Layer.

General solution   A solution dependent on exploiting the inherent weaknesses of the cryptographic system arising from its own mechanics, without the presence of any specialized circumstances.

GOSIP (Government OSI Protocol)   U.S. government standards for interoperable data communications based on the ISO's OSI Reference Model.

GOST   An algorithm from the former Soviet Union.

GSS   Generic security services

Hardware encryption   Plain text is encrypted by hardware devices online between the host computers. There are two approaches to hardware encryption: end-to-end and link (see *end-to-end* and *link*).

Hash code   Also known as message digest. A unique snapshot image of data that can be used for later comparison.

Hash function (one-way hash function)   A function that produces a message digest that cannot be reversed to produce the original.

Headers   Formatted information attached to the front of data sent through a computer network contain information used to deliver and process correctly the data being sent.

Henry the Forger   An attacker who generates completely forged network messages to try to fool victims.

Hierarchical Trust   A graded series of entities that distribute trust in an organized fashion, commonly used in X.509 issuing certifying authorities.

High-risk application   A computer application in which the enterprise operating it can suffer a significant loss through a computer incident.

Hijacking   An attack in which the attacker takes over a live connection between two entities so that he can masquerade as one of the entities.

HLD (High Level Designator)   Indicates the entry or exit point of a block in the network.

HMAC   A mechanism for message authentication that combines an iterative cryptographic hash function such as MD5 or SHA-1 with a secret shared key.

Host   A computer system that resides on a network and is capable of independently communicating with other systems on the network.

Host address   The address used by others on the network to communicate with a particular host.

HTH   Host To Host (traffic)

HTML   Hypertext markup language

HTTP (Hypertext Transfer Protocol)   The protocol used by WWW servers and clients to exchange hypertext data.

Hypertext   Associated with information on the World Wide Web. Any text that contains "links" to other documents. Specifically, words or phrases in one document that are user selectable and which cause another document to be retrieved and displayed. These "links" usually appear in a different color than the main text and are underlined.

IATA   International Air Transport Association

IBM SKMP   IBM secure-key management protocol

ICE   Integrated cryptographic engine

ICMP (Internet Control Message Protocol)   An IP protocol used for monitoring and control of an IP network.

ICSA   International Computer Security Association

ICV   Integrity Check Value

IDEA (International Data Encryption Algorithm)   An algorithm designed by Lai and Massey in 1991. Patented internationally, offered by ACSOM, a Swiss company. IDEA uses a 128-bit key and is considered strong.

Identification   Determination of the plain-text value of a cipher element or code group.

Identity Certificate   A signed statement that binds a key to the name of an individual and has the intended meaning of delegating authority from that named individual to the public key.

IEC   International Electrotechnical Commission

IEEE   Institute of Electrical and Electronics Engineers

IGMP   Internet Group Management Protocol

IKE (Internet Key Exchange)   Protocol is planned to establish IPSec-based virtual private networks on the Internet. When used together in the IKE hybrid protocol, a subset of the Oakley key exchange modes are used in the ISAKMP framework to negotiate and provide authenticated keying material for security associations in a protected manner.

ILC   International commercial communications

Index of Coincidence (IC)   The ratio of observed number of coincidences in a given body of text to the number of coincidences expected in a sample of random text of the same size.

Indicator   An element inserted within the text or heading of the message to serve as a guide to the selection of derivation and application of the correct system and key for the prompt decryption of the message.

Information security   Technical security measures that involve communications security, cryptography, and computer security.

In-line encryptor   A product that plies encryption automatically to all data passing along a data link.

Integrity   Knowing or having assurance that data are transmitted from source to destination without undetected alteration, or not modified by unauthorized persons during storage or transmittal.

Internet   The global set of networks interconnected using TCP/IP.

Internet Architecture Board (IAB)   Oversees the development of Internet standards and protocols and acts as a liaison between the Internet Society (ISOC) and other standards bodies.

Internet Assigned Numbers Authority (IANA)   Located at the Information Sciences Institute at the University of Southern California in Marina del Rey, CA, the IANA oversees registration for various Internet Protocol parameters, such as port numbers, protocol and enterprise numbers, options, codes, and types.

Internet Engineering Steering Group (IESG) Operational management arm of the Internet Engineering Task Force (IETF).

Internet Engineering Task Force (IETF) Formed by the Internet Architecture Board, the IETF is an international, voluntary body of network designers, engineers, researchers, vendors, and the like, who work together to resolve technical and operational problems on the Internet and develop Internet standards and protocols. The IETF meets three times a year; however, the bulk of the collaboration and work takes place on the various mailing lists maintained by its participants.

Internet Society (ISOC) An international organization, founded in 1992, dedicated to the expansion, development, and availability of the Internet.

Internetwork switches Switches that connect multiple data networks; classified according to the OSI protocol level at which they operate. Bridges are internetworking devices operating at Level 2, the Data Link level. Routers operate at OSI Level 3, the Network level and gateways operate at any level above Level 3.

InterNIC (Internet Network Information Center) Under a cooperative agreement with the National Science Foundation (NSF), certain companies (called interNICs) administer second-level domain name registration services in the top-level domains, for example, com, net, mil, org. Some also provide information and education services. AT&T provides directory and database services.

Internet Stack Layers Physical (copper wire, fiber optic cable); Network Access (ethernet, ATM); Internet Protocol (IP); Transport (TCP, UDP); and Application (HTTP, NNTP, POP, IMAP).

Interoperability The condition achieved among communications-electronics systems or equipment when information or services can be exchanged directly and satisfactorily between them and their users.

Interval A distance between two points or occurrences, especially between recurrent conditions or states. The number of units between a letter, digraph, code group, and the recurrence of the same letter, digraph, counting either the first or second occurrence of both.

Intranet A private network, usually within an organization, that uses the Internet protocols but is not directly connected to the global Internet.

IP (Internet protocol) Moves packets of data from node to node. Works above Layer 3 (network) of the OSI reference model like an OSI Layer 3 $\frac{1}{2}$.

IP address (numbers)   The standard way to identify a computer connected to the Internet. Each IP address consists of eight octets expressed as four numbers between 0 and 255, separated by periods, for example: 176.31.23.13.

IPARS (International Program Airline Reservation System)   IPARS code is used in airline communications.

IPPCP   Internet Protocol Payload Compression Protocol

IPSec (IP Security Protocol   A way that businesses can open up an encrypted link to a trading partner's network.

IPX   Internet Packet Exchange

IS   Information systems

ISAKMP   The Internet Security Association and Key Management Protocol defines procedures and packet formats to establish, negotiate, modify, and delete Security Associations (SA). ISAKMP defines payloads for exchanging key generation and authentication data. These formats provide a consistent framework for transferring key and authentication data, which is independent of the key generation technique, encryption algorithm, and authentication mechanism. ISAKMP is designed to support many different key-exchange protocols, but does not establish session keys itself.

ISDN (Integrated Services Digital Network)   Supports transmission of voice, data, and image-based communications in an integrated form.

ISEC (Information Security Exploratory Committee)   Formed by the NSTAC.

ISO (International Organization for Standardization)   Created the seven-layer OSI structure for telecommunications.

ISP   Internet service provider

ISSB   Information Systems Security Board proposed by the NSTAC.

IT   Information technology

ITAR   International Traffic in Arms Regulations

JEIDA   Japan Electronic Industry Development Association

Kappa I.C.   In comparing two superimposed sequences of text, the ratio of the observed number of coincidences to that expected for random.

Kerberos   A trusted-third-party authentication protocol developed at MIT.

Key, keyword, key sequence A sequence of symbols used with a cryptographic algorithm, which enables encryption and decryption. The security of the cryptosystem is dependent on the security of the key.

Key distribution center (KDC) A device that provides secret keys to allow pairs of hosts to encrypt traffic directly between themselves.

Key encrypting key (KEK) A crypto key used to encrypt session or data keys, and never used to encrypt the data itself.

Key escrow A mechanism for storing copies of crypto keys so that third parties can recover them if necessary to read information encrypted by others.

Key exchange The process for getting session keys into the hands of the conversants.

Key length The number of bits representing the key size; the longer the key, the stronger it is.

Key management The overall process of generating and distributing cryptographic keys to authorized recipients in a secure manner.

Key Management Proxy A node implementing a key management protocol on behalf of some other node.

Key recovery A mechanism for determining the key used to encrypt some data.

Key splitting A process for dividing portions of a single key between multiple parties, none having the ability to reconstruct the whole key.

Keysize Number of bits in a key.

Khufu An algorithm from Xerox.

Knapsack algorithm The first generalized public-key encryption algorithm, developed by Ralph Merkle and Martin Hellman.

Label set The combination of roles-based label values associated with specific data that is used to describe authorized roles with access to the data.

LAN Local area network

LATA Local access and transport area

Layer Usually referring to one of the OSI basic reference model levels.

Least privilege A feature of a system in which operations are granted the fewest permissions possible in order to perform their tasks.

LEC Local exchange carrier

LFSR   Linear feedback shift register

Lightweight crypto   A set of crypto capabilities that is as strong as possible but still sufficiently weak to qualify for favorable treatment under U.S. export regulations.

Link   The existence of communications facilities between two points.

Link (hardware) encryption   Performed through a series of switches (nodes) before the data reaches its destination; an encryption device is needed at each node; the source and destination are kept secret; the header need not be in clear text; the encryption devices are transparent to the data on the lines and the data does not affect the processors at each end.

Local Area Network (LAN)   A network that consists of a single type of data link and can reside entirely within a physically protected area.

Low risk application   Computer applications that, if penetrated or disrupted, would not cause a serious loss for an enterprise.

LSB   Least Significant Bit

Lucifer   An IBM-developed, private-key encryption system.

MAA (Message Authenticator Algorithm)   An ISO standard that produces a 32-bit hash, designed for IBM mainframes.

MAC (Message Authentication Code)   Key-dependent one-way hash function, requiring the use of the identical key to verify the hash.

Mandatory protection   A security mechanism in a computer that unconditionally blocks particular types of activities. For example, most multiuser systems have a "user mode" that unconditionally blocks users from directly accessing shared peripherals. In networking applications, some vendors use mandatory protection to prevent attacks on Internet servers from penetrating other portions of the host system.

Man-in-the-Middle (MIM)   An attack against a public-key exchange in which the attacker substitutes his/her own public key for the requested public key; also called a *bucket brigade attack*.

Masquerade   An attack in which an entity takes on the identity of a different entity without authorization.

MATIP   Mapping of Airline Traffic over Internet Protocol or Mapping of airline reservation, ticketing, and message traffic over IP.

MD2   Message Digest 2

MD4   Message Digest 4

MD5   Message Digest 5

Medium-risk application   A computer application in which a disruption or other security problems could cause losses to the enterprise, some of which are an acceptable cost of doing business.

Medium-strength crypto   A set of crypto capabilities that may qualify for favorable export treatment by the U.S. government if the vendor is actively developing crypto products that contain key escrow features.

Message   Information sent from one entity to another on the network. A single message may be divided into several packets for delivery to the destination and then reassembled by the receiving host.

Message digest   A number that is derived from a message. Change a single character in the message and the message will have a different message digest.

Message Security Protocol (MSP)   An email crypto protocol developed as part of the Secure Data Network System and used in the Defense Message System.

MIB   Management Information Base

MIC (Message Integrity Code)   Originally defined in PEM for authentication using MD2 or MD5. Micalg (message integrity calculation) is used in secure MIME implementations.

MIME (multipurpose Internet mail extensions)   Lets one transfer nontextual data, for example, graphics.

MLS   Multilevel security

MMB (Modular Multiplication-based Block)   Based on IDEA, Joan Daemen developed this 128-bit key/128-bit block size symmetric algorithm; not used because of its susceptibility to linear cryptanalysis.

Mode   One of several ways to apply a block cipher to a data stream; includes CBC, CFB, and OFB.

Modulus   In public-key crypto, part of the public key.

Monoalphabetically   A characteristic of encrypted text that indicates that it has been produced by means of a single cipher alphabet. The frequency distribution is characterized by troughs and peaks, which are announced.

MOSS (MIME Object Security Service)   Defined in RFC 1848; facilitates encryption and signature services for MIME, including key management based on asymmetric techniques.

MSB Most Significant Bit

MSP (Message Security Protocol) The military equivalent of PEM; an X.400-compatible application-level protocol for securing email, developed by NSA in late 1980.

MTU Message Transfer Unit

Munition Anything that is useful in warfare; crypto systems are munitions according to U.S. law. This is the rationale behind export controls on crypto systems.

Name Server A computer that has both the software and the data (zone files) needed to match domain names to IP addresses

Name Service A service that provides individuals or organizations with domain name-to-P address matching by maintaining and making available the hardware, software, and data needed to perform this function.

Nanoteq An algorithm from South Africa.

NAT (Network Address Translator) Defined in RFC 1631, a router connecting two networks together; one, designated as inside, is addressed with either private or obsolete addresses that need to be converted into legal addresses before packets are forwarded onto the other network (designated as outside).

National Computer Security Center (NCSC) A U.S. government organization that evaluates computing equipment for high-security applications.

National Institute of Standards and Technology (NIST) An agency of the U.S. government that establishes national standards.

National Science Foundation (NSF) An independent U.S. government agency that sponsors, funds, and fosters research and development in science and engineering. The NSF became involved in wide area networking in the mid-1980s and founded NSFNET, which connected academic and research institutions. NSFNET was later connected to the Advanced Research Projects Agency Network (ARPANET), and eventually developed into the network that we now refer to as the Internet. The NSF has gradually transitioned its role and responsibility in the Internet to the private sector; however, it continues to be involved in a number of experimental networking efforts.

National Security Agency (NSA) An agency of the U.S. government responsible for intercepting foreign communications for intelligence reasons and for developing crypto systems to protect U.S. government communications.

NetBEUI   NetBIOS extended user interface protocol introduced by IBM in 1985.

NetBIOS (Network Basic Input/Output)   Network programming interface allowing applications to communicate across a network.

Network   An organization of stations capable of intercommunication; a combination of circuits and terminals serviced by a single switching or processing center.

Network encryption   Crypto services applied to information above the data link level but below the application software level. This allows crypto protections to use existing networking services and existing application software transparently.

Network protocol attack   A software package that provides general-purpose networking services to application software, independent of the particular type of data link being used.

NIC (Network Information Center)   The organizational authority that administers the registration of domain names on the Internet, a.k.a. interNIC in the United States.

NII   National Information Infrastructure

NIST   National Institute for Standards and Technology (Dept. of Commerce)

NLSP   Network layer security protocol

NNTP   Network News Transfer Protocol

Node   A point of concentrated communications; a central point of communications. Switching devices are often called nodes because they form the junctions between routes or trunks in a data network.

Nonce   A random value sent in a communications protocol exchange; often used to detect replay attacks.

Nonrepudiation   A receiver knowing or having assurance that the sender of some data did in fact send the data even though the sender later may desire to deny ever having sent the data.

Normal frequency   The standard frequency of a textual unit or letter, as disclosed by a statistical study of large volume of homogenous text.

NSA   National Security Agency

NSP   Network service provider

NSTAC The President's National Security Telecommunications Advisory Committee

Oakley A protocol by which two authenticated parties can agree on secure and secret keying material. The basic mechanism is the Diffie-Hellman key-exchange algorithm. The OAKLEY protocol supports Perfect Forward Security, compatibility with the ISAKMP protocol for managing security associations, user-defined abstract group structures for use with the Diffie-Hellman algorithm, key updates, and incorporation of keys distributed via out-of-band mechanisms.

OC Open Confirm (MATIP command)

ODN Open Data Network

OEM Original equipment manufacturer

One-time pad A Vernam cipher in which one bit of a new, purely random key is used for every bit of data being used.

One-time password A password that can be used only once; usually produced by special password-generating software or by a hardware token.

One-way hash A hash function for which it is extremely difficult to construct two blocks of data that yield exactly the same hash result. Ideally it should require a brute-force search to find two data blocks that yield the same result.

Open System Interconnection (OSI) A system capable of transparently operating in telecommunications environments of dissimilar computers.

Orange Book The National Computer Security Center book entitled "Department of Defense Trusted Computer Systems Evaluation Criteria" that defines security requirements.

OSI (open systems interconnection (interface)) Usually refers to the International Standard Organization (ISO) seven-layered protocol model for the exchange of information between open systems—a model for the connection of generalized data systems through communications networks. The seven layers are physical, data link, network, transport, session, presentation, and application.

Output feedback A block cipher mode in which the cipher is used to generate the key stream; also called *autokey mode*.

P1024B SITA implementation of the ALC, the IBM airlines-specific protocol. It uses 6-bit padded characters (IPARS) and IA/TA for physical addressing.

P1024C SITA implementation of the UTS, the UNISYS terminal protocol. It uses 7-bit (ASCII) characters and RID/ SID for physical addressing.

Packet A sequence of data and control characters (binary digits) in a specified format that is switched/transferred as a whole.

Packet-Switching The process of routing and transferring data by means of addressed packets so that a channel is occupied only during the transmission of the packet. No physical connection is necessary. The packets are routed throughout the network toward their destination where the entire message is reconstructed. Upon completion of the transmission, the channel is made available for the transmission of other traffic.

PAD (packet assembler/disassembler) A device that assembles character strings into packets that includes routing information and later dissembles the packets.

PAP (Password Authentication Protocol) An authentication protocol that allows PPP peers to authenticate one another; does not prevent unauthorized access but merely identifies the remote end.

Passive attack An attack in which data is observed but not modified. This is the type of attack performed by Peeping Tom.

Password, pass code A sequence of characters or words that a subject submits to a system for purposes of authentication, validation, or verification.

Password sniffing An attack in which someone examines data traffic that includes secret passwords in order to recover the passwords, presumably to use them later in masquerades.

PC Personal computer

PCMCIA card A credit card size memory or PC card that meets the PC Card Standard, developed jointly by the Personal Computer Memory Card International Association (PCMCIA) and the Japan Electronic Industry Development Association (JEIDA).

PCT (Private Communication Technology) Protocol developed by Microsoft and Visa for secure communications on the Internet.

Peeping Tom An attacker whose attacks are based on examining network data traffic, such as password sniffing.

PEM (Privacy Enhanced Mail) A protocol to provide secure Internet mail (RFC 1421-1424), including services for encryption, authentication, message integrity, and key management; PEM uses X.509 certificates.

Pentagraph   A set of five letters.

Perimeter   The physical boundary between the inside and the outside. Security measures rely on being able to trust individuals within a perimeter, at least to some degree.

Periodic   Characterized by cyclic attributes or usage.

PFS (Perfect Forward Secrecy)   Compromise of a single key will permit access only to data protected by that key. For PFS to exist, the key used to protect transmission of data must not be used to derive any additional keys, and if the key used to protect transmission of data is derived from some other keying material, that material must not be used to derive any more keys.

Phi test   A test applied to cipher text to determine whether it is monoalphabetic or not.

Physical Level (OSI Level 1)   Functions to send the bit stream over a transmission medium.

Physical network address   A host address on a data link.

Physical star (logical ring)   A ring in a star configuration with a multistation access unit or media access unit (MAU) at the center of the star. Eliminates the single point failure feature of a ring because when a line breaks the internal circuitry of the MAU can loop the ring back on itself to bypass the break.

PKCS (Public-Key Cryptography Standards)   Set of standards for public-key cryptography developed in cooperation with an informal consortium (Apple, DEC, Lotus, Microsoft, MIT, RSA, and Sun) that includes algorithm-specific and algorithm-independent implementation standards.

Plain text (clear text)   The readable data or message before it is encrypted.

PMTU   Path Message Transfer Unit

Polyalphabetic Substitution   Substitution cipher systems using multiple alphabets for cipher components.

Polygraph   Two or more letters.

POP   Point Of Presence

Port number   A number carried in Internet transport protocols to identify which service or program is supposed to receive an incoming packet. Certain port numbers are permanently assigned to particular protocols by the IANA. For example, email generally uses port 25 and Web services traditionally use port 80.

Post Office Protocol (POP)   An Internet protocol for retrieving email from a server host.

PPP (Point-to-Point Protocol)   A protocol that provides router-to-router and host-to-network connections over synchronous and asynchronous communications links; the preferred standard for TCP/IP connections to the Internet.

Pretty Good Privacy (PGP)   An email crypto protocol that used RSA and IDEA, implemented in a software package widely distributed on the Internet.

PRF   Pseudorandom function

Privacy enhanced mail   An email crypto protocol published by the IETF and provided in some commercial products.

Private key   The privately held "secret" component of an integrated asymmetric key pair.

Probable word   A word assumed or known to be present in the underlying plain text of a cryptogram.

Protocol   The procedures that are used by two or more computer systems so they can communicate with each other.

Proxy   A facility that indirectly provides some service. Proxy crypto applies crypto services to network traffic without individual hosts having to support the services themselves. Firewall proxies provide access to Internet services that are on the other side of the firewall while controlling access to services in either direction.

Pseudorandom number generator (PRNG)   A procedure that generates a sequence of numerical values that appears random. Cryptographic PRNGs strive to generate sequences that are almost impossible to predict. Most PRNGs in commercial software are statistical PRNGs that strive to produce randomly distributed data with a sequence that may in fact be somewhat predictable.

Public key   A key used in public key crypto that belongs to an individual entity and is distributed publicly. Others can use the public key to encrypt data that only the key's owner can decrypt.

Public key algorithm   A cipher that uses a pair of keys, a public key and private key, for encryption and decryption; also called an *asymmetric algorithm*.

RACE   Research and Development in Advanced Communication Technologies in Europe

Random   In mathematics, pertaining to the chance variations from an expected norm.

Random number   A number with a value that cannot be predicted. Truly random numbers are often generated by physical events that are believed to occur randomly.

RARP   Reverse Address Resolution Protocol

RC2   Rivest Cipher 2

RC4   Rivest Cipher 4, once a proprietary algorithm of RSA Data Security, Inc.

RC5   Rivest Cipher 5

Red/black separation   A design concept for crypto systems that keeps the portions of the system that handle plain text rigidly separate from portions that handle cipher text. Portions that handle both are vigorously minimized and then very carefully implemented.

Registry   Delegates IP addresses and domain names and keeps a record of those addresses and the information associated with their delegation. Examples of regional IP registries include Reseaux IP Europeens (RIPE), Asian-Pacific Network Information Center (APNIC), and the American Registry for Internet Numbers (ARIN).

Repeating key   A key used cyclically.

Replay   An attack that attempts to trick the system by retransmitting a legitimate message.

Request For Comments (RFCs)   The official document series of the Internet Engineering Task Force (IETF) that discusses computing, computer communication, networking, Internet protocols, procedures, programs, and concepts.

Reseaux IP Europeens Network Coordination Center (RIPE NCC)   A collaborative group of approximately 400 organizations such as European Internet service providers. The RIPE NCC acts as a regional Internet Registry, providing the allocation of IP addresses to the European region.

Reusable password   A password that can be used over and over, as opposed to a one-time password. Most passwords used today are reusable passwords.

Rewrite   An attack that modifies an encrypted message's contents without decrypting it first.

RFU Reserved for Future Use

RID Remote Identifier: ASCU identifier in P1024C protocol.

Ring A networking configuration in which each workstation is connected to another adjacent workstation in a closed loop. It has the disadvantage of a single point of failure unless implemented as a physical star/logical ring.

RIPE (RACE Integrity Primitives Evaluation) European Community program to support work in communications standards and technologies to support integrated broadband communication.

RIPE-MD An algorithm developed for the European Community's RIPE project, designed to resist known cryptanalytic attacks and produce a 128-bit hash value.

Risk The likelihood that a vulnerability may be exploited or that a threat may become harmful.

Rivest Ron Rivest.

Role The set of transactions a user is authorized to perform.

Root The top of the Domain Name System (DNS) hierarchy. Examples: .com, .net, .mil.

Root server Name servers that contain authoritative data for the very top of the Domain Name System (DNS) hierarchy. Technical specifications currently limit the number of root servers to 13, located in the United States, the U.K., Sweden, and Japan.

Router An internetworking switch operating at the OSI Level 3, the Network layer.

Routing host A host that routes IP packets between networks as well as provides other services.

RPK Raike Public Key

RSA (RSA Data Security, Inc.) Also refers to the principals: Ron Rivest, Adi Shamir, and Len Adleman; or to the algorithm they invented. The RSA algorithm is used in public-key cryptography and is based on the fact that it is easy to multiply two large prime numbers together, but hard to factor them out of the product.

RSADSI RSA Data Security, Inc.

SA Security association

SAD Security association database

SAFE (Security and Freedom through Encryption) A congressional act to ease export controls on encryption products.

SAFER (Secure And Fast Encryption Routine)   A Cylink algorithm. Nonproprietary block cipher 64-bit key encryption algorithm. Not patented, available license free. Developed by Massey, who developed IDEA.

SALT   A random string that is concatenated with passwords before being operated on by a one-way function; helps prevent against successful dictionary attacks.

SC   Session Close (MATIP command)

SCR   System and Communication Reference (IATA document).

SDSI (Simple Distributed Security Infrastructure)   A new PKI proposal from Ronald L. Rivest (MIT), and Butler Lampson (Microsoft). A means of defining groups and issuing group-membership, access-control lists, and security policies. SDSI's design emphasizes like local name spaces rather than a hierarchical global name space.

SEAL (Software-optimized Encryption Algorithm)   A fast stream cipher for 32-bit machines designed by Rogaway and Coppersmith.

Second Level Domain   In the Domain Name System (DNS), the level of the hierarchy immediately underneath the top-level domains. In a domain name, that portion of the domain name that appears immediately to the left of the top-level domain, for example, the icsa in icsa.net.

Secret key   A crypto key that is used in a secret key (symmetric) algorithm. The secrecy of encrypted data depends solely on the secrecy of the secret key.

Secret key algorithm   A crypto algorithm that uses the same key to encrypt data and to decrypt data; also called a *symmetric algorithm*.

Secure   Safe, protected, free from attack or damage.

Secure channel   A means of conveying information from one entity to another such that an adversary does not have the ability to reorder, delete, insert, or read (SSL, IPSEC, whispering in someone's ear).

Security Association   The set of security information relating to a given network connection or set of connections. SAs contain all the information required for execution of various network security services such as the IP layer services of header authentication, payload encapsulation, and transport or application layer services such as self-protection of negotiation traffic.

Security Association Bundle (SA Bundle)   A sequence of SAs through which traffic must be processed to satisfy a security policy that is not achievable with a single SA.

Security services   Authentication, privacy, confidentiality, integrity, nonrepudiation, authorization, administration, audit, and so forth.

Seed, random   A random data value used when generating a random sequence of data values with a PRNG.

SEPP (Secure Electronic Payment Protocol)   Open specification for secure bank card transactions over the Internet. Developed by IBM, Netscape, GTE, Cybercash, and MasterCard.

Sequence   An ordered arrangement of symbols (letter, digits, etc.) having continuity. The members of a component of a cipher alphabet; the symbols in a row, column, or diagonal of the cipher square in order; key letters or key figures in order.

Server   Computer devices or processes that provide service to clients in a client/server architecture.

SESAME (Secure European System for Applications in a Multivendor Environment)   European research and development project that extended Kerberos by adding authorization and access services.

Session   A single communication transaction.

Session key   The secret (symmetric) key used to encrypt each set of data on a transaction basis. A different session key or set of session keys is used for each communication session.

SET (Secure Electronic Transaction)   Provides for secure exchange of credit card numbers over the Internet.

SHA (secure hash algorithm)   Specified secure hash standard, developed by the National Institute for Standards and Technology (NIST).

SHA-1   1994 revision to SHA, which is considered more secure.

Shim   A software component inserted at a well-known interface between two other software components. Shim versions of IPSec are often implemented at the device driver interface, below the host's TCP/IP network protocol stack.

SID (Station Identifier) (station identifier)   Terminal identifier in P1024C protocol.

Simple Key Interchange Protocol (SKIP)   A protocol that establishes session keys to use with IPSec protocol headers. SKIP data is carried in packet headers and travels in every IPSec-protected packet.

Simple Mail Transfer Protocol (SMTP) An Internet protocol for transmitting email between email servers.

SITA Societe International de Telecommunications Aeronautiques

SKIP (simple key-management for Internet protocols) Developed by Sun Microsystems, Inc.

Skipjack The 80-bit key encryption algorithm contained in NSA's Clipper chip. The algorithm is classified; NSA will not release information on how it works.

Smartcard Tamper-resistant hardware devices that store private keys and other sensitive information.

SMDS (Switched Multi-megabit Data Service) A high-speed (1.544 Mbps and 45 Mbps), connectionless, packet-switched service.

S/MIME A standard email protocol developed by RSA Data Security. It enables a secure email environment that authenticates the identity of the sender and receiver, verifies message integrity, and ensures privacy of the message contents and all attachments.

SMTP Simple Mail Transfer Protocol

SNA System Network Architecture (IBM)

Snake oil A derogatory term applied to a product whose developers describe it with misleading, inconsistent, or incorrect technical statements.

SNF Sequence number field

Sniffing An attack that collects information from network messages by making copies of their contents. Password sniffing is the most widely publicized example.

SNMP Simple network management protocol

SO Session Open (MATIP command)

Sockets The package of subroutines that provide access to TCP/IP on most systems.

Software encryption Encryption accomplished by software operations.

Solution (1) The process or result of solving a cryptogram or cryptosystems by cryptanalysis; a.k.a. *Cracking*. (2) The approach to solving a network connection or security problem.

SONET Synchronous optical network

Splitting The process of dividing a crypto key into two separate keys so that an attacker cannot reconstruct the actual crypto key even if one of the split keys is intercepted.

SQL (Structured Query Language) Set of commands used to create, access, query, modify, and otherwise manage relational databases.

SSH (Site Security Handbook) A working group of the IETF has been working since 1994 to produce a pair of documents designed to educate the Internet community on security. The first document is a complete reworking of RFC 1244 targeted at system and network administrators and decision makers.

SSL (Secure Sockets Level) Developed by Netscape to provide security and privacy over the Internet. Supports server and client authentication and maintains the security and integrity of the transmission channel. Operates at the transport layer and mimics the "sockets library," allowing it to be application independent. Encrypts the entire communication channel and does not support digital signatures at the message level.

SSO (Single Sign On) One log-on provides access to all resources of the network, LAN, WAN, and so forth.

SSPI Security support programming interface

SSSO Secure single sign on

SST (Secure Transaction Technology) A secure payment protocol developed by Microsoft and Visa as a companion to the PCT protocol.

Stream cipher A cipher that operates on a continuous data stream instead of processing a block of data at a time.

Strong crypto Crypto facilities that exceed the standards for lightweight or medium-strength crypto and therefore face significant restrictions under U.S. export rules.

STU-III (Secure Telephone Unit) NSA-designed phone for secure voice and low-speed data communications for use by the U.S. Department of Defense and its contractors.

Subkey splits The multiple, separate components used in the generation of CONNECT: conceal symmetric session keys.

Subroutines A set of instructions, appearing within a computer program, for performing a specific task.

Substitution cipher The characters of the plain text are substituted with other characters to form the cipher text.

Superencryption A further encryption of the text of a cryptogram for increased security.

Symmetric algorithm A crypto algorithm that uses the same crypto key for encrypting and decrypting; also called a *secret key algorithm*.

Symmetric key Same key used to encrypt and decrypt data.

Symmetric key encryption Process using one and only one key to perform both the encryption and decryption processes.

Synchronous transmission The entire message is sent with control information surrounding the text portion of the transmission.

T1 A digital communications line that has a capacity of 1.544 Mbps.

T3 A digital communications line having a capacity of 44.736 Mbps.

TA (Terminal Address) Terminal identifier in P1024B protocol.

TCP (Transmission Control Protocol) Verifies correct delivery of data from client to server; uses virtual circuit routing. Occupies Layer 4 (transport) of the OSI reference model. Electronic mail uses TCP as its transmission control.

TCP/IP Transmission control protocol/Internet protocol

TDM Time division multiplexing

TDMA Time division multiple access

TELNET Virtual terminal protocol that enables remote log-ons to computers across a network.

Text Part of the message containing the basic information the originator desires to be communicated.

Timestamping Recording the time of creation or existence of information.

TLS (Transport Layer Security) A software-based security protocol based on minor changes to Netscape's secure sockets layer version 3.0. Provides data source authentication, data integrity, and confidentiality. Submitted to the IETF for change control in 1996.

TLSP (transport layer security protocol) ISO 10736, draft international standard

Token, authentication A hardware device that generates a one-time password to authenticate its owner; also sometimes applied to software programs that generate one-time passwords.

Token, email A data item in the header of an encrypted email message that holds an encrypted copy of the secret key used to encrypt the message; usually encrypted with the recipient's public key so that only the recipient can decrypt it.

Token-passing   A deterministic access method that allows only one station at a time the right to access the network. A special data structure called a *token* passes from station to station in sequence. A station that has data to transmit, grabs the token and changes a bit, making the token into a packet header. When the data are received, the altered token is placed back on the ring as an acknowledgment from the intended recipient that the data were received without error. The transmitting station then generates a new token and passes it to the next station on the network.

Token Ring   Networking using token-passing on a ring configuration.

Top Level Domain (TLD)   In the Domain Name System (DNS), the highest level of the hierarchy after the root. For example, the com in icsa.com.

Traffic, traffic analysis   Branch of cryptology that deals with the external characteristics of signal communications and related materials for the purpose of obtaining information concerning the organization and operation of a communication system.

Traffic flow confidentiality   Concealing the existence of the traffic flowing through a connection.

Transmission Control Protocol (TCP)   The Internet protocol that provides a reliable connection between a server and a client.

Transparency   Allowing an application to perform on a circuit/connection without impacting on the usual operations or the operators of the circuit.

Transport   To carry from one place to another, especially over long distances.

Transposition cipher   The plain text remains the same but the order of the characters is transposed.

Triple DES (3DES)   An encryption configuration in which the DES algorithm is used three times with three different keys.

Trojan horse   A program with secret functions that surreptitiously access information without the operator's knowledge, usually to circumvent security protections.

Trust   A firm belief or confidence in the honesty, integrity, justice, reliability of a person, company, and so forth.

TTL (Time To Live)   Lifetime in seconds or number of transmissions of a packet.

TTP (Trusted Third Party)   A responsible party, which all participants involved agree upon in advance, to provide a service or function, such as certification by binding a public key to an entity, timestamping, or key-escrow.

Tunnel   A secure virtual connection through the Internet.

TYPE A Traffic   Interactive traffic or host to host.

TYPE B Traffic   Messaging traffic in IATA-compliant format with high level of reliability.

UDP   User Datagram Protocol

UTS   Universal Terminal System by Unisys. (See *P1024C*)

Validation   A means to provide timeliness of authorization to use or manipulate information or resources.

VAN   Value added network

Variant, variant system   A substitution system in which some or all of the plain-text letters may be represented by more than one cipher equivalent.

VC (Virtual Circuit)   A network-generated, end-to-end link sending packets in order.

VENONA   A U.S. military project to cryptanalyze Soviet one-time pad cipher text from the 1940s.

Verification   To authenticate, confirm, or to establish accuracy.

Vernam cipher   A cipher developed for encrypting teletype traffic by computing the exclusive-or of the data bits and the key bits.

Vigenere System, Vigenere square   Cipher system attributed to Blaise de Vigenere (1523-1596) having the normal sequence at the top and regular permutations of the normal in successive rows for all 26 alphabets (in English).

Virtual Private Network (VPN)   A private network built atop a public network. Hosts within the private network use encryption to talk to other hosts. The encryption excludes hosts from outside the private network even if they are on the public network.

Virus   A small program that attaches itself to a legitimate program. When the legitimate program runs, the virus copies itself onto other legitimate programs in a form of reproduction.

VLSI Very large scale integration (circuits/chips)

VN Virtual network

WAKE (Word Auto Key Encryption) Produces a stream of 32-bit words, which can be XORed with a plain-text stream to produce cipher text; invented by David Wheeler.

WAN Wide area network

Web of Trust A distributed trust model used by PGP to validate the ownership of a public key, where the level of trust is cumulative based on the individual's knowledge of the "introducers."

Weight A value assigned to units of text or key, used to evaluate results of certain cryptanalytic operations.

Wide area network (WAN) A network that connects host computers and sites across a wide geographical area.

Word pattern The characteristic arrangement of repeated letters in a word, which tends to make it readily identifiable when enciphered monoalphabetically.

Word separator A unit of one or more characters employed to indicate the space between words. It may be enciphered or in plain.

Work factor The amount of work an attacker must perform to overcome security measures.

Worm A computer program that copies itself into other host computers across a network. In 1988, the Internet Worm infected several thousand hosts.

WWW (World Wide Web) An international information network using HTTP and HTML residing on Internet host computers.

X.25 Recommendation of the CCITT (now ITU-T) that outlines procedures for switching data through a packet-switched network.

X.400 ITU-T recommendation known as Message Handling System, one of two standard architectures used for providing email services and interconnecting proprietary email systems. The other is Simple Mail Transfer Protocol (SMTP).

X.500 A specification of the directory services required to support X.400 email.

X.509v3 ITU-T digital certificate. The internationally recognized electronic document used to prove identity and public-key ownership over a communication network. It contains the issuer's name, user's identifying information, and issuer's digital signature.

xDSL Digital subscriber line

Xenocrypts, Xenos Pertaining to language ciphers or cipher systems other than English.

XOR (Exclusive-Or Operation) A mathematical bit operation to represent differences in additive states.

Zone The portion of the total domain name space stored on a particular name server.

Zone File Zone files contain the information needed to match domain names to Internet Protocol (IP) addresses.

Various recognized sources (Menezes, Schneier, Smith, Stallings, Kahn, and the Internet) were used to obtain the definitions given here. ICSA Cryptography Product Consortium members contributed terms and explanations. Charles Breed of Pretty Good Privacy, Inc., now part of Network Associates, Inc., and Randy Nichols of COMSEC Solutions provided substantial input to the process.

ANNOTATED BIBLIOGRAPHY AND RESOURCES

Algorithms

L. M. Adleman, "A subexponential algorithm for the discrete logarithm problem with applications to Cryptography," in *20th Annual Symposium on Foundations of Computer Science,* San Juan, Puerto Rico, October 29-31, 1979, pp. 55-60. Silver Spring, MD: IEEE Computer Society Press, 1979.

L. M. Adleman and K. S. McCurley, "Open problems in number theoretic complexity," in D. S. Johnson, T. Nishizeki, A. Nozaki, and H. S. Wilf, eds., *Discrete Algorithms and Complexity,* proceedings of the Japan-US Joint Seminar, Kyoto, Japan, June 4-6, 1986, pp. 237-262. Orlando, FL: Academic Press, 1987.

L. M. Adleman, C. Pomerance, and R. S. Rumely, "On distinguishing prime numbers from composite numbers," *Annals of Mathematics,* **117,** pp. 173-206, 1983.

M. Annaratone, E. Arnould, T. Gross, H. T. Kung, M. Lam, O. Menzilcioglu, and J. A. Webb, "The Warp computer: architecture, implementation and performance," *IEEE Transactions on Computers,* **C-36**(12) pp. 1523-1538, December 1987.

S. K. Banerjee, "High speed implementation of DES, Computers & Security," **1**(3), pp. 261-267, November 1982.

T. C. Bartee and D. I. Schneider, "Computation with Finite Fields," *Information and Control,* **6,** pp. 79-98, 1963.

K. E. Batcher, "Design of a massively parallel processor," *IEEE Transactions on Computers,* **C-29**(9), pp. 836-840, September 1980.

I. F. Blake, R. Fuji-Hara, R. C. Mullin, and S. A. Vanstone, "Computing logarithms in finite fields of characteristic two," *SIAM Journal on Algebraic and Discrete Methods,* **5**(2), pp. 276-285, June 1984.

I. F. Blake, R. C. Mullin, and S. A. Vanstone, "Computing logarithms in GF(2n)," in G. R. Blakley and D. Chaum, eds., *Lecture Notes in Computer Science Vol. 196: Advances in Cryptology: Proceedings of CRYPTO 84,* a Workshop on the Theory and Application of Cryptographic

Techniques, Santa Barbara, CA, August 19-22, 1984, pp. 73-82. Berlin/New York: Springer-Verlag, 1985.

G. R. Blakley, "A computer algorithm for calculating the product AB modulo M," *IEEE Transactions on Computers,* **C-32**(5), pp. 497-500, May 1983.

R. P Brent, H. T. Kung, and F. T. Luk, "Some linear-time algorithms for systolic arrays," in R. E. A. Mason, ed., *IFIP Congress Series vol. 9: Information Processing 83, Proceedings of the IFIP 9th World Congress,* Paris, France, September 19-23, 1983, pp. 865-876. Amsterdam/New York: North-Holland, 1983.

E. Brickell, D. Denning, S.Kent, D. Maher, and W. Tuchman, *SKIPJACK Review:* Interim Report, The SKIPJACK Algorithm, July 28, 1993.

E. F. Brickell, "A fast modular multiplication algorithm with application to two key cryptography," in D. Chaum, R. L. Rivest, and A. T. Sherman, eds., *Advances in Cryptology: proceedings of CRYPTO '82,* a Workshop on the Theory and Application of Cryptographic Techniques, Santa Barbara, CA, August 23-25, 1982, pp. 51-60. New York: Plenum Press, 1983.

E. F. Brickell, "Solving low density knapsacks," in D. Chaum, ed., *Advances in Cryptology: proceedings of CRYPTO '83,* a Workshop on the Theory and Application of Cryptographic Techniques, Santa Barbara, CA, August 22-24, 1983, pp. 25-37. New York: Plenum Press, 1984.

E. F. Brickell, "Breaking iterated knapsacks," in G. R. Blakley and D. Chaum, eds., *Lecture Notes in Computer Science Vol. 196: Advances in Cryptology: Proceedings of CRYPTO '84,* a Workshop on the Theory and Application of Cryptographic Techniques, Santa Barbara, CA, August 19-22, 1984, pp. 342-358. Berlin/New York: Springer-Verlag, 1985.

E. Brickell, J. Moore, M. Purtill, "Structure in the S-boxes of DES," in *Proceedings of CRYPTO '86,* A. M. Odlyzko, ed., pp. 3-8, 1987.

L. Brown, *A proposed design for an extended DES, Computer Security in the Computer Age,* W. J. Caelli, ed., Elsevier Science Publishers B.V. North Holland, IFIP, pp. 9-22, 1989.

K. W. Campbell, M. J. Wiener, "Proof the DES is Not a Group," in *Proceedings of CRYPTO '92,* 1993.

T. R. Caron and R. D. Silverman, "Parallel implementation of the quadratic scheme," *Journal of Supercomputing,* **1**(3), 1987.

H. Cohen and A. K. Lenstra, "Implementation of a new primality test," *Mathematics of Computation,* **48**(177), pp. 103-121, January 1987.

H. Cohen and H. W. Lenstra, Jr., "Primality testing and Jacobi sums," *Mathematics of Computation,* **42**(165), pp. 297-330, January 1984.

D. Coppersmith, "Another birthday attack," in H. C. Williams, ed., *Lecture Notes in Computer Science Vol. 218: Advances in Cryptology — CRYPTO '85,* proceedings of a Conference on the Theory and Applications of Cryptographic Techniques, Santa Barbara, CA, August 18-22, 1985, pp. 14-17. Berlin/New York: Springer-Verlag, 1986.

D. Coppersmith, "Fast evaluation of logarithms in fields of characteristic two," *IEEE Transactions on Information Theory,* **IT-30**(4), pp. 587-594, July 1984.

D. Coppersmith, A. M. Odlyzko, and R. Schroeppel, "Discrete logarithms in GF(p)," *Algorithmica,* **1**(1), pp. 1-15, 1986.

J. A. Davis, D. B. Holdridge, and G. J. Simmons, "Status report on factoring," in T. Beth, N. Cot, and I. Ingemarsson, eds., *Lecture Notes in Computer Science Vol. 209: Advances in Cryptology: Proceedings of EUROCRYPT 84,* a Workshop on the Theory and Application of Cryptographic Techniques, Paris, France, April 9-11, 1984, pp. 183-215. Berlin/New York: Springer-Verlag, 1985.

J. D. Dixon, "Asymptotically fast factorization of integers," *Mathematics of Computation,* **36**(153), pp. 255-260, January 1981.

T. El Gamal, "A public key cryptosystem and a signature scheme based on discrete logarithms," *IEEE Transactions on Information Theory,* **IT-31**(4), pp. 469-472, July 1985.

T. El Gamal, "On computing logarithms over finite fields," in H. C. Williams, ed., *Lecture Notes in Computer Science Vol. 218: Advances in Cryptology-CRYPTO '85,* proceedings of a Conference on the Theory and Applications of Cryptographic Techniques, Santa Barbara, CA, August 18-22, 1985, pp. 396-402. Berlin/New York: Springer-Verlag, 1986.

U. Feige, A. Fiat, and A. Shamir, "Zero knowledge proofs of identity," in Proceedings of the Nineteenth Annual ACM Symposium on Theory of Computing, New York, NY, May 25-27, 1987, pp. 210-217. New York: ACM, 1987.

G. Garon and R. Outerbridge, "DES watch: an examination of the sufficiency of the Data Encryption Standard for financial institutions in the 1990's." *Cryptologia,* **XV**(3), 177-193, 1991.

J. Gill, "Computational complexity of probabilistic Turing machines," *SIAM Journal on Computing,* **6**(4), pp. 675-695, December 1977.

S. Goldwasser and S. Micali, "Probabilistic encryption," *Journal of Computer and System Sciences,* **28**(2), pp. 270-299, April 1984.

S. Goldwasser, S. Micali, and C. Rackoff, "The knowledge complexity of interactive proof systems," *SIAM Journal on Computing,* **18**(1), pp. 186-208, February 1989.

J. A. Gordon, "Strong primes are easy to find," in T. Beth, N. Cot, and I. Ingemarsson, eds., *Lecture Notes in Computer Science Vol. 209: Advances in Cryptology: Proceedings of EUROCRYPT 84,* a Workshop on the Theory and Application of Cryptographic Techniques, Paris, France, April 9-11, 1984, pp. 216-223. Berlin/New York: Springer-Verlag, 1985.

J. Grollman and A. L. Selman, "Complexity measures for public-key cryptosystems," *SIAM Journal on Computing,* **17**(2), pp. 309-335, April 1988.

J. Hastad, "Solving simultaneous modular equations of low degree," *SIAM Journal on Computing,* **17**(2), pp. 336-341, April 1988.

P. S. Henry, "Fast decryption algorithm for the knapsack cryptographic system," *Bell System Technical Journal,* **60**(5), pp. 767-773, May-June 1981.

E. Horowitz and S. Sahni, *Fundamentals of Computer Algorithms,* Rockville, MD: Computer Science Press, 1978.

D. B. Johnson, S. M. Matyas, A. V. Le, J. D. Wilkins, "Design of the Commercial Data Masking Facility Data Privacy Algorithm," *Proceedings 1st ACM Conference on Computer & Communications Security,* Fairfax, VA, pp. 93-96, November 1993.

R. R. Jueneman, "Analysis of certain aspects of output feedback mode," in D. Chaum, R. L. Rivest, and A. T. Sherman, eds., *Advances in Cryptology—Proceedings of CRYPTO '82,* a Workshop on the Theory and Application of Cryptographic Techniques, Santa Barbara, CA, August 23-25, 1982, pp. 99-127. New York: Plenum Press, 1983.

R. R. Jueneman, "A high speed manipulation detection code," in A. M. Odlyzko, ed., *Lecture Notes in Computer Science Vol. 263: Advances in Cryptology—CRYPTO '86,* proceedings of a Conference on Theory and Applications of Cryptographic Techniques, Santa Barbara, CA, August 11-15, 1986, pp. 327-346. Berlin/New York: Springer-Verlag, 1987.

E. Kranakis, *Primality and Cryptography,* Westchester, New York: John Wiley & Sons, 1986.

J. C. Lagarias and A. M. Odlyzko, "Solving low-density subset sum problems," in 24th Annual Symposium on Foundations of Computer Science, Tucson, AZ, November 7-9, 1983, pp. 1-10. Silver Spring, MD: IEEE Computer Society Press, 1983. Revised version in *Journal of the Association for Computing Machinery,* **32**(1), pp. 229-246, January 1985.

Xuejia Lai, "On the Design and Security of Block Ciphers," *ETH Series in Information Processing,* **1,** 1992. (Article defines the IDEA Cipher.)

Xuejia Lai and James L. Massey, "A Proposal for a New Block Encryption Standard," *Advances in Cryptology — Eurocrypt '90 Proceedings,* pp. 55-70, 1992.

S. Lakshmivarahan, "Algorithms for public key cryptosystems: theory and application," *Advances in Computers,* **22,** pp. 45-108, 1983.

B. LaMacchia and A. Odlyzko, "Computation of Discrete Logarithms in Prime Fields," in *Design, Codes, and Cryptography,* **1,** pp. 47-62, 1991.

D. J. Lehman, "On primality tests," *SIAM Journal on Computing,* **11**(2), pp. 374-375, May 1992.

A. K. Lenstra, H. W. Lenstra, Jr., and L. Lovasz, "Factoring polynomials with rational coefficients," *Mathematische Annalen,* **261,** pp. 515-534, 1982.

H. W. Lenstra, Jr., "Integer programming with a fixed number of variables," *Mathematics of Operations Research,* **8**(4), pp. 538-548, November 1983.

H. W. Lenstra, Jr., "Primality testing," in J. W. de Bakker et al., eds., *Mathematics and Computer Science,* CWI Monographs, *I,* pp. 269-287. Amsterdam/New York: North-Holland, 1986.

H. W. Lenstra, Jr., "Factoring integers with elliptic curves," *Annals of Mathematics,* **126,** pp. 649-673, 1987.

H. R. Lewis and C. H. Papadimitriou, *Elements of the Theory of Computation,* Englewood Cliffs, NJ: Prentice-Hall, 1981.

Michael Luck, "A Constraint Satisfaction Algorithm for the Automated Decryption of Simple Substitution Ciphers," in *CRYPTO '88,* pp. 598-605, 1979.

J. L. Massey, "An introduction to contemporary cryptology," *Proceedings of the IEEE,* **76**(5), pp. 533-549, May 1988.

S. Micali, "Fair Cryptosystems," Report MIT/LCS/TR-579.b, MIT Laboratory for Computer Science, Cambridge, MA, November 1993.

G. L. Miller, "Riemann's hypothesis and tests for primality," *Journal of Computer and System Sciences,* **13**(3), pp. 300–317, December 1976.

M. A. Morrison and J. Brillhart, "A method of factoring and the factorization of F7," *Mathematics of Computation,* **29**(129), pp. 183-205, January 1975.

A. M. Odlyzko, "Discrete logarithms in finite fields and their cryptographic significance," in T. Beth, N. Cot, and I. Ingemarsson, eds., *Lecture Notes in Computer Science Vol. 209: Advances in Cryptology: Proceedings of EUROCRYPT '84,* a Workshop on the Theory and Application of Cryptographic Techniques, Paris, France, April 9-11, 1984, pp. 224-314. Berlin/New York: Springer-Verlag, 1985.

G. A. Orton, M. P. Roy, P. A. Scott, L. E. Peppard, and S. E. Tavares, "VLSI implementation of public-key encryption algorithms," in A. M. Odlyzko, ed., *Lecture Notes in Computer Science Vol. 263: Advances in Cryptology—CRYPTO '86,* proceedings of a Conference on the Theory and Applications of Cryptographic Techniques, Santa Barbara, CA, August 11-15, 1986, pp. 277-301. Berlin/New York: Springer-Verlag, 1987.

R. C. Peralta, "A simple and fast probabilistic algorithm for computing square roots modulo a prime number," *IEEE Transactions on Information Theory,* **32**(6), pp. 846-847, November 1986.

S. C. Pohlig and M. E. Hellman, "An improved algorithm for computing logarithms over GF(p) and its cryptographic significance," *IEEE Transactions on Information Theory,* **IT-24**(1), pp. 106-110, January 1978.

C. Pomerance, "The quadratic sieve factoring algorithm," in T. Beth, N. Cot, and I. Ingemarsson, eds., *Lecture Notes in Computer Science Vol. 209: Advances in Cryptology: Proceedings of EUROCRYPT '84,* a Workshop on the Theory and Application of Cryptographic Techniques, Paris, France, April 9-11, 1984, pp. 169-182. Berlin/New York: Springer-Verlag, 1985.

C. Pomerance, "Fast, rigorous factorization and discrete logarithm algorithms," in D. S. Johnson, T. Nishizeki, A. Nozaki, and H. S. Wilf, eds., *Discrete Algorithms and Complexity,* proceedings of the Japan-US Joint Seminar, Kyoto, Japan, June 4-6, 1986, pp. 119-143. Orlando, FL: Academic Press, 1987.

C. Pomerance, J. W. Smith, and R. Tuler, "A pipeline architecture for factoring large integers with the quadratic sieve algorithm," *SIAM Journal on Computing,* **17**(2), pp. 387-403, April 1988.

M. J. Quinn, *Designing Efficient Algorithms for Parallel Computers,* New York: McGraw-Hill, 1987.

J.-J. Quisquater and C. Couvreur, "Fast decipherment algorithm for RSA public-key cryptosystem," *Electronics Letters,* **18**(21), pp. 905-907, October 14, 1982.

M. O. Rabin, "Probabilistic algorithms," in J. F. Traub, ed., *Algorithms and Complexity: New Directions and Recent Results, proceedings of a Symposium,* Pittsburgh, PA, April 7-9, 1976, pp. 21-39. New York: Academic Press, 1976.

C. Rackoff and M. Luby, "How to construct psuedorandom permutations from psuedorandom functions," *SIAM Journal of Computing,* **17**(2), pp. 373-386, 1988.

Authentication and Digital Signatures

S. G. Akl, "Digital signatures: a tutorial survey," *Computer,* **16**(2), pp. 15-24, February 1983.

L. Brown, J. Pieprzyk, and J. Seberry, "LOKI—a cryptographic primitive for authentication and secrecy applications," in *Proceedings of AUSTCRYPT 90,* pp. 229-236, 1990.

K. S. Booth, "Authentication of signatures using public key encryption," *Communications of the ACM,* **24**(11), pp. 772-774, November 1981.

CCITT, Draft Recommendation X.509: The Directory-Authentication Framework, Gloucester, November 1987.

D. W. Davies and W. L. Price, *The application of digital signatures based on public key cryptosystems,* NPL Report DNACS 39/80, National Physics Laboratory, Teddington, Middlesex, England, December 1980.

W. Diffie, P. van Oorschot, and M. Wiener, "Authentication and Authenticated Key Exchanges," in *Designs, Codes, and Cryptography,* **2**(2), pp. 107-125, 1992.

A. Fiat and A. Shamir, "How to prove yourself: practical solutions to identification and signature problems," in A. M. Odlyzko, ed., *Lecture Notes in Computer Science Vol. 263: Advances in Cryptology—CRYPTO '86,* proceedings of a Conference on the Theory and Applications of Cryptographic Techniques, Santa Barbara, CA, August 11-15, 1986, pp. 186-194. Berlin/New York: Springer-Verlag, 1987.

S. Goldwasser, S. Micali, and R. L. Rivest, "A digital signature scheme secure against adaptive chosen-message attacks," *SIAM Journal on Computing,* **17**(2) pp. 281-308, April 1988.

Shafi Goldwasser, Silvio Micali, "Probabilistic Encryption and How To Play Mental Poker Keeping Secret All Partial Information," *Proceedings of the Fourteenth Annual ACM Symposium on Theory of Computing,* 1982.

B. Kaliski, R. Rivest, and A. Sherman, "Is the Data Encryption Standard a Group?," *Journal of Cryptology,* **1**(1), pp. 1-36, 1988.

J. Kam and G. Davida, "A structured design of substitution-permutation encryption networks," *IEEE Trans,* Information Theory, **28**(10), pp. 747-753, 1978.

J. Kohl and C. Neuman, The Kerberos Authentication Service (V5), RFC1510, September 1993.

D. Kravitz, "Digital Signature Algorithm," U.S. Patent Number 5231668, applied for July 26, 1991, received July 27, 1993.

R. M. Needham and M. D. Schroeder, "Using encryption for authentication in large networks of computers," *Communications of the ACM,* **21**(12), pp. 993-999, December 1978.

Rolf Opplinger, *Authentication Systems For Secure Networks,* Artech House, London, 1996.

M. O. Rabin, "Digitalized signatures," in R. A. DeMillo, D. P. Dobkin, A. K. Jones, and R. J. Lipton, eds., *Foundations of Secure Computation,* pp. 155-168. New York: Academic Press, 1978.

M. O. Rabin, "Digitalized signatures and public-key functions as intractable as factorization," MIT Laboratory for Computer Science, Technical Report LCS/TR-212, January 1979.

Ron Rivest, A. Shamir, and L. Adleman, "A Method for Obtaining Digital Signatures and Public Key Cryptosystems," *Communications of the ACM,* **21,** 1978.

C. Schnorr, "Procedures for the Identification of Participants as well as the Generation and Verification of Electronic Signatures in a Digital Exchange System," German Patent Number 9010348.1, patent applied for February 24, 1989, patent received August 29, 1990.

C. P. Schnorr and H. W. Lenstra, Jr., "A Monte Carlo factoring algorithm with linear storage," *Mathematics of Computation,* **43**(167), pp. 289-311, July 1984.

C. Schnorr, "Method for Identifying Subscribers and for Generating and Verifying Electronic Signatures in a Data Exchange System," U.S. Patent Number 4995082, patent applied for February 23, 1990, patent received February 19, 1991.

A. Shamir, "A polynomial-time algorithm for breaking the basic Merkle-Hellman cryptosystem," *IEEE Transactions on Information Theory,* **IT-30**(5), pp. 699-704, September 1984.

A. Shamir, "On the cryptocomplexity of knapsack systems," in Proceedings of the Eleventh Annual ACM Symposium on Theory of Computing, Atlanta, GA, April 30-May 2, 1979, pp. 118-129. New York: ACM, 1979.

M. Shand, P. Bertin, and J. Vuillemin, "Hardware speedups in long integer multiplication," presented at the Second ACM Symposium on Parallel Algorithms and Architectures, Crete, July 2-6, 1990.

A. Shimizu and S. Miyaguchi, "Fast data encipherment algorithm FEAL," *EUROCRYPT '87,* pp. 267-278, 1988.

G. J. Simmons, "How To Insure that Data Acquired to Verify Treaty Compliance are Trustworthy," in "Authentication without secrecy: A secure communications problem uniquely solvable by asymmetric encryption techniques," *IEEE EASCON 79,* Washington, pp. 661-662, 1979.

S. Von Solms and D. Naccache, "On Blind Signatures and Perfect Crimes," *Computers and Security,* **11**(6) pp. 581-583, October 1992.

R. Solovay and V. Strassen, "A fast Monte-Carlo test for primality," *SIAM Journal on Computing,* **6**(1), pp. 84-85, March 1977. Erratum: **7**(1), p. 118, February 1978.

A. Sorkin, "LUCIFER: a cryptographic algorithm," *Cryptologia,* **8**(1), pp. 22-35, 1984. Warner Amendment systems: (10 U.S.C. 2315 and 44 U.S.C. 3502[2]) applies to digital signatures.

C. C. Wang, T. K. Truong, H. M. Shao, L. J. Deutsch, J. K. Omura, and I. S. Reed, "VLSI architectures for computing multiplications and inverses in GF(2m)," *IEEE Transactions on Computers,* **C-34**(8), pp. 709-717, August 1985.

M. Wiener, "Efficient DES Key Search," presentation at Rump Session of Crypto (August 1993), Santa Barbara, CA. Available as TR-244, School of Computer Science, Carleton University, Ottawa, Canada, May 1994.

M. Wiener, "Efficient DES Key Search—An Update," *RSA Laboratories Cryptobytes,* Autumn 1997.

A. C. Yao, "Theory and applications of trapdoor functions," in *23rd Annual Symposium on Foundations of Computer Science,* Chicago, IL, November 3-5, 1982, IEEE Computer Society Press, pp. 80-91, 1982.

Biometric Encryption

Albert Bodo, "Method for producing a digital signature with aid of a biometric feature," German patent DE 42 43 908 A1, 1994.

J. Daugman, "High confidence visual recognition of persons by a test of statistical independence," *IEEE Trans. on Pattern Analysis and Machine Intelligence,* **15,** pp. 1148-1161, 1993.

J. W. Goodman, *Introduction to Fourier Optics,* McGraw-Hill, 1968.

W. B. Hahn, Jr., and K. A. Bauchert, "Optical correlation algorithm development for the Transfer of Optical Processing to Systems (TOPS) program," *Proc. SPIE,* **1959,** 48-54, 1993.

B. V. K. Vijaya Kumar, "Tutorial survey of composite filter designs for optical correlators," *Applied Optics,* **31,** 4773-4801, 1992.

B. V. K. Vijaya Kumar and L. Hassebrook, "Performance Measures for Correlation Filters", *Applied Optics,* **29,** 2997-3006, 1990.

H. C. Lee and R. E. Gaensslen, eds., *Advances in Fingerprint Technology,* New York: CRC Press, Elsevier, 1991.

Abhijit Mahalanobis, B. V. K. Vijaya Kumar, and David Casasent, "Minimum average correlation energy filters," *Appl. Opt.,* **26,** 3633-3640, 1987.

Danny Roberge, Colin Soutar, and B. V. K. Vijaya Kumar, "Optimal correlation filter for fingerprint verification," *Proc. SPIE,* **3386,** 123-133, 1998.

Ph. Réfrégier, "Optimal trade-off filters for noise robustness, sharpness of the correlation peak, and Horner efficiency," *Opt. Lett.,* **16,** 829-831, 1991.

Bruce Schneier, *Applied Cryptography,* 2d ed., New York: John Wiley & Sons, Inc., 1996.

Colin Soutar, Danny Roberge, Alex Stoianov, Rene Gilroy, and B. V. K. Vijaya Kumar, "Biometric Encryption™ using image processing," *Proc. SPIE,* **3314,** 178-188, 1998.

Colin Soutar, Danny Roberge, Alex Stoianov, Rene Gilroy, and B. V. K. Vijaya Kumar, "Biometric Encryption™ Enrollment and Verification Procedures," *Proc. SPIE,* **3386,** 24-35, 1998.

E. G. Steward, *Fourier Optics: an introduction,* Ellis Horwood Limited, 1983.

D. Stinson, *Cryptography: theory and practice,* Boca Raton, FL: CRC Press, Inc., 1995.

Alex Stoianov, Colin Soutar, and Al Graham, "High-speed fingerprint verification using an optical correlator," *Proc. SPIE,* **3386,** 242-252, 1998.

A. VanderLugt, *Optical Signal Processing,* New York: John Wiley & Sons, Inc., 1992.

Certificate Authorities

M. Moeller, "Digital IDs: offering an expanded view of users: VeriSign's next digital certificates extend electronic IDs to include personal data," *PC Week* **14**(5), p. 2, Feb. 3, 1997.

J. Rapoza, "Sentry CA cross-checks certificates; Review: Xcert uses LDAP directory secured via SSL for flexible authentication between authorities," *PC Week,* **14**(15), p. 46, April 14, 1997.

Classical Cryptography

ACA and You, Handbook For Members of the American Cryptogram Association, ACA publications, 1995.

ACME Complete Seven Figure Code, Acme Code Co., 507 West 33rd St., NYC, NY. No 6015, 1 January 1934.

Alberti, Treatise De Cifris, Meister Papstlichen, Princeton, NJ: Princeton University Press, 1963.

Ibrahim A., al-Kadi, "Origins of Cryptology: The Arab Contributions," *Cryptologia,* **XVI**(2), pp. 97-127, April 1992.

Army Security Agency, *Historical and Cryptologic Summary of Cryptosystems*; ASAG 23; **1,** 1948.

Sir Francis Bacon, *De Augmentis Scientiarum,* tr. by Gilbert Watts (1640) or tr. by Ellis, Spedding, and Heath (1857, 1870).

Barker, W., ed., *History of Codes and Ciphers in the U.S., During the Period between World Wars, part I, 1919-1929*, Laguna Hills, CA: Aegean Park Press, 1979.

Barker, W., ed., *History of Codes and Ciphers in the U.S., During the Period between World Wars, part II, 1930-1939*, Aegean Park Press, 1990.

F. L. Bauer, *Decrypted Secrets: Methods and Maxims of Cryptology*, Berlin: Springer, 1997.

Duc de Broglie, *Le Secret du roi: Correspondance secrete de Louis XV avec ses agents diplomatiques 1752-1774*, 3d ed., Paris: Calmann Levy, 1879.

William G. Bryan, *Practical Cryptanalysis—Periodic Ciphers—Miscellaneous,* vol. 5, American Cryptogram Association, 1967.

Augusto Buonafalce, *Giovan Battista Bellaso E Le Sue Cifre Polialfabetiche,* Milano, 1990.

J. A. Davis and D. B. Holdridge, "Factorization using the quadratic sieve algorithm," in D. Chaum, ed., *Advances in Cryptology: proceedings of CRYPTO 83,* a Workshop on the Theory and Application of Cryptographic Techniques, Santa Barbara, CA, August 22-24, 1983, pp. 103-113. New York: Plenum

C. A. Deavours, *Breakthrough '32: The Polish Solution of the ENIGMA,* Laguna Hills, CA: Aegean Park Press, 1988.

C. A. Deavours, "Analysis of the Herbern Cryptograph using Isomorphs," *CRYPTOLOGIA,* **I**(2), April 1977.

F. Delastelle, *Traité Elementaire de Cryptographie, Mathematiques appliquees,* Paris: Gauthier-Villars, 1902.

F. Delastelle, *Cryptographie nouvelle assurant l'inviolabilité absolue des correspondances chiffrees Maire of Saint-Malo,* Paris: P. Dubreuil, 1893.

F. Delastelle, *Cryptographie universelle,* Paris, 1893.

The Friedman Legacy: A Tribute to William and Elizabeth Friedman, National Security Agency, Central Security Service, Center for Cryptological History, 1995.

William F. Friedman, *Elements of Cryptanalysis,* Laguna Hills, CA: Aegean Park Press, 1976.

William Friedman, *Advanced Military Cryptography,* Laguna Hills, CA: Aegean Park Press, 1976.

William F. Friedman, *Elementary Military Cryptography,* Laguna Hills, CA: Aegean Park Press, 1976.

William F. Friedman, *Solving German Codes in World War I,* Laguna Hills, CA: Aegean Park Press, 1977.

William F. Friedman and Lambros D. Callimahos, *Military Cryptanalytics Part I—Volume 1,* Laguna Hills, CA: Aegean Park Press, 1985.

William F. Friedman and Lambros D. Callimahos, *Military Cryptanalytics Part I—Volume 2,* Laguna Hills, CA: Aegean Park Press, 1985.

William F. Friedman and Lambros D. Callimahos, *Military Cryptanalytics Part III,* Laguna Hills, CA: Aegean Park Press, 1995.

William F. Friedman and Lambros D. Callimahos, *Cryptanalytics Part IV,* Laguna Hills, CA: Aegean Park Press, 1995.

William F. Friedman, *Cryptanalysis—Part I,* Laguna Hills, CA: Aegean Park Press, 1980.

William F. Friedman, *Military Cryptanalysis—Part II,* Laguna Hills, CA: Aegean Park Press, 1980.

William F. Friedman and Lambros D. Callimahos, *Military Cryptanalytics Part II—Volume 1,* Laguna Hills, CA: Aegean Park Press, 1985.

William F. Friedman and Lambros D. Callimahos, *Military Cryptanalytics Part II—Volume 2,* Laguna Hills, CA: Aegean Park Press, 1985.

William F. Friedman, *The Index of Coincidence and Its Applications In Cryptography,* Publication 22, The Riverbank Publications, Laguna Hills, CA: Aegean Park Press, 1979.

Helen Fouche Gaines, *Elementary Cryptanalysis,* Dover, 1956.

James L. Gilbert and John P. Finnegan, eds. *U.S. Army Signals Intelligence in World War II: A Documentary History,* Center of Military History, United States Army, Washington, D.C., 1993.

B. D. Glover, *Secret Ciphers of The 1876 Presidential Election,* Laguna Hills, CA: Aegean Park Press, 1991.

Cyrus H. Gordon, *Forgotten Scripts: Their Ongoing Discovery and Decipherment,* New York: Basic Books, 1982.

L. S. Hill, "Concerning the Linear Transformation Apparatus in Cryptography." *American Mathematical Monthly,* **38**:135-154, 1931.

F. H. Hinsley, *History of British Intelligence in the Second World War,* Cambridge: Cambridge University Press, 1979-1988.

F. H. Hinsley et al., *British Intelligence in The Second World War: Its Influence on Strategy and Operations,* London, HMSO vol. I, 1979, vol, II, 1981, vol, III, 1984 and 1988.

Takahashi Hisashi, "Military Friction, Diplomatic Suasion in China, 1937-1938," *The Journal of International Studies,* Sophia Univ. vol. 19, July 1987.

Col. Parker Hitt, *Manual for the Solution of Military Ciphers,* Laguna Hills, CA: Aegean Park Press, 1976.

Abrahim A. al-Kadi, "Cryptography and Data Security: Cryptographic Properties of Arabic," *Proceedings of the Third Saudi Engineering Conference,* Riyadh, Saudi Arabia: Nov. 24-27, **2:**910-921, 1991.

David Kahn, *The Codebreakers,* New York: Macmillian Publishing Co., 1967, 2d ed., 1997.

David Kahn, *Kahn On Codes — Secrets of the New Cryptology,* New York: Macmillan Co., 1983.

David Kahn, An Enigma Chronology, *Cryptologia,* **XVII**(3), July 1993.

David Kahn, *Seizing The Enigma: The Race to Break the German U-Boat Codes 1939-1943,* New York: Houghton Mifflin, 1991.

Major F. W. Kasiski, *Die Geheimschriften und die Dechiffrir-kunst,* Schriften der Naturforschenden Gesellschaft in Danzig, 1872.

Kerckhoff, "la Cryptographie Militaire," *Journel des Sciences militaires,* 9th series, IX, (January and February 1883, Libraire Militaire de L. Baudoin & Co., Paris. English trans. by Warren T. McCready of the University of Toronto, 1964.

Wladyslaw Kozaczuk, *Enigma: How the German Machine Cipher was Broken and How it Was Read by the Allies in WWII,* University Publications, 1984.

I Gaj, Krzysztof, "Szyfr Enigmy: Metody zlamania," *Warsaw Wydawnictwa Komunikacji i Lacznosci,* 1989.

J. Levine, "U.S. Cryptographic Patents 1861-1981," *Cryptologia,* Terre Haute, 1983.

Louis C. S. Mansfield, *The Solution of Codes and Ciphers,* London: Alexander Maclehose & Co., 1936.

Denis L. Mavenel, *Lettres, Instructions Diplomatiques et Papiers d' Etat du Cardinal Richelieu, Historie Politique,* Paris 1853-1877 Collection.

Mohammad Mrayati, Yahya Meer Alam, and Hassan al-Tayyan, *Ilm at-Ta'miyah wa Istikhraj al-Mu'amma Ind al-Arab,* vol 1, Damascus: The Arab Academy of Damascus, 1987.

Albert Myer, *Manual of Signals,* Washington, D.C.: USGPO, 1879.

Emile V. T. Myszkowski, *Cryptographie indechiffrable basee sur de nou-*

velles combinaisons rationelles, Paris 1902. 69 pp. 8 vol., NN, DLC, Boston Public Library, John Crerar Library, Great Britain War Office Library, Belgium War Library, BN.

Randall K. Nichols, *Classical Cryptography Course, Volume I,* Laguna Hills, CA: Aegean Park Press (C-74), 301 pp, 1995.

Randall K. Nichols, *Classical Cryptography Course, Volume II,* Laguna Hills, CA: Aegean Park Press (C-76), 400 pp., 1996.

NSA: Masked Dispatches: Cryptograms and Cryptology in American History, 1775-1900. Series 1, Pre World War I volume I, National Security Agency, Central Security Service, NSA Center for Cryptological History, 1993.

Maurice Pope, *The Story of Decipherment: From Egyptian Hieroglyphic to Linear B.,* Thames and Hudson Ltd., 1975.

"PT109 Cipher Message (President Kennedy)," SO62, *The Cryptogram,* American Cryptogram Association, 1962.

Friedman, William F., *The Riverbank Publications, volumes 1*-3, Laguna Hills, CA: Aegean Park Press, 1979.

Marian Rejewski, "Mathematical Solution of the Enigma Cipher," *Cryptologia,* **6**(1), pp. 1-37, January 1982.

Jurgen Rohwer, "Comparative Analysis of Allied and Axis Radio-Intelligence in the Battle of the Atlantic," *Proceedings of the 13th Military History Symposium,* USAF Academy, pp. 77-109, 1988.

Generale Luigi Sacco, *Manuale di Crittografia,* 3d ed., Rome, 1947.

David Shulman, *An annotated Bibliography of Cryptography,* New York: Garland Publishing, 1976.

International Code Of Signals For Visual, Sound, and Radio Communications, Defense Mapping Agency, Hydrographic/Topographic Center, United States ed., 1981 (revised).

David E. Smith, "John Wallis as Cryptographer," *Bulletin of American Mathematical Society,* **XXIV,** 1917.

Clarence E. Tyner, Jr. and Randall K. Nichols, "ENIGMA95—A Simulation of Enhanced Enigma Cipher Machine on A Standard Personal Computer," *ACA Computer Supplement,* November 1995.

"Viet-Nam: Essential Matters—History of the Cryptographic Branch of the Peoples Army of Viet-Nam, 1945-1975," *U.S. Cryptological History Series,* series V, NSA CSS, CH-E32-94-02, 1994.

Ralph Edward Weber, *United States Diplomatic Codes and Ciphers,* 1775-1938, Chicago: Precedent Publishing, 1979.

Herbert O. Yardley, *The American Black Chamber,* New York: Bobbs-Merrill, 1931.

Cryptanalysis

L. M. Adleman, "On breaking the iterated Merkle-Hellman public-key cryptosystems," in D. Chaum, R. L. Rivest, and A. T. Sherman, eds., *Advances in Cryptology: proceedings of CRYPTO 82, a Workshop on the Theory and Application of Cryptographic Techniques,* Santa Barbara, CA, August 23-25, 1982, pp. 303-308, New York: Plenum Press, 1983.

D. Andelman and J. Reeds, "On the cryptanalysis of rotor and substitution-permutation networks." *IEEE Transactions on Information Theory,* **28**(4), pp. 578-584, 1982.

D. A. August, "Cryptography and Exploitation of Chinese Manual Cryptosystems—Part I: The Encoding Problem," *Cryptologia,* **XIII**(4), October 1989.

D. A. August, "Cryptography and Exploitation of Chinese Manual Cryptosystems—Part II: The Encrypting Problem," *Cryptologia,* **XIV**(1), August 1990.

Wayne G. Barker, *Cryptanalysis of the Hagelin Cryptograph,* Laguna Hills, CA: Aegean Park Press, 1977.

John Bennett, "Analysis of the Encryption Algorithm Used in the WordPerfect Word Processing Program," *Cryptologia,* **11**(4), pp. 206-210, 1987.

H. A. Bergen and W. J. Caelli, "File Security in WordPerfect 5.0," *Cryptologia,* **15**(1), pp. 57-66, January 1991.

"Bifid and Trifid Cryptography," MJ59, *The Cryptogram,* American Cryptogram Association, 1959.

E. Biham and A. Shamir, "Differential cryptanalysis of DES-like cryptosystems," *Journal of Cryptology,* **4**(1), pp. 3-72, 1991.

E. Biham and A. Shamir, *Differential Cryptanalysis of the Data Encryption Standard,* Springer-Verlag, 1993.

E. Biham and A. Shamir, "Differential cryptanalysis of Snefru, Khafre, REDOC-II, LOKI and LUCIFER," in *Proceedings of CRYPTO '91,* ed. by J. Feigenbaum, pp. 156-171, 1992.

E. F. Brickell and A. M. Odlyzko, "Cryptanalysis: a survey of recent results," *Proceedings of the IEEE,* **76**(5), pp. 578-593, 1988.

William Maxwell Bowers, *The Bifid Cipher,* Practical Cryptanalysis, II, ACA, 1960.

William Maxwell Bowers, *The Trifid Cipher,* Practical Cryptanalysis, III, ACA, 1961.

William Maxwell, Bowers, *The Digraphic Substitution,* Practical Cryptanalysis, I, ACA, 1960.

William Maxwell Bowers, *Cryptographic ABC's: Substitution and Transposition Ciphers,* Practical Cryptanalysis, IV, ACA, 1967.

Rosario Candela, *Isomorphism and its Application in Cryptanalytics,* New York: Cardanus Press, 1946.

John Carrol and Lynda Robbins, "Automated Cryptanalysis of Polyalphabetic Ciphers," *Cryptologia,* **11**(4), pp. 193-205, 1987.

D. Chaum, ed., *Lecture Notes in Computer Science Vol. 196: Advances in Cryptology: Proceedings of CRYPTO 84,* a Workshop on the Theory and Application of Cryptographic Techniques, Santa Barbara, CA, August 19-22, 1984, pp. 269-275. Berlin/New York: Springer-Verlag, 1985.

Course in Cryptanalysis, OP-20-G, Navy Department, Office of Chief of Naval Operations, Washington, 1941.

Helen Fouche Gaines, *Cryptanalysis,* New York: Dover, 1956.

E. Kranakis, *Primality and Cryptography,* Westchester, NY: John Wiley & Sons, 1986.

Solomon Kullback, *Statistical Methods in Cryptanalysis,* Laguna Hills, CA: Aegean Park Press, 1976.

Solomon Kullback, *Information Theory and Statistics,* New York: Dover, 1968.

I. J. Kumar, *Cryptology: System Identification and Key-Clustering,* Laguna Hills, CA: Aegean Park Press, 1997.

J. C. Lagarias, "Performance analysis of Shamir's attack on the basic Merkle-Hellman knapsack system," in J. Paredaens, ed., *Lecture Notes in Computer Science Vol. 172: Automata, Languages and Programming: 11th Colloquium,* Antwerp, Belgium, July 16-20, 1984, pp. 312-323. Berlin/New York: Springer-Verlag, 1984.

Frank W. Lewis, *Solving Cipher Problems—Cryptanalysis, Probabilities and Diagnostics,* Laguna Hills, CA: Aegean Park Press, 1992.

M. Matsui, "Linear Cryptanalysis of DES Cipher," in *Proceedings Eurocrypt '93,* 1993.

C. Meyer, "Ciphertext/plaintext and ciphertext/key dependence vs. number of rounds for the Data Encryption Standard," *AFIPS Conference Proceedings,* **47,** pp. 1119-1126, 1978.

A. M. Odlyzko, "Cryptanalytic attacks on the multiplicative knapsack cryptosystem and on Shamir's fast signature scheme," *IEEE Transactions on Information Theory,* **IT-30**(4), July pp. 594-601, 1984.

J. Reeds, "Cracking a Random Number Generator," *Cryptologia,* **1**(1), pp. 20-26, 1977.

R. Rueppel, *Design and Analysis of Stream Ciphers,* Springer-Verlag, 1986.

Abraham Sinkov, *Elementary Cryptanalysis,* The Mathematical Association of America, New York University, 1966.

Elliptic Curve Cryptography

L. Adleman, J. DeMarrais, and M. Huang, "A subexponential algorithm for discrete logarithms over the rational subgroup of the jacobians of large genus hyperelliptic curves over finite fields," in *Algorithmic Number Theory,* Lecture Notes in Computer Science, vol. 877, Springer-Verlag, pp. 28-40, 1994.

G. Agnew, R. Mullin, and S. Vanstone, "An implementation of elliptic curve cryptosystems over F_2^{155}," *IEEE Journal on Selected Areas in Communications,* **11,** pp. 804-813, 1993.

D. Atkins, M. Graff, A. K. Lenstra, and P. C. Leyland, "The magic words are SQUEAMISH OSSIFRAGE," *Advances in Cryptology—ASIACRYPT '94,* Lecture Notes in Computer Science, vol. 917, Springer-Verlag, pp. 263-277, 1995.

M. Blaze, W. Diffie, R. Rivest, B. Schneier, T. Shimomura, E. Thompson, and M. Wiener, *Minimal Key Lengths for Symmetric Ciphers to Provide Adequate Commercial Security,* January 1996.

D. Boneh and R. Lipton, "Algorithms for black-box fields and their applications to cryptography," *Advances in Cryptology—CRYPTO '96,* Lecture Notes in Computer Science, vol. 1109, Springer-Verlag, pp. 283-297, 1996.

J. P. Buhler, H. W. Lenstra Jr., and C. Pomerance, "Factoring integers with the number field sieve," in *The Development of the Number Field Sieve,* Lecture Notes in Mathematics, vol. 1554, Springer-Verlag, pp. 11-42, 1993.

J. Crowie, B. Dodson, R. Elkenbracht-Huizing, A. Lenstra, P. Montgomery, and J. Zayer, "A worldwide number field sieve factoring record: on to 512 bits," *Advances in Cryptology — ASIACRYPT '96,* Lecture Notes in Computer Science, vol. 1163, Springer-Verlag, pp. 382-394, 1996.

W. Diffie and M. Hellman, "New directions in cryptography," *IEEE Transactions on Information Theory,* vol. 22, pp. 644-654, 1976.

T. El Gamal, "A public-key cryptosystem and a signature scheme based on discrete logarithms," *IEEE Transactions on Information Theory,* **31,** pp. 469-472, 1985.

FIPS 186, Digital signature standard, National Institute for Standards and Technology, 1993. (Available from *http://csrc.ncsl.nist.gov/fips/*)

R. Flassenberg and S. Paulus, *Sieving in function fields,* preprint, 1997.

G. Frey and H. Rück, "A remark concerning m-divisibility and the discrete logarithm in the divisor class group of curves," *Mathematics of Computation,* **62,** pp. 865-874, 1994.

Course in Cryptanalysis, OP-20-G, Navy Department, Office of Chief of Naval Operations, Washington, 1941, pp. 124-138, 1993.

N. Koblitz, "Elliptic curve cryptosystems," *Mathematics of Computation,* **48,** pp. 203-209, 1987.

N. Koblitz, *A Course in Number Theory and Cryptography,* 2d edition, Springer-Verlag, 1994.

N. Koblitz, "CM-curves with good cryptographic properties," *Advances in Cryptology — CRYPTO '91,* Lecture Notes in Computer Science, vol. 576, Springler-Verlag, pp. 279-287, 1992.

B. A. LaMacchia and A. M. Odlyzko, "Computation of discrete logarithms in prime fields," *Designs, Codes and Cryptography,* **1,** pp. 47-62, 1991.

A. K. Lenstra, H. W. Lenstra Jr., M. S. Manasse, and J. M. Pollard, "The number field sieve," in *The Development of the Number Field Sieve,* Lecture Notes in Mathematics, vol. 1554, Springer-Verlag, pp. 11-42, 1993.

H. W. Lenstra, "Factoring integers with elliptic curves," *Annals of Mathematics,* **126,** pp. 649-673, 1987.

A. Menezes, T. Okamoto, and S. Vanstone, "Reducing elliptic curve logarithms to logarithms in a finite field," *IEEE Transactions on Information Theory,* **39,** pp. 1639-1646, 1993.

A. Menezes, *Elliptic Curve Public Key Cryptosystems,* Kluwer Academic Publishers, 1993.

A. Menezes, P. van Oorschot, and S. Vanstone, *Handbook of Applied Cryptography,* CRC Press, 1997. [Menezes and Vanstone are world-class experts in ECC.]

V. Miller, "Uses of elliptic curves in cryptography," *Advances in Cryptology CRYPTO '85,* Lecture Notes in Computer Science, vol. 218, Springer-Verlag, pp. 417-426, 1986.

A. Miyaji, "On ordinary elliptic curve cryptosystems," *Advances in Cryptology—ASIACRYPT '91,* Lecture Notes in Computer Science, vol. 218, Springer-Verlag, pp. 460-469, 1993.

M. A. Morrison and J. Brillhart, "A method of factoring and the factorization of F_7," *Mathematics of Computation,* **29,** pp. 183-205, 1975.

K. Nyberg and R. Rueppel, "Message recovery for signature schemes based on the discrete logarithm problem," *Designs, Codes, and Cryptography,* **7,** pp. 61-81, 1996.

A. Odlyzko, "The future of integer factorization," *CryptoBytes* [the technical newsletter of RSA Laboratories] **1**(2), pages 5-12, Summer 1995. (Also available from *http://www.rsa.com/*)

P. van Oorschot and M. Wiener, "Parallel collision search with cryptanalytic applications," to appear in *Journal of Cryptology.* An earlier version appeared in the Proceedings of the 2nd ACM Conference on Computer and Communications Security, Fairfax, VA, November 2-4, pp. 210-218, 1994.

S. Pohlig and M. Hellman, "An improved algorithm for computing logarithms over $GF(p)$ and its cryptographic significance," *IEEE Transactions on Information Theory,* **24,** pp. 106-110, 1978.

J. Pollard, "Monte Carlo methods for index computation mod p," *Mathematics of Computation,* **32,** pp. 918-924, 1978.

C. Pomerance, "The quadratic sieve factoring algorithm," *Advances in Cryptology EUROCRYPT '84,* Lecture Notes in Computer Science, vol. 209, Springer-Verlag, pp. 169-182, 1985.

M. O. Rabin, "Digitalized signatures and public-key functions as intractable as factorization," MIT/LCS/TR-212, MIT Laboratory for Computer Science, 1979.

R. L. Rivest, A. Shamir, and L. M. Adleman, "A method for obtaining digital signatures and public-key cryptosystems," *Communications of the ACM,* **21,** pp. 120-126, 1978.

C. P. Schnorr, "Efficient signature generation by smart cards," *Journal of Cryptology,* **4,** pp. 161-174, 1991.

O. Schirokauer, "Discrete logarithms and local units," *Philosophical Transactions of the Royal Society of London A,* **345,** pp. 409-423, 1993.

V. Shoup, "Lower bounds for discrete logarithms and related problems," *Advances in Cryptology—EUROCRYPT '97,* Lecture Notes in Computer Science, vol. 1233, Springer-Verlag, pp. 256-266, 1997.

J. Solinas, "An improved algorithm for arithmetic on a family of elliptic curves," *Advances in Cryptology—CRYPTO '97,* Lecture Notes in Computer Science, vol. 1294, Springer-Verlag, pp. 357-371, 1997.

H. C. Williams, "A modification of the RSA public-key encryption procedure," *IEEE Transactions on Information Theory,* **26,** pp. 726-729, 1980.

R. Zuccherato, *New Applications of Elliptic Curves and Function Fields in Cryptography,* Ph.D. thesis, University of Waterloo, Canada, 1997.

Email

S. Crocker, *Internet Privacy Enhanced Mail,* The Third CPSR Cryptography and Privacy Conference Source Book, June, 1993.

D. W. Davies, "Applying the RSA digital signature to electronic mail," *Computer,* **16**(2), pp. 55-62, February 1983.

Simson Garfinkel, *PGP: Pretty Good Privacy,* Sebastopol, CA: O'Reilly and Associates, Inc., 1995.

S. Kent, *Internet Privacy Enhanced Mail,* Communications of the ACM, **36**(8), pp. 48-59, August 1993.

J. Linn and S. T. Kent, "Privacy for DARPA-Internet mail," in *Proceedings of the 12th National Computer Security Conference,* Baltimore, MD, October 10-13, pp. 215-229, 1989.

J. Linn, Privacy Enhancement for Internet Electronic Mail: Part I: Message Encryption and Authentication Procedures, RFC1421, Feb 1993.

E. Rescorla and A. Schiffman, INTERNET-DRAFT, *The Secure Hyper-Text Transfer Protocol,* Enterprise Integration Technologies, December 1994

Bruce Schneier, *e-mail Security,* New York: John Wiley and Sons, 1995.

William Stallings, *Protect Your Privacy: A Guide for PGP Users,* Upper Saddle River, NJ: Prentice Hall PTR, 1995.

Financial

American Bankers Association, Management and Use of Personal Identification Numbers, ABA Bank Card Statement, ABA, Catalog No. 207213, 1979.

American National Standard X9.17-1985, Financial Institution Key Management (Wholesale), American Bankers Association, Washington, DC, 1985.

American National Standard for Financial Institution Key Management (Wholesale), ANSI X9.17, Washington Publishing Company, P.O. Box 203, Chardon, OH 44024-0203.

D. W. Davies and W. L. Price, *Security for Computer Networks: An Introduction to Data Security in Teleprocessing and Electronic Funds Transfer,* 2d ed., New York: Wiley, 1989.

U.S. Department of Treasury, Criteria and Procedures for Testing, Evaluating, and Certifying Message Authentication Devices for Electronic Funds Transfer Use, May, 1, 1985, Washington, D.C., 1985.

General

Edward Amoroso, *Fundamentals of Computer Security Technology,* Upper Saddle River, NJ: Prentice Hall PTR, 1994.

Paul W. Blackstock and Frank L Schaf, Jr., *Intelligence, Espionage, Counterespionage and Covert Operations,* Detroit, MI: Gale Research Co., 1978.

D. Bolinger and D. Sears, *Aspects of Language,* 3d ed., New York: Harcourt Brace Jovanovich, Inc., 1981.

J. Bologna, *Handbook of Corporate Fraud: Prevention, Detection, Investigation,* Boston: Butterworth-Heinemann, 1993.

Bruce Bosworth, *Codes, Ciphers and Computers: An Introduction to Information Security,* Rochelle Park, NJ: Hayden Books, 1990.

Russell J. Bowen, *Scholar's Guide to Intelligence Literature: Bibliography of the Russell J. Bowen Collection,* National Intelligence Study Center, Frederick, MD, 1983.

R. Burling, *Man's Many Voices: Language in Its Cultural Context,* New York: Holt, Rinehart & Winston, 1970.

Computer Security Act of 1987, Public Law 100-235 (H.R. 145), 101 Stat., 1724-1730.

FM 34-60, *Counterintelligence,* Department of the Army, February 1990.

Cipher A. Deavours and Louis Kruh, *Machine Cryptography and Modern Cryptanalysis,* New York: Artech, 1985.

Defending Secrets, Sharing Data: New Locks and Keys for Electronic Information, Office of Technology Assessment, 1988.

Dorothy E. R. Denning, *Cryptography and Data Security,* Reading: Addison Wesley, 1983.

S. Garfinkel and G. Spafford, *Practical UNIX Security,* Sebastopol, CA: O'Reilly & Assoc., 1991.

M. Gasser, *Building a Secure Computer System,* New York: Van Nostrand Reinhold, 1988.

Andrew Hodges, *Alan Turing: The Enigma,* New York: Simon and Schuster, 1983.

W. J. Holmes, *Double-Edged Secrets: U.S. Naval Intelligence Operations in the Pacific During WWII,* Annapolis, MD: Naval Institute Press, 1979.

House Report 100-153, 1987, Part 2, the Committee on Government Operations' Report on the Computer Security Act of 1987, Washington, DC.

A. E. Hutt, S. Bosworth, and D. B. Hoyt, eds., *Computer Security Handbook,* 3d ed., New York: John Wiley & Sons, 1995.

Harry Katzen, Jr., *Computer Data Security,* New York: Van Nostrand Reinhold, 1973.

Neal Koblitz, *A Course in Number Theory and Cryptography,* 2d ed., New York: Springer-Verlag, 1994.

Alan G. Konheim, *Cryptography — A Primer,* New York: John Wiley, 1981.

C. P. Pfleeger, *Security in Computing,* Englewood Cliffs, NJ: Prentice-Hall, 1989.

Public Cryptography Study Group, 1981, Report of the Public Cryptography Study Group, American Council on Education, February 1981.

L. J. Rose, *NetLaw: Your Rights in the Online World,* New York: Osborne/McGraw-Hill, 1994.

K. S. Rosenblatt, *High-Technology Crime: Investigating Cases Involving Computers,* San Jose, CA: KSK Publications, 1995.

D. Russell and G. T. Gangemi Sr., *Computer Security Basics,* Sebastopol, CA: O'Reilly & Assoc., 1991.

W. Schwartau, *Information Warfare,* 2d ed., New York: Thunder's Mouth Press, 1997.

C. E. Shannon, "The Communication Theory of Secrecy Systems," *Bell System Technical Journal,* **28,** October 1949.

D. J. Stang et al., *Network Security Secrets,* San Mateo, CA: IDG Books Worldwide Inc., 1993.

D. R. Stinson, *Cryptography, Theory and Practice,* London: CRC Press, 1995.

A. S. Tanenbaum, *Computer Networks,* Englewood Cliffs, NJ: Prentice-Hall, 1981.

Don J. Torrieri, *Principles of Military Communication Systems,* New York: Artech, 1981.

John Vacca, *Internet Security Secrets,* New York: IDG Books, 1996.

Peter Wayner, *Disappearing Cryptography,* New York: Academic Press, 1996.

Dominic Welsh, *Codes and Cryptography,* New York: Oxford Science Publications, 1993.

A. Yao, "Computational Information Theory," in *Complexity in Information Theory,* ed. by Abu-Mostafa, 1988.

Internet

Derek Atkins et al., *Internet Security: Professional Reference,* Indianapolis, New Riders, 1996.

R. J. Bates, Jr., *Disaster Recovery Planning: Networks, Telecommunications, and Data Communications,* New York: McGraw-Hill, 1992.

T. A. Bernstein, B. Bhimani, E. Schultz, and C. A. Siegel, *Internet Security for Business,* New York: John Wiley & Sons, 1996.

D. B. Chapman, and E. D. Zwicky, *Building Internet Firewalls,* Sebastopol, CA: O'Reilly & Associates, 1995.

W. Cheswick and S. Bellovin, *Firewalls and Internet Security: Repelling the Wily Hacker,* Reading, MA: Addison Wesley, 1994.

D. J. Cronin, *Microcomputer Data Security: Issues and Strategies for Business,* New York: Brady Books, Prentice-Hall, 1986.

L. J. Hughes, Jr., *Actually Useful Internet Security Techniques,* Indianapolis: New Riders Publishing, 1995.

IAB Privacy and Security Research Group, Privacy enhancement for Internet electronic mail: Part I: Message encipherment and authentication procedures, RFC 1113B, December 18, 1990.

Andrew Kantor and Michael Neubarth, "Off the Charts—the Internet 1996," *Internet World,* December 1996.

Vance McCarthy, "Web Security: How Much is Enough?" *Datamation,* **43**(1), January 1997.

Richard E. Smith, *Internet Cryptography,* New York: Addison-Wesley, 1997.

Key Management

J. Gordon, "Strong RSA keys," *Electronics Letters,* **20**(12), pp. 514-516, June 7, 1984.

S. M. Matyas and C. H. Meyer, "Generation, distribution, and installation of cryptographic keys," *IBM Systems Journal,* **17**(2), pp. 126-137, 1978.

W. F. Ehrsam, S. M. Matyas, C. H. Meyer, and W. L. Tuchman, "A cryptographic key management scheme for implementing the Data Encryption Standard," *IBM Systems Journal,* **17**(2), pp. 106-125, 1978.

S. M. Menke, K. Power, and S. Graves, "New FIPS defines key use," *Government Computer News* **16**(7), p. 3, Mar 17, 1997.

R. Flynn and A. S. Campasano, "Data dependent keys for a selective encryption terminal," in S. P. Ghosh and L. Y. Liu, eds., *AFIPS Conference Proceedings,* vol. 47: National Computer Conference, Anaheim, CA, June 5-8, 1978, pp. 1127-1129, Montvale, NJ: AFIPS Press, 1978.

Michael Smith, P. C. Van Oorschot, and M. Willett, "Cryptographic Information Recovery Using Key Recovery," White Paper, Key Recovery Alliance, June 17, 1997.

Network and Protocols

Tom Austin, "Tunnel Vision," *Infosecurity News,* p. 34 ff., May 1997.

M. Blaze, "Protocol Failure in the Escrowed Encryption Standard," White Paper, May 31, 1994.

W. Diffie, "Network security problems and approaches," *Proceedings of the National Electronics Conference,* **38,** pp. 292-314, 1984.

D. Dolev and A. C. Yao, "On the security of public key protocols," in *22nd Annual Symposium on Foundations of Computer Science,* Nashville,

TN, October 28-30, 1981, pp. 350-357. Silver Spring, MD: IEEE Computer Society Press, 1981.

Lincoln D. Faurer, "Computer Security Goals of the Department of Defense," *Computer Security Journal,* Summer 1984.

M. E. Kabay, *The NCSA Guide to Enterprise Security: Protecting Information Assets,* New York: McGraw-Hill, 1996.

Charlie Kaufman, R. Perlman, and M. Speciner, *Network Security — Private Communication in a Public World,* Upper Saddle River, NJ: Prentice Hall, 1995.

Frank Lyons, "A Network Security Review," *Infosecurity,* 8(2), News, March-April 1997.

R. C. Merkle, "Protocols for public key cryptosystems," in G. J. Simmons, ed., *Secure Communications and Asymmetric Cryptosystems,* pp. 73-104, Boulder, CO: Westview Press, 1982.

J. H. Moore, "Protocol failures in cryptosystems," *Proceedings of the IEEE,* 76(5), pp. 594-602, May 1988.

G. J. Popek and C. S. Kline, "Encryption protocols, public key algorithms and digital signatures in computer networks," in R. A. DeMillo, D. P. Dobkin, A. K. Jones, and R. J. Lipton, eds., *Foundations of Secure Computation,* pp. 133-153, New York: Academic Press, 1978.

G. L. Popek and C. S. Kline, "Encryption and secure computer networks," *ACM Computing Surveys,* 11(4), pp. 331-356, December 1979.

W. Price and D. Davies, *Security for computer networks,* New York: Wiley, 1984.

M. Rotenberg, "Communications Privacy: Implications for Network Design," *Communications of the ACM,* 36(8), pp 61-68, August 1993.

D. Russel and G. Gangemi, *Computer Security Basics,* Sebastopol, CA: O'Reilly, 1991.

W. Stallings, *Network and Internetwork Security: Principles and Practice,* Englewood Cliffs, NJ: Prentice Hall, 1995.

A. Tanenbaum, *Computer Networks,* 3d ed., Upper Saddle River, NJ: Prentice Hall PTR, 1996.

Policy

H. R. 3627, A Bill to Amend the Export Administration Act of 1979 with respect to the control of computer and related equipment, 1993.

Association For Computing Machinery, Codes, Keys and Conflicts: Issues in U.S. Crypto Policy, Report of a Special Panel of ACM U.S. Public Policy Committee (USACM), June 1994.

Administrative Office of the United States Courts, Report on Applications for Orders Authorizing or Approving the Interception of Wire, Oral, or Electronic Communications (Wiretap Report) 1993.

D. Banisar, "Statistical Analysis of Electronic Surveillance," presentation at the National Institute of Standards and Technology, Computer System Security and Privacy Advisory Board, June 3, 1993.

J. Chandler, D. Arrington, and L. Gill, *Foreign Encryption Technology Controls,* George Washington University, National Law Center, 1993.

J. Chandler, D. Arrington, and L. Gill, *Issues Regarding the Use of Cryptographic Technologies in the Commercial Sector,* George Washington University, National Law Center, 1993.

Communications Security Establishment, The Canadian Trusted Computer Product Evaluation Criteria Version 3.0e. Canadian System Security Centre, CSE, 1993. Available from Criteria Coordinator / S5B InfoSec Standards and Evaluations / Communications Security Establishment / P.O. Box 9703 Terminal / Ottawa K1G 3Z4. Tel. 613-991-7331; fax 613-991-7323; email *criteria@manitou.cse.dnd.ca*

Communications Security Establishment, Trusted Systems Environment Guideline, CID/09/17 (Ottawa), 1992.

W. Diffie, "Communication security and national security business, technology, and politics," *Proceedings of the National Communications Forum,* vol. 40, pp. 734-751, 1986.

Lance J. Hoffman, *Building In Big Brother: The Cryptographic Policy Debate,* New York: Springer-Verlag, 1995.

Lance J. Hoffman et al., "Cryptography Policy," *Communications of the ACM,* **37,** pp. 109-117, 1994.

International Organization for Standards, Draft International Standard ISO/DIS 7498-2, Information processing systems—Open Systems Interconnection Model—Part 2: Security Architecture, 1987.

International Traffic in Arms Regulation (ITAR), 22 CFR 120-130.

D. Kohls and Lance J. Hoffman, "TurboTrade: A National Information Infrastructure Cost/Risk/Benefit Model," Report GWU-IIST-93-17, Department of Electrical Engineering and Computer Science, The George Washington University, Washington, D.C., September 1993.

Lance Hoffman, Faraz A. Ali, Steven L. Heckler, and Ann Huybrechts, "Cryptography: Policy and Technology Trends," December 1, 1993, revised January 30, 1994, under contract DE-AC05-84OR21400.

Privacy

James Bamford, *The Puzzle Palace: A Report on America's Most Secret Agency,* Boston: Houghton Mifflin, 1982.

Charles E. H. Franklin, *Business Guide to Privacy and Data Protection Legislation,* The Hague: ICC Publishing, Kluwer Law International, 1996.

Ellen Alderman and Carolyn Kennedy, *The Right To Privacy,* New York: Knopf Publishing, 1995.

OTA (1993): Protecting Privacy in Computerized Medical Information, U.S. Congress Office of Technology Assessment, U.S. Government Printing Office #OTA-TCT-576 (Washington, DC), 1993.

"Protecting Your Privacy—A Comprehensive Report On Eavesdropping Techniques and Devices and Their Corresponding Countermeasures," Telecommunications Publishing Inc., 1979.

Public-Key Cryptography

D. Angluin and D. Lichtenstein, *Provable Security in Crypto-systems: A survey,* Yale University, Department of Computer Science, #288, 1983.

H. Beker and F. Piper, *Cipher Systems, The Protection of Communications,* New York: John Wiley and Sons, 1982.

T. Beth, M. Frisch, and G. Simmons, *Public Key Cryptography: State of the Art and Future Directions,* Lecture Notes in Computer Science, no. 578, Springer-Verlag, 1992.

T. Beth, "Algorithm engineering for public key algorithms," *IEEE Selected Areas of Communication,* **1**(4), pp. 458-466, 1990.

D. K. Branstad, "Encryption protection in computer data communications," in *Proceedings of the 4th Data Communications Symposium, IEEE,* pp 8.1-8.7, October 7-9, 1975.

G. Brassard, "A note on the complexity of cryptography," *IEEE Transactions on Information Theory,* **IT-25**(2), pp. 232-233, March 1979.

G. Brassard, "Relativized cryptography," *IEEE Transactions on Information Theory,* **IT-29**(6), pp. 877-894, November 1983.

G. Brassard, *Modern Cryptology: A Tutorial,* Lecture Notes in Computer Science, vol. 325, Berlin: Springer-Verlag, 1988.

E. F. Brickell, "A survey of hardware implementations of RSA," in G. Brassard, ed., Lecture Notes in Computer Science vol. 435: *Advances in Cryptology—Proceedings of CRYPTO '89,* pp. 368-370, Berlin/New York: Springer-Verlag, 1990.

H. S. Bright and R. L. Enison, "Cryptography using modular software elements," in S. Winkler, ed., *AFIPS Conference Proceedings,* vol. 45: National Computer Conference, New York, June 7-10, 1976, pp. 113-123. Montvale, NJ: AFIPS Press, 1976.

D. Coppersmith, "Cryptography," *IBM Journal of Research and Development,* **31**(2), pp. 244-248, March 1987.

S. T. Cobb, *NCSA Guide to PC and LAN Security,* New York: McGraw-Hill, 1995.

Datapro, Inc., *Datapro Report on Encryption Devices,* Delran, NJ, March 1993.

M. Davio and J. Goethals, "Elements of cryptology," in *Secure Digital Communications,* G. Longo, ed., pp. 1-57, 1983.

R. DeMillo and M. Merritt, "Protocols for data security," *Computer,* **16**(2), pp. 39-50, February 1983.

D. E. Denning, "Secure personal computing in an insecure network," *Communications of the ACM,* **22**(8), pp. 476-482, August 1979.

D. E. Denning, "Protecting public keys and signature keys," *Computer,* **16**(2), pp. 27-35, February 1983.

D. E. Denning and G. M. Sacco, "Timestamps in key distribution protocols," *Communications of the ACM,* **24**(8), pp. 533-536, August 1981.

D. E. R. Denning, *Cryptography and Data Security,* Reading, MA: Addison-Wesley, 1983.

W. Diffie, "Conventional versus public key cryptosystems," in G. J. Simmons, ed., *Secure Communications and Asymmetric Cryptosystems,* pp. 41-72, Boulder, CO: Westview Press, 1982.

W. Diffie, "The first ten years of public-key cryptography," *Proceedings of the IEEE,* **76**(5), pp. 560-577, May 1988.

W. Diffie and M. E. Hellman, "Multiuser cryptographic techniques," in S. Winkler, ed., *AFIPS Conference Proceedings,* vol. 45: National Computer Conference, New York, June 7-10, 1976, pp. 109-112, Montvale, NJ: AFIPS Press, 1976.

W. Diffie and M. E. Hellman, "New directions in cryptography," *EEE Transactions on Information Theory,* **IT-22**(6), pp. 644-645, November 1976.

W. Diffie and M. Hellman, "Privacy and Authentication: An introduction to cryptography," *IEEE Proceedings,* **67**(3), pp. 397-427, 1979.

W. Diffie, *Data Security for EFT and Automated Business, New Problems — New Solutions,* San Jose, CA: SBS Publishing, 1978.

W. Diffie, "Cryptographic Technology: Fifteen Year Forecast," in Gustavus J. Simmons, *Secure Communications and Asymmetric Cryptosystems,* AAAS Selected Symposium No. 69, Westview Press, 1982.

Y. Desmedt, J. Vandewalle, and R. J. M. Govaerts, "A critical analysis of the security of knapsack public key algorithms," *IEEE Transactions on Information Theory,* **IT-30**(4), pp. 601-611, July 1984.

H. Feistel, "Cryptography and Computer Privacy," *Scientific American,* **228**(5), pp. 15-23, 1973.

H. Feistel, H. W. Notz, and J. Lynn Smith. "Some cryptographic techniques for machine-to-machine data communications," *IEEE Proceedings,* **63**(11), pp. 1545-1554, 1975.

Foreign Intelligence Surveillance Act, 50 U.S.C. Sec.1801, et seq.

H. Gustafson, E. Dawson, and W. Caelli, "Comparison of block ciphers," in *Proceedings of AUSCRYPT '90,* J. Seberry and J. Piepryzk, eds., pp. 208-220, 1990.

M. E. Haykin and R. B. J. Warnar, "Smart card technology: new methods for computer access control," NIST Special Publication 500-157, September 1988.

M. Hellman, "The mathematics of public key cryptography," *Scientific American,* pp. 130-139, 1979.

C. S. Kline and G. J. Popek, "Public key vs. conventional key encryption," in R. E. Merwin, ed., *AFIPS Conference Proceedings,* **48:** National Computer Conference, June 4-7, 1979, New York, pp. 831-837, Montvale, NJ: AFIPS Press, 1979.

J. Massey, "An introduction to contemporary cryptology," *IEEE Proceedings,* **76**(5), pp. 533-549, 1988.

R. J. McEliece, "A public-key cryptosystem based on algebraic coding theory," *DSN Progress Report,* 42-44, Jet Propulsion Laboratory, pp. 114-116, 1978.

R. C. Merkle, "Secure communications over insecure channels," *Communications of the ACM,* **21**(4), pp. 294-299, April 1978.

R. C. Merkle, *Secrecy, Authentication, and Public Key Systems.* Ann Arbor: UMI Research Press, 1982.

R. C. Merkle and M. E. Hellman, "Hiding information and signatures in trapdoor knapsacks," *IEEE Transactions on Information Theory,* **24**(5), pp. 525-530, September 1978.

Alfred J. Menezes, P. C. van Oorschot, and S. A. Vanstone, *Handbook of Applied Cryptography,* New York: CRC, 1997.

Ralph Merkle and Martin E. Hellman, "On the Security of Multiple Encryption," *Communications of the ACM,* **24,** pp. 465-67, 1981.

R. Merkle, "Fast software encryption functions," in *Proceedings of CRYPTO '90,* Menezes and Vanstone, eds., pp. 476-501, 1991.

C. Meyer and S. Matyas, *Cryptography: A new dimension in computer security,* New York: Wiley, 1982.

P. Neumann, *Computer-Related Risks,* Reading, MA: Addison-Wesley, ACM Press, 1994.

James Nechvatal, *Public-Key Cryptography,* Security Technology Group, National Computer Systems Laboratory, National Institute of Standards and Technology, Gaithersburg, MD 20899, 1989.

National Research Council, *Computers at Risk: Safe computing in the Information Age,* Washington, D.C., National Academy Press, 1991.

Rhee, Man Young, *Cryptography and Secure Communications,* New York: McGraw Hill Co., 1994.

D. Riebensehl, "Hyperbolische Komplex Raume und die Vermutung von Mordell," *Math Ann.* **257,** pp. 99-100, 1981.

Ron Rivest, "Ciphertext," *The RSA Newsletter,* **1,** 1993.

R. L. Rivest, "RSA chips (past/present/future)," in T. Beth, N. Cot, and I. Ingemarsson, eds., Lecture Notes in Computer Science vol. 209: *Advances in Cryptology: Proceedings of EUROCRYPT '84,* a Workshop on the Theory and Application of Cryptographic Techniques, Paris, France, April 9-11, 1984, pp. 159-165. Berlin/New York: Springer-Verlag, 1985.

R. L. Rivest, "The MD4 message digest algorithm," February 1990.

R. Rivest, "The MD5 Message-Digest Algorithm," *RFC1321,* April 1992.

R. L. Rivest and A. T. Sherman, "Randomized encryption techniques," in D. Chaum, R. L. Rivest, and A. T. Sherman, eds., *Advances in Cryptology: Proceedings of CRYPTO '82,* a Workshop on the Theory and

Application of Cryptographic Techniques, Santa Barbara, CA, August 23-25, 1982, pp. 145-163. New York: Plenum Press, 1983.

R. Rivest, "Responses to NIST's Proposal," *Communications of the ACM,* **35**(7), pp. 41-47, July 1992.

Norbert Ryska and Siegfried Herda, *Kryptographische Verfahren in der Datenverarbeitung,* Gesellschaft fur Informatik, Berlin: Springer-Verlag, 1980.

A. Salomaa, *Public-key cryptography,* Springer-Verlag, 1990.

Bruce Schneier, *Applied Cryptography: Protocols, Algorithms, and Source Code C,* New York: John Wiley and Sons, 1994; 2d ed., 1995.

C. Schnorr, "Efficient Identification and Signatures for Smart Cards," *Advances in Cryptology-Crypto '89,* New York: Springer-Verlag, pp. 239-251, 1990.

H. Sedlak, "The RSA Cryptography Processor," in D. Chaum and W. L. Price, eds., Lecture Notes in Computer Science vol. 304: *Advances in Cryptology—EUROCRYPT '87,* a Workshop on the Theory and Applications of Cryptographic Techniques, Amsterdam, The Netherlands, April 13-15, 1987, pp. 95-105. Berlin/New York: Springer-Verlag, 1988.

G. J. Simmons, "Symmetric and asymmetric encryption," *ACM Computing Surveys,* **11**(4), pp. 305-330, December 1979.

G. J. Simmons, "How to ensure that data acquired to verify treaty compliance are trustworthy," *Proceedings of the IEEE,* **76**(5), pp. 621-627, May 1988.

G. Simmons, ed., "Contemporary Cryptology: the Science of Information Integrity," *IEEE Press,* 1991.

M. E. Smid, "Integrating the data encryption standard into computer networks," *IEEE Transactions on Computers,* **COM-29**(6), pp. 762-772, June 1981.

M. E. Smid and D. K. Branstad, The Data Encryption Standard: past and future, *Proceedings of the IEEE,* Vol. 76, No. 5, pp. 550-559, May 1988.

N. R. Wagner and M. R. Magyarik, "A public-key cryptosystem based on the word problem," in G. R. Blakley and D. Chaum, eds., *Lecture Notes in Computer Science Vol. 196: Advances in Cryptology—Proceedings of CRYPTO '84,* a Workshop on the Theory and Applications of Cryptographic Techniques, Santa Barbara, CA, August 19-22, 1984, pp. 19-36. Berlin/New York: Springer-Verlag, 1985.

H. C. Williams, "A modification of the RSA public-key encryption procedure," *IEEE Transactions on Information Theory,* **IT-26**(6), pp. 726-729, November 1980.

Random Number Generation

M. Blum and S. Micali, "How to generate cryptographically strong sequences of pseudo-random bits," *SIAM Journal on Computing,* **13**(4), pp. 850-864, November 1984.

J. Boyar, "Inferring Sequences Produced by Pseudo-Random Number Generators," *Journal of the ACM,* 1989.

Standards

Datapro Networking Report 2783, ISO Reference Model for Open Systems Interconnection (OSI), p. 7, August 1991.

FIPS 186, Digital Signature Standard (DSS), specifies a Digital Signature Algorithm appropriate for applications requiring a digital rather than a written signature.

FIPS 185, Escrowed Encryption Standard (EES), specifies a voluntary technology available for protecting telephone communications (e.g., voice, fax, modem).

FIPS 180, Secure Hash Standard (SHS), specifies a Secure Hash Algorithm (SHA) for use with the Digital Signature Standard. Additionally, for applications not requiring a digital signature, the SHA is to be used whenever a secure hash algorithm is required for federal applications.

FIPS 46-2, Data Encryption Standard (DES), provides the technical specifications for the DES.

FIPS 113, Computer Data Authentication, specifies a Data Authentication Algorithm, based upon the DES, which may be used to detect unauthorized modifications to data, both intentional and accidental. The Message Authentication Code as specified in ANSI X9.9 is computed in the same manner as the Data Authentication Code as specified in this standard.

FIPS 140-1, Security Requirements for Cryptographic Modules, establishes the physical and logical security requirements for the design and manufacture of modules implementing NIST-approved crypto-graphic algorithms.

FIPS 171, Key Management Using ANSI X9.17, adopts ANSI X9.17 and specifies a particular selection of options for the automated distribution of keying material by the federal government using the protocols of ANSI X9.17.

National Bureau of Standards, Federal Information Processing Standards Publication 46: Data Encryption Standard, January 15, 1977.

National Bureau of Standards, Federal Information Processing Standards Publication 81: DES Modes of Operation, December 2, 1980.

National Bureau of Standards, Federal Information Processing Standards Publication 74: Guidelines for Implementing and Using the NBS Data Encryption Standard, April 1, 1981.

National Bureau of Standards, Data Encryption Standard, FIPS PUB 46-1, 1987.

National Computer Security Center (1983-). Rainbow Series. Monographs on many aspects of information systems security.

National Institute of Standards and Technology, Publication XX: Announcement and Specifications for a Digital Signature Standard (DSS), August 19, 1991, Washington, DC.

National Institute of Standards and Technology, 1994, Federal Information Processing Standard Publication 185, Escrowed Encryption Standard, February 9, 1994, Washington, DC.

National Institute of Standards and Technology, 1994, Federal Information Processing Standards Publication 186: Digital Signature Standard (DSS), May 19, 1994, Washington, DC.

National Institute of Standards and Technology, 1994, Approval of Federal Information Processing Standards Publication 185, Escrowed Encryption Standard, *Federal Register,* **59**(27), February 9, 1994, Washington, D.C.

National Institute of Standards and Technology and National Security Agency, 1989, Memorandum of Understanding between the Director of the National Institute of Standards and Technology and the Director of the National Security Agency concerning the Implementation of Public Law 100-235, March 24, 1989, Washington, DC.

The Orange Book is DOD 520 0.28-STD, published December 1985 as part of the rainbow book series. Write to Department of Defense, National Security Agency, ATTN: S332, 9800 Savage Road, Fort

Meade, MD 20755-6000, and ask for the Trusted Computer System Evaluation Criteria. Call 301-766-8729.

RSA Data Security, Inc., Cryptographic Message Syntax Standard, PKCS-7, Nov. 1, 1993.

William Stallings, *Networking Standards: A Guide to OSI, ISDN, LAN, and MAN Standards,* Reading, MA: Addison Wesley, 1993.

Selected Web Sources

A large amount of information about Cryptography can be found using any Browser or Web Ferret search engines. Here is a small sample of some of the URLs found with searches on the keywords "Classical Cryptography" and "Cryptography":

Authentication Protocols

http://www.cis.ohio-state.edu/hypertext/faq/usenet/kerberos-faq/ user/faq.html

ftp://athena-dist.mit.edu/pub/kerberos

http://www.cs.hut.fi/ssh/crypto/algorithms.html

Bibliographies

http://mnementh.cs.adfa.oz.au/htbin/bib_lpb http://glimpse.cs. arizona.edu/bib/

http://liinwww.ira.uka.de/bibliography/index.html

ftp://ftp.doc.ic.ac.uk/computing/bibliographies/Karlsruhe/index.html

http://liinwww.ira.uka.de/bibliography/Theory/crypto.security.html

ftp://ftp.doc.ic.ac.uk/computing/bibliographies/Karlsruhe/Theory/ computational.number.theory.html

http://theory.lcs.mit.edu/~rivest/homepage.html http://theory.lcs.mit.edu/~rivest/crypto.bib http://theory.lcs.mit.edu/~rivest/algorithms2.bib

ttp://theory.lcs.mit.edu/~rivest/crypto-security.html

Cookies

http://www.epic.org/privacy/internet/cookies/default.html

DES

ftp://ftp.uu.net/pub/security/des

E-Commerce

http://www.jcp.co.uk/research.html

http://www.zdnet.com/pcmag/news/trends/t970221a.htm

http://www.jcp.co.uk/research.html

http://www.digicash.com/ecash/

http://www.cybercash.com/cybercash/shoppers/shopsteps.html

http://www.zdnet.com/pcmag/news/trends/t961220a.htm

http://www.zdnet.com/pcmag/news/trends/t960201d.htm

http://www.news.com/News/Item/0,4,15222,00.html

http://www.zdnet.com/pcweek/news/0526/26apro.html

http://www.digicash.com/news/archive/bigbro.html

http://www.auricweb.com/ecgateway.htm

http://www.zdnet.com/pcweek/news/0317/21mimall.html

Elliptical Curves

http://www.ama.caltech.edu/resources.html ftp://ftp.mcs.com/mcsnet
  .users/eh.crypto

ftp://csua.berekely.edu/pub/cypherpunks/ciphers

ftp://ftp.datashopper.dk/pub/users/pethern/file/curve_encrypt_22
  .sea.hqx

ftp://ftp.dsi.unimi.it/pub/security/crypt/code/curve_encrypt_22
  .sea.hqx

http://theory.lcs.mit.edu/~rivest/publications.html

Government

http://ana.arc.nasa.gov/usps/

http://www.cse.dnd.ca/ http://www.itd.nrl.navy.mil/ITD/NRL-ITD

http://infosec.nosc.mil/infosec.html http://hightop.nrl.navy.mil/
  rainbow.html

http://www.users.interport.net/~sagal/ajax.html http://www.fbi.gov/

http://www.fbi.gov/deca.htm

Laws

http://cwis.kub.nl/~frw/people/koops/lawsurvy.htm

http://www.epic.org/crypto/legislation/s1587.html

http://www.vtw.org/ http://www.epic.org/crypto/legislation/s1587_ analysis.html

http://www.law.miami.edu/~froomkin/personal-u se.txt ftp://ftp .cygnus.com/pub/export/itar.in.full

http://www.pls.com:8001/his/usc.html, http://www.epic.org/crypto/

http://www.eff.org/pub/Privacy/ITAR_export/

http://www.qualcomm.com/people/pkarn/export/index.html http:// ssdc.ucsd.edu/gpo/

http://www.io.org/~samwise/crypto/Introduction.html

http://www.us.net/~steptoe/ http://world.std.com/~franl/crypto.html

Lenstra's Large Integer Package

ftp://sable.ox.ac.uk/pub/math/freelip/

PGP

Phillip R. Zimmerman:prz@acm.org

http://draco.centerline.com:8080/~franl/pgp/pgp-2.6.2-doc1.html

http://draco.centerline.com:8080/~franl/pgp/

Privacy

http://www.cl.cam.ac.uk/users/rja14/#SR

ftp://ftp.cl.cam.ac.uk/users/rja14/

http://www.rsa.com/rsalabs/cryptobytes http://www2.indigo-net.com/ Indigo/Indigo.html

http://www.privacy.org/alert/gopher://ns1.infor.com/ gopher://ns1 .infor.com/77/.bin/s_kw?cryptography

http://www.aegeanpress.com/books/

http://www.wiley.com/ http://www.openmarket.com/info/ cryptography/applied_cry ptography.html http://www.crcpress.com/PRODS/8521.HTM

http://www.crcpress.com/

http://bibd.unl.edu/~stinson/ssbib.html http://bibd.unl.edu/~stinson/acbib.html

http://www-mitpress.mit.edu/mitp/recent-books/comp/pgp-source.html

http://www-mitpress.mit.edu/

http://www.springer-ny.com/

http://www-leland.stanford.edu/~phillin/red_paper.gif

http://www.digicash.com/digicash/digicash/profile

http://www.zdnet.com/intweek/print/970609/inwk0040.html

Primes

ftp://sable.ox.ac.uk/pub/math/primes tables

Random Numbers

http://www.cs.berkeley.edu/~daw/netscape-randomness.html

http://www.clark.net/pub/cme/html/ranno.html

http://www.cis.ohio-state.edu/htbin/rfc/rfc1750.html

http://www.ddj.com/ddj/1994/1994.11/index.htm

RIPE

ftp://ripem.msu.edu/pub/

ftp://ftp.infonexus.com/pub

http://ftpsearch.unit.no/ftpsearch/

http://www.cs.indiana.edu/ripem/dir.html

Technical Reports

http://www.itribe.net/CTRS

http://www.cs.waikato.ac.nz/~sirvine http://bibd.unl.edu/~stinson/acbib.html

http://bibd.unl.edu/~stinson/ssbib.html

http://triode.apana.org.au:8080/~cskinner/cybanim.html

http://www.isse.gmu.edu/~csis/bibliography/ref_essays.html

http://www.cs.purdue.edu/coast/archive/data/category_in dex.html

ftp://coast.cs.purdue.edu/pub/doc/cryptography/ http://www.cs .purdue.edu/coast/archive/data/categ12.html, http://www .zblmath.fiz-karlsruhe.de/cgi-bin/LNCS-500-1000

http://avalon.ira.uka.de/eiss/EISS-Reports/index.html

SSL

http://search.netscape.com/newsref/std/SSL_old.html

TRUSTe

http://www.etrust.org/webpublishers/studies_BCG.html

Quantum Cryptography

http://www.iro.umontreal.ca/people/crepeau/Biblio-QC.html

http://www.iro.umontreal.ca/labs/theorique/index_en.htm

http://vesta.physics.ucla.edu/~smolin/

http://eve.physics.ox.ac.uk/QCresearch/cryptoanalysis/qc.html

University References

ftp://sable.ox.ac.uk/pub/math/primesrsa129/ ftp://furmint.nectar.cs .cmu.edu/security

http://weber.u.washington.edu/~phantom/cpunk/index.html ftp://ftp. funet.fi/pub/crypt/cypherpunks

ftp://ftp.psy.uq.oz.au/pub/Crypto

ftp.psy.uq.oz.au/pub/Crypto

ftp://ftp.wimsey.bc.ca/pub/crypto http://clipper.uvic.ca/crypt

ftp://pgp.rasip.fer.hr ftp://ftp.datashopper.dk/pub/users/pethern

ftp://ftp.funet.fi/pub/crypt

ftp://garbo.uwasa.fi/pc/security http://www.cs.hut.fi/ssh/crypto

http://www.cnam.fr/Network/Crypto ftp://ftp.darmstadt .gmd.de/pub/crypto

ftp://ftp.informatik.uni-hildesheim.de/pub/security/ ftp://ftp

.uni-stuttgart.de / pub / doc / security / crypto / http:// www.thur.de / ulf / krypto / index.html

ftp:// ftp.informatik.uni-hamburg.de / pub / pgp ftp:// ftp.informatik.uni-hamburg.de / pub / crypt

http:// www.cert.dfn.de / eng ftp:// ftp.kfki.hu / pub / packages / security

ftp:// ftp.dsi.unimi.it / pub / security / crypt ftp:// utopia.hacktic.nl / pub / replay / pub / disk /

ftp:// ftp.unit.no / pub / unix / security ftp:// ftp.kiae.su / unix / crypto

ftp:// ftp.sunet.se / pub / security / tools / crypt ftp:// ftp.ox.ac.uk / pub / crypto

ftp:// FTP.CSN.ORG / mpj / README

http:// www.eff.org / pub / Net_info / Tools / Crypto / ftp:// ftp.eff.org / pub / Net_info / Tools / Crypto /

http:// www.cl.cam.ac.uk:80 / users / rja14 /

http:// avalon.ira.uka.de / eiss / indexe.html http:// www.ens.fr / ~grecc / papers.html

http:// www.ens.fr / ~grecc / index_en.html

http:// www.ul b.ac.be / di / scsi / defscsi.html

http:// www.informatik.uni-hildesheim.de / ~sirene / lit / sirene.lit.html

http:// www.informatik.uni-hildesheim.de / ~sirene / index.html

http:// www.swcp.com / ~iacr / jofc / jofc.html

USS Pampanino

http:// www.maritime.org / ecm2.shmtl

VPNs

[Note: The Internet drafts are in *ftp:// ftp.ietf.org / internet-drafts / XXXX* and the RFCs are in *ftp:// ds.internic.net / rfc / rfcXXXX.txt*. Also, both the Internet drafts and RFCs are evolving documents and may have greater revision numbers.]

Frederick M. Aviolio, *Firewalls and Virtual Private Networks,* TIS White Paper, 1998. Available from *www.tis.com*

S. Bradner, *Key Words for Use in RFCs to Indicate Requirement Levels,* RFC 2119, March 1997.

The Business Case for Secure VPN's, TimeStep Corporation, Kanata, Ontario, 1998. Available from *www.Timestep.com*

CiPro Conceptual Guide: A Theoretical Guide to Virtual Private Network (VPN), RADGUARD, Ltd., 1998. Available from *www.radguard.com*

Stephen Cobb, *NCSA Guide to PC and LAN Security,* McGraw-Hill Computing, New York, 1996.

Stephen Cobb, *Security Issues in Internet Commerce,* NCSA White Paper, Version 2.0, 1997. Available from *www.ICSA.net*

Frederick J. Cooper et al., *Implementing Internet Security,* New Riders Publishing, Indianapolis, IN, 1995.

Cryptosystem White Paper: The Secured Solution For the Internetworking Revolution, RADGUARD, Ltd., 1998. Available from: *www.radguard.com*

D. Harkins and D. Carrel, *The Internet Key Exchange,* draft-ietf-ipsec-isakmp-oakley-07.txt, February 1998.

Eli Herscovitz, *Virtual Private Networks: The Future of Data Communications,* RADGUARD, Ltd., 1998. Available from *www.radguard.com*

ICSA Announces First IPSec Certified Products, ICSA Press Release, May 20, 1998. Available from *www.ICSA.net*

ICSA Cryptography Product Certification Program, Version 1.0, 10 December 1997. Available from *www.ICSA.net*

ICSA Program for IPSec Product Certification, Version 1.0, May 15, 1998. Available from *www.ICSA.net*

IP Security, Cisco Systems, 1998. Available from *www.cisco.com*

P. Karn et al., *The ESP DES-CBC Transform,* RFC 1829, August 1995.

S. Kent and R. Atkinson, *IP Authentication Header,* draft-ietf-ipsec-auth-header-06.txt, February 1998.

S. Kent, *IP Encapsulating Security Payload,* draft-ietf-ipsec-esp-v2-05.txt, February 1998.

Lars Klander, *Hacker Proof: The Ultimate Guide to Network Security,* JAMSA Press, Las Vegas, 1997.

H. Krawczyk et al., *HMAC: Keyed-Hashing for Message Authentication,* RFC 2104, February 1997.

Douglas Maugjam et al., *Internet Security Association and Key Management Protocol (ISAKMP),* draft-ietf-ipsec-isakmp-09.txt, 26 July 1997.

Randall K. Nichols, *ICSA Guide to Cryptography*, McGraw-Hill Professional Publishing, New York. For release, November 1998. Beta version available from: *www.betabooks.mcgraw-hill.com*

H. K. Orman, *The OAKLEY Key Determination Protocol*, draft-ietf-ipsec-oakley-02.txt, undated.

Derrell Piper, *The Internet IP Security Domain of Interpretation for ISAKMP*, draft-ietf-ipsec-ipsec-doi-09.txt

PyroWall White Paper: The Secured Solution For the Internetworking Revolution, RADGUARD, Ltd., 1998. Available from *www. radguard.com*

B. Rogers, *Use of Block Ciphers for Message Authentication*, draft-rogers-cbc-mac-00.txt, 12 February 1998.

Karen M. Sage, *Network Management Solutions for IP-VPN Services*, Cisco Systems, 1998. Available from *www.cisco.com*

Charlie Scott, Paul Wolfe, and Mike Erwin, *Virtual Private Networks*, O'Reilly, Cambridge, MA, 1998.

Security Briefcase Handbook, AXENT Technologies, Inc., Rockville, MD, 1998. Available from *www.Axent.com*

Richard Smith, *Internet Cryptography*, Addison Wesley, New York, 1997.

Solutions for Virtual Private Dialup Networks, Cisco Systems, 1998. Available from *www.cisco.com*

William Stallings, "A Secure Foundation For VPNs," *Information Security*, March 1998.

William Stallings, *Cryptography and Network Security: Principles and Practice*, 2d ed., Prentice Hall, New York, 1998.

Understanding the IPSec Protocol Suite, TimeStep Corporation, Kanata, Ontario, 1998. Available from *www.Timestep.com*

John Vacca, *Internet Security Secrets*, IDG Books, Foster City, CA 1995.

VPN Solutions: Understanding Today's Choices for Building Service Provider Virtual Private Networks, Cisco Systems, 1998. Available from *www.cisco.com*

VPN Solutions: IP VPN Frequently Asked Questions, Cisco Systems, 1998. Available from *www.cisco.com*

What's a VPN Anyway? Or The Cloud's Silver Lining in Your Net, VPNET Technologies, 1998. Available from *www.VPNet.com*

IAAA

[Note: The Internet drafts are in *ftp://ftp.ietf.org/internet-drafts/XXXX* and the RFCs are in *ftp://ds.internic.net/rfc/rfcXXXX.txt*. Also, both the Internet drafts and RFCs are evolving documents and may have greater revision numbers.]

Anonymous, *Maximum Security: A Hacker's Guide to Protecting Your Internet Site and Network,* Sams Net, Indianapolis, IN, 1997.

Vijay Ahuja, *Network & Internet Security,* Academic Press, New York, 1996.

Derik Atkins et al., *Internet Security: Professional Reference,* New Riders Publishing, Indianapolis, IN., 1996.

Edward Amoroso, *Fundamentals of Computer Security Technology,* Prentice Hall, Upper Saddle River, NJ, 1994.

Frederick M. Avolio, *Firewalls and Virtual Private Networks,* TIS White Paper, 1998. Available from: *http://www.tis.com*

F. L. Bauer, *Decrypted Secrets: Methods and Maxims of Cryptology,* Springer, Berlin, 1997.

The Business Case for Secure VPN's, TimeStep Corporation, Kanata, Ontario, 1998. Available from: *http://www.Timestep.com*

CiPro Conceptual Guide: A Theoretical Guide to Virtual Private Network (VPN), RADGUARD, Ltd., 1998. Available from: *http://www.radguard.com*

Stephen Cobb, *NCSA Guide to PC and LAN Security,* McGraw-Hill Computing, New York, 1996.

Stephen Cobb, *Security Issues in Internet Commerce,* NCSA White Paper, Version 2.0, 1997. Available from: *http://www.ICSA.net*

Frederick J. Cooper et al., *Implementing Internet Security,* New Riders Publishing, Indianapolis, IN, 1995.

Cryptosystem White Paper: The Secured Solution For the Internetworking Revolution, RADGUARD, Ltd., 1998. Available from: *http://www.radguard.com*

Kenneth W. Dam and Herbert S. Lin, *Cryptographers Role In Securing The Information Society,* National Research Council, National Academy Press, Washington, DC, 1996.

Jan H. P. Eloff and Sebastiaan H. Von Solms, *Information Security—the Next Decade,* Chapman and Hill, London, 1995.

D. Elledge, "Keep Out Prying Eyes," *Information Week,* (629):102, May 5, 1997.

Lincoln D. Faurer, *Computer Security Goals of the Department of Defense,* Computer Security Journal, Summer, 1984.

Charles E. H. Franklin, *Business Guide to Privacy and Data Protection Legislation,* ICC Publishing, Kluwer Law International, The Hague, 1996.

Gail L. Grant, *Understanding Digital Signatures: Establishing Trust over the Internet and other Networks,* McGraw-Hill, San Francisco, CA, 1998.

D. Harkins and D. Carrel, *The Internet Key Exchange,* draft-ietf-ipsec-isakmp-oakley-07.txt, February 1998.

Eli Herscovitz, *Virtual Private Networks: The Future of Data Communications,* RADGUARD, Ltd., 1998. Available from: *http://www.radguard.com*

L. J. Hughes, Jr., *Actually Useful Internet Security Techniques,* New Riders Publishing, Indianapolis, IN, 1995.

A. E. Hutt, S. Bosworth, and D. B. Hoyt, eds., *Computer Security Handbook,* 3rd ed., John Wiley & Son, New York, 1995.

Michel E. Kabay, *The NCSA Guide to Enterprise Security: Protecting Information Assets,* McGraw-Hill, New York, 1996.

M. E. Kabay, *Identification, Authentication and Authorization on the World Wide Web: an NCSA White Paper,* draft 20, unpublished manuscript, 1997.

P. A. Karger and R. R. Schell, *Multics Security Evaluation: Vulnerability Analysis,* (ESD-TR-74-193), Electronics Systems Division, USAF, Hanscom Air Force Base, Bedford, MA, 1974 (NTIS: AD A001120)

P. Karn et al., *The ESP DES-CBC Transform,* RFC 1829, August 1995.

Charlie Kaufman, Radia Perlman, and Mike Spenser, *Network Security: Private Communication in a Public World,* Prentice Hall, Upper Saddle River, NJ, 1995.

S. Kent and R. Atkinson, *IP Authentication Header,* draft-ietf-ipsec-auth-header-06.txt, February 1998.

S. Kent, *IP Encapsulating Security Payload,* draft-ietf-ipsec-esp-v2-05.txt, February 1998.

Lars Klander, *Hacker Proof: The Ultimate Guide to Network Security,* JAMSA Press, Las Vegas, NV, 1997.

H. Krawczyk et al., *HMAC: Keyed-Hashing for Message Authentication,* RFC 2104, February 1997.

Frank Lyons, "A Network Security Review," *Infosecurity,* **8**(2), News, March/April 1997.

Douglas Maugjam et al., *Internet Security Association and Key Management Protocol (ISAKMP)*, draft-ietf-ipsec-isakmp-09.txt, 26 July 1997.

Vance McCarthy, "Web Security: How Much is Enough?," *Datamation,* **43**(1), January 1997.

Alfred J. Menezes, P. C. van Oorschot, and S. A. Vanstone, *Handbook of Applied Cryptography,* CRC, New York, 1997.

Randall K. Nichols, *ICSA Guide to Cryptography,* McGraw-Hill Professional Publishing, New York. For release, November 1998. Beta version available from: *http://www.betabooks.mcgraw-hill.com*

Randall K. Nichols, *Common Industry Practices for Implementing Cryptography,* White Paper, ICSA, May 1997. Available from: *http://www.icsa.net*

Randall K. Nichols, *Virtual Private Networks (VPNs),* White Paper, ICSA, August 1998. Available from: *http://www.icsa.net*

H. K. Orman, *The OAKLEY Key Determination Protocol,* draft-ietf-ipsec-oakley-02.txt, undated.

Rolf Oppliger, *Authentication Systems for Secure Networks,* Artech House, Boston, MA, 1996.

PC Magazine, *Network Buyers Guide,* Strategic Research Corporation, Emeryville, CA, 1996.

Birgit Pfitzmann, *Digital Signature Schemes: General Framework and Fail-Stop Signatures,* Springer, Berlin, Germany, 1996.

Lee Anne Phillips, *Using HTML 4,* 4th ed., QUE publications, New York, 1998.

Derrell Piper, *The Internet IP Security Domain of Interpretation for ISAKMP,* draft-ietf-ipsec-ipsec-doi-09.txt

PyroWall White Paper: *The Secured Solution For the Internetworking Revolution,* RADGUARD, Ltd., 1998. Available from: *http://www.radguard.com*

Man Young Rhee, *Cryptography and Secure Communications,* McGraw-Hill, New York, 1994.

Daniel H. Rimer, *Stepping into the Internet Era: The Transition of Enterprise Computing,* iWord, **2**(2), April 1997. Available from: *http://www.hamquist.com/iword/iword22/istory22.html*

K. S. Rosenblatt, *High-Technology Crime: Investigating Cases Involving Computers,* KSK Publications, San Jose, CA., 1995.

Deborah Russell and G. T. Gangemi, Sr., *Computer Security Basics,* O'Reilly & Associates, Inc., 1991.

Karen M. Sage, *Network Management Solutions for IP-VPN Services,* Cisco Systems, 1998. Available from: *http://www.cisco.com*

Charlie Scott, Paul Wolfe, and Mike Erwin, *Virtual Private Networks,* O'Reilly, Cambridge, MA, 1998.

W. Schwartau, *Information Warfare,* 2d ed., Thunder's Mouth Press, New York, 1997.

Security Briefcase Handbook, AXENT Technologies, Inc., Rockville, MD, 1998. Available from: *http://www.Axent.com*

Corey Schou, *Handbook of INFOSEC Terms,* Version 2.0, CD-ROM, Idaho State University & Information Systems Security Organization, 1996. Available from: *glossary@sdsc.isu.edu*

Richard Smith, *Internet Cryptography,* Addison Wesley, New York, 1997.

Solutions for A Safer World, 4-part video, NSA, Unclassified, Information Systems Security Organization, 1996.

William Stallings, "A Secure Foundation For VPNs," *Information Security,* March 1998.

William Stallings, *Cryptography and Network Security: Principles and Practice,* 2d ed., Prentice Hall, New York, 1998.

William Stallings, *Networking Standards: A Guide to OSI, ISDN, LAN, and MAN Standards,* Addison Wesley, New York, 1993.

William Stallings, *Network and Internetwork Security: Principles and Practice,* Prentice Hall, New York, 1998.

Understanding the IPSec Protocol Suite, TimeStep Corporation, Kanata, Ontario, 1998. Available from: *http://www.Timestep.com*

John Vacca, *Internet Security Secrets,* IDG Books, Foster City, CA, 1995.

John Vacca, *Internet Security,* Charles River Media, Rockland, MA, 1997.

Peter Wayner, *Digital Cash: Commerce on the Net,* AP Professional, New York, 1996.

Digital Signatures: 1995 → Present

American Bar Association, *Digital Signature Guidelines, Information Security Committee, Science and Technology Section,* American Bar Association, Draft, Oct. 5, 1995.

Stewart A. Baker and Michael D. Hintze, "United States Government Policy on Encryption Technology," *3 Computer & Telecommunications L. Rev. 109,* June 1997.

Stewart A. Baker and Paul R. Hurst, *The Limits of Trust: Cryptography, Governments, and Electronic Commerce,* Kluwer Law International, Washington, DC, 1998.

Philippe Beguin and Jean-Jasques Quisquater: *Fast Server-Aided RSA Signatures Secure Against Active Attacks,* Crypto '95, LNCS 963, Springer-Verlag, Berlin, 1995, pp. 57–69.

CCITT Recommendation X.509, The Directory—Authentication Framework, 1988.

M. Blaze, J. Feigenbaum, and J. Lacy, "Decentralized Trust Management," Proceedings of the 1996 *IEEE Symposium on Security and Privacy,* May 1996.

Jan L. Camenisch, Jean-Marc Piveteau, and Markus A. Stadler, *Blind Signatures Based on the Discrete Logarithm Problem,* Eurocrypt '94, LNCS 950, Springer-Verlag, Berlin 1995, pp. 428–432.

David Chaum, "Achieving Electronic Privacy," *Scientific American,* Aug. 1992, pp. 96–101.

David Chaum, *Designated Confirmer Signatures,* Eurocrypt '94, LNCS 950, Springer-Verlag, Berlin 1995, pp. 86–91.

Lidong Chen and Torben P. Pedersen, *New Group Signature Schemes,* Eurocrypt '94, LNCS 950, Springer-Verlag, Berlin 1995, pp. 171–181.

Ronald Cramer and Ivan Damgard, *Secure Signature Schemes Based on Interactive Protocols,* Crypto '95, LNCS 963, Springer-Verlag, Berlin 1995, pp. 297–310.

Kenneth W. Dam and Herbert S. Lin, editors, *Cryptography's Role In Securing The Information Society,* Computer Science and Telecommunications Board, National Research Council, National Academy Press, Washington, DC, 1996.

Yair Frankel and Moti Yung, *Cryptanalysis of the Immunized LL Public Key Systems,* Crypto '95, LNCS 963, Springer-Verlag, Berlin 1995, pp. 287–296.

Charles E. H. Franklin (ed.), *Business Guide to Privacy and Data Protection Legislation,* ICC Publishing S.A., Kluwar Law International, The Hague, Netherlands, 1996.

Global Internet Liberty Campaign (GILC), *An International Survey Of*

Encryption Policy, February 1998, *http://www.gilc.org/crypto/cryptosurvey.html*

Gail L. Grant, *Understanding Digital Signatures: Establishing Trust Over The Internet and Other Networks,* Commerce Net Press [McGraw-Hill], San Francisco, CA, 1997.

Shafi Goldwasser, Silvio Mical, and Ronald L. Rivest, "A Digital Signature Scheme Secure Against Adaptive Chosen-Message Attacks," *SIAM Journal on Computing,* 17/2, 1988.

Lance J. Hoffman (ed.), *Building In Big Brother: The Cryptographic Policy Debate,* Springer-Verlag, Berlin, 1995.

Simone van der Hof and Bert-jaap Koops, *Digital Signature Law Survey, Version 2.2,* January 1998, *http://cwis.kub.nl/-frw/people/hof/DSwsu.htm*

Patrick Horster, Markus Michels, and Holger Petersen, *Meta-Message Recovery and Meta-Blind Signature Schemes Based on the Discrete Logarithm Problem and Their Applications,* Asiacrypt '94, LNCS 917, Springer-Verlag, Berlin, 1995, pp. 224–237.

Stephen Kent, *How Many Certification Authorities are Enough?,* BBN Technologies, unclassified presentation, Cambridge, MA 1997.

Stephen Kent, *Reasoning About Public-Key Certification,* presentation at RSA Data Security Conference, January 1996.

Stephen Kent, *Let a Thousand (10,000?) CAs Reign,* keynote for DIMACS Workshop on Trust Management, September 1996.

Bert-Jaap Koops, *Crypto Law Survey,* Version 12.1, March 1998, *http://cwis.kub.nl/-frw/people/koops/lawsurvy.htm#ca*

Christopher Kuner, "Cryptography Regulation in Germany: Present and Future," *3 Computer & Telecommunications L. Rev. 116,* June 1997.

Susan K. Langford, *Threshold DSS Signatures without a Trusted Party,* Crypto '95, LNCS 963, Springer-Verlag, Berlin, 1995, pp. 397–409.

Peter Leonard and Natalia Yastreboff, "Encryption and Australian Government Policy," *3 Computer & Telecommunications L. Rev. 119,* June 1997.

Alfred J. Menezes, Paul van Oorschot, and Scott A. Vanstone, *Handbook of Applied Cryptography,* CRC Press, New York, 1998.

Emmanuel Michau, Dougall Molson, and Olivier Menant, "The Utilization of an Encryption Device or Operation is Permitted if...," *3 Computer & Telecommunications L. Rev. 113,* June 1997, France.

David Naccache, David M'Raihi, Dan Raphaeli, and Serge Vaudenay, *Can D.S.A. Be Improved? Complexity Trade-Offs with the Digital Signature Standard,* Eurocrypt '94, LNCS 950, Springer-Verlag, Berlin, 1995, pp. 77–85.

Randall K. Nichols and Hart Degrafft, "Digital Signatures," Chapter 10, *The ICSA Guide to Cryptography,* McGraw-Hill, New York, 1998.

Kaisa Nyberg and Rainer R. Rueppel, *Message Recovery for Signature Schemes Based on the Discrete Logarithm Problem,* Eurocrypt '94, LNCS 950, Springer-Verlag, Berlin, 1995, pp. 182–193.

Rolf Opplinger, *Authentication Systems For Secure Networks,* Artech House, London, 1996.

Andreas Pfitzmann, Birgit Pfitzmann, Matthias Schunter, and Michael Waidner, *Vertrauens-wfirdiger Entwurf portabler BenutzerendgerAte und Sicherheitsmodule; VerIABliche IT-Systeme* (VIS '95); Dul FachbeitrAge, Vieweg, Wiesbaden 1995, pp. 329–350.

Andreas Pfitzmann, Birgit Pfitzmann, Matthias Schunter, and Michael Waidner, *Mobile User Devices and Security Modules: Design for Trustworthiness, IBM Research Report RZ 2784* (#89262) 02/05/96, IBM Research Division, Zilfich, February 1996.

Birgit Pfitzmann, *Digital Signature Schemes: General Framework and Fail-Stop Signatures,* Springer, Lecture Notes in Computer Science, Berlin, 1996.

Igor Pozhitkov, "State Policy on Encryption in the Russian Federation," *3 Computer & Telecommunications L. Rev. 123,* June 1997.

M. Reiter and S. Stubblebine, "Toward Acceptable Metrics of Authentication," *Proceedings of the 1997 IEEE Symposium on Security and Privacy,* May 1997.

E. Rescorla and A. Schiffmann, *The Secure HyperText Transport Protocol, Version 1.1; Internet-Draft, Enterprise Integration Technologies,* July 1995, *http://www.eit.conV projects/s-http/draft-ietf-wts-shttp-OO.txt.*

Matthias Schunter, *Vertrauen als integraler Bestandteil kryptografischer Spezifikationen,* rust Center, Grundlagen, Rechtliche Aspekte, Standardisierung, Realisierung, DuD achbeitrAge, Vieweg, Wiesbaden, 1995, pp. 173–179.

"SET Secure Electronic Transaction Specification," Version 1.0, May 1997.

William Stallings, *Cryptography and Networking Security: Principals and Practice,* 2d ed., Prentice Hall, New York, 1998.

U.S. Department of Commerce & U.S. National Security Agency, *A Study of the International Market for Computer Software with Encryption,* prepared for the Interagency Working Group on Encryption and Telecommunications Policy, July 1995.

U.S. National Security Agency, *MISSI Key Management Concept,* Rev. 2.5, February 1995.

Conor Ward, "Regulation of the Use of Cryptography and Cryptographic Systems in the United Kingdom: The Policy and the Practice," *3 Computer & Telecommunications L. Rev. 105,* June 1997.

M. Wiener, *Efficient DES Key Search,* presentation at Rump Session of Crypto, August 1993, Santa Barbara, CA. Available as TR-244, School of Computer Science, Carleton University, Ottawa, Canada, May 1994.

M. Wiener, "Efficient DES Key Search—An Update," *RSA Laboratories Cryptobytes,* Autumn 1997.

Sung-Ming Yen and Chi-Sung Laih, *Improved Digital Signature Suitable for Batch Verification,* IEEE Transactions on Computers 44/7, 1995, pp. 957–959.

INDEX

ACCESSING INFORMATION FROM THE CD-ROM ▬▬ ▬

To use the CD-ROM accompanying this book, load the CD-ROM into your computer's CD-ROM drive. Activate the modem to the Internet. Access the *ISCSA Guide to Cryptography* CD-ROM from any commercial browser by opening (use FILE OPEN or BROWSE and double-clicking) the INDEX file. The INDEX file includes a table made up of Internet hot links. The name of each paper, product, or demonstration listed in the table is a hot link to the paper or a functional summary/demonstration of the product. Following is an abbreviated list of the cryptography products available at the hot link's Web sites.

Company	Product
Cryotography Products	
CyberSafe™ Corp.	Trustbroker™ Security Suite v1.x
Data Fellows, Inc.	F-Secure Desktop 2.0
	F-Secure FileCrypto 3.0
	F-Secure SSH 2.0
ENGENYOUS Corp.	Universal Encryption Lock/2001™
Gradient Technologies	NetCrusader
Litronic, Inc.	Netsign™ v1.3
	Netsign PRO™ 1.4
	CryptOS™ SDK PRO 1.1
	ProFile Manager™ 1.0
Paradata Systems, Inc.	RIPnCRYPT Server Version 1.0
RADGUARD	Cryptosystem Key Management
RPK Security Systems	RPK Invisimail Professional V.2.13
Sparta, Inc.	SecurEC™ Version 1.2 for Windows 95 & UNIX
Sterling Commerce	CONNECT:Conceal™ Encryption Server
	CONNECT:Conceal™ Desktop
Western DataCom Co.	LineGuard 6000
	CryptoCom V.34
	V.90 Fordesza
Cryptography Tool Kits	
Entrust Technologies Ltd.	EntrustFile Toolkit v.3.0c
Virtual Private Networks	
Data Fellows, Inc.	F-Secure VPN 2.0
	F-Secure VPN+ 3.0
SECANT Network Technologies, Inc.	
TimeStep Corporation	PERMIT/Connect Demo
	PERMIT/Director data sheet
	PERMIT/Client
	PERMIT/Gate 2520 & 4520

836

Smartcards	
Schlumberger Limited	Cryptoflex™

SIPSec Products	
Checkpoint Software Technologies Ltd.	Checkpoint Firewall-1 v 4.0

About the Commercially Available Cryptography Products

In May and June of 1998, *ICSA* and *COMSEC Solutions* collected white papers and functional summaries on quality products that provide security services by using cryptography. The information collected may be found on this CD-ROM. An HTML file named INDEX gives a table organized by the type of cryptography products available—*General Cryptography Products, Cryptography Toolkits, Virtual Private Networks, Smartcards and IPSec VPN Products*—and indicates whether ICSA has certified the listed product or not.

The most recent list of ICSA Certified Products and the Certification Program under which they were certified are maintained by ICSA online at *www.icsa.net*—just click on the listing of certified products. COMSEC Solutions tracks the technology developments and product lines for the providers presented on the CD-ROM. On a quarterly basis, COMSEC Solutions distributes an open-source intelligence database of comparison information to subscribers of record. New subscriber information may be found at COMSEC Solutions Web site at *www.comsec-solutions.com*.

DISCLAIMER

Information contained on the attached CD-ROM has been obtained by ICSA, Inc. and COMSEC Solutions from sources believed to be reliable. However, neither ICSA, Inc., COMSEC Solutions, nor the authors guarantee the accuracy or completeness of any information contained herein and neither ICSA, Inc., COMSEC Solutions, nor the authors shall be responsible for any errors, omissions, or damages arising out of use of this information. This work is published with the understanding that ICSA, Inc., COMSEC Solutions, and the authors are supplying information but are not attempting to render engineering or other professional services. If such services are required, the assistance of an appropriate professional should be sought.